Principles of Dynamics

Also available from Stanley Thornes (Publishers) Ltd:

Mathematics for Engineers and Scientists
K. Weltner, J. Grosjean, P. Schuster and W.J. Weber

Mathematics for Engineers and Scientists Study Guide
K. Weltner, J. Grosjean, P. Schuster and W.J. Weber

A Structured Introduction to Numerical Mathematics
P.J. Hartley and A. Wynn-Evans

Fourier Series and Harmonic Analysis
K.A. Stroud

Laplace Transforms
K.A. Stroud

An Introduction to the Principles of Vibrations of Linear Systems
P. Thureau and D. Lecler (translated and adapted by J. Grosjean)

Principles of Dynamics

J. GROSJEAN BSc(Eng) CEng MIMechE AFIMA MSEE MSocCE(France)
Chevalier, Ordre National du Mérite

Head of Applied Mechanics
School of Engineering
University of Bath

Stanley Thornes (Publishers) Ltd

First published in 1986 by
Stanley Thornes (Publishers) Ltd
Old Station Drive
Leckhampton
CHELTENHAM GL53 0DN

British Library Cataloguing in Publication Data

Grosjean, J.
Principles of dynamics.
1. Dynamics
I. Title
531′.11 QA845

ISBN 0 85950 295 3

Typeset in 10/12 Times by Tech-Set, Gateshead, Tyne & Wear.
Printed and bound in Great Britain by
Hazell Watson & Viney Limited,
Member of the BPCC Group,
Aylesbury, Bucks

In this sense rational mechanics
will be the science of motions
resulting from any forces whatsoever,
and of the forces required to produce
any motions, accurately proposed and
demonstrated.

Cambridge, College of the Holy Trinity, 1686
Is. Newton

Engineers owe a great deal to many mathematicians, scientists and astronomers of the past who were the founders of the science of mechanics.

Of the many we name three of the greatest and hope that the unnamed will forgive us.

Kepler
(1571–1630)
German astronomer
He formulated the laws of planetary motion.

Galileo
(1564–1642)
Italian mathematician
He discovered the laws of falling bodies and was one of the founders of experimental methods.

Newton
(1642–1727)
English mathematician
He formulated the laws of motion, discovered the law of universal gravitation and invented the calculus.

Contents

Preface

This book is intended for students in their first year of study at a University or Polytechnic and for those who are preparing themselves for a professional examination at a Technical College. It is hoped that it will also be useful to students working independently or as a revision course on work previously studied.

The book is based on lectures given to engineering students in their first year at the University of Bath, and assumes that the reader has a knowledge of elementary algebra, trigonometry and calculus but very little knowledge of dynamics. It covers the fundamental principles required to enable the reader to solve many of the problems likely to be encountered in practice, and also provides a foundation for further study. (To this end a number of excellent texts are listed in the bibliography.)

The first five chapters deal with the dynamics of particles and rigid bodies in one and two dimensions. Since motion in the plane covers a large number of practical problems that can be solved without vector methods, these are not employed here; however, the reader is nevertheless made aware of the simple vector rules, since many of the quantities that occur in dynamics (such as displacements, velocities and forces) are vector quantities. Vector methods are, however, particularly suited to three-dimensional problems and thus Chapter 6 is an introduction to spatial dynamics, leading to Euler's equations of motion.

The book would not be complete if it did not include the elements of vibration, and these are covered in Chapter 7, where the vibrations of systems with one degree of freedom are examined, and the important topic of vibration isolation is discussed.

The author would like to express his gratitude to his friend and colleague, Tom Adam, who kindly read the manuscript and made a number of valuable suggestions, and to Chas Stammers, who used the text with first-year students.

Finally the author would like to record his sincere thanks to Janet and Sylvia for their painstaking work on preparing the script for the publisher.

J. Grosjean, Bath 1985

To the memory of my parents
and of Eva

Acknowledgements

The author and publishers would like to express their thanks to the following for permission to reproduce or adapt illustrations for use in this book:

Cementation (Muffelite) Ltd for Figure 7.30(d)
Dunlop Polymer Engineering for Figure 7.29
FIGEE, Holland for Figures 3.19–20
G. D. Griffin and the Institution of Mechanical Engineers for Figures 3.36–7 and 5.17
The Institution of Mechanical Engineers for Figures 4.26–7
James Walker & Co. Ltd for Figure 7.30(e)
Mason Industries Inc. for Figure 7.30(a)–(c)
National Aeronautics and Space Administration for the cover photograph

Symbols

As far as possible the symbols defined below are used consistently throughout the book. Where this is not so, definitions are given as the need arises.

a	acceleration
A	cross-sectional area
a, b, c, d	constants, link lengths of a four-bar linkage or mechanism
A, B, C	constants
c	damping constant
c_c	critical damping
E	modulus of elasticity, energy
f	frequency
f_n	natural frequency
F	force
g	acceleration due to gravity
G	universal gravitational constant
h, H	angular momentum
I	moment of inertia
k	radius of gyration
K, k	stiffness
m, M	mass, moment
p	linear momentum, pressure
P	power, force
r	radius, sight line in polar coordinates
R	resistance
t	time
T	kinetic energy, transmissibility
U	work
v	velocity
V	potential energy, volume
$x, y, z; X, Y, Z$	Cartesian coordinates
$\mathbf{i}, \mathbf{j}, \mathbf{k}$	unit vectors in a Cartesian frame of reference
α	angular acceleration
$\alpha, \beta, \gamma, \theta$	angles
δ	deflection
ζ	damping ratio, i.e. fraction of critical damping
η	efficiency
θ	phase angle
ρ	mass density, radius of curvature
τ	period
ω, Ω	angular velocity
ω	frequency in radians per unit time
ω_d	damped natural frequency
ω_n	undamped natural frequency
ϕ	input angle in a four-bar linkage
ψ	output angle in a four-bar linkage
μ	coefficient of friction

1

Basic Concepts

INTRODUCTION 1.1

A great deal of the work of the engineer, in particular a designer, is concerned with the forces acting on one or more bodies and with their subsequent motion. For example, consider the single-cylinder engine found on a motorbike and shown diagrammatically in Figure 1.1. A mixture of air and petrol burns rapidly within the cylinder, and as it expands applies a force on the piston, causing it to move downwards. This force varies as the mixture expands, from a high value at the start to a low value at the end of the stroke (Figure 1.2). The piston in turn applies a force to the connecting rod via the gudgeon pin, A, and this force is transmitted by the crank pin, B, to the crank, thereby producing a turning moment M on the crankshaft. This turning moment is transmitted to the back wheel, usually by means of a chain. Consequently the motorbike, together with its rider, moves forward at some speed v as a result of the tractive effort developed by friction between the road surface and the tyre.

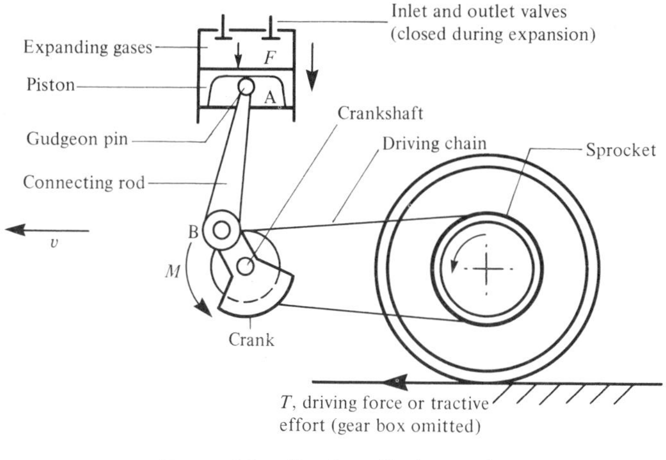

Figure 1.1 Single-cylinder engine.

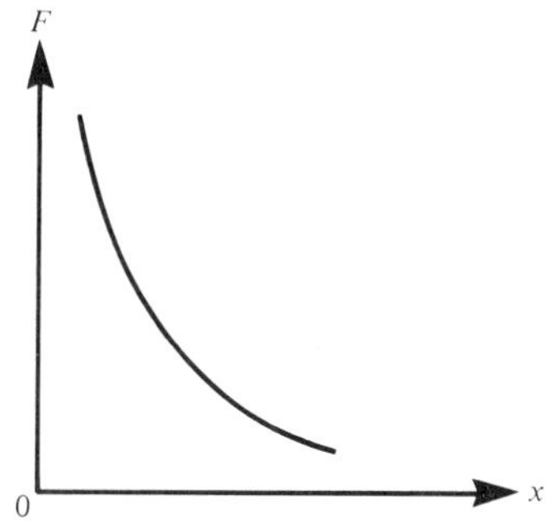

Figure 1.2 Force–displacement curve of piston.

The sizes of all the elements (cylinder, piston, connecting rod, chain, etc.) depend on the type of machine being designed, e.g. from the simple slow-speed commuter type to the high-speed racing machine.

From his knowledge of thermodynamics, the designer will know what force is being applied to the piston and, by applying the principles of dynamics, will be able to predict the acceleration and maximum speed of the machine, having taken into account other important factors such as friction, air resistance and efficiencies of machine elements.

We should not lose sight of the fact that the designer will also have to bear in mind the stresses and strains caused by the forces and hence ensure that none of the elements will break in service.

It should be fairly obvious, therefore, that the engineer/designer not only needs a wide range of knowledge but also must be able to apply this knowledge with competence based on a thorough understanding of *fundamental principles.*

In this text, we are only going to concern ourselves with the subject of *dynamics,* i.e. the study of the motion of bodies, which is usually divided into the branches of kinematics and kinetics.

Kinematics is the study of displacements, velocities and accelerations without regard to forces; this is often referred to as the geometry of motion. *Kinetics* is concerned with the relationship between forces acting on a body and the resulting motion, but does not take into account the deformations of the body as a result of these forces. In a good design, such deformations are very small and do not affect the dynamical behaviour of the body; a typical tension in a 1 m long steel rod would stretch it by only about 0.7 mm.

Our study of dynamics is based entirely on the application of the laws of motion and gravitation as well as the calculus, all due to Sir Isaac Newton (1642–1727).

1.2 UNITS

The Système International d'Unités (SI) was agreed internationally in October 1960, and is based on the following definitions:

(1) Length is a measure of the linear geometry and the displacement of a body from one position to another. The unit used nowadays is the metre (m), defined as the length equal to 1650 763.73 wavelengths in vacuum of the radiation corresponding to the transition between the energy levels $2p_{10}$ and $5d_5$ of the krypton-86 atom.

(2) Mass is a measure of the amount of material in a body, sometimes referred to as the quantity of matter. The standard mass of 1 kilogram (kg) consists of a cylinder of platinum–iridium held at Sèvres near Paris.

(3) Time is a measure of the succession of events. In 1967 the unit of time, the second (s), was defined as the interval occupied by 9192 631 770 cycles of radiation corresponding to the transition of the caesium-133 atom when unperturbed by exterior fields.

These are the fundamental units. All the other units we require in our study of dynamics (or any other subjects) will be derived from them, e.g. velocity, force, energy, power, momentum, etc.

The SI units are used throughout Europe and in other parts of the world, and are gaining ground in the USA; they are gradually replacing older units such as the pound mass, slug, pound force, horsepower, etc.

SCALAR AND VECTOR QUANTITIES 1.3

It is felt that most readers will already have had an elementary introduction to vectors, but for those new to these quantities we recall their definitions, representations and combinations.

1.3.1 Definitions and representations

A quantity that is completely defined by its magnitude is called a "scalar quantity". Mass, time, energy, speed, density, area, volume and temperature are examples of scalar quantities.

A quantity that has direction as well as magnitude is called a "vector quantity" or simply a "vector". Displacement, velocity, force, acceleration and moment are examples of vectors. A vector will be affected by a change in its direction or in its magnitude or both. The reader may already be familiar with the case of motion in a circle, where an object moves in a circle of constant radius at a constant speed. In this case the velocity vector has a constant magnitude, namely its speed, but its direction is constantly changing, with the result that the object is subjected to a radially inward acceleration known as the centripetal acceleration (see Figure 1.11).

In handwriting, a vector is represented by drawing a short line under a letter, e.g. $\underline{a}$, $\underline{F}$, $\underline{v}$. Printers, on the other hand, use a bold-face letter, e.g. **a, F, v.** The magnitude or modulus of a vector is represented by drawing two short vertical lines, thus $|\mathbf{a}|$, $|\mathbf{F}|$, $|\mathbf{v}|$, or more simply by the letter on its own in italic, i.e. *a, F, v.*

A vector is indicated graphically by an arrow. The length of the arrow is proportional to the magnitude of the vector, and the direction is shown by the angle the arrow makes with a known reference line. The sense is indicated by the arrowhead; this is illustrated in Figure 1.3, where the vector **a** starts at a point A and terminates at B, so that

$$\mathbf{a} = \overrightarrow{AB} \qquad \text{where } |\mathbf{a}| = a \text{ is the magnitude}$$

The arrow above the letters AB is often used when a vector is defined by a line joining two points.

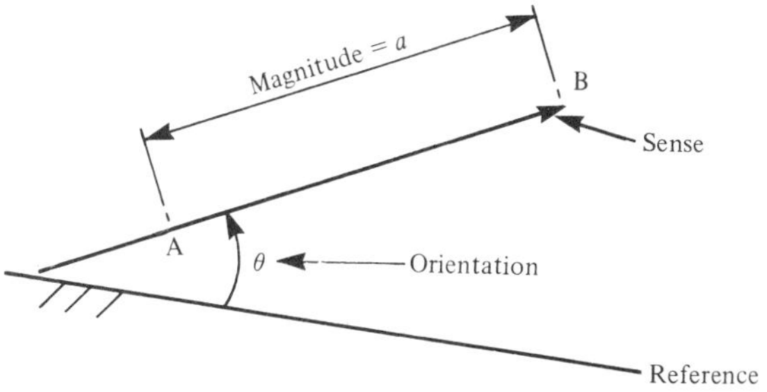

Figure 1.3 Vector representation: $\overrightarrow{AB} = \mathbf{a}$.

In many cases in practice, a vector is localised, e.g. a force applied at a particular point on a structure or the velocity of a point on the rim of a flywheel; such vectors are referred to as *bound* vectors. In general, vectors are not localised, in which case all equal and parallel vectors having the same sense will represent the same vector; they are then referred to as free vectors.

1.3.2 **Addition and subtraction of vectors**

To illustrate the addition of vectors, consider the successive displacements of a point: a displacement from A to B followed by a displacement from B to C. These two successive displacements produce the same result as a single displacement from A to C as shown in Figure 1.4(a).

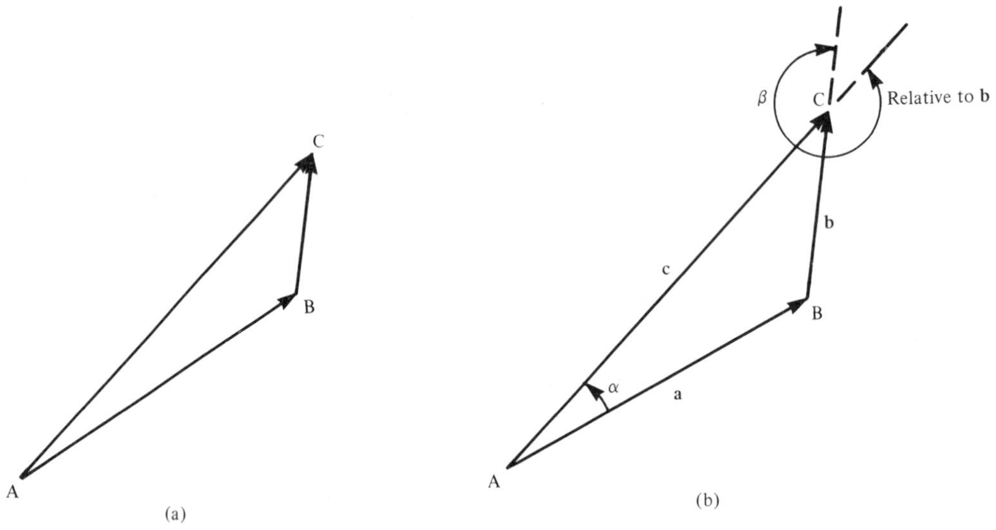

Figure 1.4 Triangle law for addition of vectors.

We call the displacement AC the vector sum of the displacements AB and BC, and write

$$\overrightarrow{AC} = \overrightarrow{AB} + \overrightarrow{BC}$$

If $\mathbf{a} = \overrightarrow{AB}$, $\mathbf{b} = \overrightarrow{BC}$ and $\mathbf{c} = \overrightarrow{AC}$, as shown in Figure 1.4(b), we have

$$\mathbf{c} = \mathbf{a} + \mathbf{b}$$

The sum vector **c** has magnitude c and a direction α relative to that of **a** or β relative to that of **b**, as shown in Figure 1.4(b). All vectors are added in accordance with the triangle law. Vectors may also be added in accordance with the parallelogram law. Consider two vectors **P** and **Q**, both with origin at O as in Figure 1.5. Their resultant **R** is obtained by constructing the parallelogram OABC so that

$$\mathbf{R} = \mathbf{P} + \mathbf{Q}$$

We notice that since $\overrightarrow{CB} = \overrightarrow{OA}$ and $\overrightarrow{AB} = \overrightarrow{OC}$ it follows that

$$\overrightarrow{OB} = \overrightarrow{OA} + \overrightarrow{AB} = \overrightarrow{OC} + \overrightarrow{CB}$$

and hence

$$\mathbf{R} = \mathbf{P} + \mathbf{Q} = \mathbf{Q} + \mathbf{P}$$

i.e. the vectors can be added in any order; this is known as the commutative law.

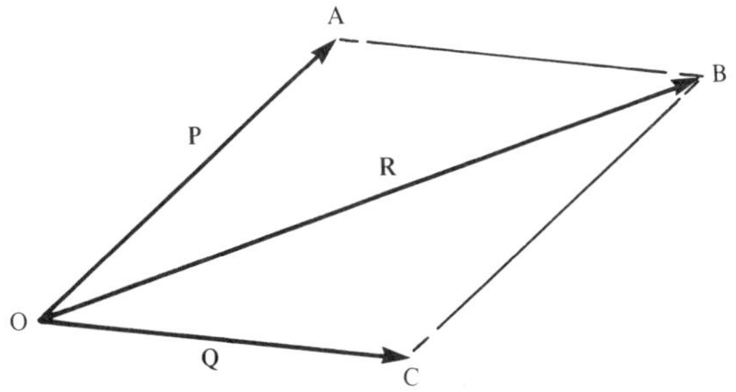

Figure 1.5 Parallelogram law for addition of vectors.

If we have n vectors $\mathbf{P}_1, \mathbf{P}_2, \mathbf{P}_3, \ldots, \mathbf{P}_n$ issuing from some point O, as in Figure 1.6(a), their resultant may be obtained by constructing one parallelogram after another as shown in Figure 1.6(b) or by placing the vectors head to tail as in Figure 1.6(c) and constructing triangles. The resultant vector is

$$\mathbf{R} = \mathbf{P}_1 + \mathbf{P}_2 + \ldots + \mathbf{P}_n$$

It follows from the above that the sum of n vectors is independent of the way the vectors are grouped.

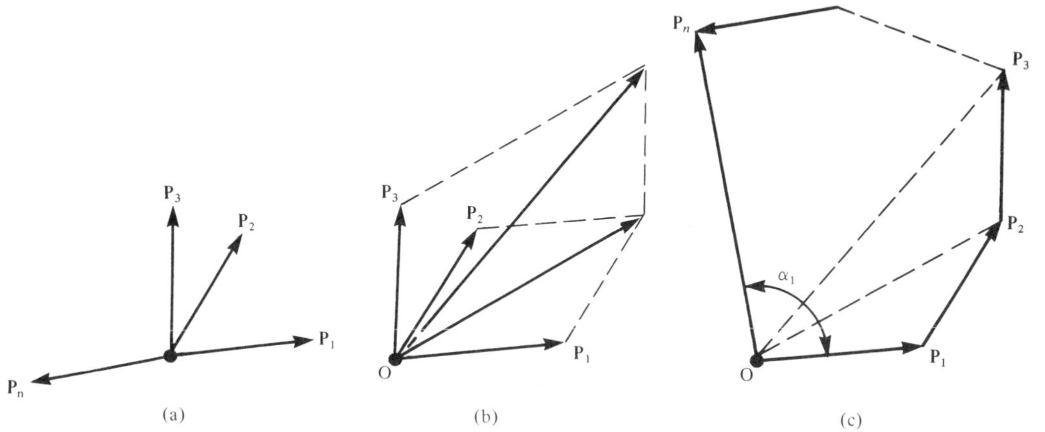

Figure 1.6 Resultant of vectors.

From a drawing to scale we can simply measure the length of the line representing $\mathbf{R}$ to obtain its magnitude R and its direction could be measured relative to any of the vectors, e.g. α_1 relative to $\mathbf{P}_1$. Thus if L is the length of $\mathbf{R}$ measured on the drawing and k the scale of the drawing, it then follows that

$$R = kL$$

The angle α_1 is, however, independent of the scale of the drawing.

To subtract two vectors, we adopt the same construction as above. This is shown in Figure 1.7(b) where

$$\mathbf{c} = \mathbf{a} - \mathbf{b} = \mathbf{a} + (-\mathbf{b})$$

i.e. we reverse the sense of vector **b** and add it to the vector **a** in accordance with the triangle law.

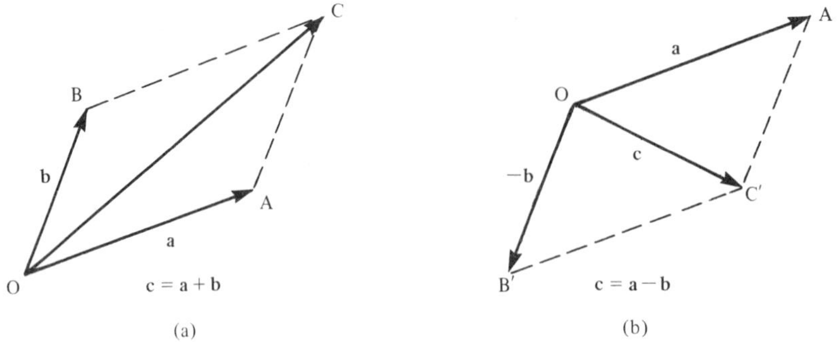

Figure 1.7 Subtraction of vectors.

If $\overrightarrow{OC'} = \mathbf{c} = 0$, this implies that $\mathbf{a} = \mathbf{b}$, and the resultant vector of zero length is called a zero or null vector.

The + and − signs are borrowed from ordinary algebra; when used with vector quantities we have to remember that direction is involved and that vectors are "added" in accordance with the triangle or parallelogram law.

These definitions for the addition or subtraction of vectors are not arbitrary but are based on the way physical quantities are compounded.

1.3.3 Multiplication and division of a vector by a scalar

Let **A** be a vector and k a positive or negative scalar. Then $\mathbf{B} = k\mathbf{A}$ is a vector whose direction is that of **A** and whose magnitude is kA, i.e. k times the magnitude of the vector **A**. The sense of **B** depends on whether k is positive or negative. If k is positive, then **B** has the same sense as **A**; but if k is negative, the sense of **B** is opposite to that of **A**.

If the vector **A** is divided by the scalar k, then the new vector **C** given by

$$\mathbf{C} = \frac{1}{k}\mathbf{A}$$

has the direction of **A** and a magnitude A/k, i.e. the magnitude of the vector **A** divided by k. The sense of **C** will depend on the sign of k, as mentioned above in the case of multiplication.

1.3.4 Unit vectors

Unit vectors are used extensively in mechanics to define particular directions. For example, it is universally accepted that the vectors **i**, **j** and **k** are unit vectors along the

x-, y- and z-axes of a Cartesian system of coordinates, whereas **t** and **n** are unit vectors along the tangent and the normal to a curve; an alternative notation is $\mathbf{e}_t$ and $\mathbf{e}_n$.

Let **a** be a vector whose magnitude is $a = \sqrt{a_x^2 + a_y^2 + a_z^2}$. Then the vector

$$\mathbf{e} = \frac{\mathbf{a}}{a} = \frac{a_x\mathbf{i} + a_y\mathbf{j} + a_z\mathbf{k}}{\sqrt{a_x^2 + a_y^2 + a_z^2}}$$

is a unit vector whose magnitude is unity and whose direction is that of **a**.

1.3.5 **Resolution of vectors**

A vector **F** may conveniently be resolved into components along specified directions. For example, let xOy be a Cartesian frame. Then this vector, whose magnitude is F, has components $F_x = F\cos\theta$ along Ox and $F_y = F\sin\theta$ along Oy, as shown in Figure 1.8(a).

If **i** and **j** are unit vectors along Ox and Oy respectively, then we can express **F** in terms of its components by writing

$$\mathbf{F} = F_x\mathbf{i} + F_y\mathbf{j} = (F\cos\theta)\mathbf{i} + (F\sin\theta)\mathbf{j}$$

If, as in Figure 1.8(b), **F** is a three-dimensional vector and Oxyz a Cartesian set of axes, then in terms of the direction angles α, β, γ we could express **F** in terms of its components thus:

$$\mathbf{F} = (F\cos\alpha)\mathbf{i} + (F\cos\beta)\mathbf{j} + (F\cos\gamma)\mathbf{k}$$

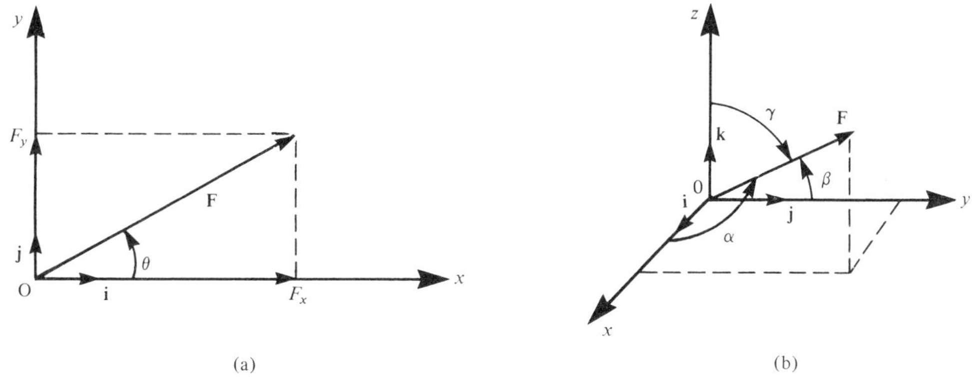

Figure 1.8 Resolving a vector in (a) two and (b) three dimensions.

In Chapter 6 we will consider the product of vectors and the elements of vector calculus to enable us to analyse the motions of particles and rigid bodies in space. For example, the analysis of the motions of aeroplanes, three-dimensional mechanisms such as robots, gyroscopes or space vehicles is much simplified by means of vectors.

Since many of the problems encountered by engineers occur in one or two dimensions, i.e. along a given direction or in a plane, the use of vector calculus is not essential and for this reason the work in the early chapters is dealt with by applying the ordinary rules of algebra and calculus. Nevertheless we must not lose sight of the fact that we shall be dealing with quantities that have direction as well as magnitude.

1.4 VELOCITY, ACCELERATION AND NEWTON'S LAWS OF MOTION

1.4.1 Velocity

Consider a body moving along the straight path Ox as shown in Figure 1.9. Ox defines a direction in space and in this case the motion will be referred to as *rectilinear motion.*

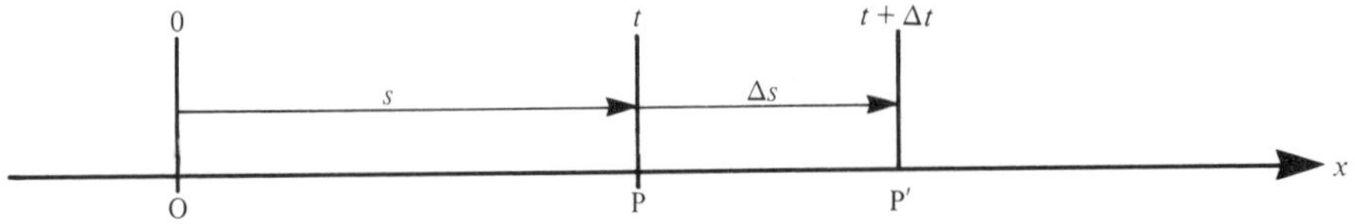

Figure 1.9 Motion in a straight line.

At time t the body is at P, a distance s from some convenient origin such as O.

At time $t + \Delta t$ the body has moved to a new position P′ at a distance $s + \Delta s$ from O.

The ratio displacement/time is defined as the average velocity, v_{av}, of the body in the particular time interval Δt or over the particular distance Δs:

$$v_{av} = \frac{\Delta s}{\Delta t}$$

Δs and Δt are both finite and can have any value. For example, on a particular day the journey from London to Bristol along the M4 motorway, a distance of 170 kilometres (km) (170 000 m), took $2\frac{1}{4}$ h. Hence $\Delta s = 170$ km, $\Delta t = 2.25$ h, so that the average velocity was

$$v_{av} = \frac{170}{2.25} = 75.6 \text{ km/h}$$

On the other hand, during the same journey we observed that in driving between the exits for Swindon and Bath, a distance of 40 km took 25 min; hence our average velocity then was

$$v_{av} = \frac{40 \times 60}{25} = 96 \text{ km/h}$$

since $\Delta s = 40$ km, $\Delta t = 25/60$ h. However, as we passed the exit for Swindon the speedometer in the car showed 110 km/h!

In dynamics we are generally more concerned with instantaneous values, i.e. at a particular instant of time t. If in Figure 1.9 we let P′ get closer and closer to P so that Δs

and Δt becomes smaller, then in the limit as $\Delta s \to 0$ we have for the instantaneous velocity v at time t the following definition:

$$v = \lim_{\Delta t \to 0} \frac{\Delta s}{\Delta t} = \frac{ds}{dt} = \dot{s} \qquad \text{in the } x\text{-direction.}$$

Since distance is usually measured in metres and time in seconds, it follows that the unit for velocity is metres/second (m/s). The magnitude of the velocity is known as the speed.

The 110 km/h we observed on the speedometer was our instantaneous speed at the instant we passed the exit for Swindon (to the accuracy of the instrumentation).

1.4.2 **Acceleration**

Again referring to the diagram in Figure 1.9, if the velocity of the body at P, at time t, is v and its velocity at P′, at time $t + \Delta t$, is $v + \Delta v$, then the average change in velocity with time is called the average acceleration a_{av} given by

$$a_{av} = \frac{\Delta v}{\Delta t}$$

The instantaneous acceleration at time t is defined by

$$a = \lim_{\Delta t \to 0} \frac{\Delta v}{\Delta t} = \frac{dv}{dt} = \dot{v} \qquad \text{in the } x\text{-direction.}$$

The unit for acceleration is therefore given by velocity/time, i.e. (metres/second/second) (or m/s^2).

1.4.3 **Newton's laws of motion**

(a) The first law

> *Every body continues in its state of rest or of uniform motion in a straight line unless a force compels it to change that state.*

This law defines inertia, a property shared by all matter; it also states that a body travelling at a constant speed along a line whose direction is fixed in space will carry on doing so unless some external agency called "force" compels it to alter its speed or direction or both.

This law also tells us that we need to define a frame of reference for all our measurements. Such a frame is called *inertial, Galilean* or *Newtonian,* and is an non-accelerating frame (see section 1.4.5).

(b) The second law

> *The change in the motion of a body is proportional to the force applied to it and takes place in the direction of the force.*

Motion is defined as the product of the mass of the body and its velocity, better known as the linear momentum.

Hence if a force **F** is applied to a body of mass m whose absolute instantaneous velocity is **v** then

$$\mathbf{F} = k\frac{d}{dt}(m\mathbf{v})$$

where k is a constant made equal to unity by a suitable choice of units.

If (and only if) the mass of the body is constant then the law becomes

$$\mathbf{F} = m\frac{d\mathbf{v}}{dt} = m\mathbf{a}$$

where **a** is the absolute acceleration of the body in the direction of the force. This acceleration is measured relative to a Newtonian frame of reference.

Thus force = mass × acceleration and the unit is called a *newton* (N),

$$1\,\text{N} = 1\,\text{kg} \times 1\,\text{m/s}^2$$

(c) The third law

To every action there is always an equal and opposite reaction.

Alternatively:

The mutual actions between two bodies are always equal and collinear, but of opposite sense.

If the speeds involved are comparable with the speed of light (2.976×10^8 m/s), then we must replace Newton's laws by those of Albert Einstein (1878–1955). In Einstein's theory of relativity it is demonstrated that the mass m of a particle is given by

$$m = \frac{m_0}{\sqrt{1-(v/c)^2}}$$

where m_0 is the mass of the particle at rest, v is the velocity and c is the velocity of light.

In the majority of problems dealt with by engineers the relevant speeds are small compared with the speed of light, and so $m \simeq m_0$.

1.4.4 Law of gravitation

Newton based this law on the work of Johann Kepler (1571–1630), who enunciated the three laws of planetary motion from an analysis of the observations of the motions of the planets by Tycho Brahe (1546–1600).

The law of gravitation states that the force of attraction between two particles is proportional to the product of the masses of the particles and inversely proportional to the square of the distance between them. Expressed mathematically it is

$$F = G\frac{m_1 m_2}{R^2}$$

where F is the force of attraction, m_1 and m_2 are the masses of the two particles, R is the distance between the two particles and G is the constant of proportionality called the universal gravitational constant ($= 6.67 \times 10^{-11}$ m^3/kg s^2).

The force exerted by the Earth on a particle lying on its surface is called the weight W of the particle. Taking the Earth as a particle of mass $m_e = 5.976 \times 10^{24}$ kg and assuming it to be a perfect sphere of radius $r_e = 6.371 \times 10^6$ m, the force of attraction anywhere on its surface is

$$F = \frac{6.67 \times 10^{-11} \times 5.976 \times 10^{24}}{(6.371 \times 10^6)^2} m_p = 9.8233 m_p \text{ N}$$

where m_p is the mass of the particle. The number 9.8233 is the value in m/s^2 of the gravitational acceleration (g) with which the Earth attracts the particle. However, the Earth is not a perfect sphere and this acceleration varies with location. For example, at a latitude of 45° it is 9.807 m/s^2, owing to the smaller radius there.

The value of g at an altitude h above the Earth's surface is given by

$$g = \frac{g_0 r_e^2}{(r + h)^2}$$

where g_0 is the local acceleration due to gravity at the Earth's surface. For most of our problems we shall take this acceleration to be 9.81 m/s^2. The force F is commonly referred to as the weight $W = mg$. In all cases where a particle is moving in a vertical plane, i.e. in a plane in which gravity has an influence, the weight of the particle must enter into the equation. For example, if a ball is thrown into the air, it is subjected to the force of gravity or its weight, and the air resistance.

1.4.5 **Frames of reference**

As a consequence of Newton's first law of motion it is essential to have a frame of reference from which we can measure distances, orientations and their time derivatives when analysing the motion of particles or of rigid bodies.

Newton's laws are valid in what is called the "inertial frame", which is regarded as fixed in space, i.e. absolutely at rest. It can be shown that Newton's laws also hold in frames of reference that are moving with constant velocity relative to the Newtonian frame, which becomes the "primary inertial frame". The force acting on a particle in any one of these frames is invariant.

For most problems in engineering, a frame of reference fixed to the Earth is regarded as a primary inertial frame, i.e. although the Earth rotates about its own axis and about the Sun, the resulting accelerations can be neglected in most cases.

1.4.6 **Particles and rigid bodies**

A particle is defined to be a body of a certain mass but of very small dimensions. For example, a radar station tracking the progress of an aeroplane shows it as a dot on the screen: the fact that it is a body of finite size is not relevant in calculating its position, velocity and acceleration; its size is still small compared with the distances involved. On the other hand, when analysing the motion of the connecting rod of the engine shown in Figure 1.1, size is important, and must be taken into account.

A rigid body, on the other hand, is a body of finite size and is such that the distance between any two points within the body remains constant under the application of forces. The connecting rod is such a rigid body. As we mentioned earlier, all bodies deform under the action of forces but these deformations are extremely small. It will become clearer as we proceed as to which bodies can be considered as particles and which as rigid bodies; these considerations will be dictated by the nature of the problem being investigated.

1.5 MOVING FRAME OF REFERENCE

Not all our frames of reference are Newtonian, and there are many situations, e.g. rocket motion or motion of an aircraft, in which the motion of particles or of rigid bodies is referred to a moving frame of reference. We shall find that it is sometimes more suitable to fix a set of axes in a body and moving with it, in which case these axes will have translation as well as rotation.

We shall consider these situations in Chapter 6 when we analyse the motion of particles and bodies in three dimensions.

As a simple illustration of the effect of a moving frame of reference, consider the case of a particle of mass m at P moving under the action of a resultant force **R** as shown in Figure 1.10. Let O be the origin of a Newtonian frame of reference and M that of a moving frame. For example, we might be carrying out an experiment in one of the carriages of an accelerating train. If **r**, **s** and **q** are the distances at time t then

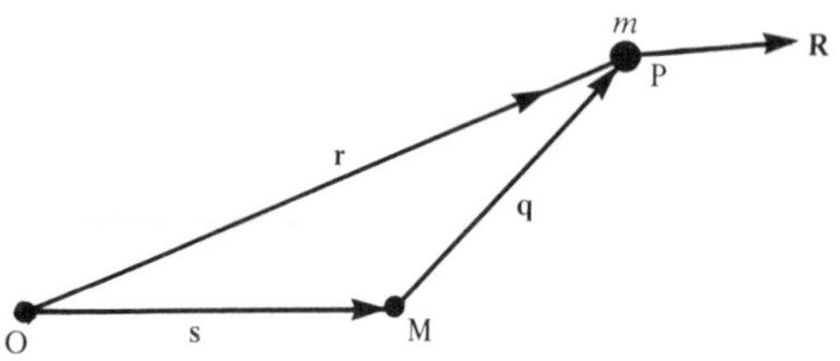

Figure 1.10 Moving frame of reference.

$$\mathbf{r} = \mathbf{s} + \mathbf{q}$$

Differentiating twice with respect to time gives

$$\ddot{\mathbf{r}} = \ddot{\mathbf{s}} + \ddot{\mathbf{q}}$$

where $\ddot{\mathbf{r}}$ is the acceleration of P as seen by O, $\ddot{\mathbf{s}}$ is the acceleration of the moving frame and $\ddot{\mathbf{q}}$ is the acceleration of P as seen by M. Hence Newton's second law gives

$$\mathbf{R} = m\ddot{\mathbf{r}} = m(\ddot{\mathbf{s}} + \ddot{\mathbf{q}})$$
$$= m\ddot{\mathbf{s}} + m\ddot{\mathbf{q}}$$

or

$$m\ddot{\mathbf{q}} = \mathbf{R} - m\ddot{\mathbf{s}}$$

This means that in a moving frame we have to subtract from the applied forces the term $m\ddot{\mathbf{s}}$ to take into account the acceleration of the frame. However, if $\ddot{\mathbf{s}} = 0$, the frame is moving with constant velocity, and both magnitude and direction are constant. For example, if M is moving in a circular path of radius d about O with a velocity **v** whose magnitude v is constant, then M has an acceleration $\ddot{s} = v^2/d$ towards the centre O, as shown in Figure 1.11. This is so because the direction of **v** is changing with time; we would, therefore, have to take into account the acceleration of M in applying Newton's second law of motion to a body viewed from M.

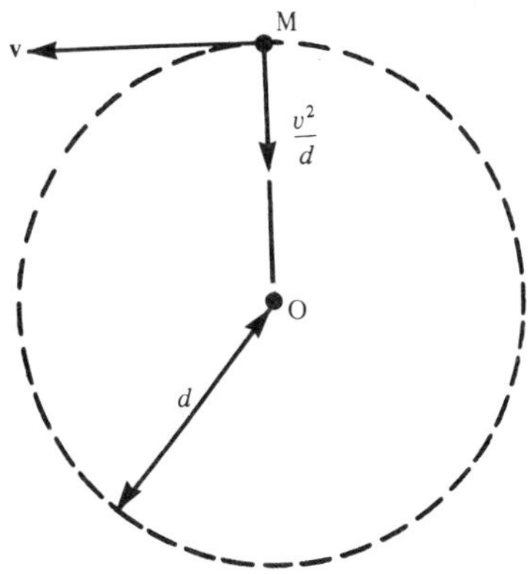

Figure 1.11 Circular motion.

FREE BODY DIAGRAMS 1.6

In order to analyse the motion of a particle or a body, we must be absolutely clear as to which forces act on it. The only way to ensure this is to draw a free body diagram every time. Such a diagram isolates the body from its surroundings and thus reveals all the forces acting on it; we are then able to apply Newton's second law of motion.

For example, consider two packages A and B touching each other and sliding down a chute as shown in Figure 1.12(a). Just by looking at the packages sliding down we cannot immediately say what forces are present. Let us take package A off the chute and investigate the forces that must be acting on it (i.e. we free it from its surroundings).

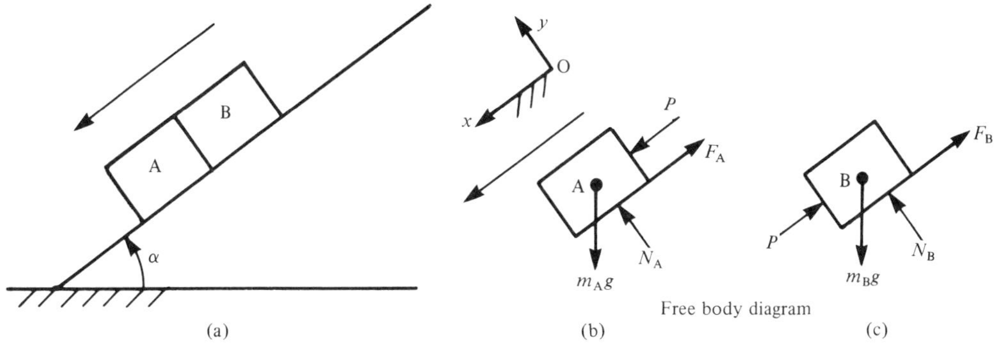

Figure 1.12 Free body diagrams for sliding on an inclined plane.

They are:

(1) its weight m_Ag,

(2) the reaction of the chute on the package, N_A normal to the chute,

(3) the frictional force F_A parallel to the chute and opposite to the motion, and

(4) the force of contact P between the two packages.

This is shown in Figure 1.12(b). A convenient frame of reference Oxy is taken such that Ox is parallel to the chute. The direction Ox of the arrow implies that all quantities measured in that direction will be taken to be positive; the same applies along Oy, normal to the chute.

Applying Newton's second law for the motion of package A, i.e. sum of the forces (Σ forces) = mass $\times$ acceleration, we have

(1) down the chute in the x-direction

$$m_A g \sin \alpha - F_A + P = m_A \ddot{x}_A$$

(2) in a direction perpendicular to the chute, along Oy

$$N_A - m_A g \cos \alpha = m_A \ddot{y}_A = 0$$

because the package has no acceleration in this direction; it is always in contact with the chute.

Figure 1.12(c) shows the free body diagram for package B; the only force in common with package A is P by Newton's third law. We shall return to this example in Chapter 4.

It is absolutely vital to draw a free body diagram every time, no matter how simple the problem, if we are to apply the laws of motion correctly. It is also essential for a proper understanding of the problem. To avoid drawing a free body diagram is asking for trouble! Experience has shown this to be true on very many occasions not only at school, technical college or university but also in industry!

EXERCISES

1.1 A force of 350 N acts at the origin of a Cartesian set of axes. The head of the vector representing this force has coordinates (400, 300, 200). Express the force in terms of the unit vectors **i**, **j** and **k**.

1.2 A force of 2500 N is directed along a line drawn from a point whose coordinates (m) are (2, 0, 4) to a point whose coordinates are (5, 1, 1). Calculate its components and direction angles. If this force acts on a particle of mass 320 kg, calculate the acceleration of that particle in magnitude and direction.

1.3 In exercise 1.2 calculate the moments of the force about the x-, y- and z-axes. (*Note:* The moment of a force about an axis or a point is equal to the product of the magnitude of the force and the perpendicular distance between the axis or the point and the line of action of the force.)

1.4 Determine the unit vector **e** along a line whose origin is the point (4, 6, −3) and which passes through the point (2, 0, 10).

1.5 A point at the end of a robotic arm has a velocity given by

$$v = 125\mathbf{i} + 210\mathbf{j} + 305\mathbf{k} \text{ mm/s}$$

Calculate the magnitude and direction of the velocity.

1.6 A crate of 1500 kg mass is suspended by three cables which meet at the origin of a set of Cartesian axes x, y and z as shown in Figure 1.13. If T_1, T_2 and T_3 are the tensions in the cables, calculate their magnitudes given the coordinates of the anchor points A, B and C. The axis Oz is parallel to the local vertical. (*Note:* A particle is in equilibrium if the vector sum of the forces acting on it is zero.)

Express all forces in terms of the unit vectors and solve the vector equations.

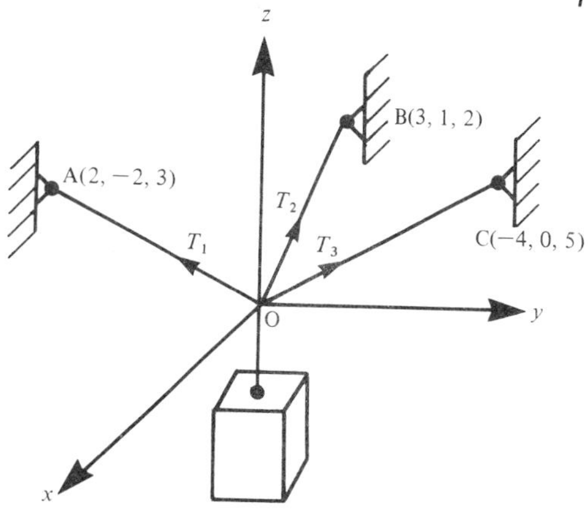

Figure 1.13

1.7 A load of 20 kN on the platform of a lorry which is lifted by means of the hydraulic ram H is prevented from slipping by the stop C as shown in Figure 1.14. When $\theta = 0°$ and $\theta = 30°$ calculate (a) the pin force at O, and (b) the force exerted by the ram. (The hydraulic ram moves at constant velocity, and friction at the pivots may be neglected. The load may be assumed to be a homogeneous block.)

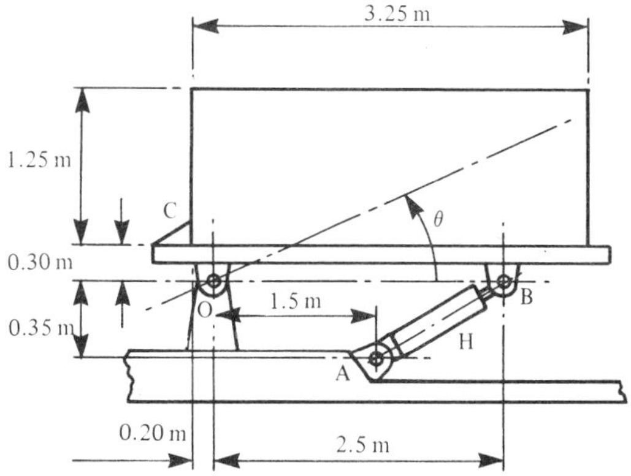

Figure 1.14

1.8 Calculate the speed with which an artificial satellite must move in order to remain in a circular orbit 350 km above the surface of the Earth. Calculate also the period of the satellite. (Assume that the Earth is a sphere.)

2

Kinematics of Particles

2.1 INTRODUCTION

Kinematics is the study of the motion of particles and rigid bodies without regard to the forces causing them. The motion can be observed from an inertial frame of reference or from a moving frame; which frame is employed depends on the nature of the problem under investigation.

A particle or rigid body moving along a straight path is said to have *rectilinear* motion, whereas if the path is curved the motion is called *curvilinear.* Furthermore, if the motion takes place in two dimensions, it is referred to as *plane* motion. Motion may also take place in three dimensions; this is referred to as motion *in space.*

Many problems dealt with in engineering are concerned with motions in one or two dimensions only, as mentioned in Chapter 1.

2.2 RECTILINEAR MOTION

This is the simplest type of motion: the piston in an engine, a billiard ball rolling on a table, an aircraft taxying on the runway, and the needle of a sewing machine are examples of rectilinear motion.

Figure 2.1 shows a particle moving along the x-axis of an xOy frame of reference. At time t it is at a distance s and, as we saw in section 1.4.1, the velocity at that instant is given by

$$v = \lim_{\Delta t \to 0} \frac{\Delta s}{\Delta t} = \frac{\mathrm{d}s}{\mathrm{d}t} = \dot{s}$$

The direction of the velocity is along the x-axis.

Similarly the acceleration is given by

$$a = \lim_{\Delta t \to 0} \frac{\Delta v}{\Delta t} = \frac{\mathrm{d}v}{\mathrm{d}t} = \dot{v}$$

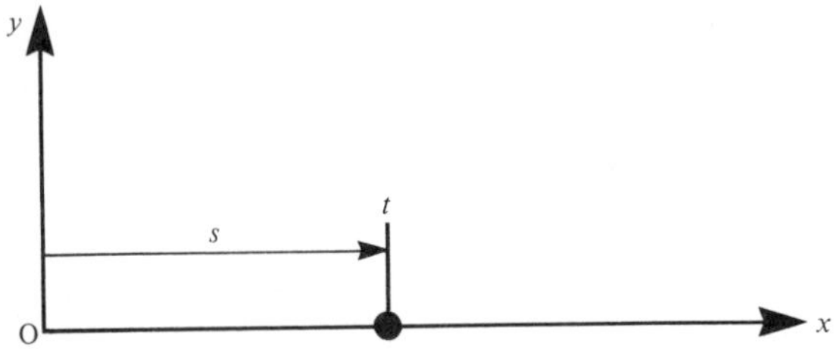

Figure 2.1 Rectilinear motion.

and its direction is also along the x-axis. (We should note that having defined a particular direction for the motion we do not need to use the vector notation **v** or **a** for the velocity or the acceleration.)

It should be fairly obvious that in order to calculate the velocity and the acceleration we need to know the displacement as a function of time, i.e. $s = f(t)$. Such a relationship may be known mathematically or graphically.

The acceleration can also be expressed in the following forms:

$$a = \frac{dv}{dt} = \frac{d}{dt}\left(\frac{ds}{dt}\right) = \frac{d^2s}{dt^2} = \ddot{s}$$

or

$$a = \frac{dv}{dt} = \frac{dv}{ds}\frac{ds}{dt} = v\frac{dv}{ds}$$

The latter form expresses the acceleration as a function of the displacement.

EXAMPLE 2.1

The displacement (in metres, of a particle moving in a straight line through a resisting medium is given by

$$s = 160(1 - e^{-0.25t}) - 20t$$

Example Cont.

Calculate (a) the velocity and the acceleration when $t = 0$ and (b) the distance travelled before coming to rest (t is measured in seconds).

SOLUTION

(a) Since

$$s = 160(1 - e^{-0.25t}) - 20t$$

the velocity is

$$v = \frac{ds}{dt} = \dot{s} = 160(+0.25e^{-0.25t}) - 20$$

When $t = 0$,

$$v_0 = 40 - 20 = 20 \text{ m/s}$$

The acceleration is

$$a = \frac{dv}{dt} = \dot{v} = 160(-0.25^2e^{-0.25t})$$

When $t = 0$,

$$a_0 = -160 \times 0.25^2 = -10 \text{ m/s}^2$$ (i.e. just over 1g)

Solution Cont.

(b) We have $v = 0$ when

$$160 \times 0.25e^{-0.25t} - 20 = 0$$

i.e. $2 = e^{0.25t}$

Taking logarithms to base e yields

$$t = 2.773 \text{ s}$$

Therefore the distance travelled,

$$d = 160(1 - e^{-0.25 \times 2.773}) - 20 \times 2.773$$
$$= 24.55 \text{ m}$$

EXAMPLE 2.2

A car with the power off came to rest in 35 s. The distance travelled was measured every 2.5 s and the results are shown in Table 2.1. Estimate the velocity and deceleration of the car at the instant the power was switched off and at $t = 20$ s.

Example Cont.

Table 2.1

t (s)	0	2.5	5	7.5	10
s (m)	0	92	157	202	234
t (s)	12.5	15	17.5	20	22.5
s (m)	256	272	283	290	293.75
t (s)	25	27.5	30	32.5	35
s (m)	296.75	299.25	301.25	302.75	303.75

SOLUTION

There are two ways of solving this problem. The first is to plot a graph and draw tangents to the curve at each point to obtain the velocity–time relationship and then calculate the acceleration by drawing tangents again. This method is not recommended as it is not easy to draw tangents to any degree of accuracy.

The best way is to tabulate the results and calculate the average velocity during each time interval using $v_{av} = \Delta s/\Delta t$. The average acceleration for each time interval is similarly calculated from $a_{av} = \Delta v_{av}/\Delta t$. In both cases Δt is 2.5 s. The results are shown in Table 2.2.

A simple method to obtain the velocities and the accelerations is to proceed as follows. Referring to Figure 2.2, let us consider the positions at $t = 10$, 12.5 and 15 s and the corresponding displacements 234, 256 and 272 m at A, B and C. The time intervals are $\Delta t = 2.5$ s in each case and the corresponding displacements are $\Delta s_1 = 256 - 234 = 22$ m and $\Delta s_2 = 272 - 256 = 16$ m. Hence in going from A to B the average velocity is

$$v_{av1} = \Delta s_1/\Delta t = 22/2.5 = 8.8 \text{ m/s}$$

and in going from B to C

$$v_{av2} = \Delta s_2/\Delta t = 16/2.5 = 6.4 \text{ m/s}$$

These values are then entered in the fourth column of Table 2.2.

If we were going to construct a velocity–time graph we would consider these average velocities to be at mid-intervals, i.e. at A′ and B′. Now the change in the velocity in going from A′ to B′ is

$$\Delta v = v_{av2} - v_{av1} = 6.4 - 8.8 = -2.4 \text{ m/s}$$

Solution Cont.

so that the average acceleration (or deceleration, since Δv is negative) is

$$a_{av} = \Delta v_{av}/\Delta t = -2.4/2.5 = -0.96 \text{ m/s}^2$$

This is the value of the deceleration at B, since B is the mid-interval between A′ and B′. Similar results are entered in the sixth column of Table 2.2

Table 2.2

t (s)	s (m)	Δs (m)	$v_{av} = \Delta s/\Delta t$ (m/s)	Δv_{av} (m/s)	$a_{av} = \Delta v_{av}/\Delta t$ (m/s^2)	Δa_{av} (m/s^2)
0	0		47.60		−5.44	
		92	36.8			
2.5	92			−10.8	−4.32	
		65	26.0			1.12
5.0	157			−8.0	−3.20	
		45	18.0			1.12
7.5	202			−5.2	−2.08	
		32	12.8			
10.0	234			−4.0	−1.60	
		22	8.8			
12.5	256			−2.4	−0.96	
		16	6.4			
15.0	272			−2.0	−0.80	
		11	4.4			
17.5	283			−1.6	−0.64	
		7.0	2.8			
20.0	290			−1.3	−0.52	
		3.75	1.5			
22.5	293.75			−0.3	−0.12	
		3.0	1.2			
25.0	296.75			−0.2	−0.08	
		2.5	1.0			
27.5	299.25			−0.2	−0.08	
		2.0	0.8			
30.0	301.25			−0.2	−0.08	
		1.5	0.6			
32.5	302.75			−0.2	−0.08	
		1.0	0.4			
35.0	303.75					

Solution Cont. **Solution Cont.**

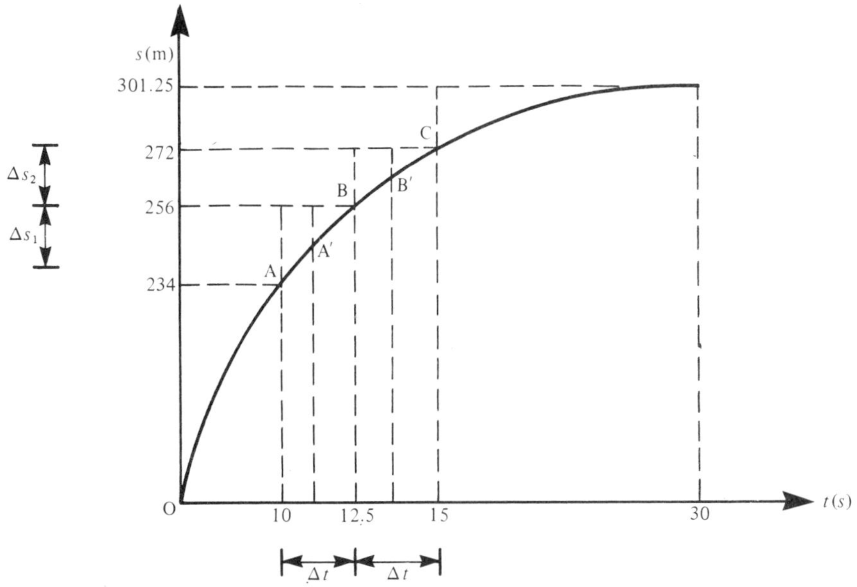

Figure 2.2 Finding velocity and acceleration from a displacement–time graph.

At $t = 0$: the velocity is $36.8 + 10.8 = 47.60$ m/s (estimated) and the acceleration is

$$-4.32 - 1.12 = -5.44 \text{ m/s}^2$$

using the value of 10.8 for the change Δv in the velocity and -1.12 for the change Δa in the acceleration.

At $t = 20$ s the velocity is $(2.8 + 1.5)/2 = 2.15$ m/s and the acceleration is -0.52 m/s^2.

The above method is a simple approach to numerical differentiation.

PLANE MOTION 2.3

If a particle is moving in a plane, the motion is said to be planar. In this case we need two coordinates to define its position at any instant; the motion is often referred to as two-dimensional and the particle is said to have two degrees of freedom. In space, the motion is three-dimensional and three coordinates are required to define the position. Motion of a particle along a curved path is referred to as curvilinear.

To define the position of a particle we have to specify a coordinate system, and the one selected is the one that best suits the problem. We shall consider three such systems: Cartesian, polar and intrinsic.

2.3.1 Cartesian coordinates

The reference frame consists of a rectangular set of axes Ox and Oy, as shown in Figure 2.3. A particle at P at time t has coordinates x_1, y_1. If at time $t + \Delta t$ the particle is at P′ whose coordinates are x_2, y_2, then the average velocity is

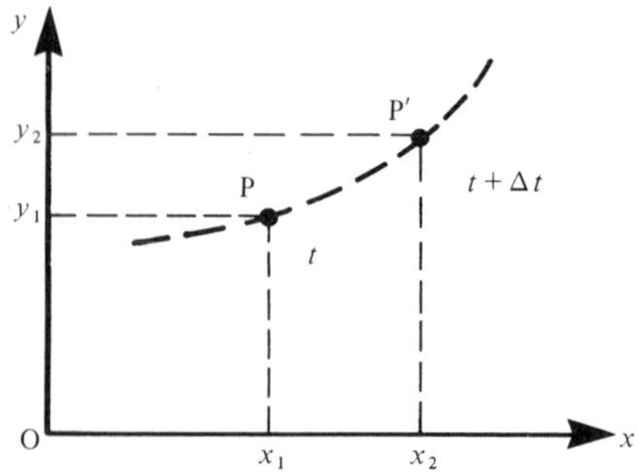

Figure 2.3 Plane motion: Cartesian coordinates.

$$v_{ax} = \frac{x_2 - x_1}{\Delta t} = \frac{\Delta x}{\Delta t}$$

parallel to the x-axis, and

$$v_{ay} = \frac{y_2 - y_1}{\Delta t} = \frac{\Delta y}{\Delta t}$$

parallel to the y-axis.

Since we are usually interested in the velocity at time t, then from our definition of instantaneous velocity we have

$$v_x = \lim_{\Delta t \to 0} \frac{\Delta x}{\Delta t} = \frac{dx}{dt} = \dot{x}$$

parallel to the x-axis, and

$$v_y = \lim_{\Delta t \to 0} \frac{\Delta y}{\Delta t} = \frac{dy}{dt} = \dot{y}$$

parallel to the y-axis.

The velocity will in general vary and the particle will accelerate or decelerate. Hence from our definition of instantaneous acceleration it follows that

$$a_x = \lim_{\Delta t \to 0} \frac{\Delta v_x}{\Delta t} = \frac{dv_x}{dt} = \dot{v}_x = \ddot{x}$$

parallel to the x-axis, and

$$a_y = \lim_{\Delta t \to 0} \frac{\Delta v_y}{\Delta t} = \frac{dv_y}{dt} = \dot{v}_y = \ddot{y}$$

parallel to the y-axis.

2.3.2 Polar coordinates

The position of a particle at P is in certain cases more conveniently expressed by means of the distance $r = \text{OP}$ and the angle θ, as shown in Figure 2.4. O is a convenient reference point and OA a line whose direction is known. The distance r is often referred to as the radius vector or the sight line, and the

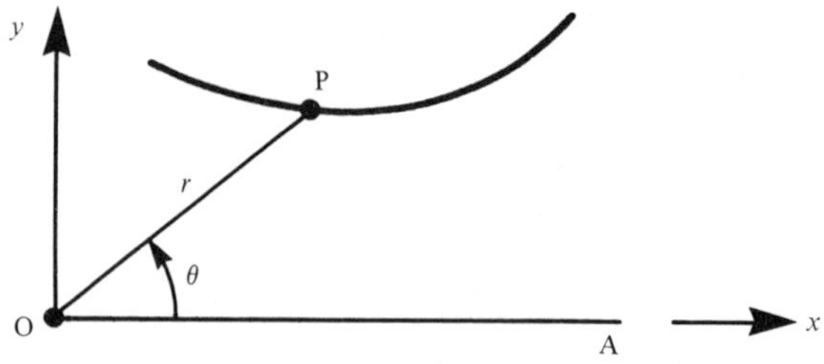

Figure 2.4 Plane motion: polar coordinates.

angle θ the elevation. If in fact OA coincides with the x-axis of a Cartesian frame, then

$$x = r\cos\theta$$

$$y = r\sin\theta$$

Differentiating with respect to time yields

$$\dot{x} = \dot{r}\cos\theta - (r\sin\theta)\dot{\theta} \qquad \text{for the velocity parallel to O}x, \tag{2.1}$$

and

$$\dot{y} = \dot{r}\sin\theta + (r\cos\theta)\dot{\theta} \qquad \text{for the velocity parallel to O}y, \tag{2.2}$$

where $\dot{r} = \dfrac{\mathrm{d}r}{\mathrm{d}t}$ is the rate of change of the sight line or radius vector

$\theta = \dfrac{\mathrm{d}\theta}{\mathrm{d}t}$ is the angular velocity of the sight line or the rate at which it is rotating; it is defined in a way similar to that for rectilinear motion:

$$\frac{\mathrm{d}\theta}{\mathrm{d}t} = \lim_{\Delta t \to 0} \frac{\Delta\theta}{\Delta t} = \dot{\theta}$$

Angular velocity is usually measured in radians/second (rad/s). If it is required in degrees/second, then we multiply rad/s by 57.3 ($= 180/\pi$). The angular velocity is usually denoted by ω, i.e. $\dot{\theta} = \omega$.

If the rotation of the sight line is not uniform, then $\dot{\theta}$ will not be constant, in which case the line is accelerating. The angular acceleration is defined as

$$\frac{\mathrm{d}\omega}{\mathrm{d}t} = \lim_{\Delta t \to 0} \frac{\Delta\omega}{\Delta t} = \dot{\omega} = \frac{\mathrm{d}^2\theta}{\mathrm{d}t^2} = \ddot{\theta} = \alpha$$

It can also be expressed in the following way:

$$\frac{\mathrm{d}\omega}{\mathrm{d}t} = \frac{\mathrm{d}\omega}{\mathrm{d}\theta}\frac{\mathrm{d}\theta}{\mathrm{d}t} = \omega\frac{\mathrm{d}\omega}{\mathrm{d}\theta}$$

giving a relationship between angular acceleration, angular velocity and angular position. (This is analogous to $a = v\,\mathrm{d}v/\mathrm{d}s$ derived previously.)

Differentiating the expressions for $\dot{x}$ and $\dot{y}$ once again with respect to time gives the accelerations

$$\begin{aligned}\ddot{x} &= \ddot{r}\cos\theta - r\dot{\theta}^2\cos\theta - r\ddot{\theta}\sin\theta - 2\dot{r}\dot{\theta}\sin\theta \\ &= (\ddot{r} - r\dot{\theta}^2)\cos\theta - (r\ddot{\theta} + 2\dot{r}\dot{\theta})\sin\theta \qquad (2.3)\end{aligned}$$

and

$$\begin{aligned}\ddot{y} &= \ddot{r}\sin\theta - r\dot{\theta}^2\sin\theta + r\ddot{\theta}\cos\theta + 2\dot{r}\dot{\theta}\cos\theta \\ &= (\ddot{r} - r\dot{\theta}^2)\sin\theta + (r\ddot{\theta} + 2\dot{r}\dot{\theta})\cos\theta \qquad (2.4)\end{aligned}$$

(*Note*: $\dfrac{\mathrm{d}}{\mathrm{d}t}(\dot{r}\cos\theta) = \ddot{r}\cos\theta + \dot{r}\dfrac{\mathrm{d}}{\mathrm{d}t}(\cos\theta) = \ddot{r}\cos\theta + \dot{r}\dfrac{\mathrm{d}}{\mathrm{d}\theta}(\cos\theta)\dfrac{\mathrm{d}\theta}{\mathrm{d}t}$

$= \ddot{r}\cos\theta - \dot{r}\dot{\theta}\sin\theta$

and the other terms are differentiated similarly.)

EXAMPLE 2.3

A radar station is following the progress of an aircraft flying at a constant velocity of 600 km/h away from the station and at a constant altitude of 1000 m. When the aircraft is at a distance of 5100 m as measured by the radar, calculate in magnitude and direction

(a) r and $\dot{r}$ of the sight line, and

(b) the rates at which the radar dish is turning in order to keep track of the aircraft.

Figure 2.5 shows the aircraft at any instant t. Its position relative to the radar station is at a horizontal distance x and an altitude y metres and with velocities v_x and v_y m/s respectively. The radar can only measure $\theta, r, \dot{\theta}, \dot{r}, \ddot{\theta}$ and $\ddot{r}$, i.e. changes in the sight line. In Figure 2.5 the velocity of the aircraft as seen by the radar station consists of two components: $\dot{r}$ along the sight line and $r\dot{\theta}$ perpendicular to it.

Example Cont.

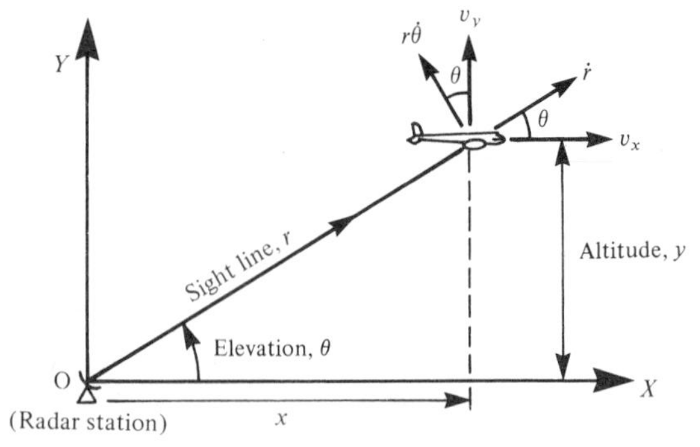

Figure 2.5 Tracking an aircraft with radar.

SOLUTION

Referring to Figure 2.5 we have

$$x = \sqrt{r^2 - y^2} = \sqrt{5100^2 - 1000^2}$$

$$= 5001 \text{ m}$$

$$\theta = \arcsin\left(\frac{y}{r}\right) = \arcsin\left(\frac{1000}{5100}\right)$$

$$= 11.31°$$

$$\dot{r} = v_x \cos\theta = 600 \times \frac{5001}{5100} = 588.35 \text{ km/h}$$

$$= 163.4 \text{ m/s}$$

From equation (2.2) we have

$$\dot{r}\sin\theta + (r\cos\theta)\dot{\theta} = 0 \qquad \text{since } \dot{y} = 0$$

Hence

$$\dot{\theta} = -\frac{\dot{r}}{r}\tan\theta = \frac{163.4}{5100} \times \frac{1000}{5001}$$

$$= -6.4 \times 10^{-3} \text{ rad/s}$$

The negative sign means that the sight line is dropping, i.e. the elevation is getting smaller as the aircraft is flying away from the radar station.

To calculate $\ddot{r}$ it is best to proceed as follows.

We know that

$$r^2 = x^2 + y^2$$

Solution Cont.

Differentiating with respect to time yields

$$r\dot{r} = x\dot{x} + y\dot{y} = x\dot{x} \qquad \text{since } \dot{y} = 0$$

Differentiating once more gives

$$r\ddot{r} + \dot{r}^2 = x\ddot{x} + \dot{x}^2 = \dot{x}^2 \qquad \text{since } \ddot{x} = 0$$

Hence

$$\ddot{r} = \frac{\dot{x}^2 - \dot{r}^2}{r} = \frac{(600/3.6)^2 - 163.4^2}{5100}$$

$$= 0.209 \text{ m/s}^2$$

To calculate $\ddot{\theta}$ we can use equation (2.4), noting that $\ddot{y} = 0$. We have

$$r\ddot{\theta} + 2\dot{r}\dot{\theta} = -(\ddot{r} - r\dot{\theta}^2)\tan\theta$$

Solving for $\ddot{\theta}$ gives

$$\ddot{\theta} = -\frac{1}{r}[\ddot{r} - r\dot{\theta}^2)\tan\theta + 2\dot{r}\dot{\theta})]$$

$$= -\frac{1}{5100}\Big\{[0.209 - 5100 \times (6.4 \times 10^{-3})^2]$$

$$\times \frac{1000}{5001} + 2 \times 163.43 \times -6.4 \times 10^{-3}\Big\}$$

Hence

$$\ddot{\theta} = -4.1 \times 10^{-4} \text{ rad/s}^2$$

Solution Cont.

If we resolve equations (2.3) and (2.4) along the sight line and perpendicular to it, we find that

$$\text{acceleration along the sight line} = \ddot{r} - r\dot{\theta}^2 \qquad (2.5)$$

and

$$\text{acceleration perpendicular to the sight line} = r\ddot{\theta} + 2\dot{r}\dot{\theta} \qquad (2.6)$$

With Cartesian coordinates the directions are fixed in advance so that displacements, velocities and accelerations do not change in direction, only in magnitude. These quantities can then be resolved into components in any other directions we care to choose, such as the radial and transverse directions, i.e. along the sight line and perpendicular to it as above.

With polar coordinates, however, both magnitude and direction change continuously, and a more visual way to study these changes than the straight differentiation previously carried out is discussed in what follows.

Consider a particle moving along a curve as shown in Figure 2.6, and let P be its position at time t, and P′ its position at time $t + \Delta t$. Then let R be the position vector which defines the position of the particle from some fixed origin O, and let θ be the angle this vector makes with a known datum direction, both at time t.

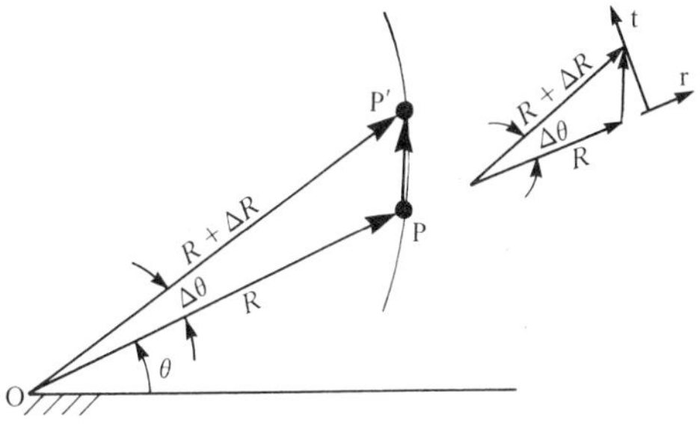

Figure 2.6 Curved trajectory: polar coordinates.

At time $t + \Delta t$ the position vector is $R + \Delta r$ and its direction is $\theta + \Delta\theta$. Let us resolve the changes in the magnitude of the position vector in the radial (r) direction and in the transverse (t) direction as shown.

The velocities in these two directions are as follows:

(a) In the radial direction:

$$v_r = \lim_{\Delta t \to 0} \frac{(R + \Delta R)\cos\Delta\theta - R}{\Delta t} = \frac{dR}{dt} = \dot{R} \qquad \text{since } \cos\Delta\theta \simeq 1.$$

(b) In the transverse direction:

$$v_t = \lim_{\Delta t \to 0} \frac{(R + \Delta R)\sin\Delta\theta}{\Delta t} = R\frac{d\theta}{dt} = R\dot{\theta} = R\omega$$

since $\sin\Delta\theta \simeq \Delta\theta$ and $\Delta R\Delta\dot{\theta} \to 0$ as $\Delta t \to 0$.

Figure 2.7 shows the velocities in the radial and transverse directions at time t and at time $t + \Delta t$. To derive expressions for the accelerations in these two directions we proceed as below, remembering that acceleration is the rate of change of velocity.

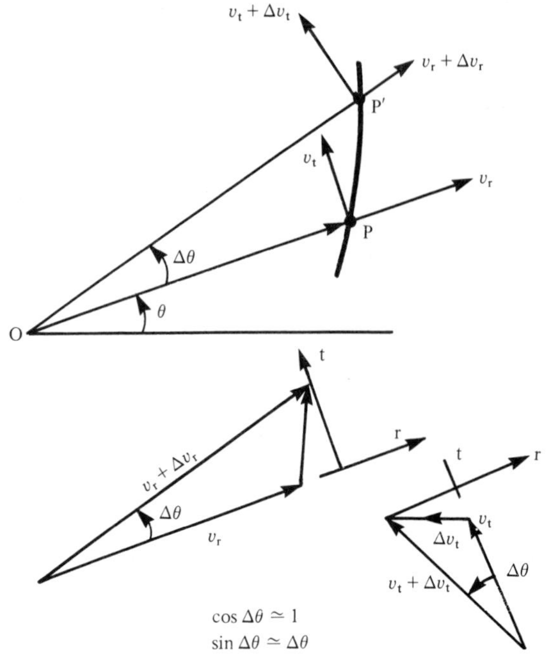

Figure 2.7 Curved trajectory: radial and transverse velocities.

(a) In the radial direction:

$$a_r = \lim_{\Delta t \to 0} \frac{(v_r + \Delta v_r)1 - v_r - (v_t + \Delta v_t)\Delta\theta}{\Delta t}$$

Since $\cos \Delta\theta \simeq 1$ and $\sin \Delta\theta \simeq \Delta\theta$. So

$$a_r = \frac{dv_r}{dt} - v_t \frac{d\theta}{dt}$$

$$= \ddot{R} - R\omega^2$$

since $v_t = R\omega$ and $dv_r/dt = \ddot{R}$.

(b) In the transverse direction:

$$a_t = \lim_{\Delta t \to 0} \frac{(v_r + \Delta v_r)\Delta\theta + (v_t + \Delta v_t)1 - v_t}{\Delta t}$$

$$= \dot{R}\omega + \frac{d}{dt}(R\omega) = \dot{R}\omega + \dot{R}\omega + R\dot{\omega}$$

$$= R\dot{\omega} + 2\dot{R}\omega$$

where $\dot{\omega}$ is the angular acceleration of the position vector.

These two expressions for the acceleration of the particle at any time t are shown in Figure 2.8. They are very important and we shall meet them again when dealing with motion along any curve and in the analysis of mechanisms. The term $2\dot{R}\omega$ is known as the *Coriolis acceleration*, after the French mathematician and physicist, Gaspard Gustave de Coriolis (1792–1843).

(1) R constant: In this case we have motion in a circle and $\dot{R} = \ddot{R} = 0$, and hence $2\dot{R}\omega = 0$, i.e. the Coriolis acceleration is zero but the particle is subjected to the centripetal acceleration $R\omega^2$.

(2) $\dot{R}$ and ω constant: In this case the position vector is rotating at constant angular velocity and the point P is moving away from O, i.e. relative to O with constant velocity. Consequently the particle is subjected to both the Coriolis acceleration $2\dot{R}\omega$ and the centripetal acceleration $R\omega^2$.

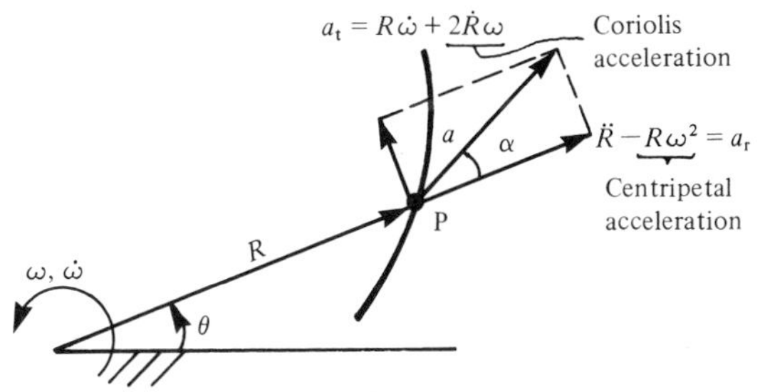

Figure 2.8 Curved trajectory: centripetal and Coriolis accelerations.

The reader should note that whenever a particle moves along a curve, whether plane or spatial, the centripetal term is always present.

EXAMPLE 2.4 **Example Cont.**

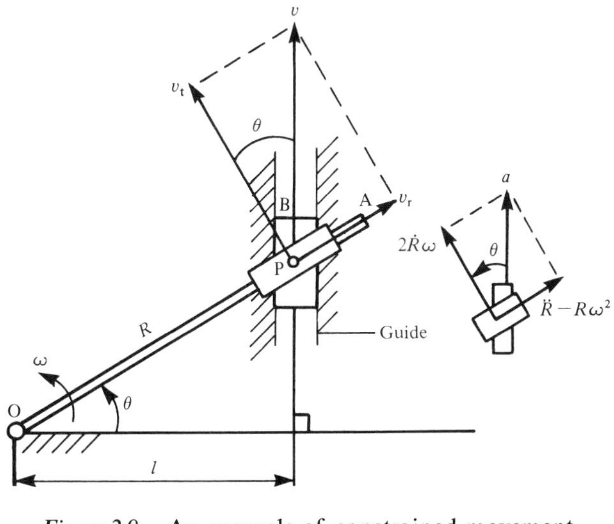

Figure 2.9 An example of constrained movement.

Example Cont.

Figure 2.9 shows a block B constrained to move along a fixed guide. Block P is pinned to B and free to slide along the rod OA, which rotates about O with a constant angular velocity ω rad/s. Hence, as the rod rotates, block P transfers its motion to B.

Example Cont.

Calculate (a) the velocity and acceleration of B and (b) the side force on the rod if the mass of the block P is m_P.

SOLUTION

Since B is constrained to move in the guide, its velocity v is in the direction shown. The velocity of block P is $v_r = \dot{R}$ radially and $v_t = R\omega$ transversely. It follows that

$$v = v_t/\cos\theta = R\omega/\cos\theta$$

but

$$R = l/\cos\theta$$

where l is the distance from O to the centre-line of the guide. Hence

$$v = \omega l/\cos^2\theta$$

In a practical situation the velocity of sliding, v_r, will be important because of wear and lubrication:

Solution Cont.

$$v_r = \dot{R} = \frac{d}{dt}\left(\frac{l}{\cos\theta}\right) = \frac{d}{d\theta}\left(\frac{1}{\cos\theta}\right)\frac{d\theta}{d\theta}$$

$$= \omega l \sin\theta/\cos^2\theta$$

The acceleration a of block B is

$$a = 2\dot{R}\omega/\cos\theta = 2\omega^2 l \sin\theta/\cos^3\theta$$

The side force F is due to the Coriolis acceleration and is given by

$$F = m_P \times a_{Coriolis} = 2m_P\dot{R}\omega$$

The reader should verify that the acceleration a is also given by

$$a = (\ddot{R} - R\omega^2)/\sin\theta$$

2.3.3 **Intrinsic or tangential coordinates**

Consider a particle moving along the path AB as shown in Figure 2.10 (a). The distance travelled by the particle is measured from A along the path. Let s be this distance at time t when the particle is at P; at $t + \Delta t$ it is at P′ a further distance Δs along the path. Two normals drawn to the path at P and P′ meet at O and make an angle $\Delta\theta$. The average velocity of the particle is $\Delta s/\Delta t$ and its velocity at time t as given by

$$v_t = \lim_{\Delta t \to 0} \frac{\Delta s}{\Delta t} = \dot{s}$$

is directed along the tangent to the path at P. The particle has no velocity along the normal at P, i.e. along OP.

Figure 2.10 (b) shows the velocities of the particle at time t, i.e. v_t along the tangent at P, and at $t + \Delta t$, i.e. $v_t + \Delta v_t$ along the tangent at P′. Expressions for the acceleration are obtained by considering changes in the velocity along the tangential direction and along the normal at P.

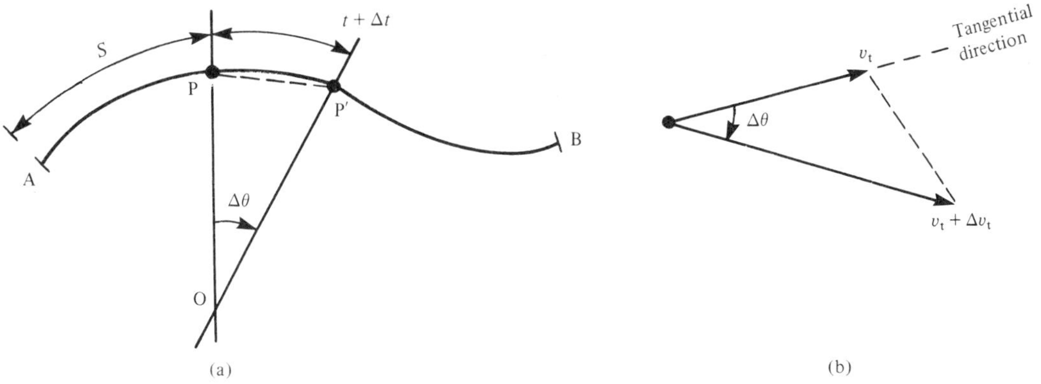

Figure 2.10 Plane motion: intrinsic or tangential coordinates.

From Figure 2.10 we see that the change in the velocity along the tangential direction is

$$(v_t + \Delta v_t)\cos\Delta\theta - v_t$$

If a_t is the tangential acceleration in that direction, then

$$a_t = \lim_{\Delta t \to 0} \frac{(v_t + \Delta v_t)\cos\Delta\theta - v_t}{\Delta t}$$

$$= \lim_{\Delta t \to 0} \frac{\Delta v_t}{\Delta t} = \frac{dv_t}{dt} = \dot{v}_t = \ddot{s} \qquad \text{since } \cos\Delta\theta \simeq 1$$

The change in the velocity in the normal direction is

$$(v_t + \Delta v_t)\sin\Delta\theta = v_t\Delta\theta + \Delta v_t\Delta\theta \qquad \text{since } \sin\Delta\theta \simeq \Delta\theta$$

If a_n is the acceleration along the normal, then

$$a_n = \lim_{\Delta t \to 0} \frac{v_t\Delta\theta + \Delta v_t\Delta\theta}{\Delta t} = v_t\frac{d\theta}{dt} = v_t\frac{d\theta}{ds}\frac{ds}{dt} = v_t^2\frac{d\theta}{ds}$$

But from the figure $OP \times \Delta\theta = \Delta s$, hence $\Delta\theta/\Delta s = 1/OP$, which in the limit is $1/\rho$, where ρ is the radius of curvature of the path at P. It follows that

$$a_n = \frac{v_t^2}{\rho}$$

directed towards O, which is the centripetal acceleration. It should be noted that this acceleration is always present when the particle moves along a curved path even if its speed is constant. This is because velocity has magnitude (speed) and direction, and along a curved path the direction is changing all the time; for example, motion in a circle is a special case of the above.

EXAMPLE 2.5

A car takes a sharp bend of 100 m radius at a constant speed of 110 km/h. Calculate its acceleration.

SOLUTION

Transversely, $a_t = 0$ since v_t is constant and, normally,

$$a_n = \frac{v_t^2}{\rho} = \left(\frac{110}{3.6}\right)^2 \frac{1}{100} = 9.34\ \text{m/s}^2 \simeq 1g$$

2.4 VELOCITY AND DISPLACEMENT FROM A KNOWLEDGE OF ACCELERATION

Situations arise where the acceleration of a particle is known (mathematically or numerically) and we wish to calculate its velocity and displacement.

Noting that the acceleration a is given by

$$a = \frac{dv}{dt} = v\frac{dv}{ds}$$

where v is the velocity and s is the displacement, we express these relationships in differential form thus:

$$dv = a\,dt \qquad \text{or} \qquad v\,dv = a\,ds$$

Figure 2.11(a) illustrates the acceleration–time relationship. During the time interval dt the area $a\,dt$ is equal to the change in the velocity of the particle. Hence during a finite time interval $t_2 - t_1$ the change in the velocity is the area under the a–t graph and is given by the integral

$$v_2 - v_1 = \int_{t_1}^{t_2} a\,dt \qquad (2.7a)$$

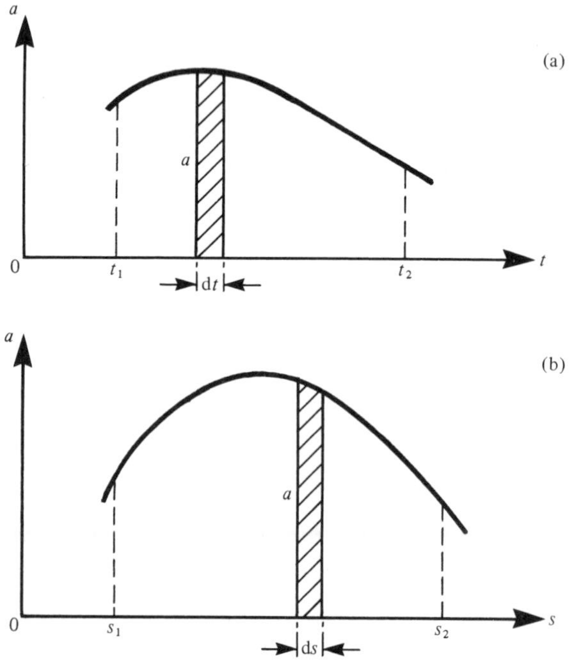

Figure 2.11 (a) Acceleration–time and (b) acceleration–displacement graphs.

If the acceleration is known as a function of the displacement, as shown in Figure 2.11(b), then the change $v\,dv$ in the velocity during the small displacement ds is given by the area $a\,ds$. Integrating this relationship between $s = s_1$ and $s = s_2$, where the velocities are $v = v_1$ and $v = v_2$ respectively, we obtain

$$\tfrac{1}{2}v_2^2 - \tfrac{1}{2}v_1^2 = \int_{s_1}^{s_2} a\,ds \qquad (2.7b)$$

which is the area under the a–s graph.

Situations occur where the acceleration is constant, as in the case of free fall under gravity or by design, e.g. in the case of the acceleration of a lift, but an unvalidated assumption can lead to disastrous results in other cases!

To obtain the displacement we use

$$v = \frac{ds}{dt} \qquad \text{or} \qquad v\,dt = ds$$

During a small time interval dt the area $v\,dt$ is equal to the change ds in the displacement of the particle, as shown in Figure 2.12. It follows that during a finite time interval $t_2 - t_1$ the change in the displacement of the particle is given by the integral

$$s_2 - s_1 = \int_{t_1}^{t_2} v\,dt \qquad (2.8)$$

which is the area under the v–t graph.

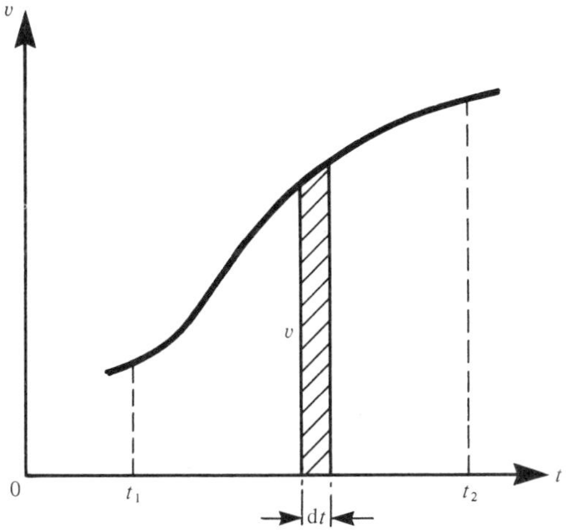

Figure 2.12 Velocity–time graph.

EXAMPLE 2.6

A lift has a constant acceleration of 0.5 m/s^2 for 4 s, zero acceleration for a further 6 s and is brought to rest with a constant deceleration of 0.75 m/s^2. Show the velocity profile for this lift and calculate the total distance travelled.

SOLUTION

Figure 2.13 (a) shows the acceleration–time graph, the deceleration being negative.

We consider this in three phases:

(1) Phase 1: We have $a = 0.5$ m/s^2, constant; $v = 0$ at $t = 0$. Hence from equation (2.7a) we have for the velocity when $t = 4$ s

$$v_4 = 0 + \int_0^4 0.5\,dt = [0.5t]_0^4$$

$$= 0.5 \times 4 = 2 \text{ m/s}$$

(2) Phase 2: We have $a = 0$, $v = 2$ m/s when $t = 4$ s, and when $t = 10$ s the velocity is

$$v_{10} = v_4 + \int_4^{10} 0\,dt = v_4 = 2 \text{ m/s}$$

Solution Cont.

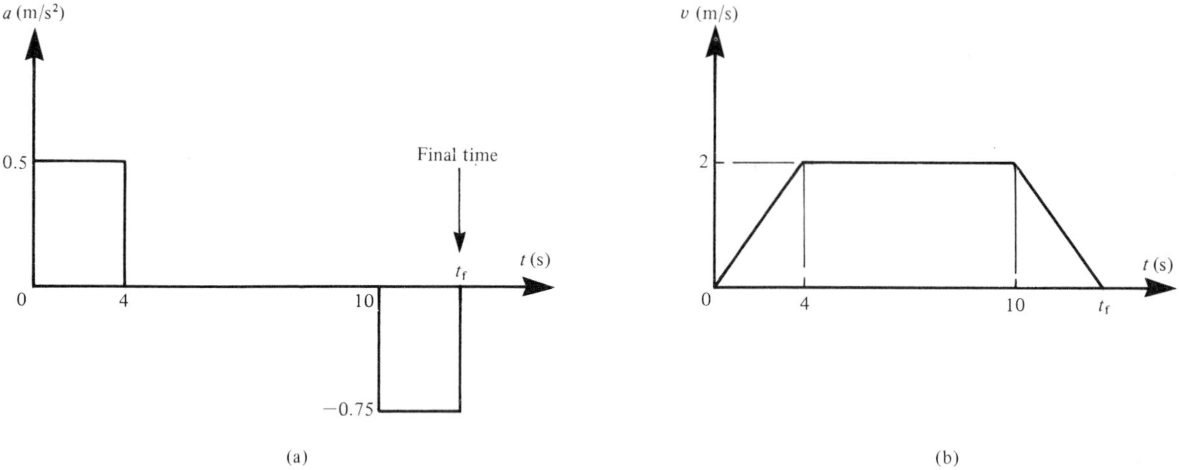

Figure 2.13 (a) Acceleration–time and (b) velocity-time graphs for a lift.

(3) Phase 3: We have $a = -0.75\ \text{m/s}^2$, constant; $v_{10} = 2$ m/s. So

$$v_f = 2 + \int_{10}^{t_f} (-0.75)\,dt = 2 - 0.75(t_f - 10)$$

$$= 9.5 - 0.75t_f$$

The lift comes to rest when $v = 0$, and hence

$$t_f = 9.5/0.75 = 12.67\ \text{s}$$

The velocity–time graph can now be plotted, as shown in Figure 2.13 (b).

For the total distance we use equation (2.8) with $s_1 = 0$ at $t_1 = 0$; hence

$$s_{total} = 0 + \int_0^{t_f} v\,dt$$

$$= \int_0^4 0.5t\,dt + \int_4^{10} 2\,dt$$

$$+ \int_{10}^{12.67} (9.5 - 0.75t)\,dt$$

$$= 18.67\ \text{m}$$

EXAMPLE 2.7

During a test the acceleration of a car starting from rest was recorded every 5 s; the values are given in Table 2.3. Draw the acceleration–time graph and hence the velocity–time graph; from the latter obtain the time taken for the car to reach 100 km/h and estimate its maximum speed on that occasion. Calculate also the distance covered in 80 s.

Example Cont.

Table 2.3

t (s)	0	5	10	15	20	25
a (m/s²)	3	1.95	1.5	1.14	0.93	0.75
t (s)	30	35	40	45	50	55
a (m/s²)	0.63	0.54	0.42	0.33	0.24	0.18
t (s)	60	65	70	75	80	
a (m/s²)	0.15	0.105	0.09	0.04	0.025	

SOLUTION

Consider the following procedure (Figure 2.14). If at time t_n the acceleration of the car is a_n and its velocity is v_n, then at time t_{n+1} the velocity will be

$$v_{n+1} = v_n + \left(\frac{a_n + a_{n+1}}{2}\right)(t_{n+1} - t_n)$$

where the last term is the area ABCD under the acceleration–time graph.

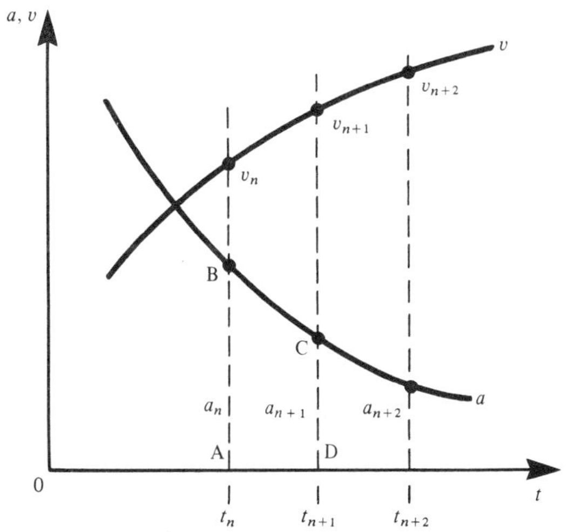

Figure 2.14 Procedure for calculating velocity when acceleration is known.

Similarly at time t_{n+2}, we have

$$v_{n+2} = v_{n+1} + \left(\frac{a_{n+1} + a_{n+2}}{2}\right)(t_{n+2} - t_{n+1})$$

When the acceleration as a function of time is not known mathematically, we may replace equation (2.7a) by the above approximation for each step.

The result of such computations is shown in Table 2.4 for the car test.

Table 2.4

t (s)	0	5	10	15	20	25
v (km/h)	0	44.6	75.6	99.4	118	133.11
t (s)	30	35	40	45	50	55
v (km/h)	145.53	156.06	164.7	171.45	176.58	180.36
t (s)	60	65	70	75	80	
v (km/h)	183.33	185.62	187.38	188.55	189.14	

The velocity–time graph is shown superimposed on the acceleration–time graph in Figure 2.15.

Solution Cont.

To illustrate the procedure, let us consider a few points on the graph. Since the car starts from rest, we know that $v_1 = 0$ at $t = 0$. Hence the velocity at 5 s is

$$v_2 = \frac{a_1 + a_2}{2}\Delta t = (a_1 + a_2)\frac{\Delta t}{2}$$

$$= (3 + 1.95) \times \frac{5}{2} \times 3.6 = 44.6 \text{ km/h}$$

(The factor of 3.6 is to convert from m/s to km/h.) Also

$$v_3 = v_2 + (a_2 + a_3)\frac{\Delta t}{2}$$

$$= 44.6 + (1.95 + 1.5) \times 2.5 \times 3.6$$

$$= 75.6 \text{ km/h}$$

$$v_4 = v_3 + (a_3 + a_4)\frac{\Delta t}{2} = 75.6$$

$$+ (1.5 + 1.14) \times 2.5 \times 3.6$$

$$= 99.36 \text{ km/h}$$

and so on until

$$v_{17} = v_{16} + (a_{16} + a_{17})\frac{\Delta t}{2}$$

$$= 188.55 + (0.04 + 0.015) \times 9$$

$$= 189.14 \text{ km/h}$$

From the velocity-time graph, the time taken to reach 100 km/h is seen to be 16 s, line A to B to C.

The maximum speed of the car corresponds to $a = 0$, zero acceleration; we see from the graph that this would occur when $t = 85$ s by extrapolation, giving

$$v_{\max} = 190 \text{ km/h}$$

To calculate the distance travelled in 80 s we can use Simpson's rule (see Appendix A.3), since it is equal to the area under the velocity-time graph by equation (2.8). Hence we have

$$s = \frac{\Delta t}{3}[v_1 + v_{17} + 4(v_2 + v_4 + \ldots + v_{16})$$

$$+ 2(v_3 + v_5 + \ldots + v_{15})]$$

$$= \frac{5}{3 \times 3.6} \times [0 + 189.4 + 4(44.6 + 99.4$$

$$+ 133.11 + 156.06 + 171.45 + 180.36$$

$$+ 185.62 + 188.55) + 2(75.6 + 118$$

$$+ 145.33 + 164.7 + 176.58 + 183.33$$

$$+ 187.38)]$$

$$= 3207 \text{ m}$$

Solution Cont. **Solution Cont.**

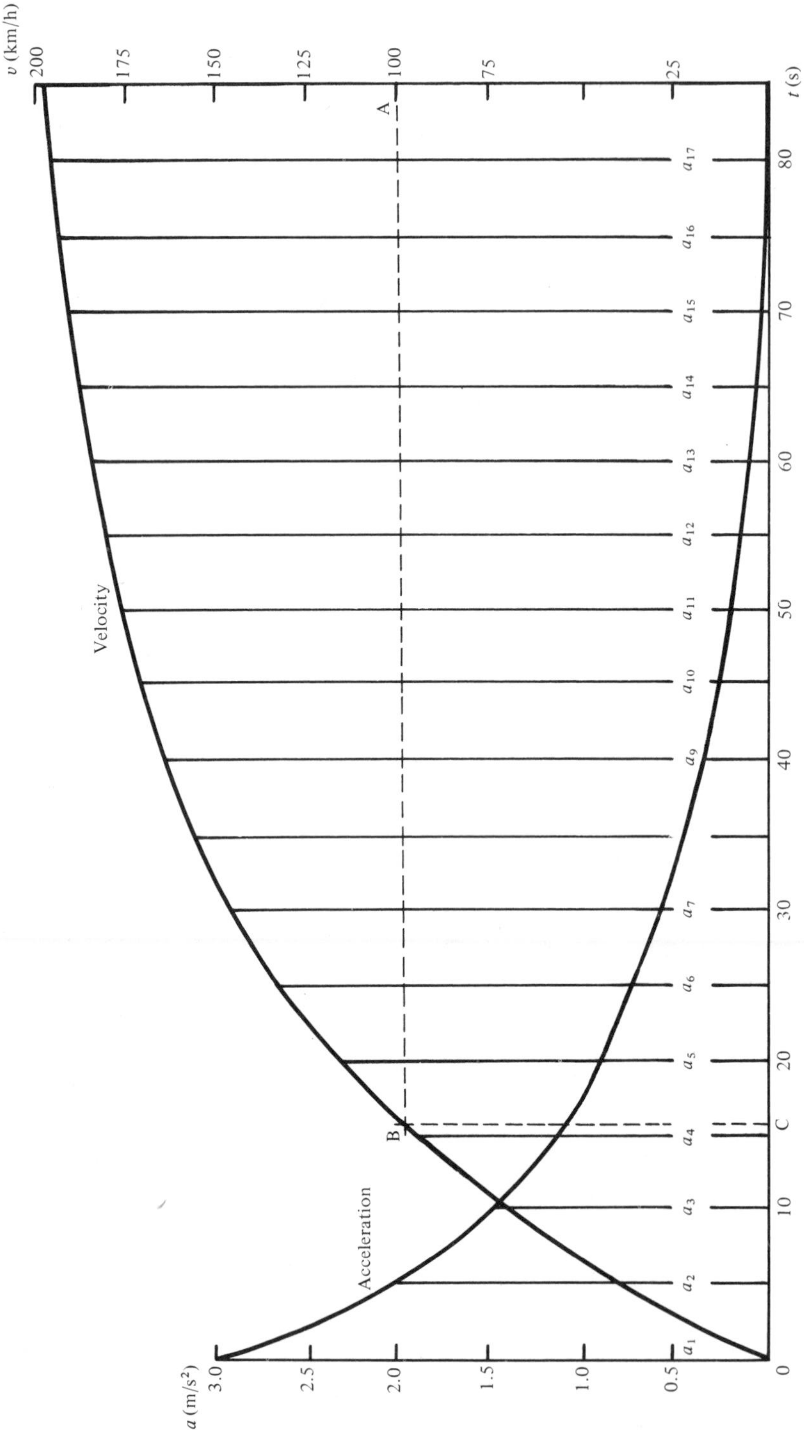

Figure 2.15 Acceleration and velocity versus time graphs for a car.

2.4.1 Acceleration as a function of velocity

The acceleration of a particle depends on a number of factors that will be discussed later in the chapter on kinetics. For the moment let us accept the fact that in many instances the acceleration is not necessarily constant; for example, all particles and bodies wholly or partially immersed in a fluid (water, air or other substance) experience a resistance that is a function of their velocity, better known as the drag force or simply the drag.

It is shown in books on fluid mechanics that the total drag D of a body divided by its projected area A (in the direction of motion) and by the dynamic pressure $\rho v^2/2$ is given by

$$\frac{D/A}{\rho v^2/2} = C_D = f(Re) \tag{2.9}$$

where C_D is the drag coefficient, $Re = vl/\nu$ is the Reynolds number, v is the velocity, ν is the kinematic viscosity of the fluid, ρ is the density of the fluid and l is a representative dimension of the body.

At high Reynolds numbers (greater than 2×10^4) the value of C_D tends to remain constant for a large number of shapes, e.g. 0.07 for a well streamlined body and about 1.0 for a circular cylinder with its axis parallel to the flow.

At very low Reynolds numbers

$$C_D \simeq 24/Re$$

In the case of complex shapes, such as aircraft, ships and cars, the value of the overall drag coefficient is usually obtained from model tests in wind tunnels or towing tanks.

The overall drag on an aircraft in flight is a function of the square of the velocity. A road vehicle, on the other hand, is subject to a resistance consisting primarily of two terms: a constant term, the rolling resistance, and a second term that depends on the square of the velocity.

For a better appreciation of the drag problem, the reader should consult the appropriate texts on fluid mechanics.

To accelerate a particle or a body the power source, e.g. an electric motor, an internal combustion engine (petrol or diesel), a gas turbine, a water wheel, etc., must be capable of overcoming the total resistance, but as soon as that power source is cut off the resistance produces a deceleration.

In general we can express the acceleration a by

$$a = a_p - f(v) \tag{2.10}$$

where a_p is the acceleration that the power source would produce in the absence of all resistance.

Since the acceleration can be expressed in two ways, namely

$$a = \frac{dv}{dt} \qquad \text{and} \qquad a = v\frac{dv}{ds}$$

equation (2.10) becomes

$$\frac{dv}{dt} = a_p - f(v) \tag{2.11a}$$

or

$$v\frac{dv}{ds} = a_p - f(v) \tag{2.11b}$$

To calculate the time t_{01} taken for the velocity to increase from v_0 at time t_0 to v_1 at time t_1 we can separate the variables in equation (2.11a) and integrate, giving

$$t_{01} = t_1 - t_0 = \int_{v_0}^{v_1} \frac{dv}{a_p - f(v)} \tag{2.12}$$

Similarly the distance s_{01} travelled in that time is obtained by separating the variables in equation (2.11b) and integrating so that

$$s_{01} = s_1 - s_0 = \int_{v_0}^{v_1} \frac{v\,dv}{a_p - f(v)} \tag{2.13}$$

With the power off, equation (2.10) becomes

$$a = -f(v)$$

so that the particle or body is decelerating.

Equation (2.10) shows that for a constant power source the acceleration decreases until $a = 0$, giving $a_p = f(v)$, and the velocity reaches its maximum value v_{max}. For example, suppose that the power source or prime mover produces a constant acceleration a_p and that $f(v) = A + Bv^2$, where A and B are constants. Then

$$a = a_p - (A + Bv^2)$$

or

$$a_p = (a - A) - Bv^2$$

When $a = 0$, $v = v_{max}$, given by

$$v_{max} = \sqrt{\frac{a_p - A}{B}} \tag{2.14}$$

The acceleration a_p produced by a prime mover is not necessarily constant. It can vary with time, distance or velocity. Figure 2.16 shows the acceleration produced by a petrol engine in going through the gears and driving a vehicle. The broken curve shows the resistance of the vehicle. Hence the acceleration at any instant is the difference between the two curves

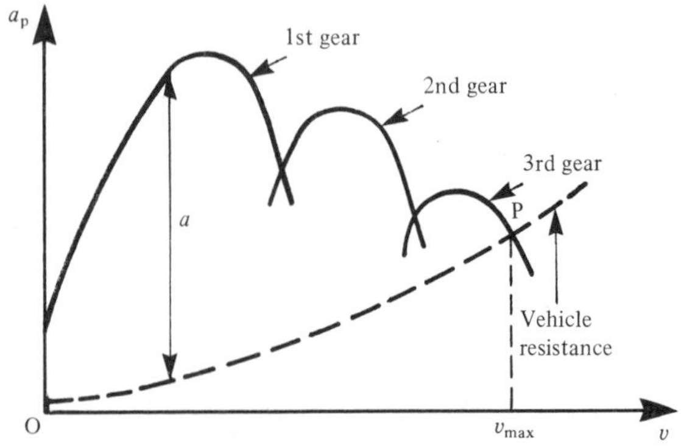

Figure 2.16 Acceleration–velocity graph for a geared vehicle.

and the point P where they meet is the equilibrium point corresponding to the maximum velocity of the vehicle. Prime-mover characteristics will be reviewed in the chapter on kinetics.

EXAMPLE 2.8

The prime mover of an electric car produces, at zero resistance, a constant acceleration $a_p = 2.95\ \mathrm{m/s^2}$. The resistance of the car to motion, in $\mathrm{m/s^2}$, is $0.06 + 0.002v^2$, where v is the velocity in m/s. Calculate (a) the initial acceleration of the car, (b) the maximum velocity of the car, (c) the time taken to reach maximum velocity from rest and (d) the distance covered by the car to reach its maximum velocity from rest.

SOLUTION

At any instant the acceleration of the car is

$$\begin{aligned} a &= a_p - (A + Bv^2) \\ &= 2.95 - (0.06 + 0.002v^2)\ \mathrm{m/s^2} \end{aligned}$$

(a) At $t = 0$, $v = 0$ since the car starts from rest. Hence

$$a_0 = 2.95 - 0.06 = 2.89\ \mathrm{m/s^2} = 0.29g$$

(b) $v = v_{max}$ when $a = 0$. Hence

$$\begin{aligned} v_{max} &= \sqrt{\frac{2.89}{0.002}} = 38\ \mathrm{m/s} \\ &= 136\ \mathrm{km/h} \end{aligned}$$

(c) We have

$$a = \frac{dv}{dt} = a_p - (A + Bv^2) = a_1 - Bv^2$$

where $a_1 = a_p - A$. To solve for t we must separate the variables so that

$$\frac{dv}{a_1 - Bv_2} = dt$$

Integrating both sides gives

$$\int \frac{dv}{a_1 - Bv^2} = t + C$$

(where C is a constant). This is a standard integral of the type

$$\int \frac{dx}{a - bx^2}$$

(see Appendix A.2) whose value is

$$\frac{1}{2ab} \ln\left(\frac{a + bx}{a - bx}\right)$$

Hence the solution is

$$t + C = \frac{1}{2\sqrt{a_1 B}} \ln\left(\frac{\sqrt{a_1} + \sqrt{B}v}{\sqrt{a_1} - \sqrt{B}v}\right)$$

From the statement of the problem, $v = 0$ at $t = 0$ so that $C = 0$. If t_m is the time taken to reach maximum velocity then

$$t_m = \frac{1}{2\sqrt{a_1 B}} \ln\left(\frac{\sqrt{a_1} - \sqrt{B}v_{max}}{\sqrt{a_1} - \sqrt{B}v_{max}}\right)$$

Now, $a_1 = 2.95 - 0.06 = 2.89\ \mathrm{m/s^2}$, $B = 0.002/\mathrm{m}$, and hence

$$\begin{aligned} t_m &= \frac{1}{1\sqrt{2.89 \times 0.02}} \times \\ &\quad \ln\left(\frac{\sqrt{2.89} + \sqrt{0.002} \times 38}{\sqrt{2.89} - \sqrt{0.002} \times 38}\right) \\ &= 57\ \mathrm{s} \end{aligned}$$

(d) We have

$$a = v\frac{dv}{ds} = a_1 - Bv^2$$

Separating the variables and integrating yields

$$\int \frac{v\,dv}{a_1 - Bv^2} = s + C_1$$

(where C_1 is a constant). The solution is (see Appendix A.2)

$$-\frac{1}{2B} \ln(a_1 - Bv^2) = s + C_1$$

When $s = 0$, $v = 0$, so that

$$C_1 = -\frac{1}{2B} \ln a_1$$

Solution Cont.

If s_{max} is the distance travelled to reach v_{max} then

$$s_{max} = \frac{1}{2B}\ln\left(\frac{a_1}{a_1 - Bv^2_{max}}\right)$$

Substituting numerical values gives

Solution Cont.

$$s_{max} = \frac{1}{2 \times 0.002}\ln\left(\frac{2.89}{2.89 - 0.002 \times 38^2}\right)$$

$$= 1820 \text{ m}$$

$$= 1.82 \text{ km}$$

2.5 CONSTANT ACCELERATION

When the rate of change of the velocity of a particle remains constant with the passing of time, the motion is said to be uniformly accelerated, i.e. the acceleration is constant or uniform. Free fall under gravity near the surface of a planet, a car slowing down as a result of the application of the brakes, with the clutch disengaged and the brake pressure is constant, and the acceleration of a lift maintained at a constant value by design are examples of constant acceleration.

In reality there are not many cases where the acceleration of a particle is truly constant but there are situations where the engineer may be justified in considering the acceleration as being effectively constant. To illustrate such a situation we propose to consider a typical industrial problem met by engineers involved in the design and installation of belt conveyors. One aspect of the problem concerns the positioning of a hopper relative to the discharge end of a conveyor.

To reduce wear on the hopper and breakage of fragile material, the location and design must take into account the path or trajectory that the material will tend to follow when discharged over a pulley. The path in still air depends on the acceleration due to gravity, the material being conveyed, the belt speed, the pulley diameter and the inclination of the conveyor. Figure 2.17 shows the discharge end of the conveyor, part of the receiving hopper and the path the material will follow. Material close to the belt will not be thrown as far as that furthest away from the belt.

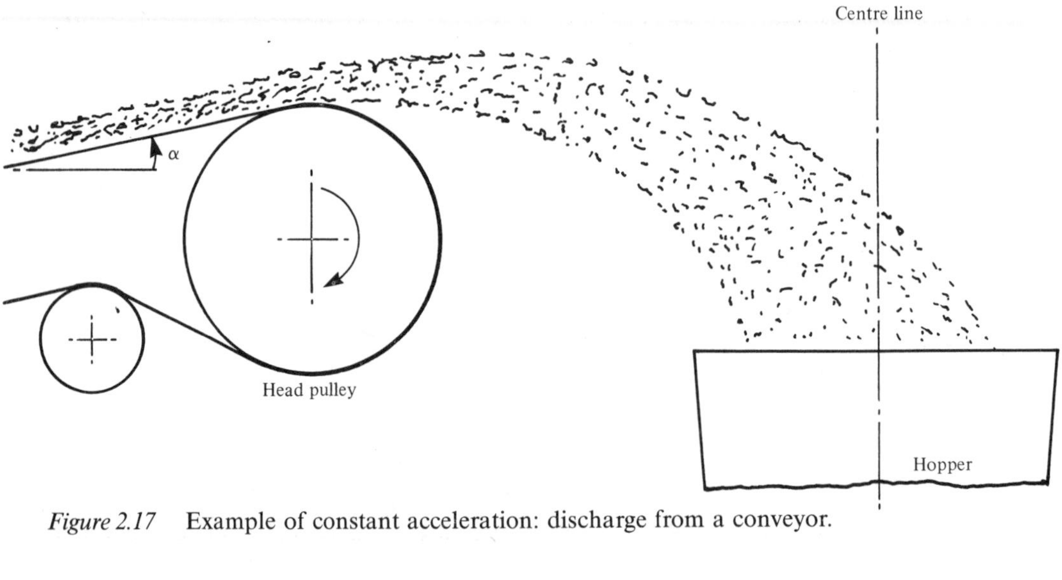

Figure 2.17 Example of constant acceleration: discharge from a conveyor.

From the broad industrial picture we isolate the relevant system (Figure 2.18). The point A where the material leaves the conveyor depends on the speed of the belt, the radius of the pulley and an allowance for the thickness of the belt and material. It can be shown that angle θ is given by

$$\cos\theta = \frac{v_0^2}{g(R+d)} = \frac{\omega^2(R+d)}{g}$$

where v_0 is the speed of the mid-line ABC and ω is the angular velocity of the pulley, as shown in Figure 2.18.

The material will leave at B if $\cos\theta = 1$, i.e. when

$$v_0 \geqslant v_c = \sqrt{g(R+d)}$$

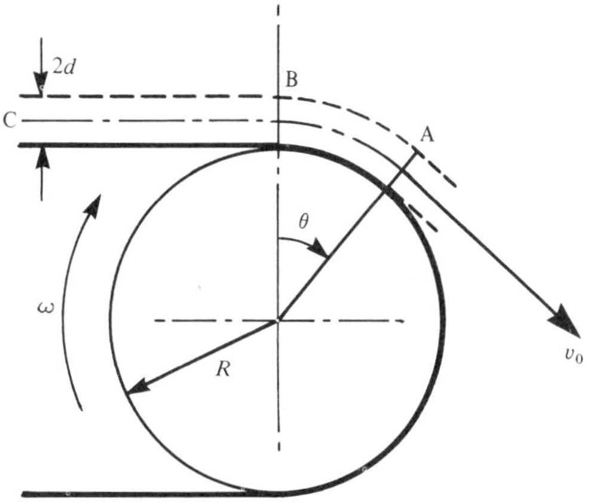

Figure 2.18 Geometry of discharge from conveyor.

The speed $v_c = \sqrt{g(R+d)}$ is referred to as the critical speed. The above equation assumes there is sufficient friction for the material not to slip on the belt as it goes around the pulley.

The trajectory is calculated on the basis that the only acceleration to which a particle is subjected after leaving the conveyor is that due to gravity, and with a velocity known both in magnitude and direction. Air resistance plays an insignificant part in the motion because the velocities involved and the particle size are small. For a granular material having particle size of 10 mm, the effect of air resistance corresponds to a deceleration of about 0.07 m/s^2 which is very small compared with g of 9.81 m/s^2.

The following example illustrates the calculations necessary to arrive at the correct positioning of a hopper to collect the material. A few years ago the author, when commissioning a conveyor plant, came across a case where most of the material fell outside the hopper!

EXAMPLE 2.9

Calculate the horizontal distance between the centre-line of the hopper and the pulley centre in the case of a conveyor discharging granular material into a hopper whose top is 2 m below the centre of the pulley. The data are given in Table 2.5.

Example Cont.

Table 2.5

Speed of the conveyor	3 m/s
Depth of material	50 mm
Thickness of belt	20 mm
Pulley diameter	640 mm
Inclination of the conveyor	15°

SOLUTION **Solution Cont.**

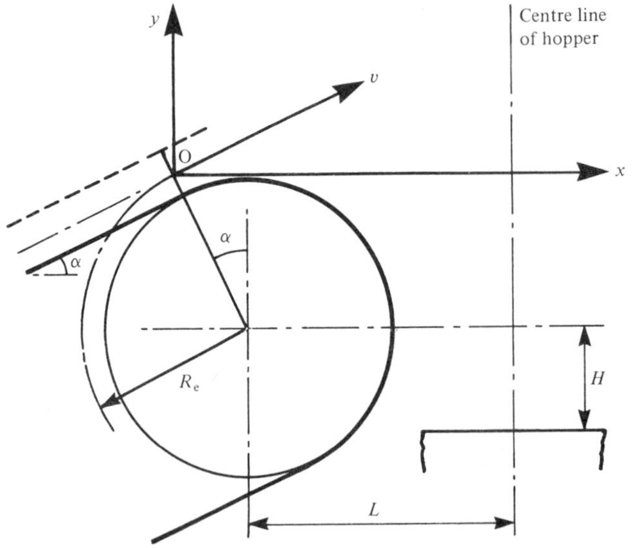

Figure 2.19 Calculating distance between hopper and pulley.

(See Figure 2.19.) Let H be the height of the pulley above the hopper and let L be the horizontal distance between the pulley and hopper centre-lines. Also let R_e be the effective radius, i.e. pulley radius + belt thickness + half thickness of material. Thus

$$\begin{aligned} R_e &= R + t + d \\ &= 0.32 + 0.02 + 0.025 \\ &= 0.365 \text{ m} \end{aligned}$$

Figure 2.19 shows the material leaving at O; if this is correct,

$$v_0 \geqslant \sqrt{g\mathrm{R_e}}$$

i.e.

$$3 \geqslant \sqrt{9.81 \times 0.365} \qquad \text{or} \qquad 3 \geqslant v_c$$

The material will therefore leave at O with a velocity of 3 m/s tangentially to the effective radius R_e.

Before proceeding with the detailed calculation it is important to define a frame of reference: a convenient one is shown in Figure 2.20. It has its origin at O, the discharge point, and axes Ox and Oy horizontally and vertically.

Consider a particle at any instant t after leaving the conveyor with an initial velocity v as shown in Figure 2.20. The only acceleration to which the particle is subjected is that due to gravity g.

If a_x and a_y are the accelerations of the particle along Ox and Oy respectively, then we have

$$a_x = 0 \qquad \text{or} \qquad \frac{dv_x}{dt} = 0$$

and

$$a_y = -g \qquad \text{or} \qquad \frac{dv_y}{dt} = -g$$

Note the sign! Gravity g acts in the opposite direction to our vertical axis.

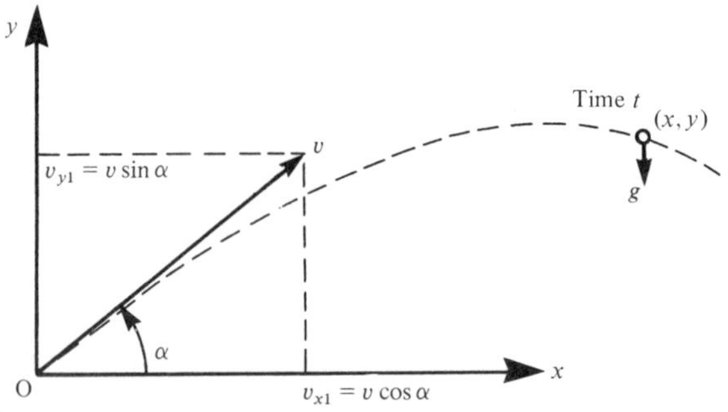

Figure 2.20 A convenient frame of reference for the conveyor problem.

Solution Cont.

To solve these equations for v_x and v_y we integrate with respect to time and obtain

$$v_x = \text{constant} \qquad v_y = -gt + \text{constant}$$

Since, when $t = 0$, $v_x = v_{x1} = v\cos\alpha$ and $v_y = v_{y1} = v\sin\alpha$, it follows that

$$v_x = v\cos\alpha \qquad v_y = v\sin\alpha - gt$$

or

$$\frac{dx}{dt} = v\cos\alpha \qquad \frac{dy}{dt} = v\sin\alpha - gt$$

where x and y are the coordinates of the particle at time t.

Since we require the position of the particle, we integrate once more with respect to time giving

$$x = vt\cos\alpha + \text{constant}$$

$$y = vt\sin\alpha - \tfrac{1}{2}gt^2 + \text{constant}$$

At $t = 0$, $x = y = 0$, and hence both constants are zero, so that the coordinates are

$$x = vt\cos\alpha \qquad y = vt\sin\alpha - \tfrac{1}{2}gt^2$$

From the first equation

$$t = \frac{x}{v\cos\alpha}$$

Solution Cont.

and substituting in the equation for y yields a quadratic in x:

$$gx^2 - (v^2\sin 2\alpha)x + 2yv^2\cos^2\alpha = 0$$

From the data we have

$$\alpha = 15^\circ \qquad v = 3\text{ m/s}$$

$$y = -(H + R_e\cos\alpha)$$

$$= -(2 + 0.365\cos 15^\circ) = -2.355\text{ m}$$

Note the sign! The top of the hopper is below the origin of our axes. Substituting in the above equation yields

$$x^2 - 0.459x - 4.174 = 0$$

with roots $x = 2.29$ m or -1.83 m (see Appendix A.6 for the roots of a quadratic equation). The practical value is 2.29 m.

It therefore follows that the centre-line of the hopper should be at a distance from the centre of the pulley given by

$$L = x - R_e\sin\alpha$$

$$= 2.29 - 0.365\sin 15^\circ$$

$$= 2.20\text{ m}$$

EXERCISES

2.1 A train rounds a curve of 750 m radius at a speed of 150 km/h. At that instant its speed is increasing at the rate of 3.25 km/h every second. Calculate the total acceleration of the train.

2.2 A space module is landing on a planet whose gravity is one-third that of the Earth; its speed of descent of 7 m/s is controlled by rocket motors. If, when at a height of 10 m, its motors cut out, calculate the speed of impact when the module hits the surface of the planet.

2.3 A train is travelling at 100 km/h. Power is shut off and the brakes are applied. If the brakes exert a constant retarding force equal to 10% of the weight of the train and all other resistances are proportional to the square of the speed and at 100 km/h are equal to 1% of the weight of the train, calculate (a) the distance travelled and (b) the time taken before coming to rest.

2.4 An aircraft is climbing at a constant speed of 225 km/h and at an angle of 15° to the horizontal after taking off from O (Figure 2.21). One minute later it levels off and its progress is being monitored by a radar station R situated 6 km from O and at the same level as O. For the instant after levelling off, calculate (a) the distance of the aircraft from the radar, (b) the rate of change of the length of the sight line, and (c) the rate at which the radar dish must be rotating in order to follow the aircraft.

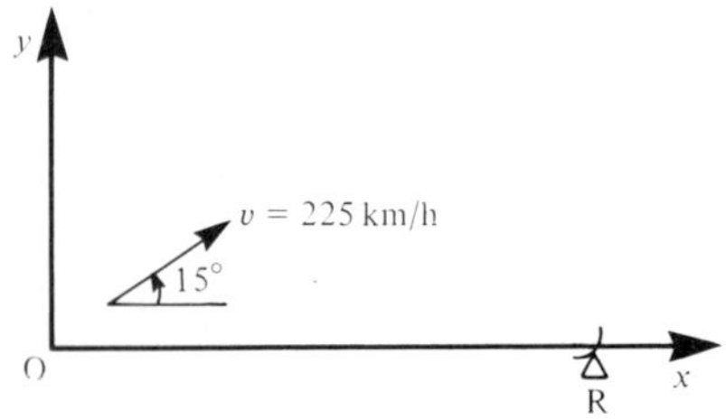

Figure 2.21

2.5 Figure 2.22 shows the acceleration of a particle starting from rest. (a) Sketch the velocity–time graph, and (b) calculate the total distance covered if at time t' the particle's velocity is zero.

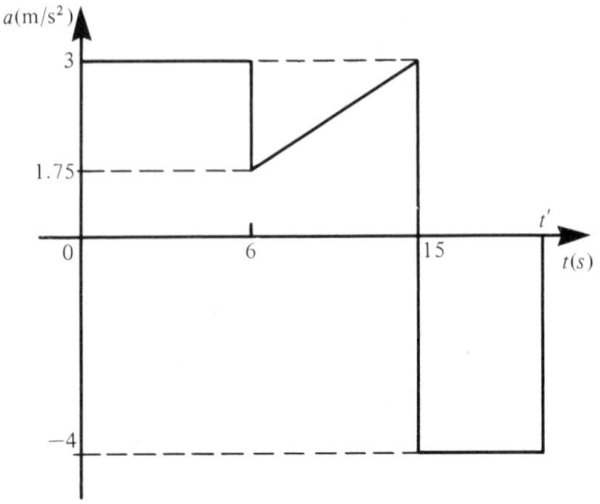

Figure 2.22

2.6 A sports car started from rest and its speed as a function of time was as follows:

t (s)	0.5	1.0	1.5	2.0	2.5	3.0	3.5
v (km/h)	19.2	36.0	49.6	60.8	68.0	72.0	70.4
t (s)	4.0	4.5	5.0	5.5	6.0	6.5	7.0
v (km/h)	65.6	63.2	64.8	72.0	83.2	92.0	96.0

Plot a graph of the acceleration of the car. At 7.0 s how far had the car travelled? If at 7.0 s the brakes were applied producing a constant deceleration of $0.5g$, how much further did the car travel?

2.7 The following table shows the variation of the lift of one of the valves in an internal combustion engine as a function of the angular position of the camshaft:

θ (deg)	0	5	10	15	20	25	30	35	40	45	50	55
y (mm)	0	0.43	1.73	3.78	5.82	7.59	9.14	10.41	11.4	12.12	12.55	12.70

Draw a graph of the displacement, velocity and acceleration of the valve as a function of the angle. The camshaft rotates at 850 rev/min.

2.8 (a) Referring to Figure 2.18, prove the formula for the angle at which the material leaves the conveyor belt, assuming no slippage. (b) Figure 2.23 shows material being discharged from a thin belt conveyor into a hopper situated 2.5 m below the centre C of the head pulley. Calculate the distance D to the centre-line of the hopper and the minimum width d to ensure that the material will fall into it. State your assumptions.

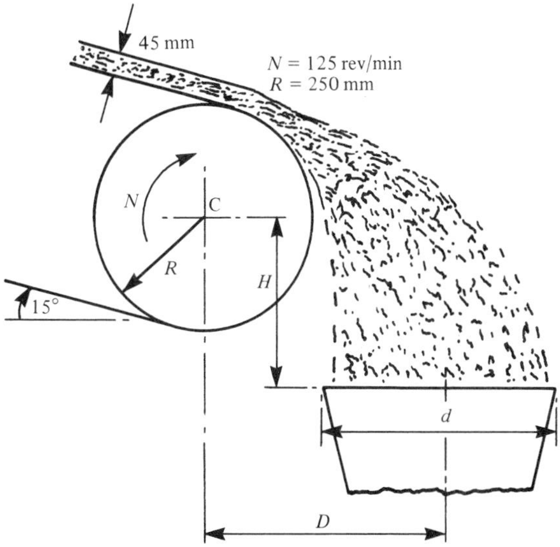

Figure 2.23

2.9 A block A is constrained to slide in the slotted lever shown in Figure 2.24 by means of a screw, not shown, with a velocity of 2.5 m/s relative to the lever. For the position shown, calculate the acceleration of A using the data given in the figure. Indicate also the direction of the Coriolis acceleration.

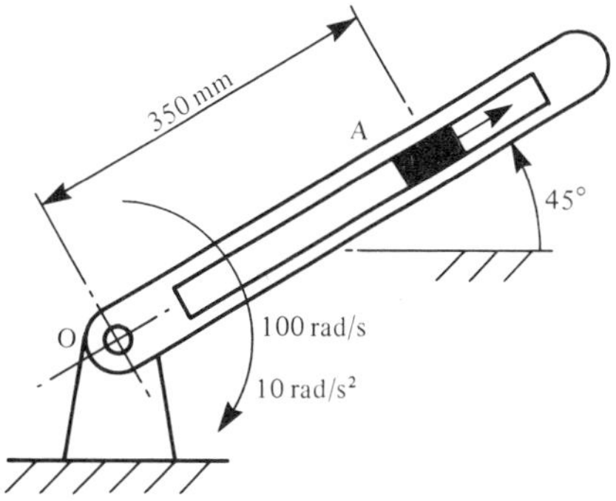

Figure 2.24

2.10 Figure 2.25 shows a simple form of cam. It consists of a circular disc of radius R pivoted at O, a distance e from its centre C. F is a point follower situated directly above O. If the cam rotates at a constant angular velocity ω, obtain an expression for the velocity of the follower. What is the total travel of the follower? In the case of a cam of 85 mm diameter rotating at 720 rev/min, calculate the maximum acceleration of the follower given that $e = 15$ mm and using the approximation that e/R is small.

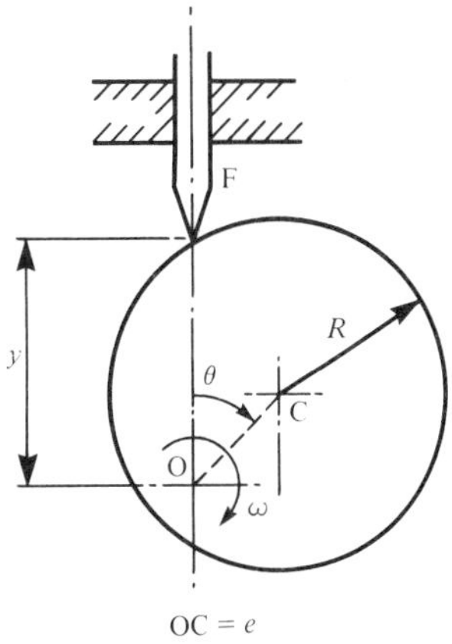

Figure 2.25

2.11 The mechanism shown in Figure 2.26 has many practical applications; it is called a "quick return mechanism" and consists of a crank OA driven by an electric motor rotating at a constant angular velocity ω. A link O′T pivoted at O′ is constrained to oscillate between T′ and T″ by means of a slider S pivoted at A. There is a second slider at T constrained to move along a fixed guide by the action of the link O′T. In a shaping machine this slider carries a tool for cutting metal or other material. Obtain expressions for the velocity $\dot{x}$ and the acceleration $\ddot{x}$ of the slider T.

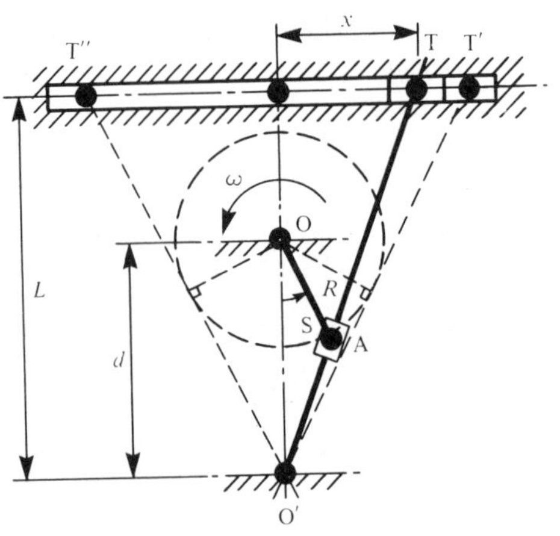

Figure 2.26

2.12 During a trial a ship was towed at a constant velocity of 7 m/s in calm waters. The towing rope was slipped and the retardation of the ship at various velocities was recorded:

v (m/s)	7	6.5	6	5.5	5	4.5	4
a (m/s^2)	0.042	0.041	0.04	0.037	0.033	0.027	0.023
v (m/s)	3.5	3	2.5	2	1.5	1	
a (m/s^2)	0.019	0.015	0.012	0.01	0.008	0.007	

Plot velocity–time and displacement–time graphs and obtain the time elapsed and the distance travelled by the ship while the velocity decreased from 7 to 2 m/s.

2.13 A fully loaded transport aircraft is flying at its maximum speed of 850 km/h and at a constant altitude of 9000 m. Each of its four engines would produce an acceleration of 0.46 m/s^2 in the absence of air resistance and on full thrust. If the resistance is proportional to the square of the speed, calculate the constant of proportionality. If while flying at that same altitude the total thrust of the engines is reduced by 25%, calculate the new maximum speed of the aircraft and the time taken to slow down to this new speed from 850 km/h.

3

Kinematics of Rigid Bodies

INTRODUCTION 3.1

We shall concern ourselves with the plane motion of rigid bodies only.

The motion of a body in a plane is either curvilinear or rotational or a combination of both, in which case the body translates and rotates simultaneously. Curvilinear motion means that the body follows a curved path without rotating, i.e. it maintains its orientation. Rectilinear translation of a body takes place in straight lines and is a special case of curvilinear motion.

To illustrate these motions let us consider the mechanism of the internal combustion engine shown diagrammatically in Figure 3.1. The main elements are the cylinder and the frame (both of which are fixed), the piston, the connecting rod and the crank connected to (or usually integrated with) the crankshaft.

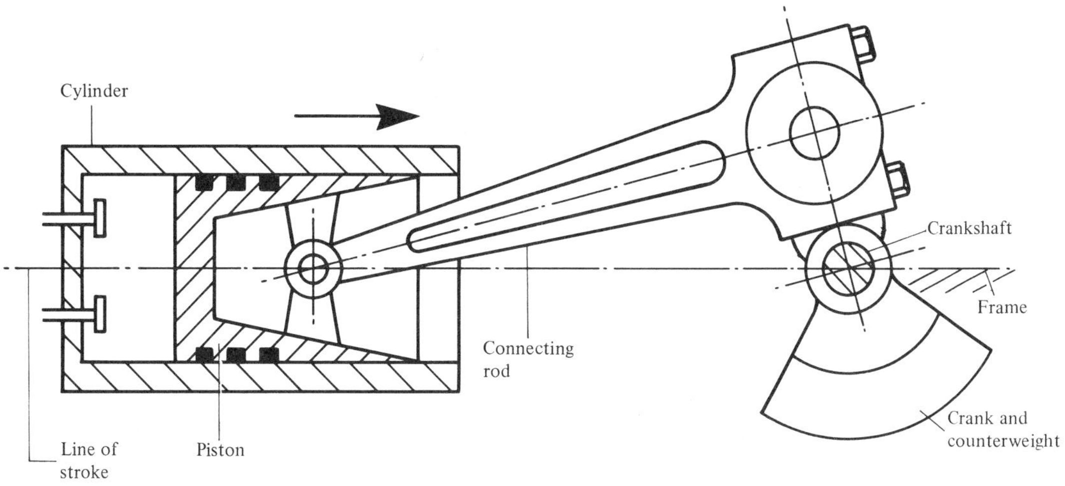

Figure 3.1 Mechanism of internal combustion engine.

The operation of the engine is such that the piston has rectilinear translation along the line of stroke, the crank has rotational motion about the axis of the crankshaft and the connecting rod has plane motion, i.e. simultaneous translation and rotation. Furthermore the motion of the piston has a to-and-fro action.

3.2 PLANE MOTION

Consider the body shown in Figure 3.2. A and B are any two points in the body and, since the body is rigid, the distance AB remains constant throughout the motion. Let the position of the body at time t be as shown. After a time Δt, A is at A_1 and B is at B_1; the motion may therefore be regarded as a translation from A to A_1 of Δl and from B to B' of Δl together with a rotation $\Delta\theta$ about A_1 to bring B' into the position B_1.

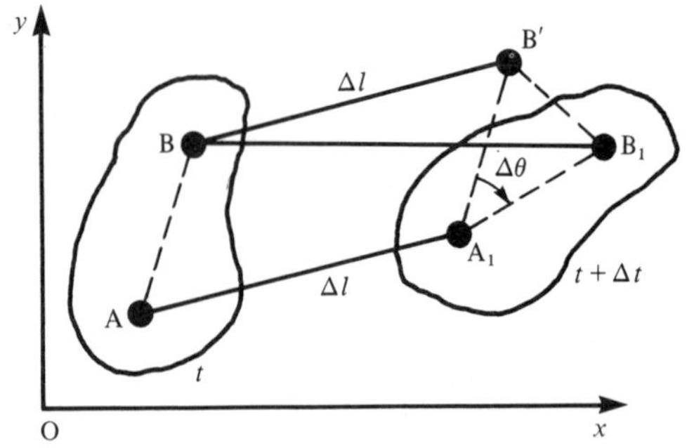

Figure 3.2 Plane motion of a rigid body.

It follows that the body in moving from the position AB to A_1B_1 has a velocity of translation given by

$$v = \lim_{\Delta t \to 0} \frac{\Delta l}{\Delta t} = \frac{dl}{dt} = \dot{l} \tag{3.1}$$

and a rotational velocity or angular velocity ω given by

$$\omega = \lim_{\Delta t \to 0} \frac{\Delta\theta}{\Delta t} = \frac{d\theta}{dt} = \dot{\theta} \tag{3.2}$$

Every point in the body is thus treated as having the velocity of translation v and every line joining any two points has the angular velocity ω.

3.3 RELATIVE VELOCITY

Let us now consider a body moving in the plane and two points A and B within it as shown in Figure 3.3(a). Let A have a velocity v_A and B a velocity v_B in the directions shown. Resolving these velocities along AB and perpendicular to AB gives

$$\begin{aligned} v_{A1} &= v_A \cos\theta_A \\ v_{B1} &= v_B \cos\theta_B \\ v_{A2} &= v_A \sin\theta_A \\ v_{B2} &= v_B \sin\theta_B \end{aligned}$$

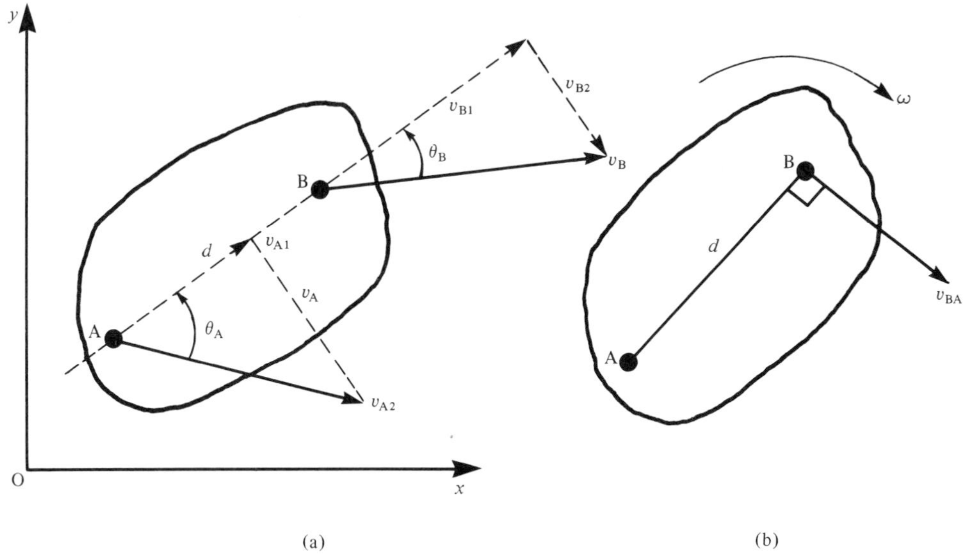

Figure 3.3 Relative velocity of two points in a rigid body.

Since the body is rigid, it follows that $v_{A1} = v_{B1}$ and the velocity of B relative to A, written v_{BA}, is given by

$$v_{BA} = v_{B2} - v_{A2}$$

whose direction is perpendicular to AB (see Figure 3.3(b)). Hence the motion of B as seen by A is one of rotation about A; it follows that the angular velocity ω of the body is given by

$$\omega = \frac{v_{BA}}{d}$$

where d is the distance AB. The absolute velocity of the point B is then given by

$$\mathbf{v}_B = \mathbf{v}_A + \mathbf{v}_{BA} \tag{3.3}$$

These must be added vectorially as shown in Figure 3.4. This equation states that the absolute velocity of B is the resultant of the absolute velocity of A and the velocity of B relative to A.

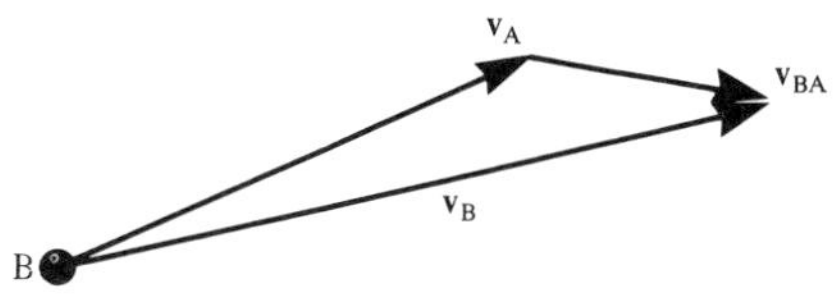

Figure 3.4 Absolute velocity.

3.4 INSTANTANEOUS CENTRE

Suppose that a point A in a rigid body has an absolute velocity $\mathbf{v}_A$ and a second point B has an absolute velocity $\mathbf{v}_B$ as shown in Figure 3.5. Then, if these velocities are different, the body has an angular velocity ω at a particular instant. Now A can be considered as rotating about some point along a perpendicular to the velocity vector $\mathbf{v}_A$, i.e. along A_1A_2, and likewise B can be considered as rotating about a point along a perpendicular to the velocity vector $\mathbf{v}_B$, i.e. along B_1B_2. We, therefore, conclude that at that particular instant the body must be rotating about the point of intersection of A_1A_2 and B_1B_2, i.e. about the point I. This point is called the *instantaneous centre,* or alternatively the *instant* or *virtual* centre. Since v_A and v_B are in general not constant, the instant centre is not a fixed point, but a point regarded as being instantaneously at rest.

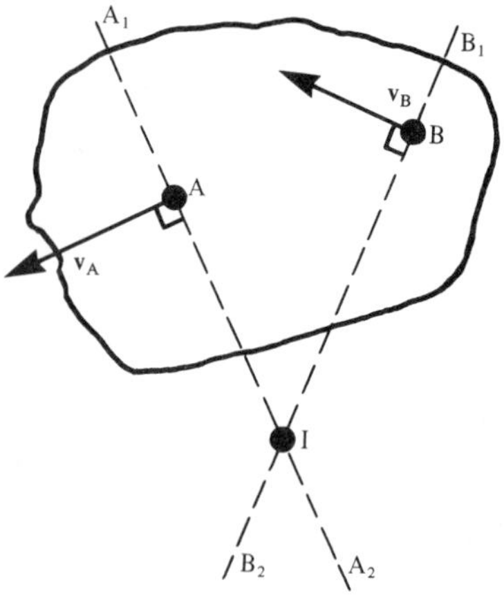

Figure 3.5 Finding the instantaneous centre.

If ω is the angular velocity of the body at that instant, it follows that

$$\omega = \frac{v_A}{IA} = \frac{v_B}{IB} \tag{3.4}$$

The use of this equation is illustrated by the following example.

EXAMPLE 3.1

The crank of the engine mechanism shown in Figure 3.1 is rotating clockwise at 3500 rev/min. The crank radius is 55 mm and the length of the connecting rod 170 mm. Calculate the velocity of the piston and the angular velocity of the connecting rod at the instant when the crank makes an angle of (a) 40° and (b) 345° with the line of stroke.

SOLUTION

Figure 3.6 is a scale drawing of the construction. The angular velocity of the crank is

$$\omega_c = \frac{2\pi \times 3500}{60} = 366.5 \text{ rad/s}$$

Hence the linear velocity of the crank pin A is $v_A = \omega_c \times$ crank radius, perpendicular to OA:

$$v_A = 366.5 \times \frac{55}{1000} = 20.16 \text{ m/s}$$

Let v_P be the velocity of the piston, which is along the line of stroke. For position 1 corresponding to an angle of 40°, draw AI_1 perpendicular to v_A and P_1I_1 perpendicular to v_{P1}. Then from equation (3.4)

$$\omega_1 = \frac{v_A}{I_1A} = \frac{v_{P1}}{I_1P_1}$$

Hence

$$v_{P1} = v_A \times \frac{I_1P_1}{I_1A}$$

$$= 20.16 \times \frac{85}{107}$$

$$= 16.01 \text{ m/s}$$

Solution Cont. **Solution Cont.**

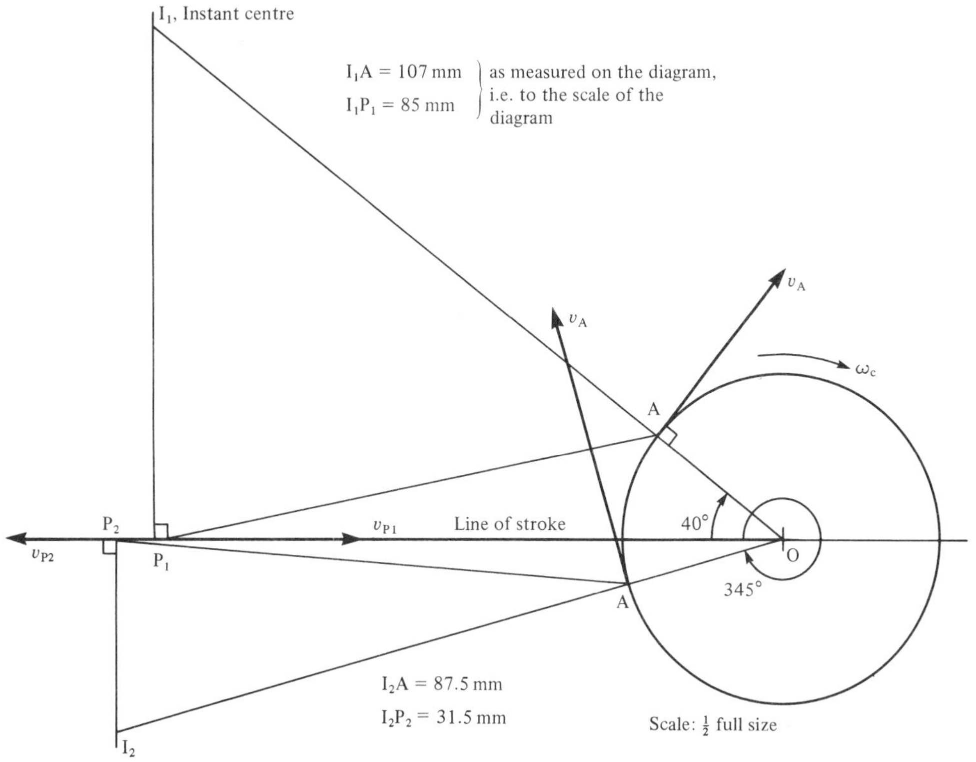

Figure 3.6 Scale drawing of the crank of an engine mechanism.

Similarly for position 2,

$$v_{P2} = v_A \times \frac{I_2P_2}{I_2A} = 20.16 \times \frac{31.5}{87.5}$$

$$= 7.26 \text{ m/s}$$

The angular velocity of the connecting rod is

$$\text{(a)} \quad \omega_1 = \frac{v_A}{I_1A} = \frac{20.16}{(0.107 \times 2)} = 94.2 \text{ rad/s}$$

(the factor of 2 is to take into account the scale of the drawing, also $I_1A = 0.107$ m) and

$$\text{(b)} \quad \omega_2 = \frac{v_A}{I_2A} = \frac{20.16}{(0.0875 \times 2)} = 115.2 \text{ rad/s}$$

The construction shows clearly that the instantaneous centre is not a fixed point.

When the crank makes an angle of 90° or 270° with the line of stroke, the instant centres are at infinity, hence IA = IB and $v_P = v_A$. For the 90° case the piston is moving to the right and for the 270° case the piston is moving to the left; also for the connecting rod $\omega = 0$, i.e. in those positions it is translating with a velocity equal to v_A in magnitude and direction.

Furthermore when the angle is 0° or 180°, $v_P = 0$ because I coincides with P, and therefore IP = 0.

The instantaneous-centre concept provides a very useful and rapid way of calculating the velocities of the moving parts of any mechanism. It may be used to set up analytical relationships, but if used graphically there are some drawbacks, e.g. limited accuracy and the need for a separate construction for each increment in the motion.

3.5 ACCELERATION OF A RIGID BODY

Consider once again the motion of a rigid body, and in particular two points A and B within it, a distance d apart, as shown in Figure 3.7. The velocities v_A and v_B of the two points will, in general, vary with time so that A and B will accelerate. Let $\mathbf{a}_A$ and $\mathbf{a}_B$ be the absolute accelerations of A and B respectively. These have components a_{A1} and a_{B1} along AB and a_{A2} and a_{B2} perpendicular to AB. Proceeding as in section 3.3, the acceleration of B relative to A has two components, $a_{B1} - a_{A1}$ along AB and $a_{B2} - a_{A2}$ perpendicular to AB.

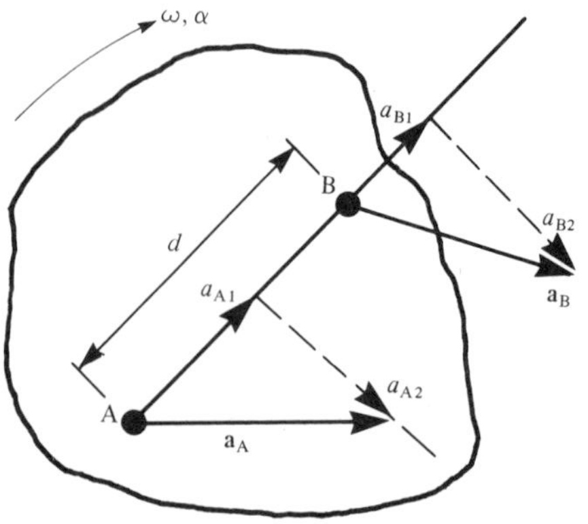

Figure 3.7 Relative acceleration of two points in a rigid body.

In section 2.3.2 we saw that a particle moving in a circle has accelerations $R\omega^2$ towards the centre of the circle and $R\alpha$ at right angles to the radius R, ω and α being the angular velocity and angular acceleration respectively.

It therefore follows that the accelerations of B relative to A are

$$a_{B1} - a_{A1} = -\omega^2 d$$

along AB (the negative sign indicating that the acceleration is directed from B towards A) and

$$a_{B2} - a_{A2} = \alpha d$$

at right angles to AB and in a direction that depends on the magnitudes of $\mathbf{a}_B$ and $\mathbf{a}_A$. In Figure 3.7 it is shown to be clockwise. These accelerations are those which an observer at A would see.

The angular velocity ω is found from the velocities v_A and v_B, and the angular acceleration α is found from the accelerations a_{B2} and a_{B1} and the geometry.

As in the case of relative velocity we deduce the following vector equation:

$$\mathbf{a}_B = \mathbf{a}_A + \mathbf{a}_{BA} \tag{3.5}$$

i.e. the absolute acceleration of B is equal to the resultant of the absolute acceleration of A and its acceleration relative to A. The acceleration $\mathbf{a}_{BA}$ has two components, unlike the relative velocity discussed in section 3.3. We should realise that the acceleration of A seen by an observer at B, namely $\mathbf{a}_{AB}$, is equal in magnitude to $\mathbf{a}_{BA}$ but the direction is reversed. Thus the absolute acceleration of A is given by the vector equation

$$\mathbf{a}_A = \mathbf{a}_B + \mathbf{a}_{AB} \tag{3.6}$$

and $\mathbf{a}_{AB}$ has two components, one parallel and one perpendicular to AB.

For the point B

$$\mathbf{a}_B = \mathbf{a}_A + \mathbf{a}_{BA} \qquad (3.7)$$

or

$$\mathbf{a}_B = \mathbf{a}_A \text{ together with } \alpha d \text{ (normal to AB) and } \omega^2 d \text{ (parallel to AB)}$$

as shown in Figure 3.8.

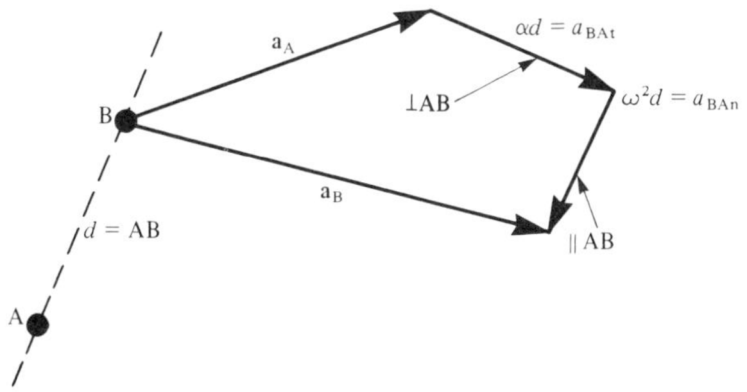

Figure 3.8 Components of absolute acceleration.

GRAPHICAL METHODS FOR DETERMINING VELOCITIES AND ACCELERATIONS 3.6

3.6.1 **Velocity diagrams**

Consider a body L and two points A and B a distance d apart as shown in Figure 3.9. Let $\mathbf{v}_A$ be the absolute velocity of A, whose magnitude and direction are known, and let the velocity of B be known in direction only, namely along the line B_1B_2.

To obtain the magnitude of the velocity of B we proceed as follows:

(1) From an arbitrary fixed point o, known as a pole, draw oa to represent the absolute velocity of A in magnitude and direction, to some convenient scale.

(2) From the point a, draw a line perpendicular to AB.

(3) From o draw a line parallel to B_1B_2. These two lines meet at point b. Then ab represents the velocity of B relative to A and ob the magnitude of the absolute velocity of B.

Suppose we now want to know the velocity of a third point C in the body. We would draw a line through point a perpendicular to AC and a line through b perpendicular to BC; where these two lines meet is the point c. Now oc represents the absolute velocity of C in magnitude and direction, cb is the velocity of C relative to B and ca the velocity of C relative to A.

The triangle abc is known as the *velocity image* of the triangle ABC and triangle abc is similar to triangle ABC.

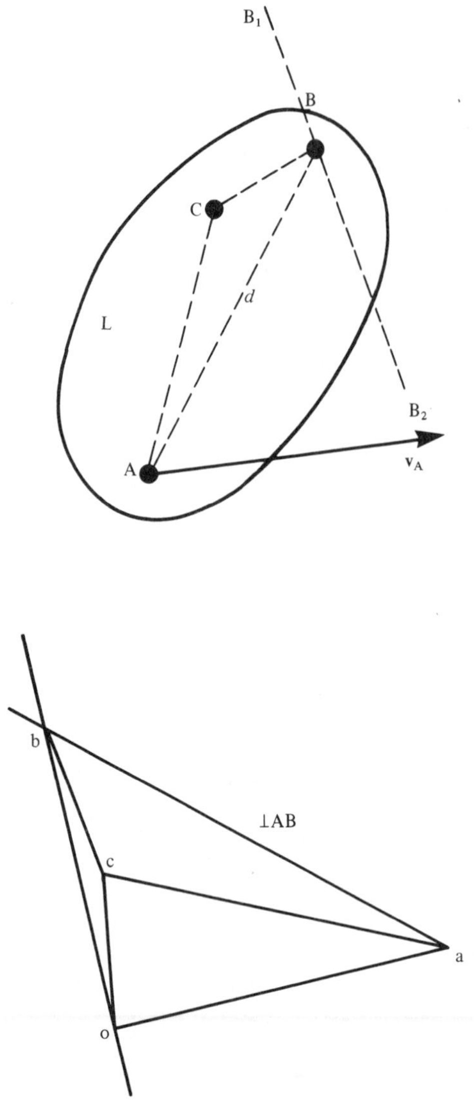

Figure 3.9 Velocity diagram.

The angular velocity ω_{AB} of the body is given by

$$\omega_{AB} = \frac{ab}{AB} = \frac{cb}{CB} = \frac{ca}{CA} \tag{3.8}$$

Thus the velocity diagram is obtained by drawing to some convenient scale the vector diagram in Figure 3.4, and this method is an alternative to that of the instantaneous centre. Which is used depends very much on the problem.

3.6.2 **Acceleration diagrams**

Consider again the body L, which could be one of the links in a mechanism. Let $\mathbf{a}_A$ be the absolute acceleration of the point A, known in magnitude and direction, while B is constrained to move along B_1B_2 as shown in Figure 3.10(a).

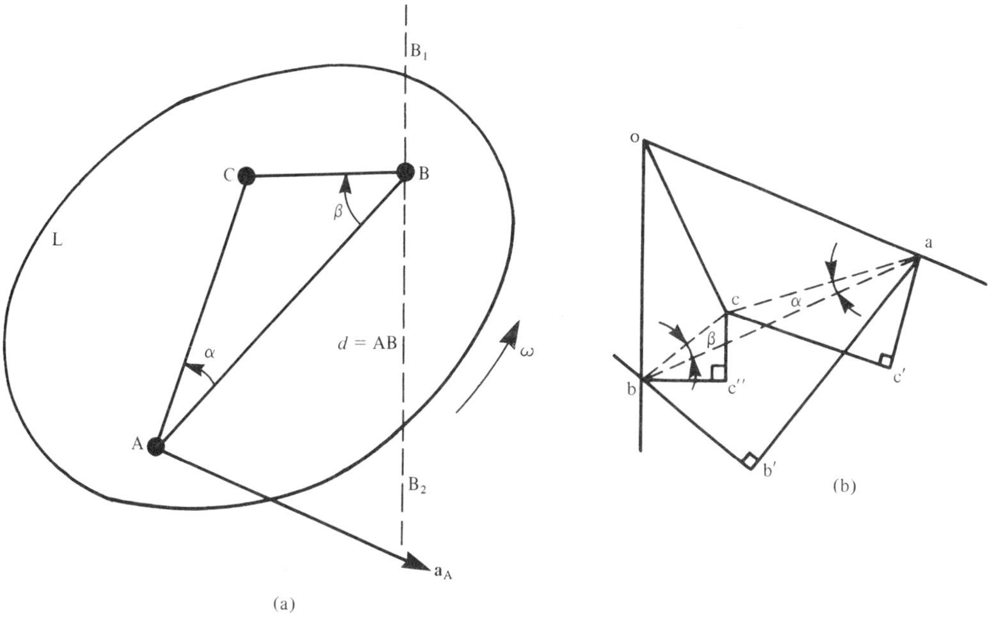

Figure 3.10 Acceleration diagram.

To obtain the magnitude of the acceleration of B, we know that it has two components of acceleration relative to A: a_{BAn}, a centripetal or normal component of magnitude $\omega^2 d$ directed towards A, and a_{BAt}, a tangential component of magnitude αd in a direction perpendicular to AB. The angular velocity ω of the body can always be obtained from a velocity or instant-centre diagram, whereas its angular acceleration α is not always given explicitly.

To obtain the acceleration of B and the angular acceleration α of the body, we proceed thus (see Figure 3.10(b)):

(1) From a pole o, draw oa to represent the absolute acceleration $\mathbf{a}_A$ of A to some convenient scale.

(2) From point a, draw $\omega^2 d = a_{BAn} = ab'$ to the same scale and parallel to BA in the direction from B towards A, since this is the centripetal acceleration.

(3) From b′ draw a line perpendicular to AB since a_{BAt} is known in direction only.

(4) From o draw a line parallel to B_1B_2.

The point b lies at the intersection of lines (3) and (4). Then ob represents the absolute acceleration of B and $\alpha = bb'/AB$ represents the angular acceleration of the body.

To calculate the accelerations of a third point c, draw a line ac′ parallel to CA of magnitude ω^2AC, giving the point c′, and a line through c′ perpendicular to AC.

Similarly, from b draw a line bc″ parallel to BC of magnitude ω^2BC and a line through c″ perpendicular to BC. The lines meet at the point c and oc is the absolute acceleration of C in magnitude and direction.

The triangle abc is the *acceleration image* of the triangle ABC, i.e. triangle abc is similar to triangle ABC.

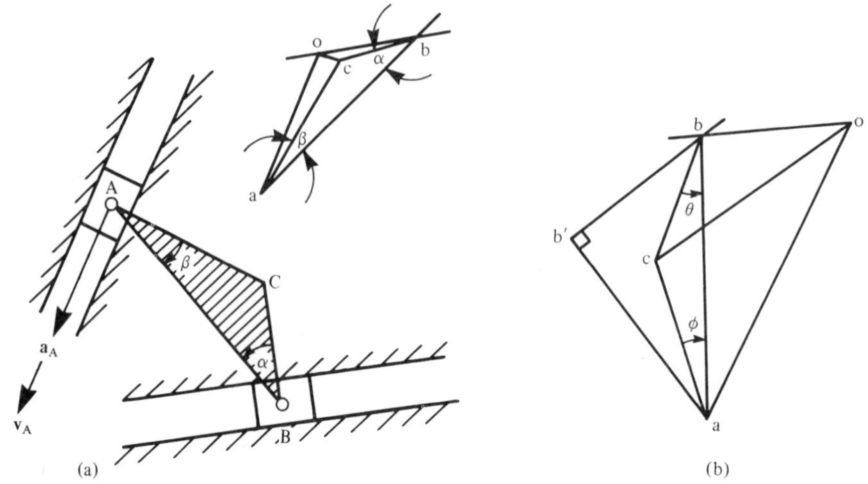

Figure 3.11 (a) Constrained link and velocity diagram; (b) acceleration diagram.

To illustrate the method consider the motion of the link ABC in Figure 3.11(a), where A and B are constrained to slide in grooves. The velocity and acceleration of A are given and we wish to obtain the accelerations of B and C. Before we can proceed with the acceleration diagram we must first obtain the angular velocity ω of the link, and for this we draw the velocity triangle oab shown in Figure 3.11(a); hence $\omega = \text{ab}/\text{AB}$.

For the acceleration diagram we first draw the absolute acceleration of A, $\mathbf{a}_A = \text{oa}$ (Figure 3.11(b)), followed by the acceleration $a_{BAn} = \omega^2\text{AB} = \text{ab}'$ and then a line through b′ perpendicular to AB. From o draw a line parallel to B's groove to locate the point b; hence the angular acceleration of the link is $\alpha = \text{bb}'/\text{AB}$ (see Figure 3.11(b)).

For the point C, c is located by drawing lines ac and bc at angles θ and ϕ as shown, where now oc is the absolute acceleration of the point C.

We shall now use the above method to calculate the velocity and acceleration of the piston of the engine mechanism of example 3.1 for the 40° position of the crank.

We know the velocity of A in magnitude and direction, the velocity of P in direction only and the velocity of P relative to A in direction only. The diagram in Figure 3.12 has been drawn to a scale of 1 cm = 2.5 m/s. From the fixed point o, the pole, $\mathbf{v}_A$ is drawn perpendicular to OA (see Figure 3.6), and so oa = $\mathbf{v}_A$. From point a, the relative velocity vector $\mathbf{v}_{PA} = \text{ap}$ is drawn perpendicular to AP. Hence the vector op = v_P is the one required. By scaling the diagram, op = 63 mm; hence $v_P =$ 15.75 m/s, which is close to the value obtained previously. The angular velocity of the connecting rod is obtained from the relative velocity vector ap so that

$$\omega = \frac{\text{ap}}{\text{AP}} = \frac{6.3 \times 2.5}{0.17} = 92.6 \text{ rad/s}$$

which is also close to the value obtained previously. However, the accuracy can easily be improved by using a better scale; for example the diagram was redrawn to twice the above scale and v_P was found to be 16 m/s.

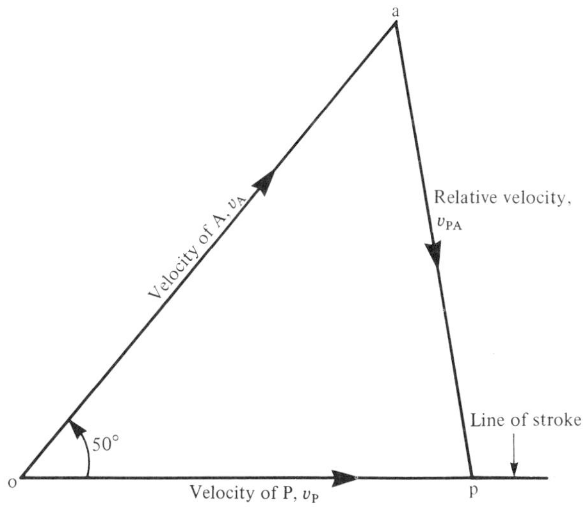

Figure 3.12 Scaled velocity diagram for piston of example 3.1.

For more complicated mechanisms the procedure is the same, but the final diagram consists of several velocity triangles like that in Figure 3.12.

Now for the acceleration of the piston (Figure 3.13). The acceleration of A is known in magnitude and direction; the acceleration of P is known in direction only. The radial component of P relative to A is known in magnitude and direction but the transverse component of the acceleration of P relative to A is known in direction only.

From the instantaneous centre or the velocity diagram we know the angular velocity of the connecting rod, i.e. $\omega_1 = 94.2$ rad/s, so that

$$\omega_1^2\text{AP} = 94.2^2 \times 0.17 = 1508 \text{ m/s}^2$$

and the acceleration of A is

$$\omega_c^2\text{OA} = 366.5^2 \times 0.055 = 7387 \text{ m/s}^2$$

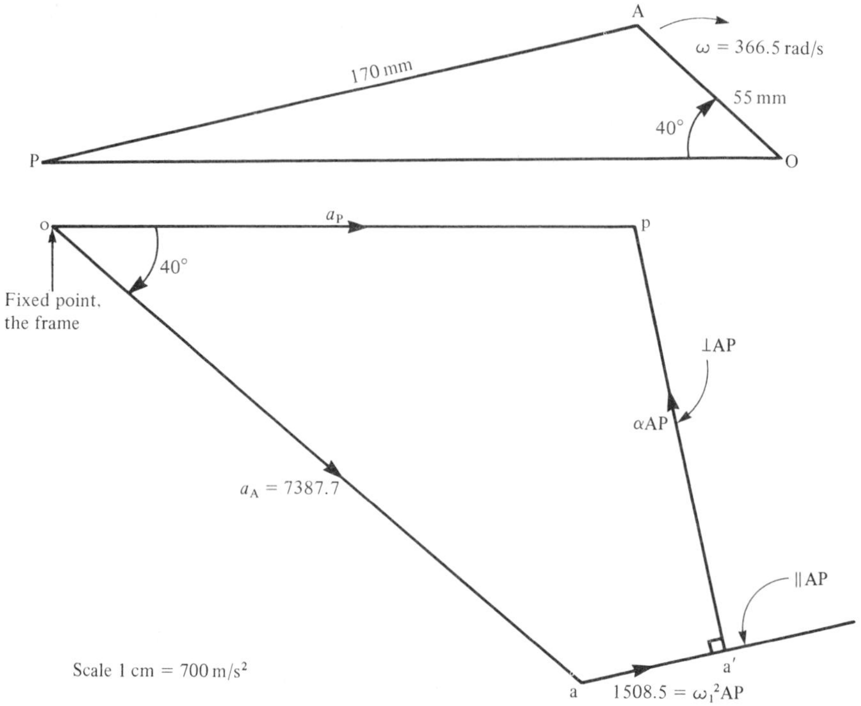

Figure 3.13 Scaled acceleration diagram for piston of example 3.1.

By scaling from the drawing (in which a′ is an intermediate point in the construction), $a_P = 8.3 \times 700 = 5810\ \text{m/s}^2$. (A drawing to a scale of $1\ \text{cm} = 400\ \text{m/s}^2$ gave $a_P = 6120\ \text{m/s}^2$, showing the importance of the choice of scale.)

From the component of acceleration perpendicular to AP, i.e. αAP, we can calculate the angular acceleration of the connecting rod. By scaling,

$$\alpha AP = 5.9 \times 700 = 4130\ \text{m/s}^2$$

and since $AP = 0.17$ m we find that

$$\alpha = \frac{4130}{0.17} = 24\,290\ \text{rad/s}^2$$

In practice, the arrows shown in the diagram are usually omitted.

3.7 MECHANISMS

Mechanisms typify rigid-body motion. They play a major role in practically every branch of engineering and to list them all would fill many pages. However, the following are typical examples: excavators, aircraft undercarriages, engine mechanisms, quick-return mechanisms, packing machines, wrapping machines, bottling machines, steering gear, car suspensions, manipulators, robotic devices, artificial limbs, sewing machines, looms in textile industries, etc., right down to timing mechanisms and door hinges.

Some mechanisms are very simple, e.g. the engine mechanisms, whereas others are extremely complicated, e.g. looms. They are made of links, slides, gears and cams operating singly or in combination and work at low or high speeds to transmit power and to modify the motion. For example, consider once more the engine mechanism: the piston slides in oscillatory translation and this motion is transformed into one of continuous rotation by means of the connecting rod.

All the elements that make up a mechanism are assumed to be rigid bodies in the sense of our definition; they do in fact deform owing to the forces acting on them, but by good design, including choice of material, these deformations are so small that they do not affect the kinematics. The more precise the mechanism, however, the more these deformations may have to be taken into account.

The problem in practice, from the point of view of design, is the choice of mechanism to perform a given task. It may be possible to use a familiar mechanism or to modify and adapt one for the job in hand. In some cases we need to find or even to invent a mechanism to do the job (if none of the well known ones are suitable). In either case we shall have to analyse the mechanism to calculate the velocities and accelerations of its various elements. A knowledge of velocity ratio between input and output is required for power transmission, and a knowledge of acceleration is important to ensure that the resulting inertia forces (mass × acceleration) are taken into account, since these will add (vectorially) to the externally applied forces, and neglecting them could be catastrophic. Consider, for example, the acceleration of the piston of example 3.1: we found it to be 5810 m/s^2 at the particular instant considered, and if its mass is 1 kg the inertia force is $5810 \times 1 = 5810$ N or $5810/(1 \times 9.81) = 592$ times its own weight!

Graphical or mathematical methods may be used to calculate displacements, velocities and accelerations. Graphical techniques are quick and visual for one position of a mechanism but become tedious if many positions are needed; the accuracy is also limited. Mathematical methods express the displacements, velocities and accelerations by means of equations, which can now be solved increasingly quickly and accurately with a calculator, programmable calculator or computer for all possible positions. Visual presentation can be restored using a computer with a graphics display, and this is what would be used in those industries concerned with the design and manufacture of mechanisms.

We are not concerned with advanced techniques here, but rather with the basic principles, since we cannot progress without a good understanding of these; and having analysed mathematically a mechanism for one complete cycle, it is good practice to check the correctness of the solution graphically for one particular position.

3.7.1 **Linkages**

Figures 3.14 and 3.15 present a sequence of linkages of increasing complexity.

Figure 3.14(a) shows two rigid links, 1 and 2, each with two holes, so that they can be connected to each other or to other links by means of pins introduced at A, B, C or D. A link with *two* holes, e.g. link 1 with holes at A and B, is referred to as a *binary* link. A link with *three* holes is called a *tertiary* link, as in Figure 3.14(d).

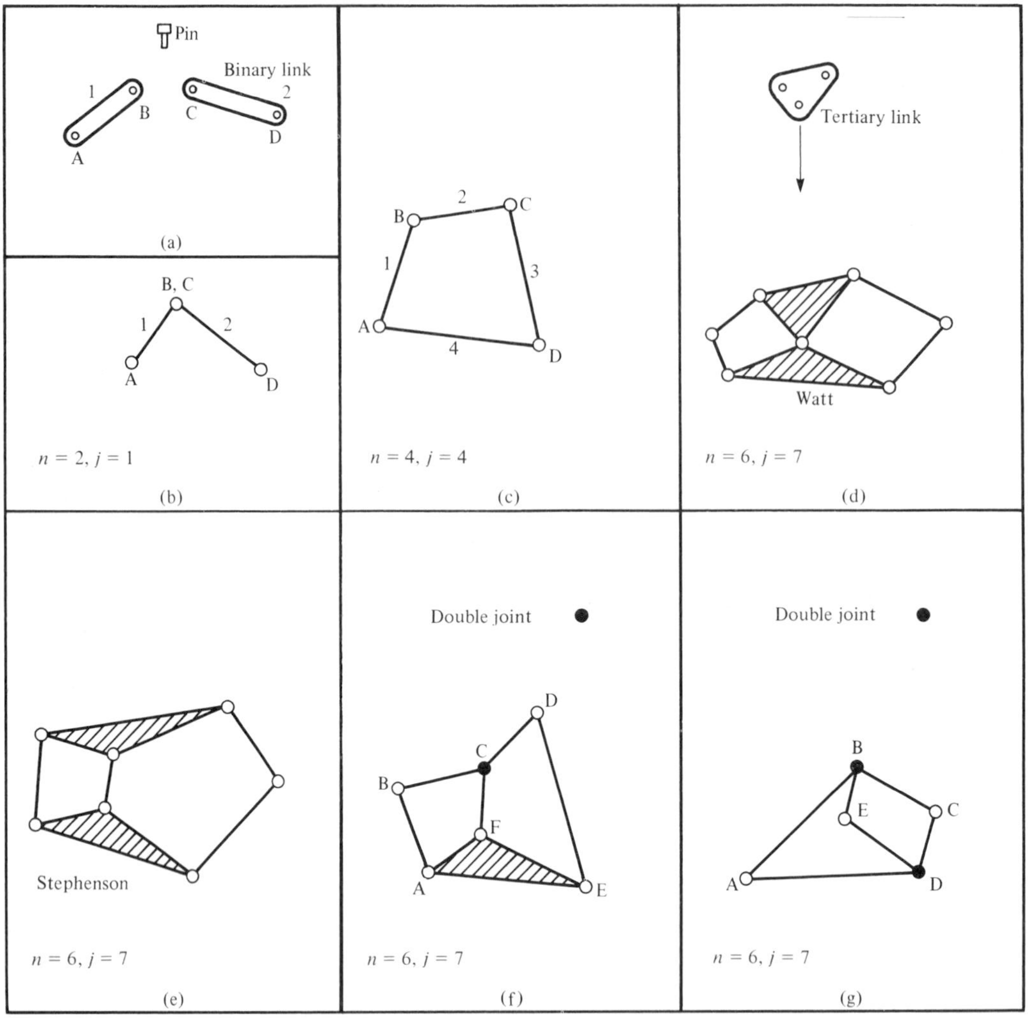

Figure 3.14 Kinematic chains.

By putting a pin through B and C, we form an *open kinematic chain,* as in Figure 3.14(b). Relative motion between the two links is possible. We say that the two links are *paired* and the joint thus formed is a *pin joint,* also known as a *revolute* (indicated by the letter R). Such a connection is also referred to as a *lower pair.*

If we now take two more links and join them to our open chain in such a way that we close the chain, we obtain the kinematic chain ABCD shown in Figure 3.14(c). We can go on adding links and make up complex chains. We may also include tertiary links, as in Figures 3.14(d) and (e), which show chains due to Watt and to Stephenson.

In Figures 3.14(f) and (g) double joints have been introduced; there is one double joint at C in the former, and there are two double joints at B and D in the latter. In order to obtain a mechanism capable of transmitting motion, we can fix any one link; i.e. if link AD of Figure 3.14(c) is fixed or grounded we have Figure 3.15(a), and if link AB is an input then an output can be taken from link CD or a shaft at D fixed to CD.

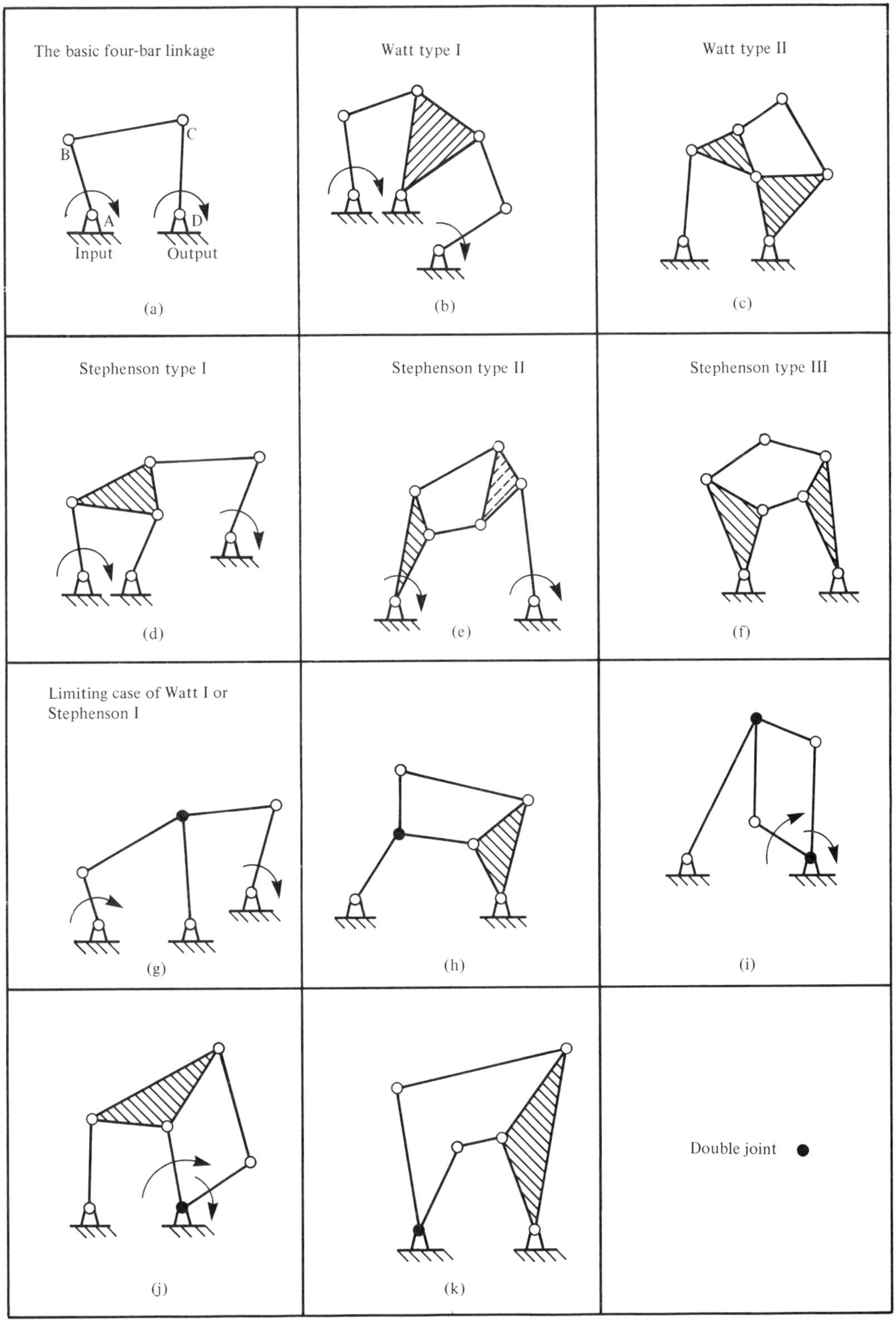

Figure 3.15 Possible mechanisms based on the kinematic chains of Figure 3.14. (*Note:* Double joints can be more economical.)

If we were to fix an alternative link such as AB in Figure 3.14(c), the absolute motion of the links will change but their relative motion remains the same. Fixing other links of a kinematic chain is known as *inversion.*

The mechanisms shown in Figure 3.15 are all formed from the kinematic chains of Figure 3.14 by fixing a particular link; the reader can verify this for himself.

If we replace a link by a slider we obtain mechanisms such as those shown in Figure 3.16; for example, Figure 3.16(a) shows the slider–crank mechanism, which is the familiar engine mechanism, with AB as the crank and BC as the connecting rod. The link CD of Figure 3.15(a) has been replaced by the slider; or the length CD is infinite.

Figure 3.17 shows a practical application of one of the mechanisms in Figure 3.15. It is suggested that the reader should discover for himself which mechanism has been used in this case by considering the linkage $A_0ABB_0B'FE$, leaving out H_0HA', which is a means of introducing power to elevate or lower the platform P. The reader should also notice that with this arrangement the platform remains horizontal throughout its motion.

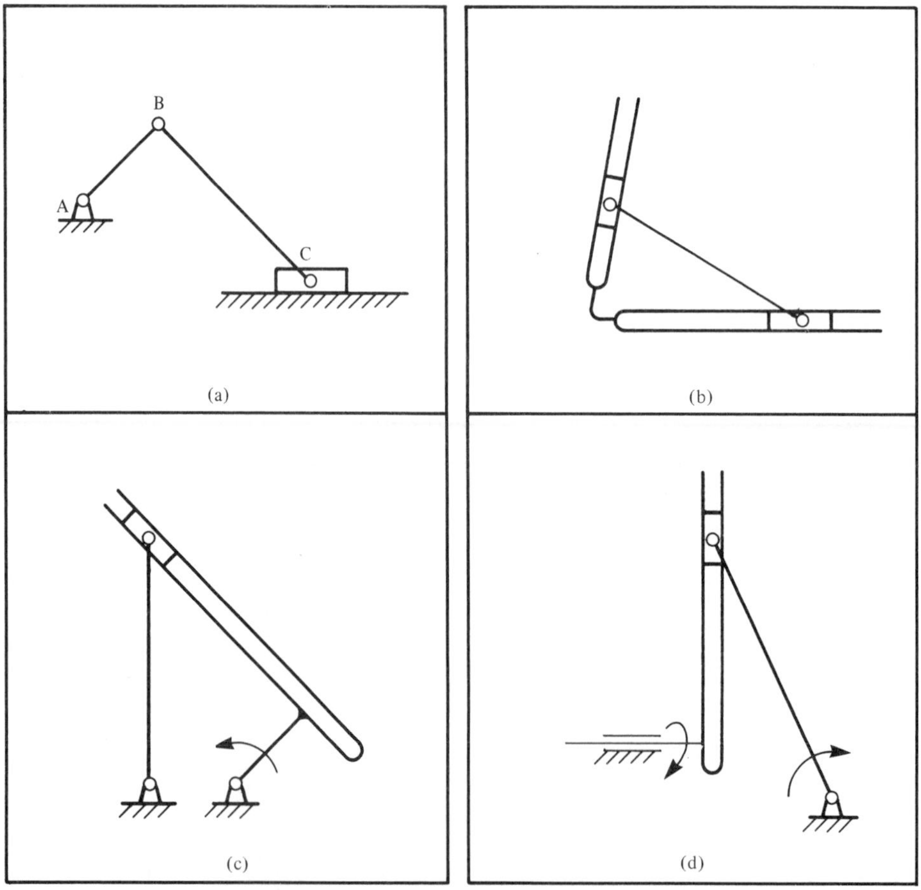

Figure 3.16 Mechanisms formed by replacing a link by a slider.

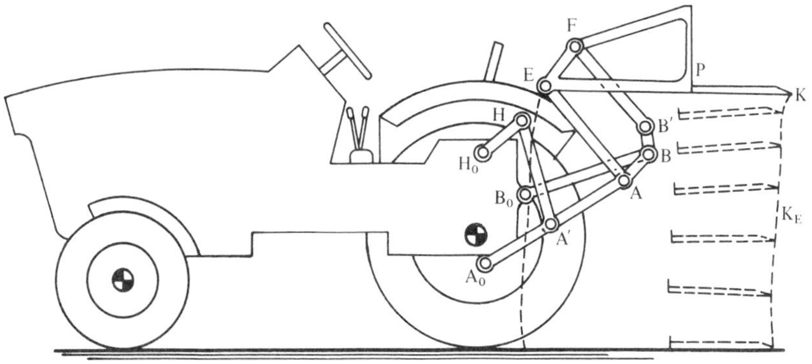

Figure 3.17 Practical application of one of the mechanisms shown in Figure 3.15.

If no relative motion is possible between links, then the mechanism is a structure. Thus if we were to add a link between A and D in Figure 3.14(b) we would obtain a triangular chain or frame. Such a triangle forms the basis of many practical structures.

In a mechanism, therefore, relative and absolute motion is necessary for the transmission of power. Apart from transmitting power, a mechanism is also a device that transforms the motion of an input. For instance, in the slider–crank mechanism, rotation of the crank is transformed into a translation of the slider and vice versa. Consequently, a mechanism has mobility or freedom of movement.

A mechanism is said to have one degree of freedom if a single coordinate is sufficient to define its position; two degrees of freedom if two independent coordinates are necessary to define its position; and so on. For example, the unconstrained link AB in Figure 3.14(a) has three degrees of freedom in the plane: two of translation and one of rotation.

In this text we shall consider mechanisms that have one degree of freedom only, a requirement for many mechanisms.

Referring to Figure 3.14(a), links AB and CD each have three degrees of freedom; by connecting B and C with a pin we remove two degrees of freedom and hence the kinematic chain in Figure 3.14(b) has four degrees of freedom. Suppose now we fix AB, i.e. AB is grounded. It follows that link CD with C pivoting at B has one degree of freedom, since it can only rotate about C. Thus fixing a link removes three degrees of freedom.

Let us now consider the four-bar chain in Figure 3.14(c): with four links and four joints the number of degrees of freedom of this kinematic chain will be $4 \times 3 - 2 \times 4 = 12 - 8 = 4$ degrees of freedom. By fixing one link, say AD, we remove three degrees of freedom and hence the four-bar linkage with one link fixed has one degree of freedom.

We can express the above arguments using the notation $f =$ number of degrees of freedom, $n =$ number of links (including the fixed link or frame) and $j =$ number of joints of the revolute type. Then

$$f = 3(n - 1) - 2j \tag{3.9}$$

For a mechanism to have one degree of freedom, $f = 1$ and

$$1 = 3n - 3 - 2j$$

Hence

$$j = \tfrac{3}{2}n - 2$$

is the number of joints required. It follows from this equation that there must be an even number of links, including those fixed.

For example, consider the mechanism shown in Figure 3.15(f): there are six links ($n = 6$) and seven joints ($j = 7$). Hence

$$f = 3(6 - 1) - 2 \times 7 = 15 - 14 = 1$$

The reader should satisfy himself that the mechanisms shown in Figure 3.15 satisfy equation (3.9).

Of all the linkages the four-bar one is extremely important, and for this reason we propose to examine it in some detail.

3.7.2 **The four-bar linkage**

The four-bar linkage or four-bar chain is fundamental in the design of mechanisms. It is widely used and takes many different shapes and sizes. It is simple, fairly inexpensive, and easy to maintain, can work at high or low speeds and transmit small or large powers and can operate in all kinds of environments, e.g. in cold, or hot and humid climates, or in dusty atmospheres. It can be used to coordinate input and output motions such as displacements, velocities and accelerations, or to generate mathematical functions to a high degree of accuracy.

The four-bar linkage consists of four bars or links AB, BC, CD and DA, pinned at A, B, C and D as shown in Figure 3.18(a), thus forming a closed chain; a, b, c, d are the link lengths.

In operation any one of the links may be fixed, resulting in different output/input relationships depending on the link lengths. This is illustrated in Figures 3.18(b), (c), (d) and (e), which demonstrate the four "inversions" of the four-bar linkage. The arrangements in Figures 3.18(b) and (c) are referred to as crank and rocker mechanisms; AB is the crank and CD the rocker. In these cases a rotary motion of the crank leads to an oscillatory motion of the rocker. (Note that the angles of swing of the link CD are not necessarily equal, i.e. $\phi \neq \theta$ in general.) Figure 3.18(d) shows a double rocker, in which links AD and BC oscillate while AB rotates. The arrangement in Figure 3.18(e) is known as the drag link mechanism, and here links AD and BC rotate.

If a designer wants a four-bar linkage to be driven by an electric motor, he has to be sure that one crank, the input, can rotate through a complete revolution; otherwise the linkage would not be of much use. There is a criterion due to Grashof (1883) which will ensure that such a requirement is possible, viz.

For a continuous relative rotation between two links of a four-bar linkage, the length of the shortest link plus that of the longest link must be less than or equal to the sum of the lengths of the other two links.

Thus, referring to Figure 3.18, we must have

$$a + b \leqslant c + d \tag{3.10}$$

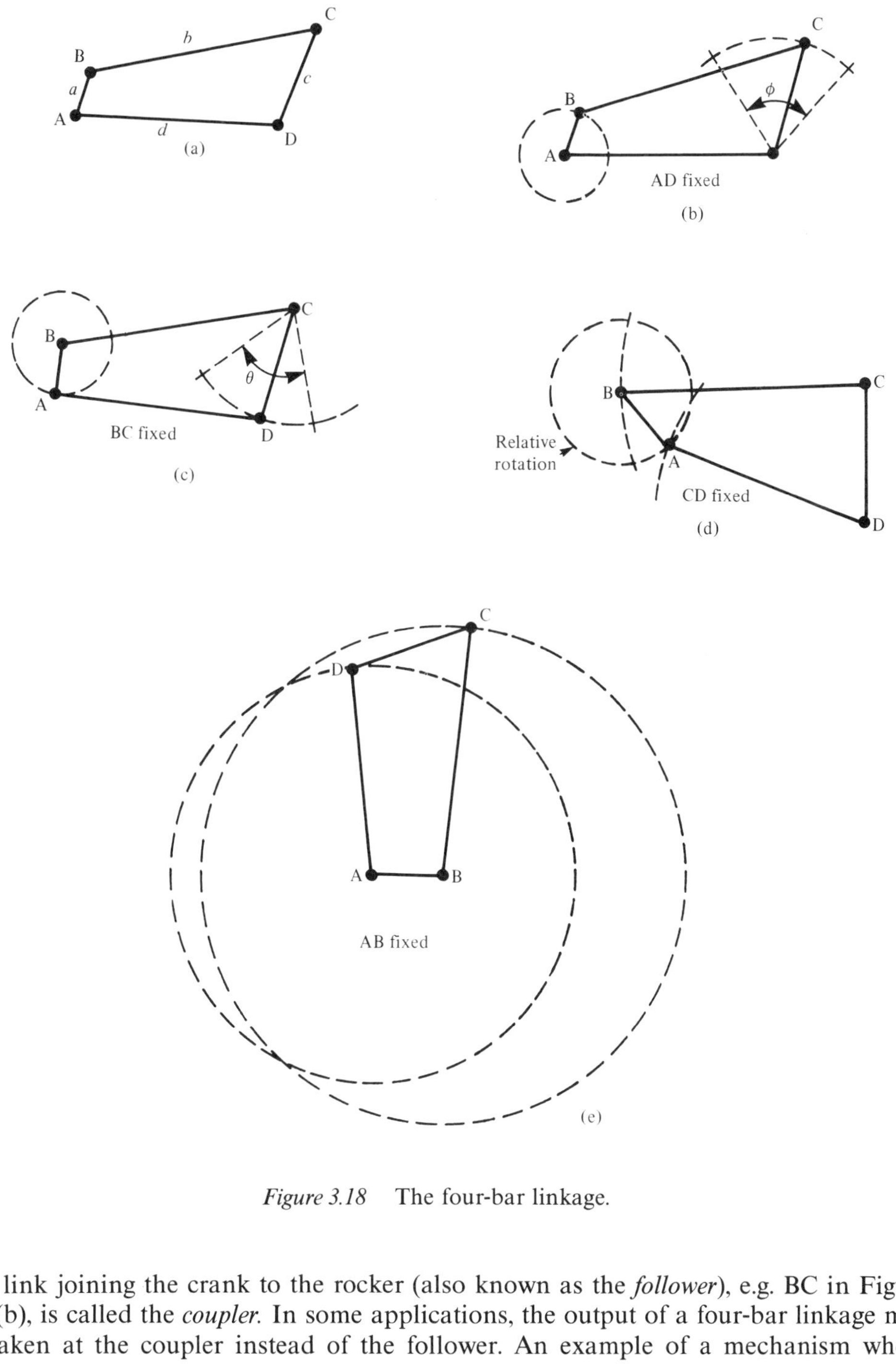

Figure 3.18 The four-bar linkage.

The link joining the crank to the rocker (also known as the *follower*), e.g. BC in Figure 3.18(b), is called the *coupler*. In some applications, the output of a four-bar linkage may be taken at the coupler instead of the follower. An example of a mechanism whose output is taken at the coupler is shown in Figures 3.19 and 3.20, where the jib of a floating crane is the coupler of a four-bar chain in which the link DC is fixed; the point E on the coupler BAEF carries the pulley to enable the load to be raised or lowered. The lengths of the links are such that E follows a straight horizontal path EE_1 over a length L

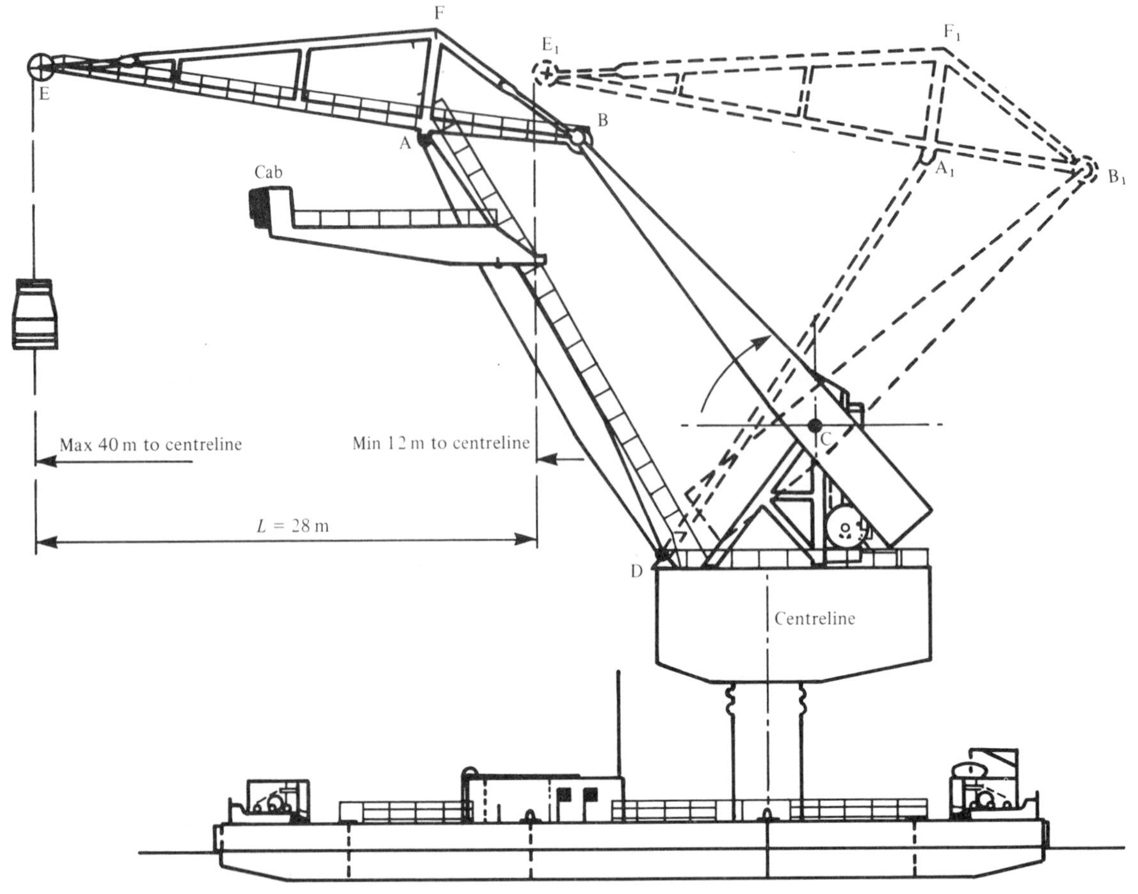

Figure 3.19 Floating crane, in which the output is taken at the coupler.

of 28 m as the input link BC is rotated through an angle ϕ of 89°. It is also an example of a double rocker mechanism.

Extensive use is made of the properties of coupler curves in all kinds of engineering situations, from the crane mentioned above to automatic assembly manipulators right down to robotic devices for helping the handicapped. An atlas containing thousands of curves generated by points on the coupler or extended coupler of a four-bar linkage was produced by Hrones and Nelson (1951) for a very wide range of link lengths; it is extremely valuable in the design of any mechanism when there is a requirement for guiding an object along a particular path.

An example taken from this atlas is shown in Figure 3.21; point E, for instance, on the coupler BCE will trace out the path shown during one complete rotation of the input link AB.

Figure 3.20 The new level luffing lemniscate type of dockside crane, as in Figure 3.19.

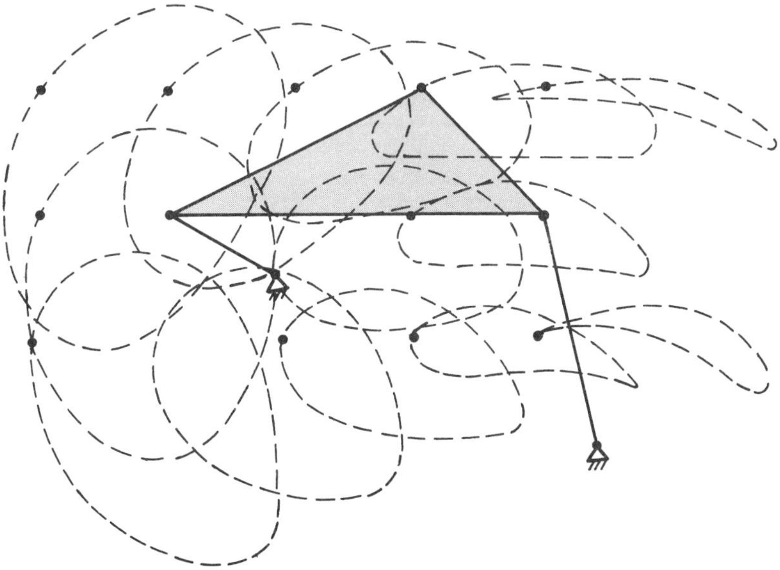

Figure 3.21 An example of curves generated by the coupler of a four-bar linkage.

3.7.3 **Analysis of the four-bar linkage**

The four-bar linkage can be analysed graphically to determine velocity and acceleration by means of the methods discussed previously. The drawbacks of these methods are that the accuracy is limited and many diagrams are required to obtain a complete picture of the behaviour of the mechanism during one cycle of operation.

In many situations it is advisable to express the problem analytically and to obtain all input and output displacements, velocities and accelerations, quality of transmission, forces, etc., with a programmable calculator or computer. Apart from the rapidity with which results are obtained for a complete cycle, it is also possible to examine quickly the effect of changing the length of a particular link or a change in any other parameter.

Having analysed a given mechanism in this way it is strongly recommended that a graphical check be carried out for one particular position to confirm the results.

Let us obtain an input–output relationship by considering the linkage shown in Figure 3.22(a), at the instant when the input link AB makes an angle ϕ with the frame of reference defined by the x- and y-axes and the fixed link AD. The position of the output could be defined by the angles α, β or ψ, the choice being arbitrary. In this text we shall use the angle ψ.

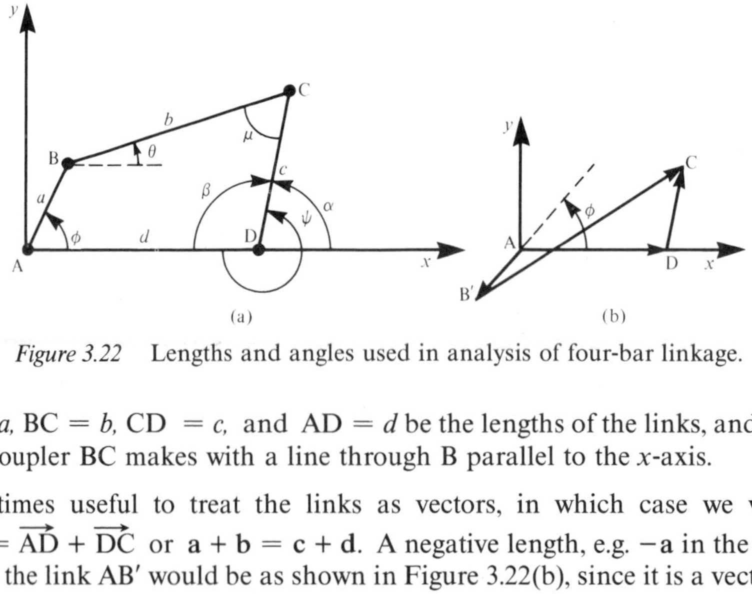

Figure 3.22 Lengths and angles used in analysis of four-bar linkage.

Let AB $= a$, BC $= b$, CD $= c$, and AD $= d$ be the lengths of the links, and let θ be the angle the coupler BC makes with a line through B parallel to the x-axis.

It is sometimes useful to treat the links as vectors, in which case we would write $\overrightarrow{AB} + \overrightarrow{BC} = \overrightarrow{AD} + \overrightarrow{DC}$ or $\mathbf{a} + \mathbf{b} = \mathbf{c} + \mathbf{d}$. A negative length, e.g. $-\mathbf{a}$ in the ϕ-direction, means that the link AB′ would be as shown in Figure 3.22(b), since it is a vector of length a but whose sense is from A to B′, i.e. opposite to AB.

The angle μ between the coupler BC and the output link CD, known as the transmission angle, plays an important role in the quality of transmission of the mechanism. Projection on the x-axis gives

$$a \cos \phi + b \cos \theta - c \cos (\psi - 180°) - d = 0$$

or

$$a \cos \phi + b \cos \theta + c \cos \psi = d \tag{3.11}$$

and projection on the y-axis gives

$$a \sin \phi + b \sin \theta - c \sin (\psi - 180°) = 0$$

or

$$a \sin \phi + b \sin \theta + c \sin \psi = 0 \tag{3.12}$$

Since we are looking for a relationship between the input ϕ and the output ψ, we need to eliminate θ from equations (3.11) and (3.12). Rewriting these equations leads to

$$b \cos \theta = d - (a \cos \phi + c \cos \psi)$$

$$b \sin \theta = -(a \sin \phi + c \sin \psi)$$

Squaring and adding yields

$$b^2 = a^2 + c^2 + d^2 + 2ac \cos (\phi - \psi) - 2ad \cos \phi - 2cd \cos \psi$$

or

$$\frac{b^2 - (a^2 + c^2 + d^2)}{2ac} + \frac{d}{c} \cos \phi + \frac{d}{a} \cos \psi = \cos (\phi - \psi) \tag{3.13}$$

This equation may be written more simply thus

$$K_1 \cos \phi + K_2 \cos \psi - K_3 = \cos (\phi - \psi) \tag{3.14}$$

where

$$K_1 = \frac{d}{c} \qquad K_2 = \frac{d}{a} \qquad K_3 = \frac{a^2 - b^2 + c^2 + d^2}{2ac} \tag{3.14a}$$

Equation (3.14) is fundamental in the design of the four-bar linkage and is known as "Freudenstein's equation". It relates the input to the output in terms of the link ratios, and is used in two ways:

(a) For a given input ϕ we can solve for the output ψ, and by differentiating obtain the velocity, acceleration and "jerk" (rate of change of the acceleration).

(b) It can be used to calculate the link ratios for a given input–output relationship; this process is known as synthesis. For example, we may wish to generate the function $\psi = 240 + 0.095\phi^{1.5}$ degrees with the initial conditions $\phi_0 = 20°$ and angular movement $\Delta\phi = 45°$; this in fact was a requirement in the design of a special-purpose machine.

In this text we are primarily concerned with analysis rather than synthesis, i.e. we start with a linkage of known dimensions and find out its properties. Returning then to equation (3.14) let us differentiate it implicitly with respect to time; this gives

$$-(K_1 \sin \phi)\dot{\phi} - (K_2 \sin \psi)\dot{\psi} = -(\dot{\phi} - \dot{\psi}) \sin(\phi - \psi)$$

Solving for $\dot{\psi}$ yields

$$\dot{\psi} = \frac{\sin (\phi - \psi) - K_1 \sin \phi}{\sin (\phi - \psi) - K_2 \sin \phi} \dot{\phi} \tag{3.15}$$

where $\dot{\psi}$ is the angular velocity of the output ψ and $\dot{\phi}$ is the angular velocity of the input ϕ.

This equation depends on ψ, the position of the output for a given position of the input ϕ. We can derive an expression for ψ by rewriting equation (3.14) as follows:

$$A \sin \psi + B \cos \psi = C \tag{3.16}$$

where

$$\begin{aligned} A &= \sin \phi \\ B &= \cos \phi - K_2 \\ C &= K_1 \cos \phi - K_3 \end{aligned}$$

Equation (3.16) is a trigonometric equation, which is easily solved by letting

$$\sin \psi = \frac{2 \tan (\psi/2)}{1 + \tan^2(\psi/2)} \qquad \text{and} \qquad \cos \psi = \frac{1 - \tan^2 (\psi/2)}{1 + \tan^2(\psi/2)}$$

(See Appendix A.5.) Substituting in equation (3.16) gives

$$(B + C) \tan^2(\psi/2) - 2A \tan (\psi/2) + (C - B) = 0$$

which is a quadratic in $\tan (\psi/2)$ whose solution is

$$\psi = 2 \arctan \left(\frac{A \pm \sqrt{A^2 + B^2 - C^2}}{B + C} \right) \tag{3.17}$$

Thus the output can take on two positions corresponding to the two roots ψ_1 and ψ_2; Figure 3.23 illustrates these positions. Position BC′D is a mirror image of BCD about the line BD. In practice, only one of the positions is the required one.

The acceleration $\ddot{\psi}$ of the output is obtained by differentiating equation (3.15) with respect to time; and we leave it to the reader to derive an expression for $\ddot{\psi}$.

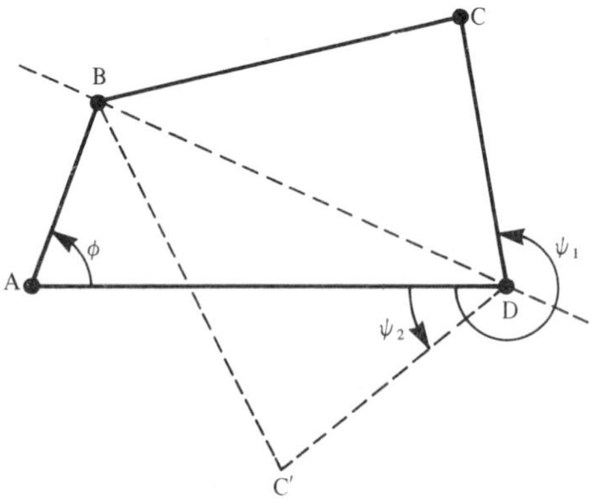

Figure 3.23 Two possible positions of four-bar linkage satisfying the equations.

We notice that although the mechanism is physically very simple, it is somewhat complicated mathematically; this is often true of mechanisms, but the analysis is necessary if we wish to gather all the information about the behaviour of a given mechanism during one cycle of its operation. It should be obvious to the reader that with programmable calculators or computers the task of translating the equations into a suitable language to compute displacements, velocities, accelerations, jerks and forces is not too difficult. We must emphasise once again that the mathematical approach gives us a complete insight into the behaviour of the mechanism; the effect of a change in a link length can be seen at a glance, whereas the graphical method requires redrawing for each position.

EXAMPLE 3.2

In the design of a special-purpose machine incorporating a four-bar linkage, the following link ratios were obtained:

$$\frac{a}{d} = -0.6601 \qquad \frac{b}{d} = 1.4553$$

$$\frac{c}{d} = -0.5042$$

Example Cont.

If $d = 150$ mm, calculate the output position and the angular velocity ratio for input values of 20° to 65° in steps of 5°.

The functional relationship was

$$\psi = 240 + 0.095\phi^{1.5} \text{ deg}$$

SOLUTION

Equation (3.15) will give us the speed ratio $\dot{\psi}/\dot{\phi}$ (output to input angular velocity); we need the value of ψ first.

Since equation (3.17) gives two values for ψ, we have to decide which one to use. We can proceed thus: since we know the functional relationship, the total angular movement of the output is

$$\begin{aligned}\Delta\psi &= 240 + 0.095 \times 65^{1.5} \\ &\quad - (240 \times 0.095 \times 20^{1.5}) \\ &= 0.095(65^{1.5} - 20^{1.5}) \\ &= 41.287°\end{aligned}$$

Now one root will give the required value but the other will not; we must, therefore, establish which one before proceeding to calculate the velocity ratio.

From equation (3.14a) we have

$$K_1 = \frac{d}{c} = \frac{1}{-0.5042} = -1.9833$$

$$K_2 = \frac{d}{a} = \frac{1}{-0.6601} = -1.5149$$

$$K_3 = -0.6429$$

Substituting in equation (3.17) for $\phi = 20°$ and 65° we have (a) with the positive root, $\Delta\psi^+ = 7.14°$, (b) with the negative root, $\Delta\psi^- = 41.41°$. Of these two roots the one we require is the negative one since it satisfies the given functional relationship.

Solution Cont.

Hence using equation (3.17) with the negative root and substituting the values in equation (3.15), the results in Table 3.1 are obtained.

Table 3.1

ϕ_1 (deg)	ψ (deg)	$\dot{\psi}/\dot{\phi}$
20	−111.57	0.6613
25	−108.11	0.7227
30	−104.34	0.7819
35	−100.29	0.8391
40	− 95.96	0.8947
45	− 91.35	0.9492
50	− 86.46	1.0033
55	− 81.32	1.0581
60	− 75.89	1.1147
65	− 70.16	1.1748

Figure 3.24 shows the mechanism in its two extreme positions; the broken lines show the mechanism corresponding to the positive root, the angles being measured in accordance with the convention adopted in this text and shown in Figure 3.22. Because of the negative signs for a and c the mechanism lies below the fixed link.

Solution Cont. Solution Cont.

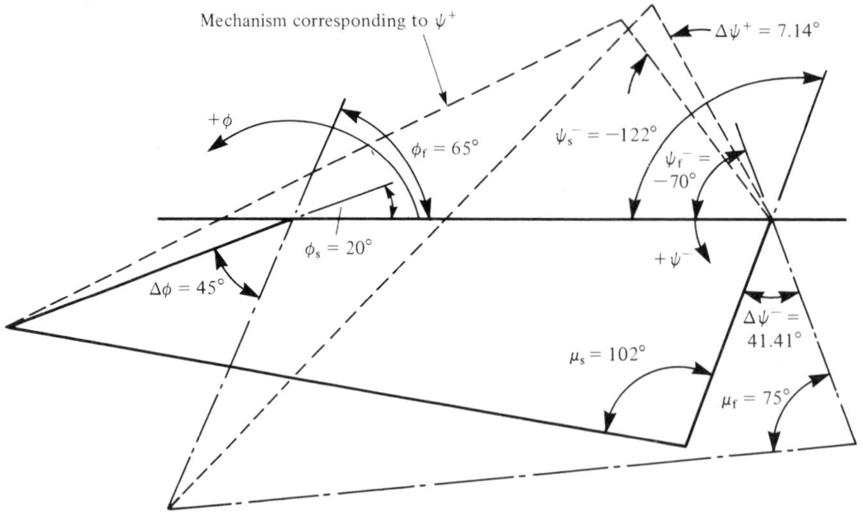

Figure 3.24 Two extreme positions of the special-purpose mechanism of example 3.2.

3.7.4 **Synthesis: coordination of input and output**

In synthesis we are concerned with the problem of selecting the size of the mechanism or linkage to perform a given function. There are basically three situations:

(a) the coordination of input and output positions,
(b) the generation of functions, and
(c) the coordination of input and output velocities and accelerations.

We shall consider here the simpler case of coordinating three input positions with three output positions.

The design of a four-bar linkage to coordinate input and output positions ϕ_i and ψ_i, where $i = 1, 2, \ldots, n$, requires the calculation of the link lengths a, b, c, d. This can be achieved very simply when $n = 3$ by considering Freudenstein's equation (3.14):

$$K_1 \cos \phi + K_2 \cos \psi - K_3 = \cos (\phi - \psi)$$

where

$$K_1 = \frac{d}{c} \qquad K_2 = \frac{d}{a} \qquad K_3 = \frac{a^2 - b^2 + c^2 + d^2}{2ac}$$

This equation has three unknowns, K_1, K_2 and K_3. Hence, with three input positions ϕ_1, ϕ_2 and ϕ_3, and the corresponding three output positions ψ_1, ψ_2 and ψ_3 required, we have the following three simultaneous equations with three unknowns:

$$K_1 \cos \phi_1 + K_2 \cos \psi_1 - K_3 = \cos (\phi_1 - \psi_1) \tag{3.18}$$

$$K_1 \cos \phi_2 + K_2 \cos \psi_2 - K_3 = \cos (\phi_2 - \psi_2) \tag{3.19}$$

$$K_1 \cos \phi_3 + K_2 \cos \psi_3 - K_3 = \cos (\phi_3 - \psi_3) \tag{3.20}$$

These equations can be solved quite simply by any one of the well-known methods, e.g. Gaussian elimination.

Knowing K_1, K_2 and K_3 we can then calculate the length of each link by fixing one of them arbitrarily. It is usual to fix either the input link, a in this case, or the fixed link. The actual lengths will in many cases depend on the space available for the mechanism; all mechanisms having the same link ratios are geometrically and kinematically equivalent.

The following example illustrates the procedure.

EXAMPLE 3.3

Figure 3.25 shows the shovel S of a mechanical digger actuated by the hydraulic cylinder H via the four-bar linkage ABCD. AB is the "fixed link" relative to the outer arm assembly ABE of the digger.

Calculate to the nearest millimetre the length of each link to coordinate the positions in Table 3.2.

Table 3.2

Input, ϕ (deg)	Output, α (deg)
135	125
82.5	50
30	−40

The distance between the pivots AB is not to exceed 325 mm.

Example Cont.

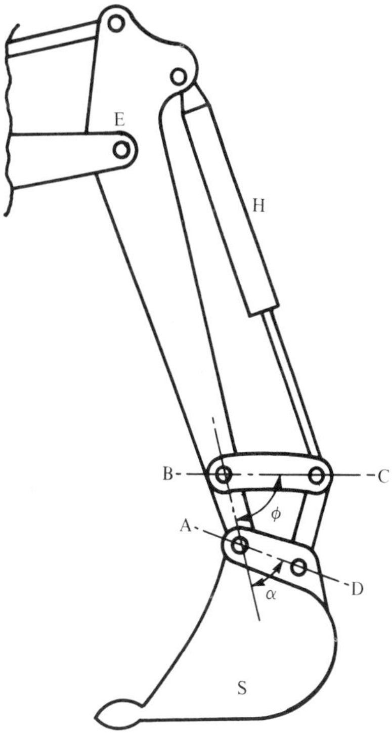

Figure 3.25 Shovel of mechanical digger.

SOLUTION

All we need do is substitute the values of the input and output angles in Freudenstein's equation (equations (3.18), (3.19) and (3.20)), having first transformed the output angles α into their equivalent ψ values; according to our conventions they are $\psi = -55°, -125°$ and $140°$.

So

Solution Cont.

$$K_1 \cos 135° + K_2 \cos(-55°) - K_3 = \cos(135° + 55°)$$

$$K_1 \cos 82.5° + K_2 \cos(-125°) - K_3 = \cos(82.5° + 125°)$$

$$K_1 \cos 30° + K_2 \cos 140° - K_3 = \cos(30° - 140°)$$

Solution Cont.

Working to five decimal places with a calculator we have

$$-0.70711\,K_1 + 0.57358\,K_2 - K_3 = -0.98481 \quad (3.18a)$$

$$0.13053\,K_1 - 0.57358\,K_2 - K_3 = -0.88701 \quad (3.19a)$$

$$0.86603\,K_1 - 0.76604\,K_2 - K_3 = -0.34202 \quad (3.20a)$$

If the reader is not familiar with the Gaussian elimination method of solution, then the simplest way to solve these equations is to eliminate K_3 by subtracting (3.19a) from (3.18a) and subtracting (3.20a) from (3.19a). Hence we find

$$-0.83763\,K_1 + 1.14715\,K_2 = -0.09780$$
$$-0.73550\,K_1 + 0.19247\,K_2 = -0.54499$$

We now have two simultaneous equations in K_1 and K_2. Dividing the first equation by -0.83764 and the second by 0.73550 yields

$$K_1 - 1.36952\,K_2 = 0.11675$$
$$-K_1 + 0.26168\,K_2 = -0.74098$$

Adding gives

$$-1.10784\,K_2 = -0.62423$$

Solution Cont.

Also

$$K_1 = 0.11675 + 1.36952 \times 0.56347$$
$$= 0.88843$$
$$K_2 = 0.56347$$

and from equation (3.18a), or any one of the other two, we have

$$K_3 = -0.70711 \times 0.88843 + 0.57358 \times 0.56347 + 0.98481$$
$$= 0.67979$$

Before proceeding any further it is wise to check these answers by substituting in either equation (3.19a) or (3.20a). Substitution in equation (3.19a) gives -0.88702 for the right-hand side, which only differs by 0.00002 from that given in equation (3.19a). Our computation is therefore acceptable.

With $d = 325$ mm we find from equations (3.14a) that

$$a = d/K_2 = 325/0.56347 = 576 \text{ mm}$$
$$c = d/K_1 = 325/0.88843 = 365 \text{ mm}$$
$$b = \sqrt{(576^2 + 365^2 + 325^2 - 2 \times 576 \times 365 \times 0.67979)}$$
$$= 534 \text{ mm}$$

An existing computer program gave the result $a = 577$ mm, $b = 534$ mm, $c = 365$ mm, which is not significantly different.

3.7.5 The angular velocity relationship in a four-bar linkage by the instantaneous-centre method

Let ω_1 be the angular velocity of a shaft A to which the link AB is fixed, ω_2 the angular velocity of shaft D to which the link CD is fixed and BC a link joining B and C, as shown in Figure 3.26. Furthermore let A be the input shaft and D the output shaft. We require the relationship between input and output; we saw how to do this analytically in section 3.7.3 (equation (3.15)). We now wish to obtain the output/input angular velocities graphically.

The mechanism is a four-bar linkage with AD as the fixed link, and with AB making an angle ϕ at a particular instant.

Consider the points B on link AB and C on link CD. The velocity of B is

$$v_B = \omega_1 AB$$

in magnitude and in a direction perpendicular to AB, the sense being as shown by the vector $\mathbf{v}_B$.

Similarly, for the point C on link CD

$$v_C = \omega_2 CD$$

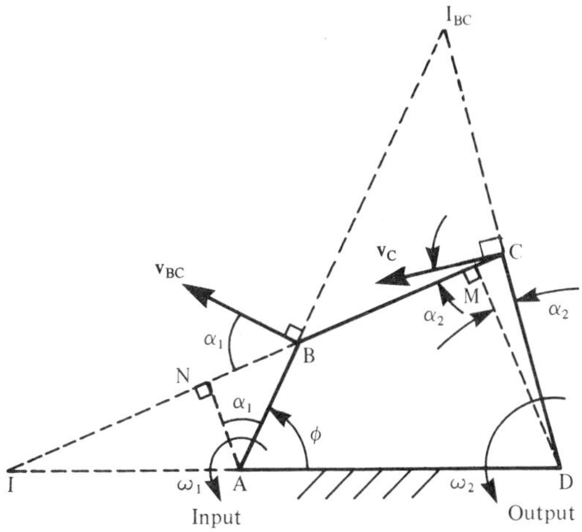

Figure 3.26 Angular velocity by the instant-centre method.

The components of the velocities of B and C along BC are

$$v'_B = \omega_1 AB \cos \alpha_1 = \omega_1 AN$$

and

$$v'_C = \omega_2 CD \cos \alpha_2 = \omega_2 DM$$

Two lines drawn along BC and AD meet at the point I; points N and M are such that AN and DM are perpendicular to IBC. Since the link BC is rigid it follows that

$$v'_B = v'_C$$

Hence

$$\omega_1 AN = \omega_2 DM$$

or

$$\frac{\omega_2}{\omega_1} = \frac{AN}{DM}$$

Also, because the triangles IAN and IDM are similar, we have

$$\frac{AN}{DM} = \frac{IA}{ID}$$

The required angular velocity ratio is therefore given by

$$\frac{\omega_2}{\omega_1} = \frac{IA}{ID} \tag{3.21}$$

I is in fact the instantaneous centre for the links AB and CD. The reader should verify that I_{BC} is the instantaneous centre for link BC (see section 3.4).

The angular velocity of link BC, the coupler, is such that

$$\omega_{BC} = \frac{v_B}{BI_{BC}} = \frac{v_C}{CI_{BC}} \tag{3.22}$$

As ϕ takes on various values (0 to 2π in many cases), I and I_{BC} will change position.

EXAMPLE 3.4

The four-bar linkage shown in Figure 3.26 has the following link lengths:

AB = 125 mm, BC = 275 mm, CD = 225 mm and DA = 200 mm.

Example Cont.

For the position where $\phi = -120°$, calculate the angular velocity of the output and of the coupler if the input angular velocity is 25 rad/s clockwise.

SOLUTION

Solution Cont.

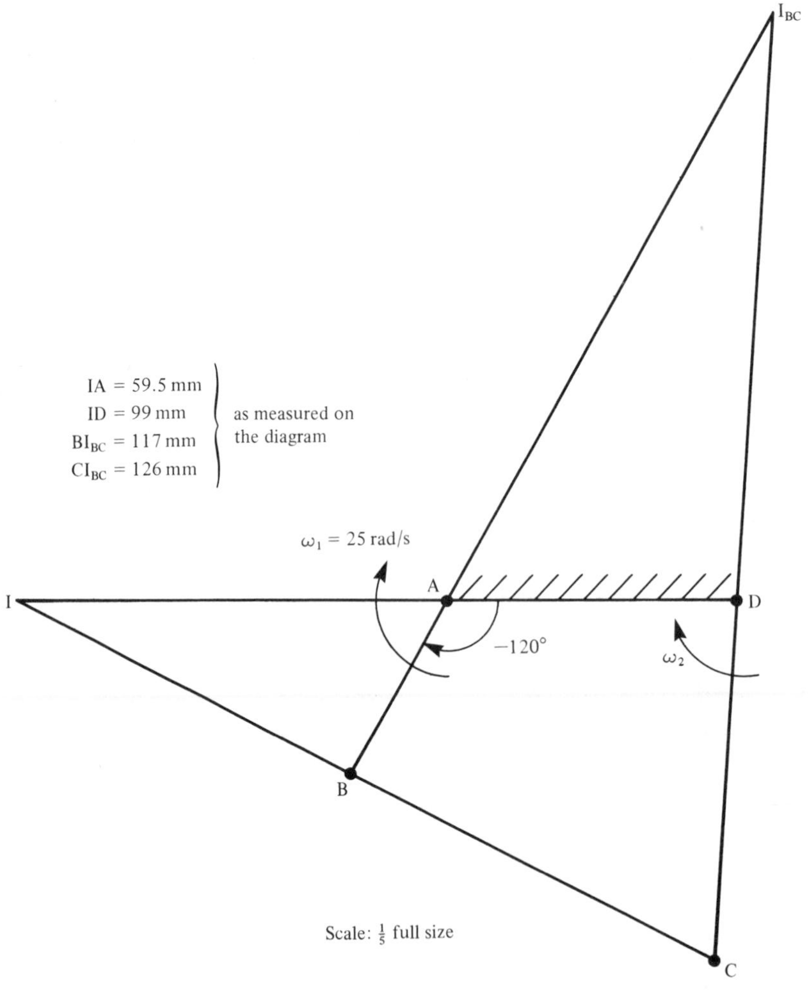

Figure 3.27 Scale drawing of four-bar linkage of example 3.4.

First we have to draw the linkage to some suitable scale in the required position as shown in Figure 3.27, noting that with $\phi = -120°$ the link AB points downwards. As we do not know where the instantaneous centres will be located, it may take one or two sketches to ensure that this will lie within the space of the paper available. In our case a scale of 1/5 full size is found to be suitable.

The point I is located at the intersection of BC and AD produced, and I_{BC} at the intersection of BA and

Solution Cont.

CD produced. Angular velocity ω_2 will have the same sense as ω_1, and

$$\begin{aligned}\omega_2 &= \omega_1 \times IA/ID \\ &= 25 \times 59.5/99 \\ &= 15.03 \text{ rad/s (clockwise)}\end{aligned}$$

from (3.21). Also

$$\begin{aligned}\omega_{BC} &= v_B/BI_{BC} = \omega_1 AB/BI_{BC} \\ &= 25 \times 125/117 \times 5 \\ &= 5.34 \text{ rad/s (clockwise)}\end{aligned}$$

from (3.22). As a check,

$$\begin{aligned}\omega_2 &= v_C/CD \\ &= \omega_{BC} CI_{BC}/CD \\ &= 5.34 \times 126 \times 5/225 \\ &= 14.95 \text{ rad/s}\end{aligned}$$

which is near enough in view of the small scale of the diagram.

(*Note:* 5 is the scale factor.)

3.7.6 **Equivalent mechanisms**

The calculation of velocities and accelerations of certain mechanisms with contact surfaces, such as cams, can be simplified by replacing these surfaces by four-bar linkages that are kinematically equivalent to them at a particular instant.

Consider the two curved elements E_1 and E_2 shown in Figure 3.28(a), used to transmit motion from shaft A to shaft D and making contact at the point P. Let B and C be the centres of curvature of E_1 and E_2 respectively for that particular position. The mechanism can then be replaced by a four-bar linkage. The original element E_1 is replaced by the link AB connecting the pivot A to the centre of curvature B; similarly, element E_2 is replaced by the link DC connecting D to the centre of curvature C. The coupler of the four-bar linkage connects the two centres of curvature B and C as shown in Figure 3.28(b).

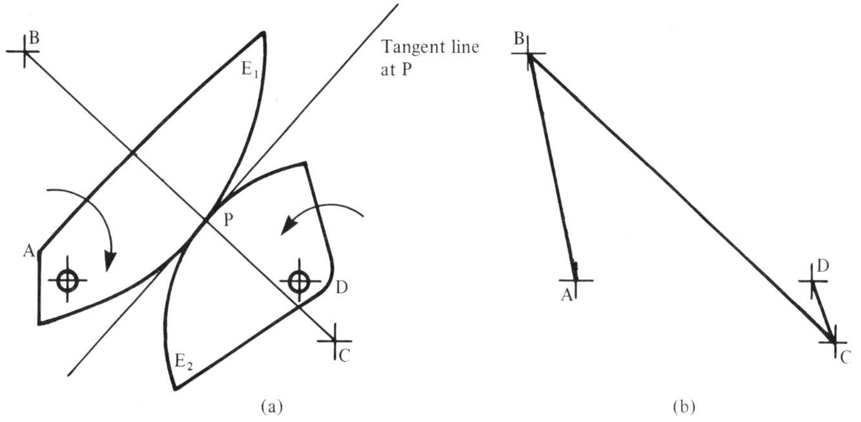

Figure 3.28 Replacing a mechanism by a four-bar linkage.

It must be remembered that a little later, when the original mechanism has moved to another position, the lengths of the equivalent mechanism will have changed.

Figures 3.29 and 3.30 illustrate the way two different types of cam can be replaced by equivalent mechanisms that are easier to analyse for a particular position. B is the centre of curvature of the cam at the point of contact P. In Figure 3.30 the equivalent mechanism is a slider–crank mechanism.

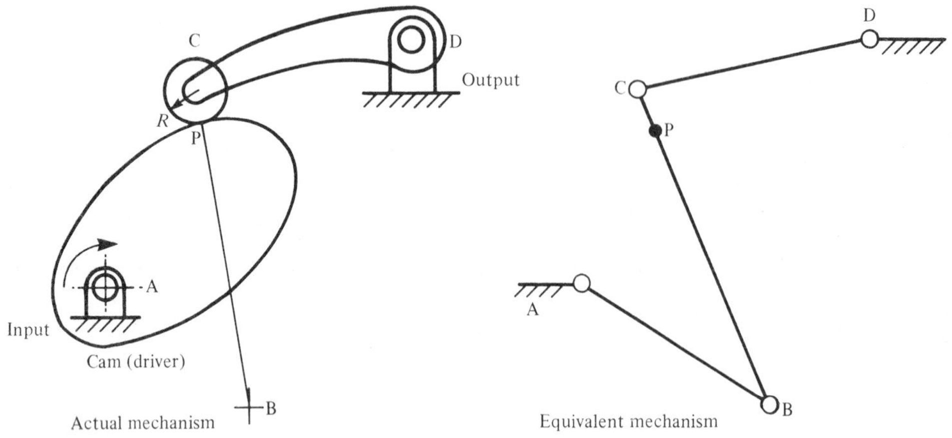

Figure 3.29 An example of an equivalent mechanism.

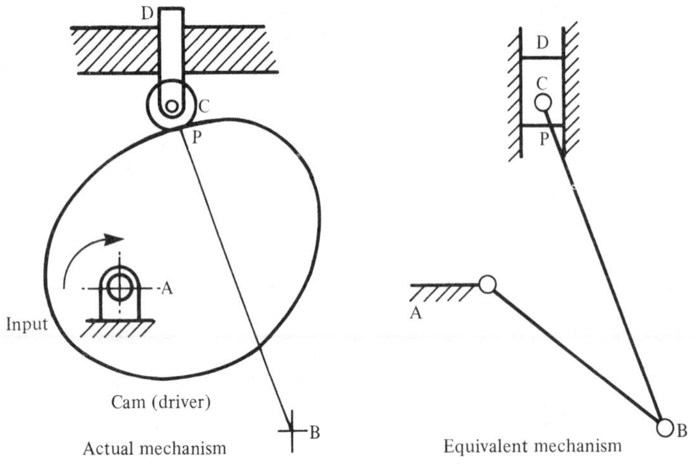

Figure 3.30 Another example of an equivalent mechanism.

3.7.7 **Analysis of the slider–crank mechanism**

The engine mechanism is in fact a slider–crank mechanism, the slider being the piston. Figure 3.31 shows the mechanism at a particular instant in time when the crank makes an angle θ with the line of stroke. Let R be the crank radius, L the length of the connecting rod and ω the angular velocity of the crank (assumed constant as in the case of an electrically driven reciprocating pump).

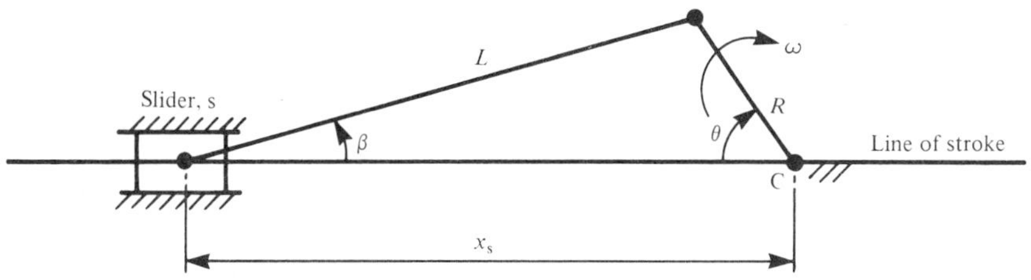

Figure 3.31 Analysis of the slider–crank mechanism.

If x_s is the position of the slider at that instant, measured from the crankshaft C, and β is the angle between the connecting rod and the line of stroke, then resolving along the line of stroke and perpendicular to it we have

$$x_s = R\cos\theta + L\cos\beta \tag{3.23}$$

and

$$L\sin\beta = R\sin\theta \tag{3.24}$$

As we are not interested in β at this stage, we may eliminate it using (3.24); thus

$$\sin\beta = \frac{R}{L}\sin\theta = q\sin\theta$$

where q = crank radius/connecting rod ratio. Since

$$\cos\beta = \sqrt{1-\sin^2\beta} = \sqrt{1-q^2\sin^2\theta}$$

substitution in equation (3.23) gives

$$x_s = R\cos\theta + L\sqrt{1-q^2\sin^2\theta} \tag{3.25}$$

This equation relates the position of the slider to that of the crank for all positions of the crank.

The velocity of the slider v_s is obtained by differentiating equation (3.25) with respect to time, remembering that $d\theta/dt = \omega$:

$$v_s = \dot{x}_s = -R\omega\left(\sin\theta + \frac{q}{2}\frac{\sin 2\theta}{\sqrt{1-q^2\sin^2\theta}}\right) \tag{3.26}$$

The reader is reminded that to differentiate the second term of equation (3.25) we proceed thus: let $u = 1 - q^2\sin^2\theta$, then

$$\frac{d}{dt}\sqrt{1-q^2\sin^2\theta} = \frac{d}{du}(u^{\frac{1}{2}})\frac{du}{d\theta}\frac{d\theta}{dt} = \tfrac{1}{2}u^{-\frac{1}{2}}(-2q^2\sin\theta\cos\theta)\omega$$

Before differentiating equation (3.26) with respect to time to obtain the acceleration we should note that in many cases in practice $q < 1$; in fact q is frequently of the order of $\frac{1}{3}$ or $\frac{1}{4}$. Hence $q^2 \ll 1$ and since $\sin^2\theta \leqslant 1$, we are justified in making the approximation that

$$(1 - q^2\sin^2\theta)^{-\frac{1}{2}} \simeq 1 + \tfrac{1}{2}q^2\sin^2\theta$$

by taking the first term of the expansion using the binomial theorem.

Substituting in equation (3.26) will give

$$v_s = -R\omega\left[\sin\theta + \frac{q}{2}\sin 2\theta\left(1 + \frac{q^2}{2}\sin^2\theta\right)\right]$$

$$= -R\omega\left(\sin\theta + \frac{q}{2}\sin 2\theta + \frac{q^3}{4}\sin 2\theta\sin^2\theta\right)$$

The third term will be small compared with the second term; hence we have for the velocity of the piston

$$v_s = -R\omega\left(\sin\theta + \frac{q}{2}\sin 2\theta\right) \tag{3.27}$$

The error in calculating the velocity of the piston in example 3.1 using equation (3.27) instead of equation (3.26) is 0.4% typically. Differentiating (3.27) gives the following expression for the acceleration a_s of the slider:

$$a_s = \dot{v}_s = \ddot{x}_s = R\omega^2(\cos\theta + q\cos 2\theta) \tag{3.28}$$

Equations (3.27) and (3.28) are the ones used most often in practice. We now propose to compare the values for the velocity and acceleration of the piston of example 3.1 obtained by the graphical method with those using the above equations. The values obtained from the graphical construction were

$$v_{P1} = 16\text{ m/s} \qquad \text{(instant-centre method)}$$
$$a_{P1} = 6120\text{ m/s}^2 \qquad \text{(larger scale drawing)}$$

Substitution in equations (3.27) and (3.28) yields

$$v_{P1} = -0.055 \times 366.5\left(\sin 40° + \frac{55}{2\times 170}\sin 80°\right) = 16.168\text{ m/s}$$

and

$$a_{P1} = -0.055 \times 366.5^2\left(\cos 40° + \frac{55}{170}\cos 80°\right) = 6074\text{ m/s}^2$$

By comparison we see that the velocities and the accelerations are in good agreement.

If we had wanted to find out the velocity and acceleration of the slider for one complete cycle of the crank, 360°, we could have done so easily and quickly using a programmable calculator. Furthermore the effect of changes in the dimensions R and/or L can be seen at a glance. The graphical technique would, on the other hand, require many drawings.

3.7.8 **Intermittent motion mechanism**

Figure 3.32(a) shows a mechanism that provides intermittent motion and is known as a "Geneva mechanism": it is an indexing device. The driver D rotates at a constant speed and drives the follower F by engaging a pin P into one of the slots. (Although the diagram shows four slots, there can be as many as 18.)

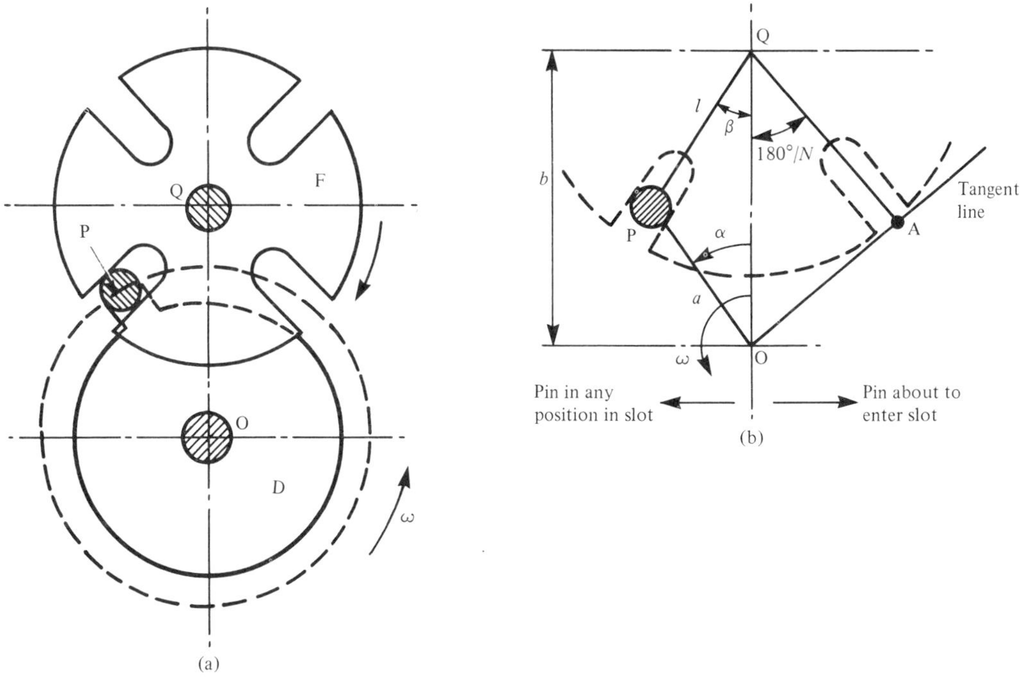

Figure 3.32 A Geneva mechanism producing intermittent motion.

From a design point of view we need to know the angular velocity and acceleration of the driven member and the velocity of sliding of the pin in the groove, which is important from a wear aspect.

To be more general, let N be the number of slots. Figure 3.32(b) shows the mechanism in any position (left-hand side of diagram) where a is the radius to the pin OP, α is the angle between the driver and the centre line OQ, b is the centre distance, l the variable distance of the pin from Q, and β the angle it makes with OQ. The right-hand side of the diagram shows the position when the pin is about to enter the slot at A. Between entering and leaving, the follower rotates through $360°/N$. Thus $\angle OQA = 180°/N$.

From the triangle OAQ,

$$b = \frac{a}{\sin(180°/N)} = ka$$

where $k = 1/\sin(180°/N)$. From the triangle OPQ we have

$$l \cos\beta + a \cos\alpha = b$$

or

$$l \cos\beta = b - a \cos\alpha \tag{3.29}$$

and

$$l \sin\beta = a \sin\alpha \tag{3.30}$$

Since l varies during the motion we will eliminate it; dividing (3.30) by (3.29) yields

$$\tan\beta = \frac{a\sin\alpha}{b - a\cos\alpha} \tag{3.31}$$

This equation gives the angle β.

To calculate the angular velocity we differentiate equation (3.31) implicitly with respect to time; this gives

$$(\sec^2\beta)\dot{\beta} = \frac{ab\cos\alpha - a^2}{(b - a\cos\alpha)^2}\,\dot{\alpha} \tag{3.32}$$

Since

$$\sec^2\beta = 1 + \tan^2\beta = 1 + \frac{a^2\sin^2\alpha}{(b - a\cos\alpha)^2}$$

substituting in (3.32) yields

$$\dot{\beta} = \frac{(ab\cos\alpha - a^2)\omega}{a^2 + b^2 - 2ab\cos\alpha} \qquad \text{since } \dot{\alpha} = \omega$$

or

$$\dot{\beta} = \frac{(k\cos\alpha - 1)\omega}{1 + k^2 - 2k\cos\alpha} \tag{3.33}$$

We leave it to the reader to show that the angular acceleration of the driven member is given by

$$\ddot{\beta} = \frac{k\sin\alpha\,(1 - k^2)}{(1 + k^2 - 2k\cos\alpha)^2}\,\omega^2 \tag{3.34}$$

To visualise equations (3.33) and (3.34) the angular velocity and angular acceleration ratios have been plotted and are shown in Figure 3.33 for $N = 3, 4, 5, 6, 7$ and 8 slots.

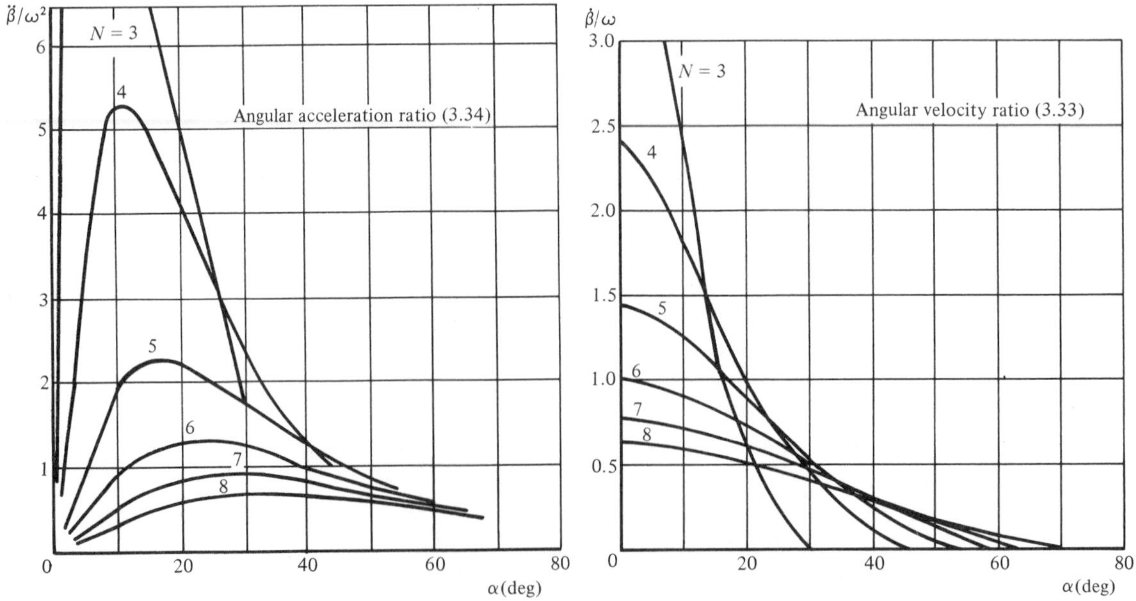

Figure 3.33 Output performance of the Geneva mechanism.

Let us examine the sliding of the pin in the slot. Figure 3.34 shows the triangle OQP of Figure 3.32. Let v_P be the velocity of sliding of the pin in the slot; then we have

$$v_P = a\omega \cos \psi$$

But $\psi = 90° - (\alpha + \beta)$ and hence

$$v_P = a\omega \sin(\alpha + \beta) \qquad (3.35)$$

It follows that the velocity of sliding is a maximum when

$$\alpha + \beta = 90°$$

Hence

$$v_{P\,max} = a\omega$$

This value is important when lubrication is being considered.

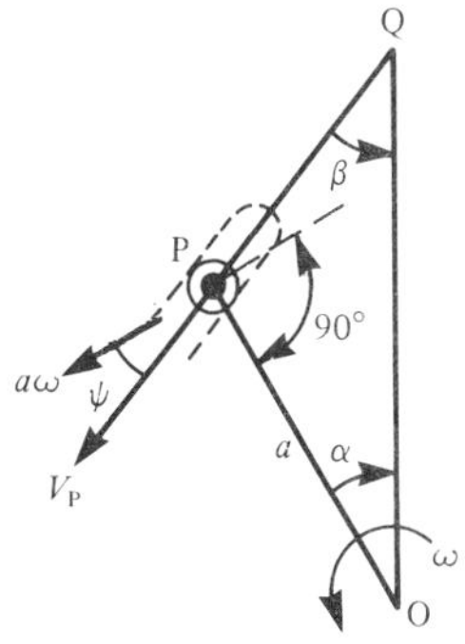

Figure 3.34 Sliding of the pin in the Geneva mechanism.

COMPUTER PROGRAMS: AN EXAMPLE 3.8

Computer programs to facilitate the analysis and synthesis of mechanisms are available commercially; they range from very simple ones to very advanced ones costing around £3500 (1985 prices).

The output from such a computer program designed by two final-year students* is shown in Figure 3.35. It is written in BASIC and intended for use on a PET microcomputer linked to a plotter and/or printer. The program can be used for either the analysis or the synthesis of four-bar linkages. Linkages produced by the synthesis routine are automatically analysed.

The analysis routine gives graphical information on the position of the output (PSI), the velocity ratio, the transmission angle (MU) and the acceleration of the output as a function of the input angle. The effect on the performance due to a change in any one link length can be seen fairly quickly. The locus of any point on the coupler can also be drawn, and all results can be obtained in tabular form if desired.

*S. Beck and M. Chapman, unpublished undergraduate thesis, Bath University, 1985.

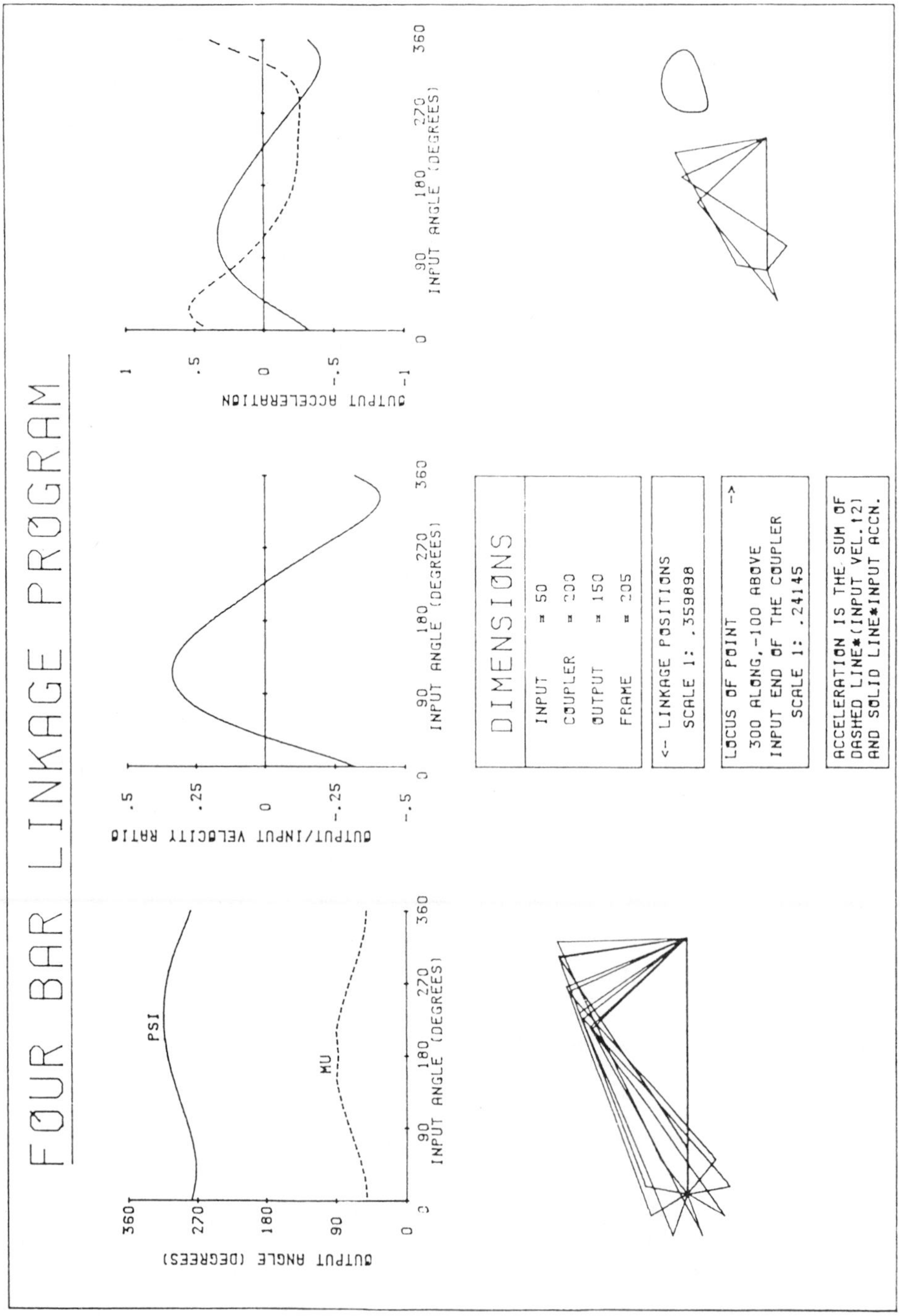

Figure 3.35 An example of output from a computer program.

LINKAGES IN OUTER SPACE 3.9

Figure 3.36 of the space shuttle *Orbiter* illustrates further applications of linkages. Figure 3.36(a) shows one of the four-bar linkages ABCD operating the payload bay door, which is 18.29 m long, and hinged at thirteen hinge points. AD is the fixed link, i.e. the shuttle's structure; AB is the input link, in the shape of a bellcrank, and actuated by means of a link PQ; BC is the coupler; and CD is the follower, or output link, which is the bay door itself. In the open position B moves to B′ and C to C′ corresponding to an angular movement of 180°, while the input link rotates through an angle of 103°. The torque shaft for each bay door is actuated by two motors through the geared system shown in Figure 5.17, Chapter 5.

Other bellcranks and linkages operated by actuators are used in the various latch systems required to secure the payload bay doors and the umbilical doors underneath *Orbiter,* and are shown in Figure 3.36(b).

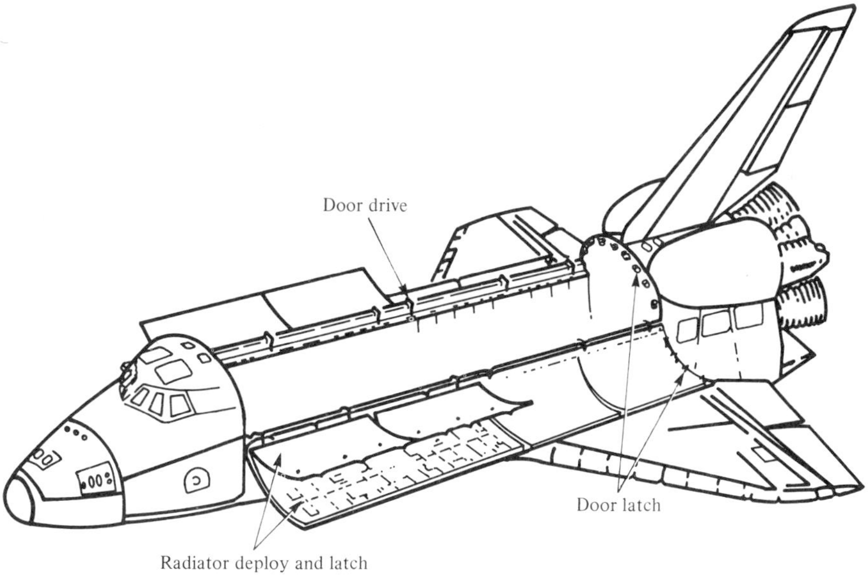

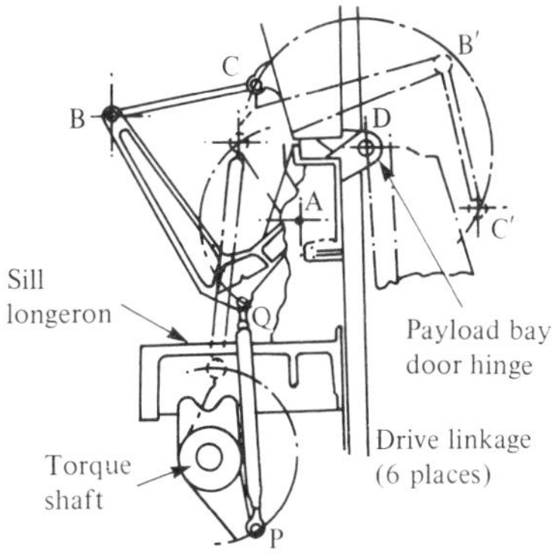

Figure 3.36(a) Space shuttle *Orbiter:* payload bay door mechanisms.

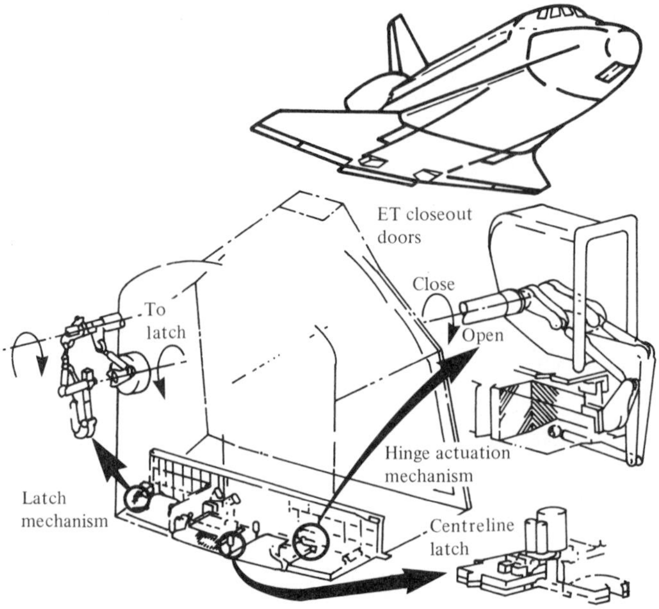

Figure 3.36(b) Space shuttle *Orbiter:* umbilical door mechanisms.

Figure 3.37 shows the landing gear, which is essentially of a conventional aircraft tricycle configuration with steerable nose gear and a braking and anti-skid system for the aft main landing gear, each comprising a number of linkages. The *Orbiter* landing speed is, however, about twice that of most aircraft.

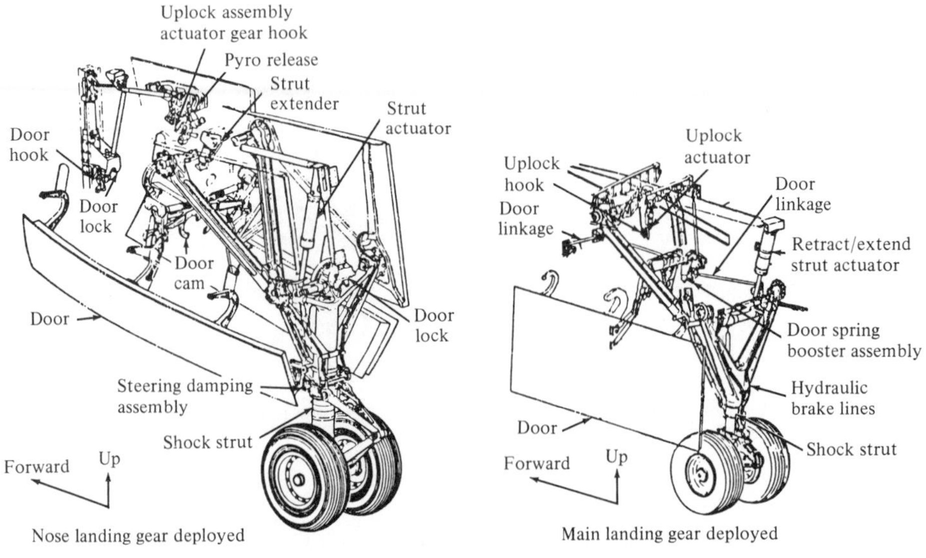

Figure 3.37 Space shuttle *Orbiter:* landing/deceleration system.

EXERCISES

3.1 Figure 3.38 shows the slider–crank mechanism with the slider B driving. Using the data shown calculate graphically the angular velocity and acceleration of the crank OA. Check your answers analytically.

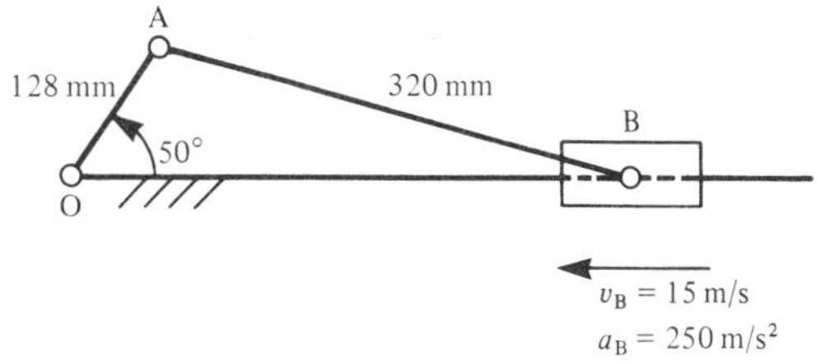

Figure 3.38

3.2 Figure 3.39 shows the dimensions of the links of the crane shown in Figure 3.19. Using the instantaneous-centre method, calculate the horizontal velocity of the point E on the jib EAB in the two extreme positions of the crane. The input link BC has an angular velocity of 0.08 rad/s.

Check your answers by drawing the velocity diagrams corresponding to these two positions.

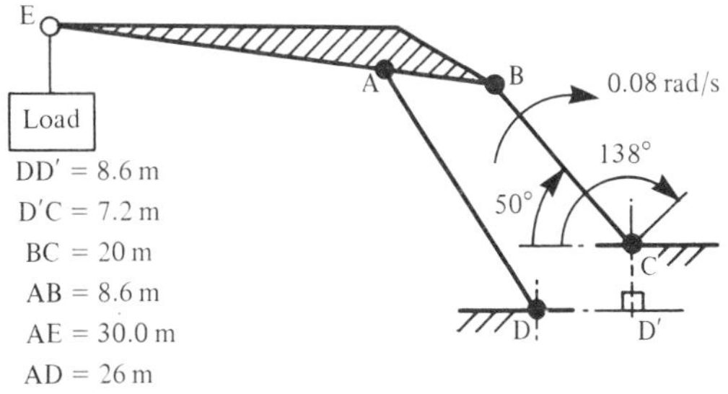

Figure 3.39

3.3 Figure 3.40 shows diagrammatically a mechanism for operating the arm AOB of an earth excavator. OA = 0.35 m, AC = 0.85 m, OB = 2.85 m, $v_C = 0.5$ m/s. Calculate the velocity and acceleration of the point B when OA makes an angle of 60° with OC. The rod PC moves along a straight line through O. Check your answers analytically. What is the magnitude of the acceleration of B at the extreme positions?

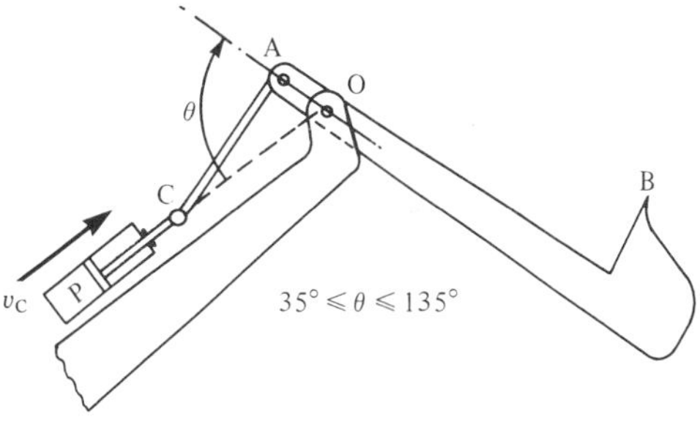

Figure 3.40

3.4 Figure 3.41 shows the offset nose wheel of an airliner. A, D and E are pivots fixed to the frame of the aircraft. C is a pivot fixed to the undercarriage leg and F is a pivot fixed to the nose wheel door. For the position where the nose wheel makes an angle of 30° with the vertical and the link AB rotates at 0.25 rad/s in the direction shown, calculate graphically the velocity of G, the angular velocity of the leg DG and the angular velocity of the door EF. The dimensions are AB = 432 mm, BC = 229 mm, CF = 330 mm, EF = 229 mm, DH = 254 mm, ch = 63.5 mm (perpendicular to DH), DG = 990 mm; A is 584 mm to the left of D and 229 mm above D; E is 127 mm to the right of D and 63.5 mm below D.

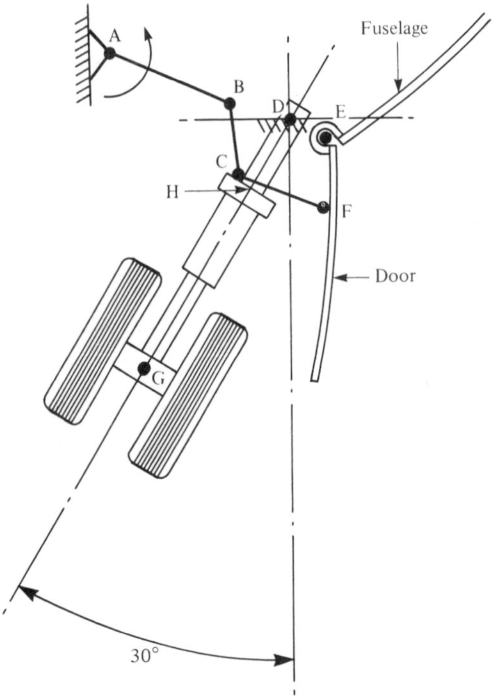

Figure 3.41

3.5 Figure 3.42 shows a four-bar linkage A_0ABB_0. Calculate graphically (a) the angular velocity of the coupler AB, (b) the angular velocity of the output link BB_0, (c) the velocity of the point B, (d) the angular acceleration of the coupler, (e) the angular acceleration of the output link. Dimensions are in metres.

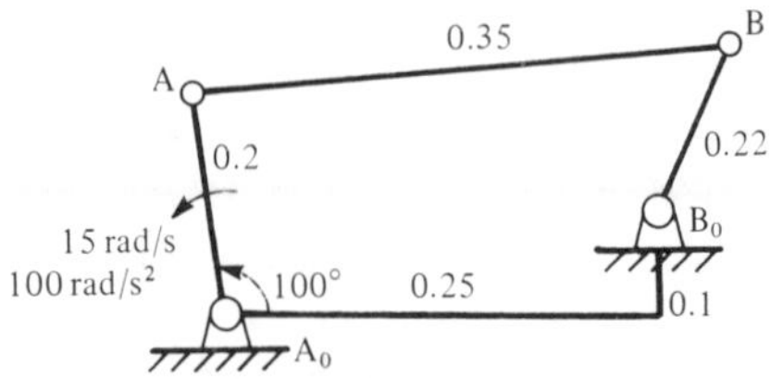

Figure 3.42

3.6 Calculate the angular acceleration of the links CP, PA and AQ as well as the acceleration of the slider P, shown in Figure 3.43. The crank OC rotates at 250 rev/min. Dimensions are in millimetres.

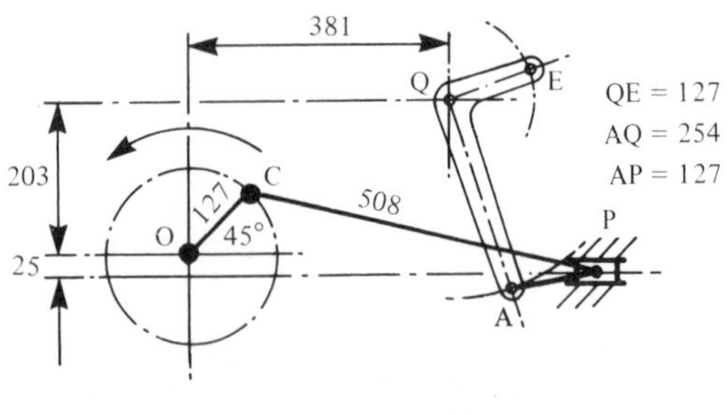

Figure 3.43

3.7 The dimensions of a stone-crusher mechanism are shown in Figure 3.44. When the crank OA is in the position shown and rotating at the constant angular velocity of 75 rev/min, calculate the velocity of the point X.

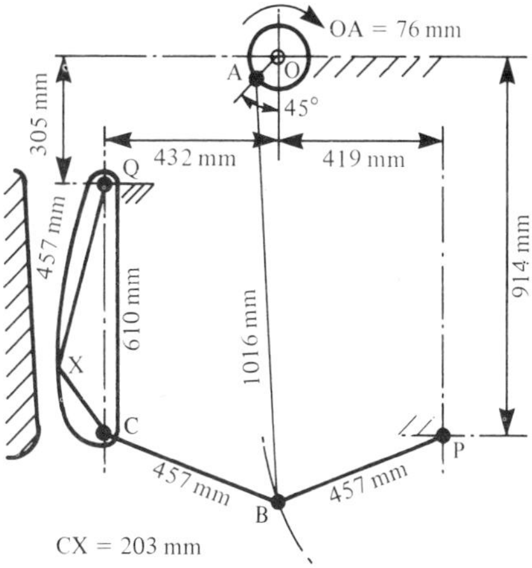

Figure 3.44

3.8 Figure 3.45 shows a type of quick-return mechanism for a slotting machine. The toothed sector gear drives the rack R which carries the tool, not shown. When the crank OP rotates at 65 rev/min, calculate the velocity of the rack R.

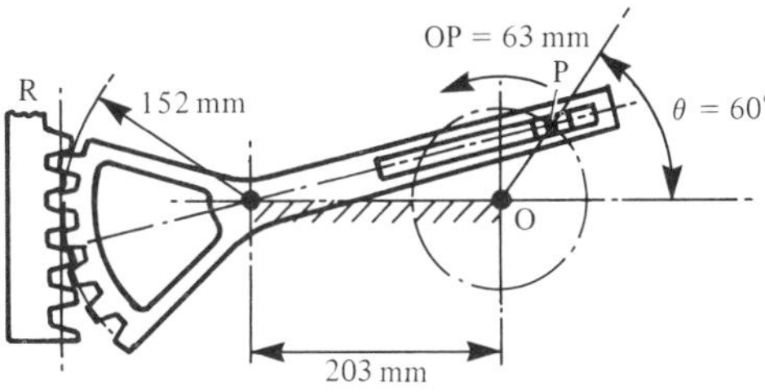

Figure 3.45

3.9 The dimensions of a differential stroke engine mechanism are as shown in Figure 3.46. OA and QB are geared together so that QB turns at twice the speed of OA and in the opposite sense. For the given configuration calculate the velocity of the piston when OA rotates at 700 rev/min.

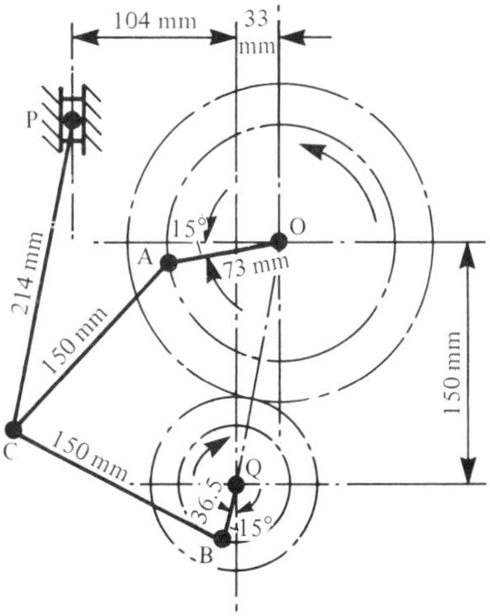

Figure 3.46

3.10 Referring to exercise 3.5 calculate analytically the angular velocity and acceleration of the coupler AB and the output link BB_0.

3.11 Figure 3.47 shows a quick-return mechanism used to save time in a machine which cuts in one direction only (time is money!). At the end of the crank BE, rotating at 60 rev/min, is a pin E sliding in the link DF, which slides on a fixed pin A at one end. At the other end a pin D slides in a fixed slot CC′. Obtain an analytical expression for the velocity of D in terms of θ, ω and the lengths a, b and r. If $a = 178$ mm, $b = 165$ mm, $r = 57$ mm, $\theta = 60°$, calculate (a) the total stroke of D, (b) the velocities of D as it passes the mid-stroke position in each direction and (c) the acceleration of D when $\theta = 60°$.

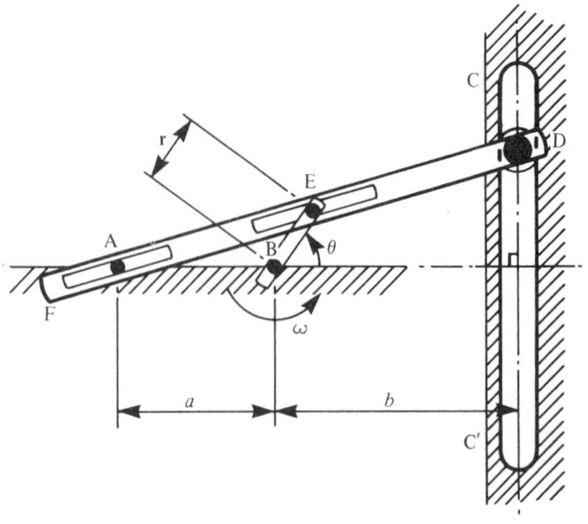

Figure 3.47

3.12 A four-bar linkage is to be used to coordinate three input and three output positions and to fit in a space of 450 mm × 350 mm. Calculate the dimensions of the links to one decimal place. Referring to Figure 3.22, calculate also the transmission angle for each position: input angle, 30°, 45°, 60°; output angle, 200°, 235°, 270°.

4

Kinetics of Particles

MOTION OF PARTICLES 4.1

We now investigate the motion of particles under the action of forces. If a particle is free of any constraints, e.g. a golf ball, a rocket, or material falling off a conveyor belt, the path it takes will be dictated by the nature of the forces acting on it, but if it is constrained to follow a particular path then its motion will be affected by the presence of reactions in accordance with Newton's third law, and by frictional forces.

Consider a free particle of mass m moving in a horizontal plane, acted upon by a number of forces whose resultant is **R** as shown in Figure 4.1(a). Then according to Newton's second law it will have an acceleration **a** (of magnitude R/m) in the direction of **R**.

However, if that same particle, acted upon by the same force **R**, is constrained to move in a guide parallel to the x-axis as shown in Figure 4.1(b), it can now accelerate only in the direction of the guide, whatever the direction of **R**.

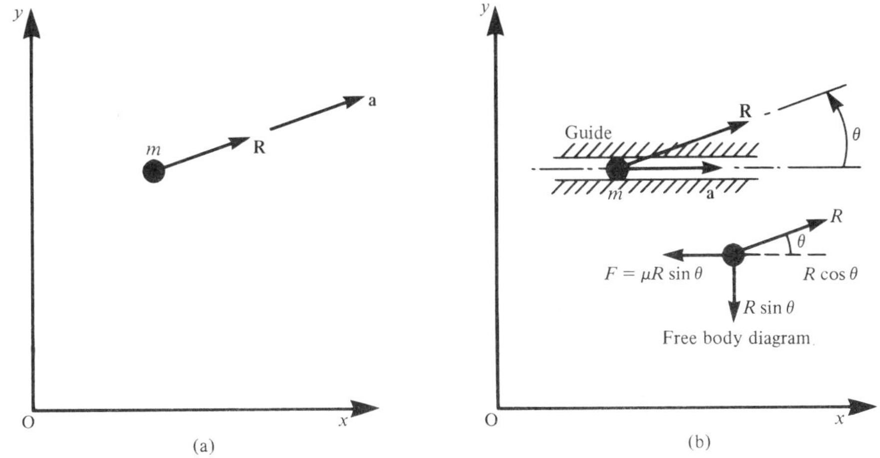

Figure 4.1 Motion of (a) a free particle and (b) a constrained particle.

Furthermore the particle is now subjected to three forces as shown in the free body diagram; $R \sin\theta$ is the reaction of the guide on the particle and F is the frictional force.

The magnitude of the acceleration of the particle is given by

$$a = R(\cos\theta - \mu\sin\theta)/m \qquad (4.1)$$

which is very different from that of the free particle.

Many problems in engineering are concerned with the constrained motion of particles (and rigid bodies), e.g. mechanisms and railways.

In practice, different kinds of forces are encountered:

(a) *Constant forces:* Examples are the force of gravity near the surface of the Earth or other planet, the force exerted by a hydraulic ram working at constant pressure, dry friction and the thrust of a jet engine. In these cases **R** is constant (in magnitude and direction).

(b) *Variable forces:* Examples are the force of gravity as we move away from the surface of a planet, the resistance offered by the air to the motion of an aircraft, the force exerted on the piston of an internal combustion engine and forces exerted by springs. In these cases $\mathbf{R} = f(\mathbf{x}, \dot{\mathbf{x}}, t)$ in general, i.e. the resultant force is a function of displacement, velocity and time. For example, a spring exerts a force that is a function of the displacement, so that $\mathbf{R} = f(\mathbf{x})$; the drag on a particle is a function of the velocity, so that $\mathbf{R} = f(\mathbf{v})$; whereas the effect of the imbalance of the rotor of a fan gives rise to an inertia force varying with time, so that $\mathbf{R} = f(t)$.

An aircraft in flight is subjected to lift and drag forces, which are functions of the square of the velocity, and a constant thrust from the engines. There are also reactive forces in accordance with Newton's third law, as in Figure 4.1(b).

4.2 FRICTION

4.2.1 Introduction

When a surface slides on another surface, a tangential force is developed between them, which depends on the nature of the two surfaces; this force is known as a frictional force.

Frictional forces are very important and must not be neglected. They may lead to a loss of power, as in bearings, or wherever there is a rubbing action. On the other hand, we can make use of friction to transmit power, as in belt drives, in clutches such as the ones used in car transmission. Furthermore a train could not move if it were not for the friction between the wheels and the rails. The loss of power due to friction appears as heat, and leads to wear of the surfaces in contact.

The kinds of friction are as follows:

(a) *Dry friction,* which is known as Coulomb friction, occurs where the surfaces in contact are not lubricated or the lubrication is very sparse.

(b) *Fluid friction* occurs where two surfaces are separated by a film of fluid such as oil.

(c) *Rolling friction* is the resistance to the rolling of circular bodies such as the wheels of a train on the rails, and is due to a local deformation of the surfaces.

(d) *Internal friction* or *hysteresis* occurs in materials under stress due to the cyclic application of forces. This leads to a loss that is quite small for elastic materials, but can be very large in non-elastic materials, or materials that undergo plastic deformations.

4.2.2 Sliding friction

In this text we are primarily concerned with dry and rolling friction.

In 1781 Coulomb made a clear distinction between static and sliding friction:

(i) Static friction is the force required to start the motion.

(ii) Sliding friction is the force required to maintain the motion. Sliding friction is smaller than static friction.

Experiments on a wide range of materials have shown that:

(i) the frictional force is independent of the contact area,

(ii) at low speeds the force of friction is independent of the velocity, and

(iii) the force of friction is proportional to the normal force between the surfaces in contact and acts in a direction opposite to the relative velocity.

Figure 4.2(a) shows a block of material A resting on a horizontal surface B. A force P is applied to A; this force will be resisted by the frictional force F developed between the block and the surface, as shown in the free body diagram in Figure 4.2(b).

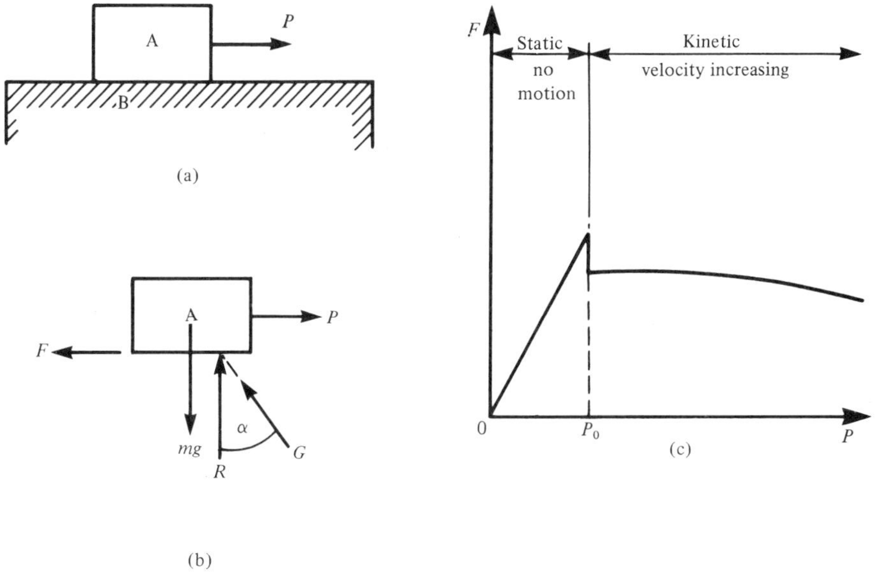

Figure 4.2 Sliding friction.

The free body diagram shows all the forces acting on A: mg is the weight, R is the normal reaction and F the frictional force opposite to the applied force P. From $P = 0$ to some value P_0 the block remains at rest and F increases with P and reaches a maximum value given by the relationship $F = \mu_s R$, where μ_s is a constant that depends on the nature of the surfaces of A and B. This constant is called the coefficient of static friction. When P_0 is reached, sliding motion is about to take place and the coefficient drops to a value μ_k called the coefficient of kinetic friction, and $F = \mu_k R$. As P is increased beyond P_0, the velocity of the block increases while the frictional force remains constant, until, at high velocities, the force starts to fall again. F and R may be combined to give a resultant G.

The frictional force is usually written as $F = \mu R$ and the appropriate value for μ is used to suit a particular situation, but $\mu_s R$ is the maximum frictional force that can exist between any two given surfaces and is known as the limiting friction. The coefficient of friction between any two surfaces can vary from day to day, owing to the presence of dust or grease. Typical values are given in Appendix A.7.

The angle α between R and G shown in Figure 4.2(b) is called the friction angle, and is given by

$$\alpha = \arctan\left(\frac{F}{R}\right) = \arctan \mu \tag{4.2}$$

EXAMPLE 4.1

Referring to Figure 1.12 which showed two packages in contact sliding down a chute, let the mass of A be 25 kg, the mass of B be 40 kg, the angle of the chute to the horizontal be 35° and the coefficients of friction be $\mu_A = 0.3$ and $\mu_B = 0.4$. Calculate the time taken for the packages to slide down the chute a distance of 7.5 m and the velocity reached by the packages if their initial velocity was 1.5 m/s. Do the packages remain in contact? What is the minimum angle the chute must make to the horizontal to ensure that the packages will slide down?

SOLUTION

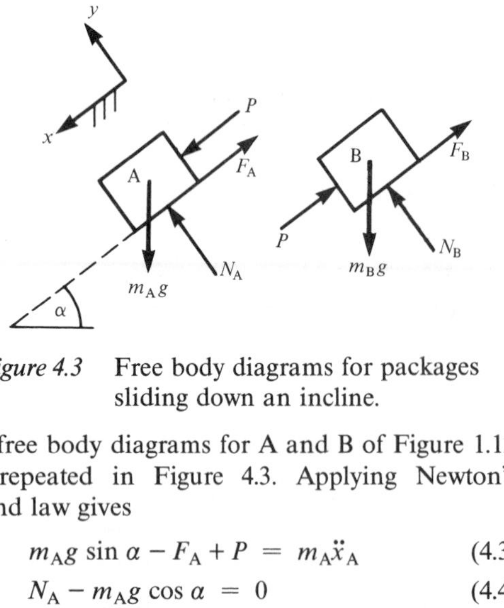

Figure 4.3 Free body diagrams for packages sliding down an incline.

The free body diagrams for A and B of Figure 1.12 are repeated in Figure 4.3. Applying Newton's second law gives

$$m_A g \sin\alpha - F_A + P = m_A \ddot{x}_A \tag{4.3}$$

$$N_A - m_A g \cos\alpha = 0 \tag{4.4}$$

$$F_A = \mu_A N_A \tag{4.5}$$

From (4.5) and (4.4) we have

$$F_A = \mu_A m_A g \cos\alpha$$

Substituting in (4.3) yields

$$m_A g(\sin\alpha - \mu_A \cos\alpha) + P = m_A \ddot{x}_A \tag{4.6}$$

Similarly for B except that the force of contact P acts up the incline in accordance with Newton's law of reaction; hence

$$m_B g(\sin\alpha - \mu_B \cos\alpha) - P = m_B \ddot{x}_B \tag{4.7}$$

The packages will remain in contact provided that $P > 0$, i.e. if

$$m_A g(\sin\alpha - \mu_A \cos\alpha) \leqslant m_B g(\sin\alpha - \mu_B \cos\alpha)$$

or

$$m_A(\sin\alpha - \mu_A \cos\alpha) \leqslant m_B(\sin\alpha - \mu_B \cos\alpha)$$

Now

$$m_A(\sin\alpha - \mu_A \cos\alpha) = 25(\sin 35° - 0.3 \cos 35°) = 8.195 \text{ kg}$$

and

$$m_B(\sin\alpha - \mu_B \cos\alpha) = 40(\sin 35° - 0.4 \cos 35°) = 9.836 \text{ kg}$$

Hence the condition is satisfied. It follows, therefore, that

$$\ddot{x}_A = \ddot{x}_B = a$$

Solution Cont.

Adding equations (4.6) and (4.7) gives

$$g[(m_A + m_B)\sin\alpha - (m_A\mu_A + m_B\mu_B)\cos\alpha] = (m_A + m_B)a$$

Substituting numerical values and solving for a yields

$$a = \frac{9.81}{65}[65\sin 35° - (25 \times 0.3 + 40 \times 0.4)\cos 35°]$$
$$= 2.72\ \text{m/s}^2$$

To solve for the velocity at the end of the chute we know that

$$v\frac{dv}{dx} = a$$

Separating the variables and integrating gives

$$\int v\,dv = \int a\,dx + \text{constant}$$

i.e.

$$\tfrac{1}{2}v^2 = ax + \text{constant}$$

When $x = 0$, $v = v_0$, so that

$$\text{constant} = \tfrac{1}{2}v_0^2$$

Hence

$$v^2 = v_0^2 + 2ax$$

Solution Cont.

If v_1 is the velocity at the bottom of the chute when $x = x_1$, then

$$v_1 = \sqrt{v_0^2 + 2ax_1}$$
$$= \sqrt{1.5^2 + 2 \times 2.72 \times 7.5} = 6.56\ \text{m/s}$$

To calculate the time we have

$$\frac{dv}{dt} = a$$

Proceeding as above we find that

$$v = at + v_0$$

If t_1 is the time to reach the bottom of the chute, then

$$t_1 = \frac{v_1 - v_0}{a} = \frac{6.56 - 1.5}{2.72} = 1.86\ \text{s}$$

The minimum angle α to ensure that the packages will slide down is given by

$$\alpha = \arctan\mu_A \quad \text{or} \quad \arctan\mu_B$$

Since $\mu_B > \mu_A$ the minimum angle is given by

$$\alpha = \arctan\mu_B = \arctan 0.4 = 21.8°$$

(*Note:* arctan 0.3 = 16.7°.)

4.2.3 **Rolling friction**

A wheel of radius R rolling without sliding on a flat surface will experience a resistance due to the very small local deformation that takes place, i.e. a kind of ridge is formed in front of the wheel as shown exaggerated in Figure 4.4; this gives rise to the force F_R, whose line of action passes through the centre C of the wheel. If W is the weight of the wheel and P the horizontal force necessary to balance the horizontal component F_h of F_R, we must have

$$F_v e = PR$$

but

$$F_v = W$$

Hence

$$P = \frac{e}{R}W$$

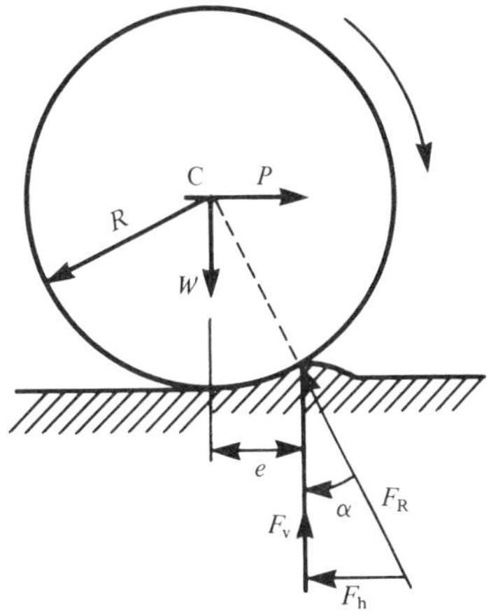

Figure 4.4 Rolling friction.

Here e is the horizontal distance between the vertical component F_v of F_R and the weight W. The ratio $e/R = \mu_R$ is called the coefficient of rolling friction. The distance e depends on the type and nature of the surfaces in contact, the speed and the radius R of the wheel, although experiments indicate that the radius has little influence. Typical values are $\mu_R = 0.006$ for steel on steel and 0.02–0.04 for rubber tyres on concrete surfaces.

To illustrate friction further let us consider three everyday situations.

Figure 4.5 shows one of the wheels of a diesel shunting locomotive driven by means of the coupling rod AB. Motion is transferred to the wheel by means of the crank OA. Provided there is no slipping at the point of contact P, this point is at rest, and consequently a frictional force or tractive effort T acts on the wheel in the direction of motion.

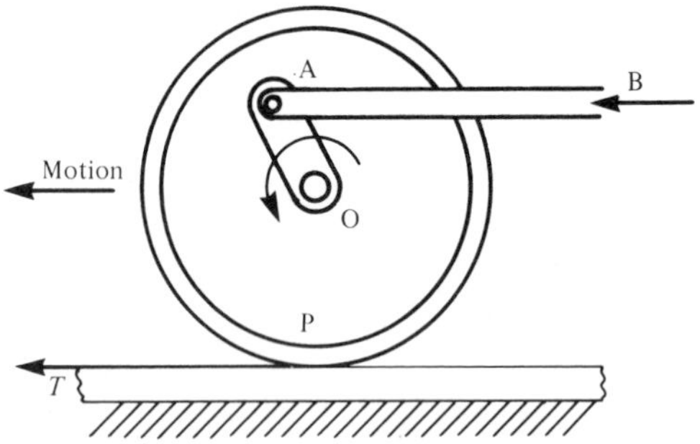

Figure 4.5 Wheel of a locomotive.

Figure 4.6 shows the non-driven wheel of a car; if there were no friction between the tyre and the road, the wheel would not rotate, it would slide. It is the friction force F opposite to the motion that causes the wheel to rotate.

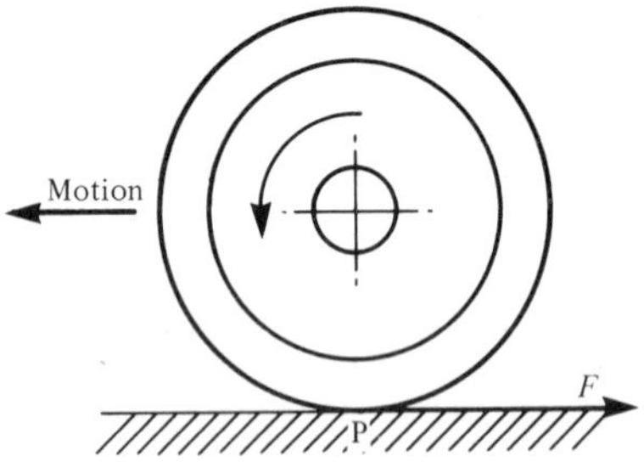

Figure 4.6 Non-driven wheel of a car.

Figure 4.7 illustrates the action of the brakes to reduce the speed of travel. Frictional forces F_1 between the brake pads B and the brake drum D provide a couple tending to slow down the rotation of the wheel. A frictional force F at P acts opposite to the motion, giving rise to a deceleration of the wheel.

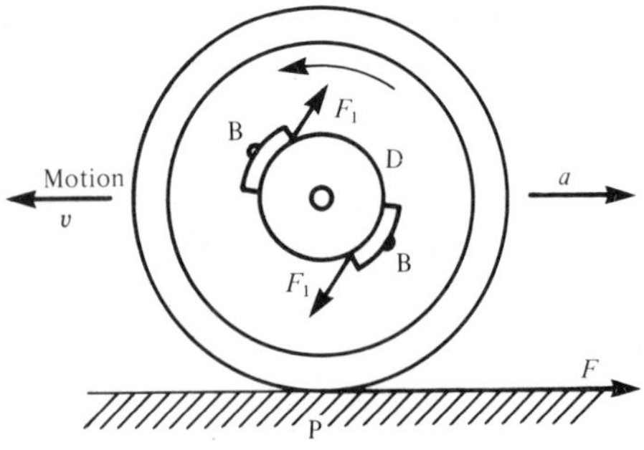

Figure 4.7 Brake action.

In these three cases it is assumed that there is no slipping at the point of contact P. Thus point P is instantaneously at rest.

4.2.4 **Belt friction**

As an example of the use of friction to transmit power, consider the drive shown in Figure 4.8(a), where a motor M drives a pulley A which is linked to a pulley B by means of a flat belt.

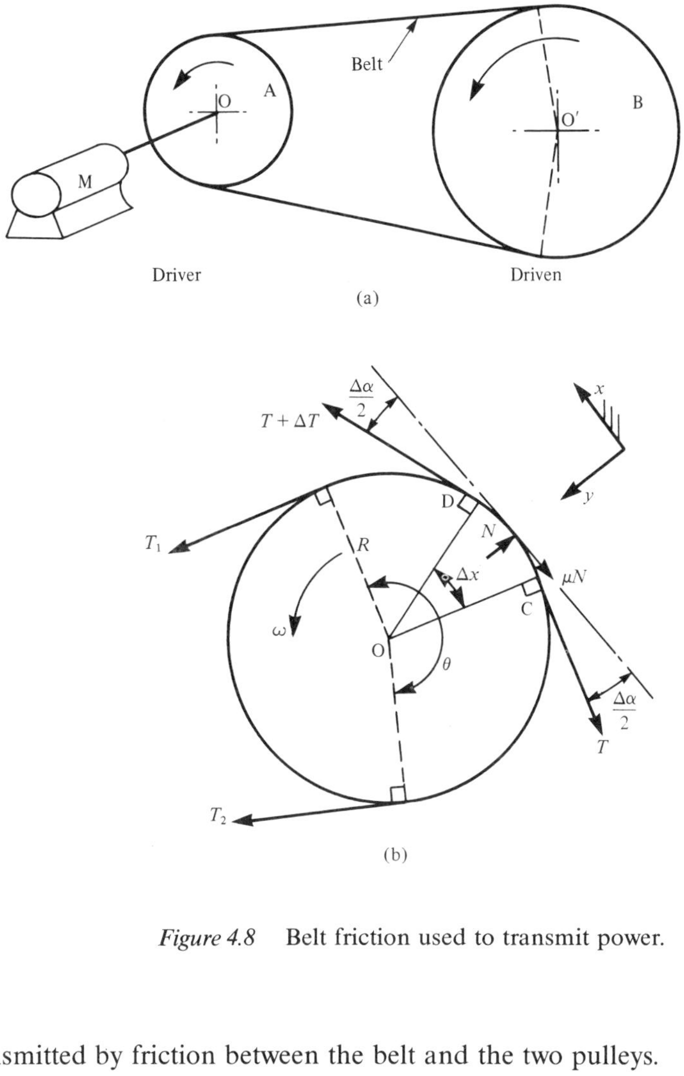

Figure 4.8 Belt friction used to transmit power.

Power is transmitted by friction between the belt and the two pulleys.

An examination of the forces acting on an element of belt CD that subtends an angle $\Delta\alpha$ at the centre O of the pulley of mean radius R shows that there are tensions T and $T + \Delta T$ in the belt at C and D respectively (Figure 4.8(b)). N is the normal reaction per unit length between the belt and the pulley and ω the angular velocity, usually constant after run up.

Let μ be the coefficient of static friction and ρ the mass of the belt per unit length. Then by Newton's second law we have the following:

(a) Resolving along the x-axis gives

$$\sum F_x = 0$$

$$-T\cos(\Delta\alpha/2) - \mu NR\Delta\alpha + (T + \Delta T)\cos(\Delta\alpha/2) = 0$$

If $\Delta\alpha$ is small, $\cos(\Delta\alpha/2) \simeq 1$ so that

$$-\mu NR\Delta\alpha + \Delta T = 0$$

i.e.

$$\frac{\mathrm{d}T}{\mathrm{d}\alpha} = \mu NR$$

(b) Resolving along the y-axis gives

$$\sum F_y = \text{mass} \times \text{acceleration}$$

$$\sum F_y = (\rho R\Delta\alpha)\omega^2 R$$

where $\rho R\Delta\alpha$ is the mass of the element and $\omega^2 R$ the centripetal acceleration of the belt. Hence

$$(T + \Delta T)\sin(\Delta\alpha/2) + T\sin(\Delta\alpha/2) - NR\Delta\alpha = \rho R^2\omega^2\Delta\alpha = \rho v^2\Delta\alpha$$

where v is the peripheral velocity of the belt. Since $\sin(\Delta\alpha/2) \simeq \Delta\alpha/2$ for small angles, it follows that

$$T\Delta\alpha - NR\Delta\alpha = \rho v^2\Delta\alpha$$

or

$$T - \rho v^2 = NR$$

Substituting for NR from (a) yields

$$\mu(T - \rho v^2) = \frac{\mathrm{d}T}{\mathrm{d}\alpha}$$

Separating the variables and integrating,

$$\int_{T_2}^{T_1} \frac{\mathrm{d}T}{T - \rho v^2} = \int_0^\theta \mu\,\mathrm{d}\alpha$$

Hence

$$\frac{T_1 - \rho v^2}{T_2 - \rho v^2} = \mathrm{e}^{\mu\theta}$$

where θ is the angle of "lap". The term ρv^2 is the centripetal force, which reduces the tension in the belt and depends only on the mass per unit length and not on the length of belt in contact with the pulley.

In practice "Vee" belts are frequently used. The sections of such belts are trapezoidal as shown in Figure 4.9, and fit into a groove in the pulley subtending an angle 2β. The reader should verify for himself that with these belts the coefficient of static friction μ is effectively increased to $\mu' = \mu/\sin\beta$ so that greater power can be transmitted.

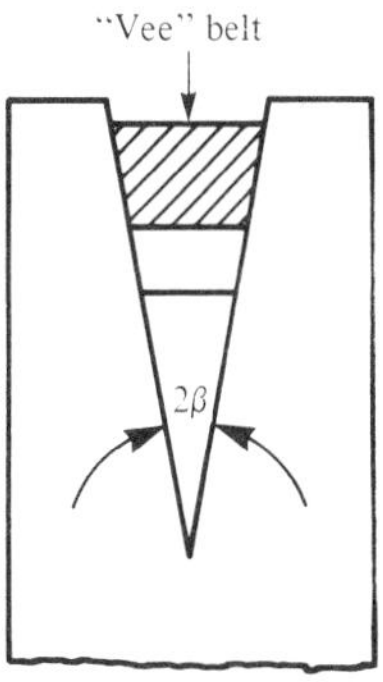

Figure 4.9 A "Vee" belt.

Belts are not only used for transmitting power; they find application in conveyors for transporting materials such as coal, sand ores or other loose materials. These belt conveyors can be very long, reaching lengths of 3 km, operating at speeds of 150 m/min, transporting 200 t of material per hour and powered by a single 150 kW motor. Figure 4.10 illustrates a horizontal conveyor discharging at intermediate stations A and B or the end C.

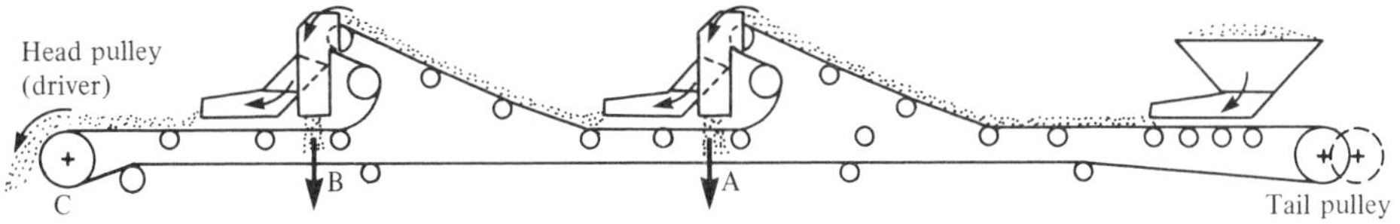

Figure 4.10 Horizontal conveyor using belt friction.

To obtain a greater carrying capacity the belt is given a through shape as shown in Figure 4.11, and is supported on three independent rollers or idlers with the outer ones inclined at an angle of 20°. The idlers run on roller bearings.

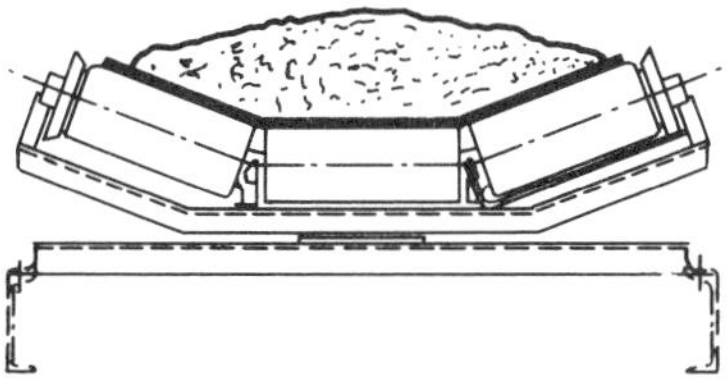

Figure 4.11 Trough shape of belt for greater capacity.

PRIME MOVER CHARACTERISTICS 4.3

When we get into a car or on a motorbike and switch on the engine, we call upon its characteristics to get started. The pilot of an aircraft calls upon the characteristics of the engine(s) in order to take off. Similarly when we switch on a fan to get a little air in an office or factory on a very hot day we call upon the characteristics of an electric motor to drive a fan.

The car, motorbike and aircraft engines, as well as the electric motor, are types of prime mover, which derive their power from a fuel: petrol and kerosene in the case of an internal combustion engine and gas turbine respectively, and coal or atomic energy in power stations to provide the electricity from generators or alternators driven by turbines. In these cases the energy in the fuel is converted into mechanical or electrical energy.

The characteristic or output performance of a prime mover depends on a number of factors. For instance, in the case of an internal combustion engine, its characteristic is a function of the way the gases expand in the cylinder, the kinematics of the slider–crank mechanism which transforms the rectilinear motion of the piston into a continuous rotation of the crankshaft, the number of cylinders and the firing order of the cylinders, to name but a few.

The characteristic of such an engine is expressed by its torque–speed relationship. The torque available at the crankshaft is what is needed to drive a car or a generator or any other device. In the case of a car we should have to ensure that the choice of engine results in a satisfactory performance; this means that we need to match the engine to the car correctly.

The devices driven by prime movers are usually referred to as loads.

The dynamic performance of a prime-mover–load system depends on the characteristics of both the prime mover and the load. For example, the engine of a car has to overcome a resistance which is basically a function of the speed of the car; this resistance determines the load characteristic of the car.

Examples of actual prime mover characteristics are shown on the next few pages.

The characteristic of the internal combustion engine is measured by the torque available at the crankshaft as a function of the speed of rotation of the crank. The torque–speed or output characteristic at full throttle of a modern petrol engine is shown in Figure 4.12; the power curve has also been plotted. We notice that the torque remains fairly level in the middle speed range but drops at high and low speeds. Such a characteristic is typical of most internal combustion engines. The characteristic can be shifted up or down, keeping much the same shape, by admitting more or less fuel, using the throttle.

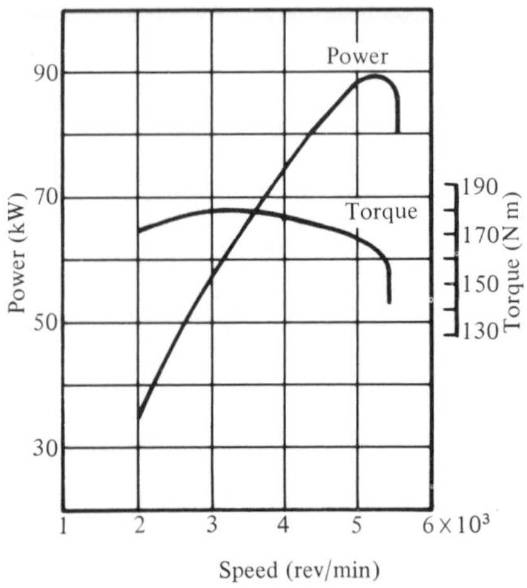

Figure 4.12 Torque and power curves for a 2.2-litre internal combustion engine.

Figure 4.13 shows the tractive effort–speed characteristic of a recently introduced electric locomotive for passenger and freight traffic. It is designed for maximum speeds of 160 km/h when hauling 700 t passenger trains and 100 km/h when hauling 1500 t freight trains. An important aspect of the characteristic is its very high tractive effort at zero and low speeds, an important feature for getting the train started not only on the level but also on an incline.

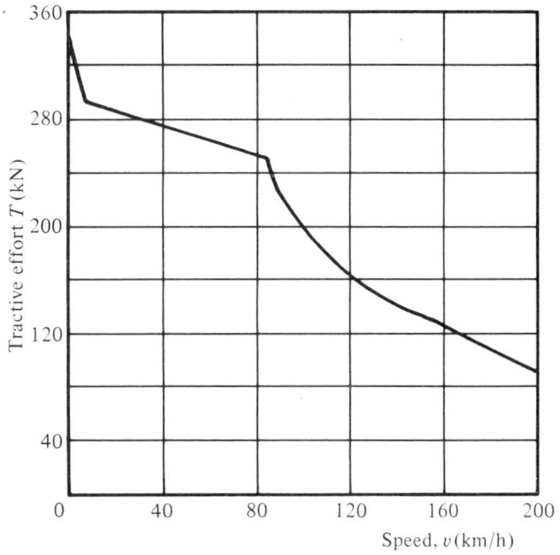

Figure 4.13 Tractive effort versus speed for a locomotive.

The characteristics shown in Figure 4.14 are those of a hydraulic motor. We notice that for a given supply pressure the torque remains practically constant throughout the speed range, except for a slight drop at zero speed. By increasing the supply pressure these characteristics are shifted up or down. Hydraulic motors are used extensively in industry, e.g. in earth-moving machinery, tractors, mining equipment, marine winches and many other applications.

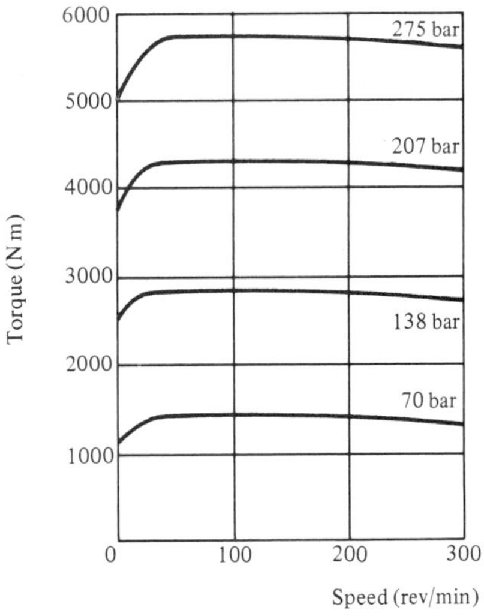

Figure 4.14 Characteristics of a hydraulic motor.

Figure 4.15 shows the torque–speed characteristic of a 60 W induction electric motor. It is typical of the type of motor used to drive small fans or small mechanical devices.

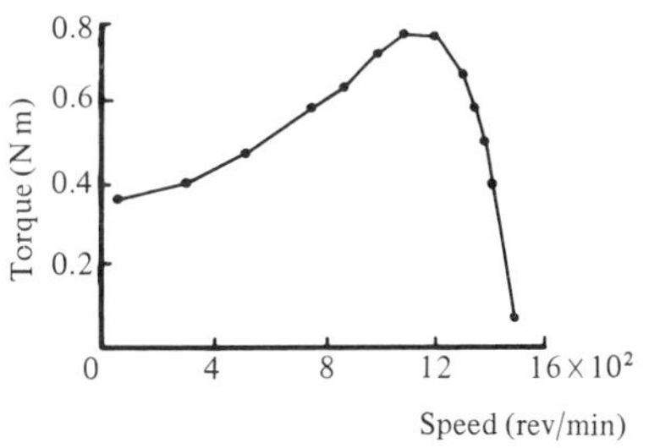

Figure 4.15 Torque-speed characteristic of an electric motor.

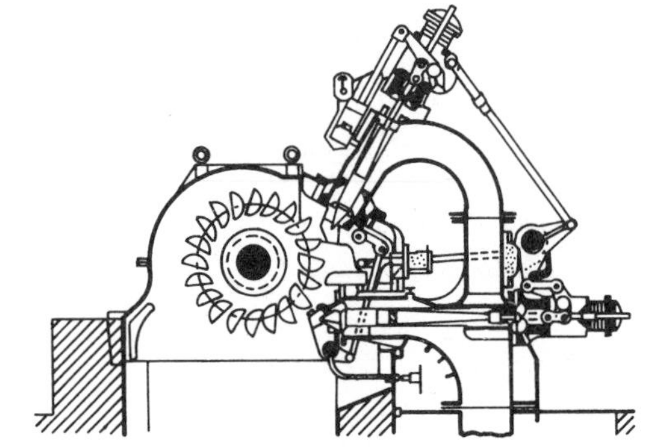

Figure 4.16 Double-jet Pelton wheel; 4.6 MW at 1500 r.p.m., head of water 820 m, wheel diameter 750 mm.

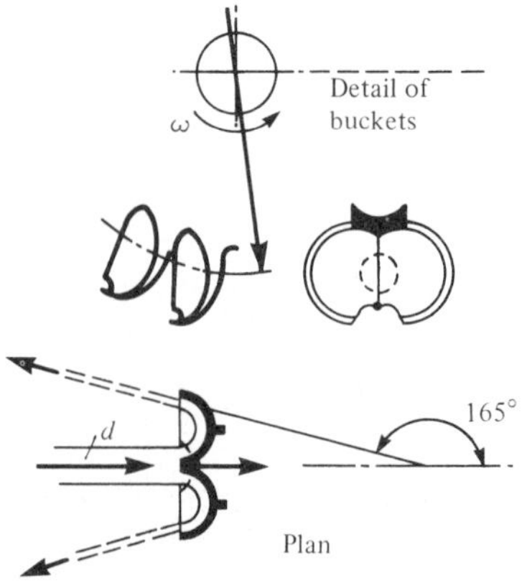

Figure 4.17 The buckets of the Pelton wheel.

Figure 4.16 illustrates a type of prime mover used in hydro-electric installations. It is an impulse turbine, better known as a Pelton wheel. One or more nozzles project water brought down a pipe from a reservoir or dam (150 to 2000 m above the Pelton wheel) on to a number of buckets attached to the wheel or runner as shown in Figure 4.17. The change in direction of the water jet produced by the shape of the bucket results in a force on the buckets, in accordance with the impulse-momentum relation, whose action causes the wheel to rotate. The wheel is coupled to a generator to produce electricity. The torque output can be controlled by the flow of water, which is regulated by means of a needle valve. The torque-speed characteristic of a 240 kW Pelton wheel is shown in Figure 4.18. Figure 4.19 shows the runner of a Pelton wheel where the buckets are bolted on, whereas Figure 4.20 shows an integral construction.

We mentioned above that the problem in practice is to match the prime mover to the load and predict their dynamic performance. As an illustration consider the dynamic behaviour of the induction motor (see Figure 4.15) driving a small fan. The two

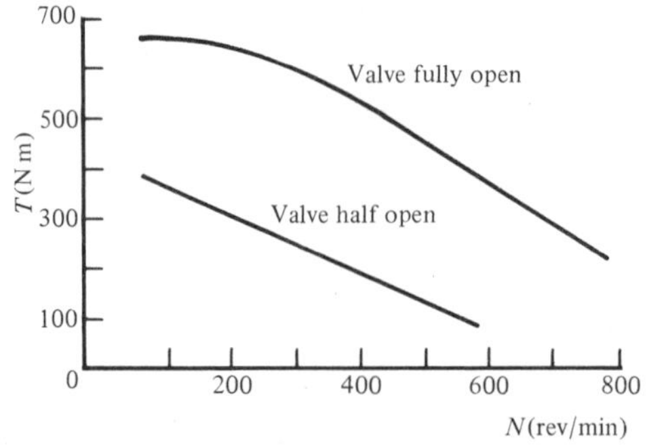

Figure 4.18 Characteristic of a Pelton wheel.

Figure 4.19 A Pelton wheel with buckets bolted on.

Figure 4.20 An integral Pelton wheel.

characteristics are shown superimposed in Figure 4.21. When we switch on the supply the torque available at the motor shaft T_S is more than sufficient to overcome the small resistance T_0, and the system (motor plus fan) accelerates. The initial resistance is mainly due to bearing friction. We see that at any speed N the motor torque T_M is greater than the load torque demand of the fan T_L. Hence since $T_M > T_L$ the system is still accelerating and goes on accelerating until a speed N_0 is reached corresponding to point P where the characteristics cross, i.e. where $T_M = T_L$. N_0 is referred to as the equilibrium speed and P the matching point. Provided there are no disturbances, the system (motor plus fan) goes on operating at that speed.

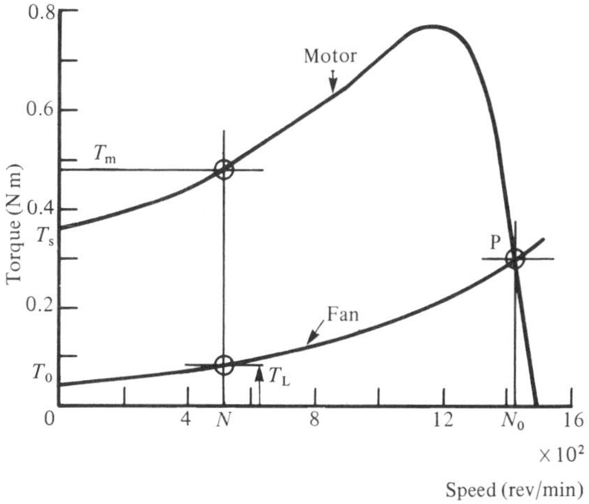

Figure 4.21 Characteristics of an inductor motor and fan.

The reader should notice that during the accelerating phase, $N = 0$ to N_0, the acceleration is not constant, but is proportional to $(T_M - T_L)$, and varies from a starting value proportional to $(T_S - T_0)$ to zero at the matching point, passing through a maximum somewhere in between.

Whatever systems we have to deal with, such as an internal combustion engine driving a lorry, an electric motor driving a machine tool or a Pelton wheel driving a generator, their dynamic behaviour will be similar to the motor fan just discussed. The only difference will be in their characteristics and stability.

It is important that when a system has reached its operating point it should be stable; it must be capable of returning to that point when subjected to some disturbance such as a fluctuation in the load or in the fuel supply to the prime mover. The stability of a system at its operating point is a function of the characteristics of the prime mover and its load. It can be shown that for stability we must satisfy the following relationship:

$$\frac{\partial T_M}{\partial N} < \frac{\partial T_L}{\partial N}$$

4.3.1 **Motion in a resisting medium: load characteristics**

All bodies moving in a fluid such as air or water are subject to a resistance which is a function of the velocity. In many cases this resistance is proportional to the velocity for bodies moving relatively slowly and to the square of the velocity at higher velocities, and it always acts in a direction opposite to the motion. Thus we may write:

$$\text{resistance} \propto v \qquad R = kv$$

or

$$\text{resistance} \propto v^2 \qquad R = Kv^2$$

where k and K depend on the shape and size of the body as well as the properties of the medium.

In section 2.4.1, we mentioned the fact that this latter resistance R or drag D is given by the following equation:

$$R \text{ or } D = \tfrac{1}{2} C_D \rho A v^2$$

where ρ is the density of the fluid, A is the projected area of the body, v is the relative velocity of the body and C_D is the drag coefficient.

Car manufacturers have taken to quoting a C_D value for their cars; a typical value is 0.4 for a well designed car. For example, taking a modern family saloon having clean lines, a projected area of 1.9 m^2 and with $\rho = 1.19$ kg/m^3, the resistance would be

$$R = \tfrac{1}{2} \times 0.4 \times 1.19 \times 1.9v^2$$

$$= 0.452v^2 \text{ N}$$

At the legal maximum speed of 70 m.p.h. (112 km/h) on motorways in Great Britain this resistance would be

$$R = 0.452\left(\frac{112}{3.6}\right)^2 = 437.5 \text{ N}$$

R is also known as the aerodynamic drag, and for a car we must add to this the rolling resistance. If $\mu_R = 0.02$ (a typical value), this resistance is 0.02 mg, and with a total mass when laden of 1200 kg the total resistance of the car will be

$$R_t = 0.02 \times 1200 \times 9.81 + 0.452v^2$$
$$= 235.4 + 0.452v^2 \text{ N}$$

Thus at the legal speed limit

$$R_t = 672.9 \text{ N}$$

The resistance of an aircraft in flight is of the form Kv^2 but the same aircraft on the runway prior to take off has a resistance of the form $A + Kv^2$ where A is the rolling resistance.

The resistance of a ship is also proportional to the square of the velocity except at very low speeds (of the order of 1.5 m/s), when it is proportional to the velocity.

The resistance of a train is of the form $A + BV + CV^2$; the $A + BV$ terms predominate at low speeds (of the order of 15 m/s).

The rotor of a fan or of a centrifugal pump has a resistance proportional to the square of the speed of rotation.

The prime movers that drive the car, the aircraft, the train, the fan or any other device have to overcome resistances of the kinds mentioned above.

We will now analyse the motion of particles (or of bodies which can be considered as particles as discussed previously) under the action of forces, some tractive and some resistive, when moving along a straight line in a known direction such as the x-axis of a Newtonian frame of reference.

Applying Newton's second law to a particle of mass m we have:

$$m\ddot{x} = T - \sum R$$

where T is the tractive force developed by the prime mover, i.e. the prime mover characteristic, and $\sum R$ is the sum of all resistances and constitutes the load characteristic. To these must be added the force of gravity (i.e. the weight) whenever the particle is moving in a gravitational field. This force or a component of it will be either positive or negative; the tractive effort of a train going up an incline will have to overcome the component of its weight parallel to the incline.

EXAMPLE 4.2

A high-speed train has a resistance given by

$$R = (5000 + 180v + 8v^2) \text{ N}$$

where v is in m/s (I.Mech.E. figures, 1977). If the tractive effort at the wheels is constant at 130 kN up to

Example Cont.

80 km/h (Figure 4.22), calculate the time taken for the train to reach that speed from rest on a level track. The total mass of the train is 383 t. What is the maximum acceleration of the train?

SOLUTION

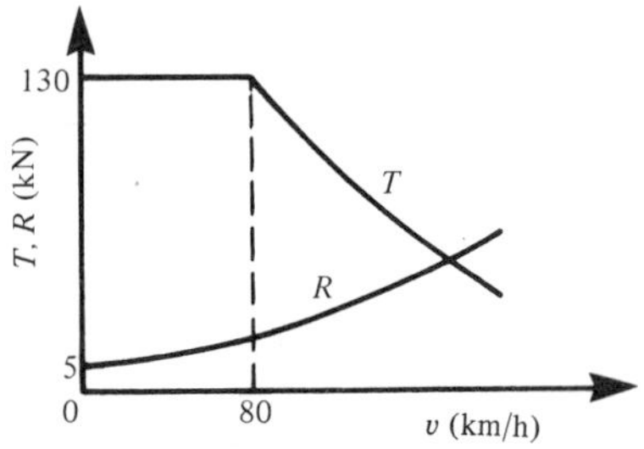

Figure 4.22 Resistance and tractive effort of train of example 4.2.

By Newton's second law,

$$m\frac{dv}{dt} = T - R$$

where T is the tractive effort and R is the resistance. Substituting numerical values gives

$$383 \times 10^3 \frac{dv}{dt} = 130 \times 10^3 - 5000 - 180v - 8v^2$$

or
$$383\frac{dv}{dt} = 125 - 0.18v - 0.008v^2$$

The acceleration is a maximum when $v = 0$, so that

$$\left(\frac{dv}{dt}\right)_{max} = \frac{125}{383} = 0.326 \text{ m/s}^2$$

Solution Cont.

To calculate the time we must separate the variables and integrate, i.e.

$$383\int\frac{dv}{125 - 0.18v - 0.008v^2} = t + \text{constant}$$

The integral is a standard one and will be found in Appendix A.2. In this case since $b^2 - 4ac > 0$ the solution is

$$\frac{1}{x}\ln\left(\frac{2cv + b - x}{2cv + b + x}\right)$$

where

$$x = \sqrt{b^2 - 4ac}$$

with $b = -0.18$, $c = -0.008$ and $a = 125$; thus

$$x = \sqrt{0.18^2 - (4 \times 125 \times -0.008)} = 2.008$$

from the initial conditions: $v = 0$ when $t = 0$. The constant is given by:

$$\text{constant} = \frac{383}{2.008}\ln\left|\frac{-0.18 - 2.008}{-0.18 + 2.008}\right| = 34.29$$

If t_1 is the time to reach 80 km/h = 22.2 m/s then

$$t_1 = \frac{383}{2.008}\ln\left|\frac{-0.016 \times 22.2 - 0.18 - 2.008}{-0.016 \times 22.2 - 0.18 + 2.008}\right| - 34.29 = 70 \text{ s}$$

EXAMPLE 4.3

The tractive effort T and the resistance R of the high-speed train of example 4.2 as a function of the speed v are given in Table 4.1. Calculate the maximum speed of the train and the distance travelled to reach 160 km/h from rest on a gradient of 1 in 200. The total mass of the train is 383 t.

Example Cont.

Table 4.1

v (km/h)	0	20	40	60	80	100
T (kN)	130	130	130	130	130	105
R (kN)	5	6.2	7.5	10	12.5	15
v (km/h)	120	140	160	180	200	220
T (kN)	85	72.5	61	52.5	42	35
R (kN)	18	23	28	34	41	50

SOLUTION

Since the train is going up an incline we must subtract from the tractive effort the component of the weight down the incline, i.e.

$$mg \sin \alpha = 383 \times 10^3 \times 9.81/200$$
$$= 18.8 \text{ kN} \quad (\text{using } \sin\alpha \approx \tan\alpha)$$

or add this component to the resistance, to give R_1 as in Table 4.2.

Table 4.2

v (km/h)	0	20	40	60	80	100
R_1 (kN)	23.8	25	26.3	28.8	31.3	33.8
v (km/h)	120	140	160	180	200	220
R_1 (kN)	36.8	41.8	46.8	52.8	59.8	68.8

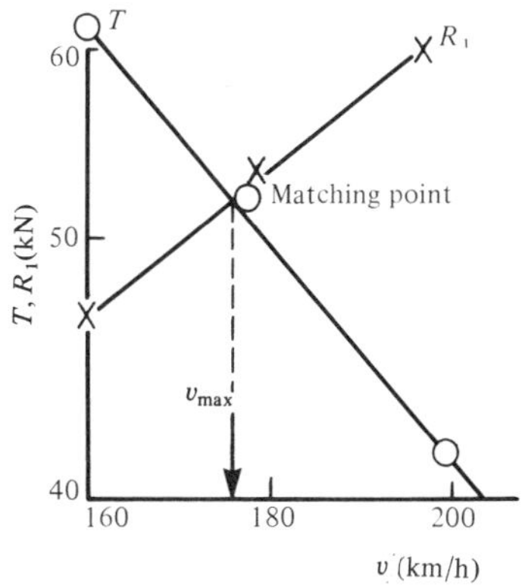

Figure 4.23 Resistance and tractive effort of train of example 4.3.

By comparing the tables we notice that $T = R_1$ close to 180 km/h. Hence the maximum velocity can be obtained more accurately by drawing the graphs of T and R_1 in the neighbourhood of 180 km/h, as shown in Figure 4.23. The maximum velocity of the train up the incline is 178 km/h; this in fact confirms the figure quoted by British Rail.

By Newton's second law,

$$mv\frac{dv}{dx} = T - R - mg \sin \alpha$$

Solution Cont.

Separating the variables and integrating for $v = 0$ to $v = v_{max}$ gives for the distance x

$$x = \frac{m'}{3.6^2}\int\frac{v\,dv}{T' - R' - m'g\sin\alpha}$$

$$= \frac{m'}{3.6^2}\int\frac{v\,dv}{T' - R_1'}$$

where m', T' and R' are in thousands of units and the factor of 3.6^2 is to reduce v and Δv to m/s. Since the relationship between $(T' - R_1')$ and v is not given mathematically we must evaluate the integral numerically. To do this we can use either Simpson's rule or the trapezium rule, the former being the more accurate (see Appendix A.3). Whichever method we use, the first thing to do is to calculate $v/(T' - R_1')$ as a function of v, as shown in Table 4.3, together with the y-coordinates for reference.

Table 4.3

v	0	20	40	60	80
$v/(T' - R_1')$	0	0.19	0.386	0.593	0.811
Ordinate	y_0	y_1	y_2	y_3	y_4
v	100	120	140	160	
$v/(T' - R_1')$	1.40	2.49	4.56	11.27	
Ordinate	y_5	y_6	y_7	y_8	

(a) Using Simpson's rule we have

$$x = \frac{383}{3.6^2}\times\frac{20}{3}[0 + 11.27 + 4(0.19 + 0.593 + 1.40 + 4.56) + 2(0.386 + 0.811 + 2.49)]$$

$$= 9 \text{ km (5.6 miles)}$$

(b) Using the trapezium rule yields (for comparison)

$$x = \frac{383}{3.6^2}\times 20\,[\tfrac{1}{2}(0 + 11.27) + 0.19 + 0.386 + 0.593 + 0.811 + 1.4 + 2.49 + 4.56]$$

$$= 9.5 \text{ km (5.9 miles)}$$

Generally if we require more accurate results we can plot a graph of the function under the integral sign and read off as many values as we wish.

EXAMPLE 4.4

A 15 t lorry pulls a 30 t trailer up a hill of 1 in 10 with a constant tractive effort of 65 kN in a low gear. If it starts from rest at the bottom of the hill, calculate the distance travelled up the hill when its speed has increased to 15 km/h. The rolling resistance is 1% of the total weight and it is known that the lorry and trailer have a maximum speed of 140 km/h on a level road under a tractive effort of 7 kN. Assume that the drag is proportional to the square of the speed and that the drag of the trailer is 50% greater than that of the lorry. Calculate also the maximum tension in the coupling device during that time.

SOLUTION

The rolling resistance

$$R = 0.01 \times 45 \times 10^3 \times 9.81 = 4.42 \text{ kN}$$

If kv^2 is the drag of the lorry, then $1.5kv^2$ is the drag of the trailer and the total drag is

$$D = kv^2 + 1.5kv^2 = 2.5kv^2$$

At the maximum speed of 140 km/h on the level we have

$$T = R + D$$

i.e.

$$7 \times 10^3 = 4.42 \times 10^3 + 2.5kv_{max}^2$$

Solving for k yields

$$k = \frac{(7 - 4.42) \times 10^3}{2.5 \times (140/3.6)^2} = 0.68 \text{ kg/m}$$

Hence the total drag, $D = 1.7v^2$ N, where v is in m/s. Referring to the free body diagram in Figure 4.24 we have by Newton's second law

$$(m_1 + m_2)v\frac{dv}{dx} = T - (m_1 + m_2)g \sin \alpha - R - 2.5kv^2$$

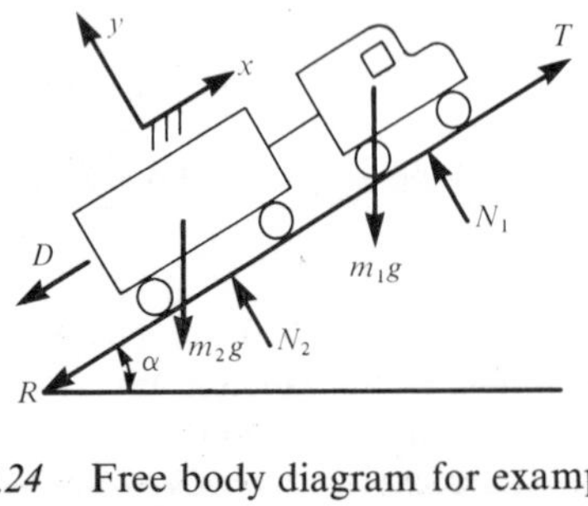

Figure 4.24 Free body diagram for example 4.4.

Substituting numerical values gives

$$45v\frac{dv}{dx} = 65 - \frac{45 \times 9.81}{10} - 4.42 - 1.7 \times 10^{-3}v^2$$

or

$$v\frac{dv}{dx} = (0.37 - 3.78 \times 10^{-5}v^2) \quad (4.8)$$

which is of the form

$$v\frac{dv}{dx} = a - bv^2$$

$$a = 0.37, \quad b = 3.78 \times 10^{-5}$$

Separating the variables and integrating (see Appendix A.2) gives

$$-\frac{1}{2b}\ln(a - bv^2) = x + \text{constant}$$

The initial conditions are: when $x = 0$, $v = v_0$. Hence

$$\text{constant} = -\frac{1}{2b}\ln(a - bv_0^2)$$

Substituting in the equation yields for $v = v_1$ the distance

$$x = \frac{1}{2b}\ln\left(\frac{a - bv_0^2}{a - bv_1^2}\right)$$

where $v_0 = 0$ and $v_1 = 15$ km/h. Hence

$$x = \frac{10^5}{7.56}\ln\left(\frac{0.37}{0.37 - 3.78 \times 10^{-5} \times 4.23^2}\right)$$

$$= 24.2 \text{ m}$$

Solution Cont.

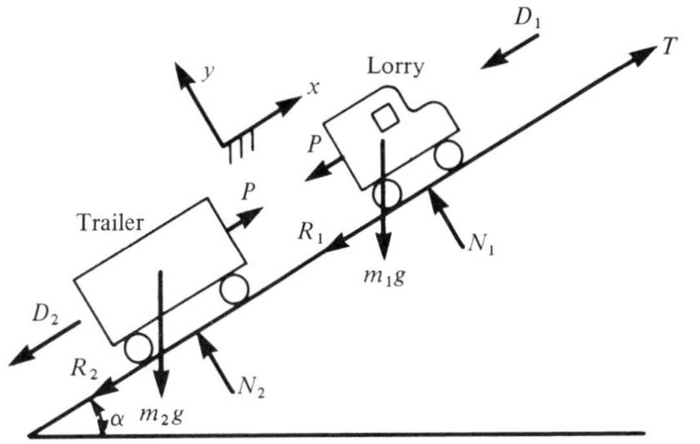

Figure 4.25 Free body diagram for separated trailer and lorry of example 4.4.

Figure 4.25 shows the free body diagram for the lorry and trailer. P is the tension in the coupling in the direction shown; it is responsible for the acceleration of the trailer and by Newton's third law $-P$ acts on the lorry. Applying Newton's second law to the lorry gives

$$m_1\ddot{x}_1 = T - R_1 - D_1 - P - m_1g \sin \alpha$$

Solution Cont.

Solving for P yields

$$P = T - R_1 - m_1g \sin \alpha - D_1 - m_1\ddot{x}_1 \quad (4.9)$$

But $\ddot{x}_1 = \ddot{x}_2$ and is given by equation (4.8), i.e.

$$\ddot{x}_1 = \ddot{x}_2 = 0.37 - 3.78 \times 10^{-5}v^2$$

Hence

$$P = 65 \times 10^3 - \frac{15 \times 9.81 \times 10^3}{100} - 0.68v^2$$

$$- \frac{15 \times 9.81 \times 10^3}{10} - 15 \times 10^3$$

$$\times (0.37 - 3.78 \times 10^{-5}v^2)$$

P will have its maximum value at the bottom of the hill where $v = 0$; hence

$$P_{max} = (65 - 1.47 - 14.72 - 5.55) \times 10^3$$

$$= 43.3 \text{ kN}$$

Figure 4.26 shows the results of deceleration tests on three different types of road tanker, carried out on an unopened stretch of motorway with a constant gradient of 0.173%, and Figure 4.27 shows typical curves of power losses in kilowatts (kW) due to aerodynamic drag and rolling resistance for laden and unladen road tankers. (For a discussion of power see section 4.4.) The results demonstrate clearly that the total resistance to motion consists of a constant term and a term which depends on the velocity.

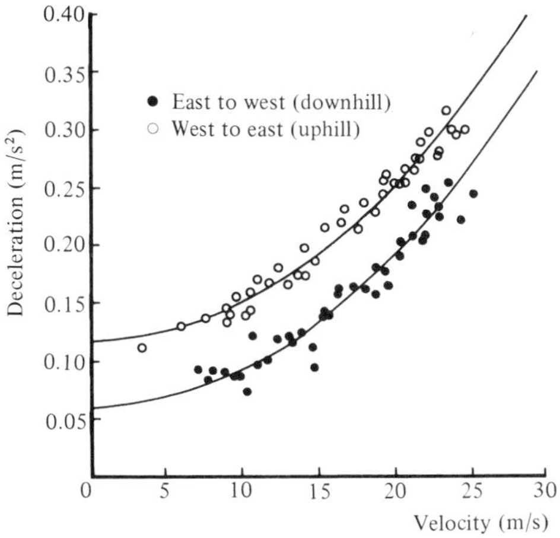

Figure 4.26 Deceleration versus velocity for road tankers.

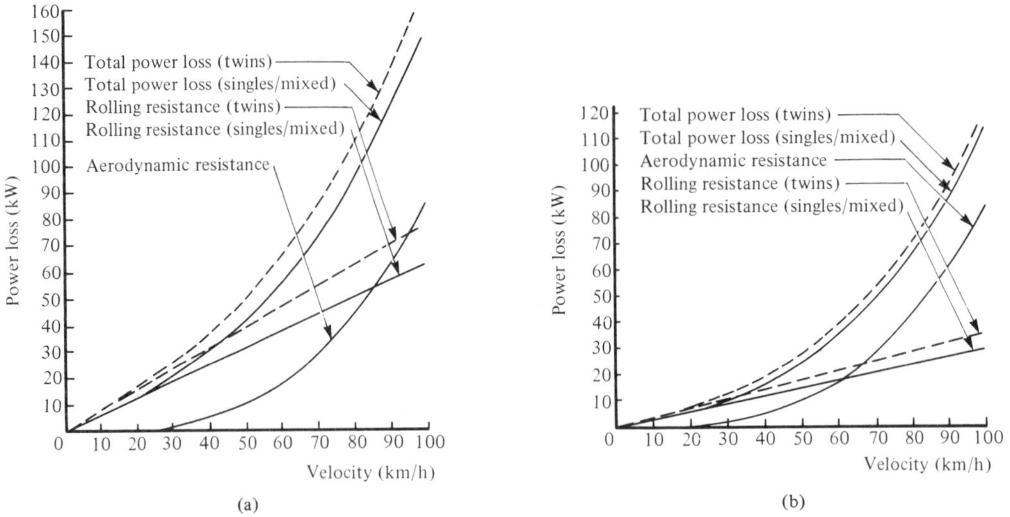

Figure 4.27 Typical power losses caused by aerodynamic resistance and rolling resistance: (a) laden tankers; (b) unladen tankers. (*Note:* "twins", "singles" and "mixed" refer to tyres.)

4.4 WORK, POWER AND EFFICIENCY

4.4.1 Work

If we had to push a 1000 kg car to get it started again because of a flat battery we would probably have to exert a force of about 200 N to overcome the rolling resistance on a level road. Suppose we pushed the car with that force a distance of 20 m, then we would say that we had done $200 \times 20 = 4000$ N m of work.

Thus work is defined as the product of the force and the displacement along the line of action of the force. If two men pushed the car, one at each corner, and each exerts a force of 120 N m at an angle of 20° to the direction of motion, then the work done by them would be $120 \times \cos 20° \times 20 \times 2 = 4510$ N m. A crane lifting a 500 kg container to a height of 15 m does $500 \times 9.81 \times 15 = 73\,575$ N m of work.

Suppose that a constant force P acts on a particle at A as shown in Figure 4.28 and it moves to the position B such that $AB = s$; furthermore, if the line of action of the force makes a constant angle θ with AB, the work done is $F = (P \cos \theta)s$ or $P(s \cos \theta)$, i.e. the work done is also the product of the force and the component of the displacement in the direction of the force. If $\theta = 0$, the work done is Ps and if $\theta = 90°$, the work done is zero; but if $\theta > 90°$ the work done is negative. If P is a friction force then its work will be negative.

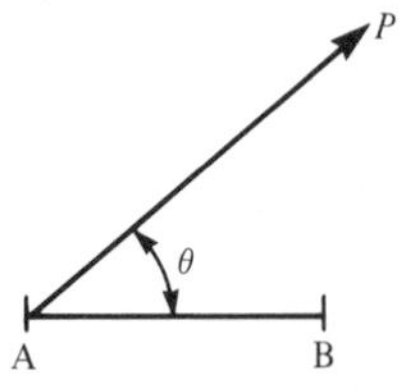

Figure 4.28 Force acting at an angle.

Generally if a particle moves along a curved path under the action of a variable force P as shown in Figure 4.29, the work done ΔU during a displacement Δs is given by

$$\Delta U = (P \cos \theta)\Delta s$$

where θ is the angle between the line of action of the force and the tangent to the curve.

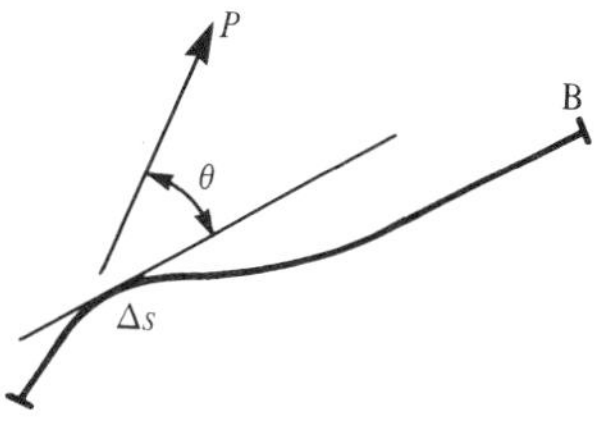

Figure 4.29 Variable force acting on a particle.

The total work done during a displacement from A to B is

$$U = \int_A^B (P \cos \theta)\, ds \quad (4.10)$$

If several forces $P_1, P, \ldots, P_n$ act on a particle, the work done during a displacement Δs is

$$(P_1 \cos \theta_1)\Delta s + (P_2 \cos \theta_2)\Delta s + \ldots + (P_n \cos \theta_n)\Delta s$$

where $\theta_1, \theta_2, \ldots, \theta_n$ are the angles between the lines of action of the forces and the tangents to the path. Thus we see that the total work done is

$$(P_1 \cos \theta_1 + P_2 \cos \theta_2 + \ldots + P_n \cos \theta_n)\Delta s$$

and during a finite displacement from A to B along the path the work done U is

$$U = \int_A^B \sum_{i=1}^{n} (P_i \cos \theta_i)\, ds = \sum_{i=1}^{n} \int_A^B (P_i \cos \theta_i)\, ds \quad (4.11)$$

U is the algebraic sum of the work done by all the forces.

The unit of work is the newton metre (N m) or joule (J):

$$1\,\text{N m} = 1\,\text{J}$$

Work is a scalar quantity.

EXAMPLE 4.5

The gases inside the cylinder of an engine expand according to the relation $pV^{1.4} = 0.25$ where p is the pressure inside the cylinder in N/m^2 and V is the volume in m^3. If the displacement of the piston is from 10 to 120 mm and the cylinder diameter is 60 mm, calculate the net work done during the expansion process assuming a frictional force between the piston and the cylinder of 30 N.

SOLUTION

Let x be the displacement of the piston from the end of the cylinder and A be the cross-sectional area of the cylinder (see Figure 4.30). Then

$$A = \frac{\pi}{4}\left(\frac{60}{1000}\right)^2 = 2.827 \times 10^{-3}\ \text{m}^2$$

The force P on the piston is

$$P = pA$$

$$= \frac{0.25A}{V^{1.4}}$$

Solution Cont.

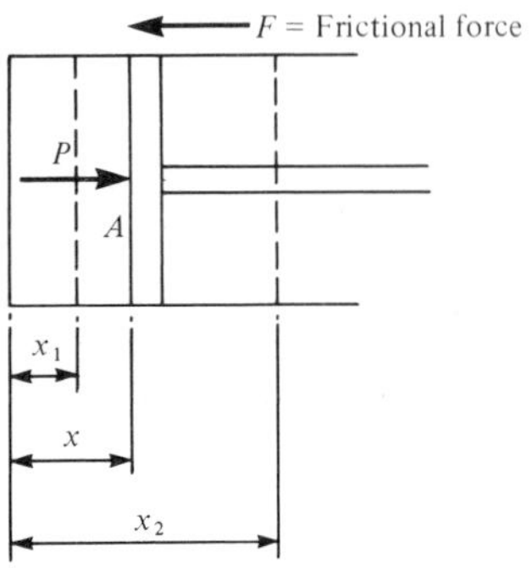

Figure 4.30 The piston of example 4.5.

In this case we have two forces, so that the work done U is given by

$$U = \int_{x_1}^{x_2} (P - F)\,dx$$

by equation (4.11). F acts in a direction opposite to the motion. Because F is constant we have

$$U = \int_{x_1}^{x_2} P\,dx - F\int_{x_1}^{x_2} dx$$

$$= \int_{x_1}^{x_2} P\,dx - F(x_2 - x_1)$$

Solution Cont.

The work done by P in a displacement Δx is

$$\Delta U_P = P\Delta x = \frac{0.25A\Delta x}{V^{1.4}} = \frac{0.25\Delta V}{V^{1.4}}$$

since $\Delta V = A\Delta x$. The total work done during a displacement from $x_1 = 0.01$ m to $x_2 = 0.12$ m is

$$U_P = \int_{x_1}^{x_2} P\,\mathrm{d}x = 0.25\int_{V_1}^{V_2} \frac{\mathrm{d}V}{V^{1.4}}$$

$$= \frac{0.25}{-0.4}\left[\frac{1}{V^{0.4}}\right]_{V_1}^{V_2}$$

$$= \frac{0.25}{0.4 \times A^{0.4}}\left[\frac{1}{x_1^{0.4}} - \frac{1}{x_2^{0.4}}\right]$$

$$= \frac{0.25}{0.4 \times (2.827 \times 10^{-3})^{0.4}}\left(\frac{1}{0.01^{0.4}} - \frac{1}{0.12^{0.4}}\right)$$

$$= 26\text{ N m} = 26\text{ J}$$

The work done by F is

$$U_F = F(x_2 - x_1) = 30 \times 0.11 = 3.3\text{ J}$$

The net work done is then given by

$$U_P - U_F = 26 - 3.3 = 22.7\text{ J}$$

4.4.2 **Power and efficiency**

The rate at which work is done is called the power; thus if we took 15 s to move the car in section 4.4.1 a distance of 20 m, the power would be

$$200 \times \frac{20}{15} = 266.7\text{ N m/s}$$

The unit of power is the watt (W); it is defined as 1 joule per second:

$$1\text{ W} = 1\text{ J/s} = 1\text{ N m/s}$$

The kilowatt (kW) is frequently used instead of the watt. Engineers often quote the power of a prime mover in horsepower (HP); 1 HP = 746 W = 0.746 kW.

If W is the power of, and U is the work done by, a constant force F, then

$$W = \frac{\mathrm{d}U}{\mathrm{d}t} = \frac{\mathrm{d}}{\mathrm{d}t}(Fs) = F\frac{\mathrm{d}s}{\mathrm{d}t} = Fv \tag{4.12}$$

where v is the velocity in m/s.

The efficiency (η) is defined as the ratio of the work available at the output to the work at the input, and since these occur during the same interval of time,

$$\eta = \frac{\text{output power}}{\text{input power}} \tag{4.13}$$

In all machines work, and therefore power, is lost mainly because of friction, which generates heat. In some situations work lost appears as sound, e.g. in a pile driver. One of the aims of a designer is to achieve as high an efficiency as possible, and although it is theoretically possible to predict the overall efficiency of a machine, only tests can reveal the actual efficiency since it is affected by many parameters, e.g. poorer lubrication than expected, badly fitting parts, etc.

If $\eta_1, \eta_2, \ldots, \eta_n$, are the efficiencies at various stages of a machine the overall efficiency η is given by the product

$$\eta = \eta_1\eta_2\ldots\eta_n \tag{4.14}$$

For example, a double reduction gearbox consisting of two sets of meshing gears in series, each set having an efficiency of 98%, would have an overall efficiency $\eta = 0.98^2 = 0.96 = 96\%$. Hence 4% of the power input to the gearbox would be lost because of friction at the bearings and the sliding action at the point of contact where the teeth mesh.

ENERGY 4.5

Consider a particle of mass m moving under the action of a force P along a straight line Ox from position A to position B. By Newton's second law we have

$$m\ddot{x} = P \qquad \text{or} \qquad v\frac{\mathrm{d}v}{\mathrm{d}x} = P$$

To calculate the velocity we separate the variables and integrate between the limits A and B. Hence

$$\int_A^B mv\,\mathrm{d}v = \int_A^B P\,\mathrm{d}x$$

or

$$\tfrac{1}{2}mv_B{}^2 - \tfrac{1}{2}mv_A{}^2 = \int_A^B P\,\mathrm{d}x \tag{4.15}$$

The integral on the right-hand side is the work done by the force, and to evaluate it we must know P as a function of x. If P is a constant the work done is $P(x_B - x_A)$.

The left-hand side of the equation involves the change in the square of the velocity; for example we may solve for v_B, the velocity at the end of the travel.

Energy is usually referred to as the capacity for doing work and the term $\frac{1}{2}mv^2$ is referred to as the kinetic energy of the particle. There are many forms of energy, e.g. mechanical, electrical, chemical and nuclear. In this text we are primarily concerned with the mechanical forms of energy, i.e. potential and kinetic energy. The symbol T is used for kinetic energy (KE), due to motion, and V for potential energy (PE), due to position.

Energy is a scalar quantity.

To illustrate potential energy consider a spring, an element with many applications in engineering, compressed or stretched by an amount δ. A graph of load versus deflection is shown in Figure 4.31 and in many cases is linear; if P is the load corresponding to the deflection δ, the slope of the graph is called the stiffness K. Hence

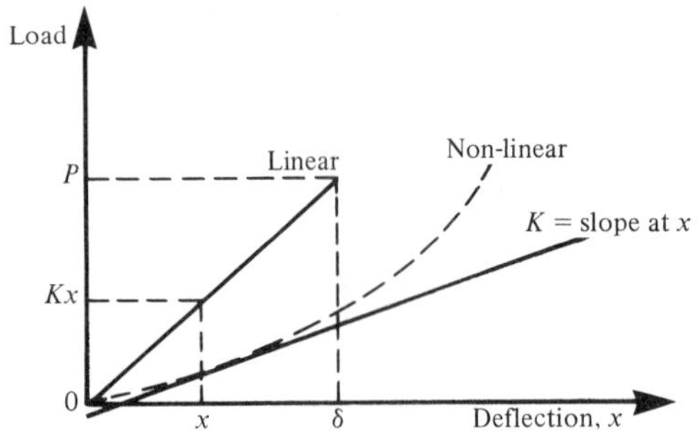

Figure 4.31 Load–deflection curve for a spring.

$$K = P/\delta$$

The force for any deflection x is Kx and the work done during a displacement δ is given by

$$\int_0^\delta Kx\,\mathrm{d}x = \tfrac{1}{2}K\delta^2$$

Certain types of springs, e.g. rubber, have a non-linear load–deflection characteristic, in which case the stiffness K is a function of the deflection, as can be seen in Figure 4.29; in this case $K = \mathrm{d}P/\mathrm{d}x$.

The work done on the spring is stored in it as potential energy V, and can be recovered when the spring is released. Hence for a spring with a linear load–deflection characteristic:

$$V = \tfrac{1}{2}K\delta^2 \tag{4.16}$$

Gravity is responsible for another example of potential energy; the work done U in raising a mass through a distance H is

$$U = -mgH$$

The negative sign is to take into account the fact that the force is opposite to the motion. The potential energy V possessed by this mass is then

$$V = -U = mgH$$

This is positive because the mass will do work when released.

Equation (4.15) is more conveniently written in the form

$$U_{AB} = \Delta T_{AB} \tag{4.17}$$

which is read as follows:

The work done by all forces during a displacement from A to B is equal to the change in the kinetic energy.

The forces will include those that have a potential such as gravity and springs.

It should be clearly understood that equation (4.17) is an integrated form of Newton's second law. It adds nothing new to the behaviour of a particle subjected to forces; it simply relates changes in its velocity to the work done by these forces. It is useful in cases where we are not concerned with acceleration and the forces are constant or a function of displacement.

EXAMPLE 4.6

A 15 t wagon travelling at 3.6 m/s is brought to rest by a buffer (a spring) having a stiffness of 7.5×10^5 N/m.

Example Cont.

Calculate the deflection of the buffer if there is a constant rolling friction force of 800 N.

SOLUTION

By equation (4.17) if Δ is the deflection to bring the wagon to rest, we have

$$-\tfrac{1}{2}K\Delta^2 - F\Delta = \tfrac{1}{2}mv_2^2 - \tfrac{1}{2}mv_1^2$$

where $-\frac{1}{2}K\Delta^2$ is the work done on the spring, $-F\Delta$ is the work done against friction, $\frac{1}{2}mv_2^2$ and $\frac{1}{2}mv_1^2$ are the final and initial kinetic energy, respectively. The negative signs are used because work is being done against the spring and against friction. Since $v_2 = 0$ we have

$$K\Delta^2 + 2F\Delta = mv_1^2$$

or

$$K\Delta^2 + 2F\Delta - mv_1^2 = 0$$

Substituting numerical values gives

Solution Cont.

$$7.5 \times 10^5\Delta^2 + 2 \times 800 \times \Delta - 15 \times 10^3 \times 3.6^2 = 0$$

or

$$750\Delta^2 + 1.6\Delta - 194.4 = 0$$

This is a quadratic in Δ whose roots are

$$\Delta = \frac{-1.6 \pm \sqrt{1.6^2 + 4 \times 750 \times 194.4}}{1500}$$

Hence $\Delta = 0.508$ m, the negative root having no physical significance.

We should note that it has been assumed that the action is smooth, i.e. without rebound when the wagon comes into contact with the buffer.

Forces such as spring and gravitational forces are referred to as *conservative forces* because the work done against them is fully recoverable and is independent of the path taken. On the other hand, forces such as frictional forces and drag on bodies are *non-conservative* because the work done on them cannot be recovered and appears mainly in the form of heat; the work done in this case depends on the path taken.

In situations where all the forces are conservative, a particle under their action will move from position A to another position B in accordance with equation (4.17); hence

$$U_{AB} = \Delta T_{AB} = T_B - T_A = \text{change in KE}$$

and since the forces are conservative, the potential energy is $V = -U$, so that

$$U_{AB} = -(V_B - V_A) = -\text{change in PE}$$

Equation (4.17) then becomes

$$-(V_B - V_A) = T_B - T_A$$

and rearranging yields

$$T_A + V_A = T_B + V_B$$

i.e.

$$\text{total energy at A} = \text{total energy at B}$$

There is conservation of mechanical energy.

4.6 LINEAR MOMENTUM

Let P be the resultant force on a particle. By Newton's second law

$$m\ddot{x} = P$$

or

$$m\frac{dv}{dt} = P$$

Separating the variables and integrating for motion from position A to another position B gives

$$\int_A^B m\, dv = \int_A^B P\, dt$$

or

$$mv_B - mv_A = \int_A^B P\, dt \qquad (4.18)$$

The terms mv_B and mv_A are called the linear momenta of the particle at B and A respectively and the integral is called the impulse. Both are vector quantities. Thus equation (4.18) expresses the fact that the change in the linear momentum is equal to the impulse, I.

The impulse is the product of a force and time, and its unit is the newton second (N s). To evaluate the integral in equation (4.18) we must know P as a function of time.

The concept of impulse is useful in practice in cases where the forces involved are large and the time very short, e.g. a pile driver. We can thus measure the value of the impulse by the change in the momentum.

EXAMPLE 4.7

A 1200 kg pile is being driven into the ground by blows from a 900 kg tup released from a height of 2 m. There is no rebound and the pile sinks 110 mm at each blow. Calculate the average resistance of the ground.

SOLUTION

There are three stages to consider: (a) the tup falls freely and its potential energy is converted into kinetic energy, (b) the impact between the tup and pile, and (c) the motion of the tup and pile into the ground.

(a) By equation (4.17)

$$-(V_2 - V_1) = T_2 - T_1$$

Hence

$$0 + mgH = \tfrac{1}{2}mv^2 - 0$$

where H is the drop and v the velocity of the tup as it reaches the pile. Solving for v gives

$$v = \sqrt{2gH} = \sqrt{2 \times 9.81 \times 2} = 6.26 \text{ m/s}$$

Solution Cont.

(b) Consider what happens at impact; Figure 4.32 shows the tup and pile at impact. Let I be the impulse. Then by equation (4.18), if u is the velocity of the tup and pile as a result of I, we have for the tup

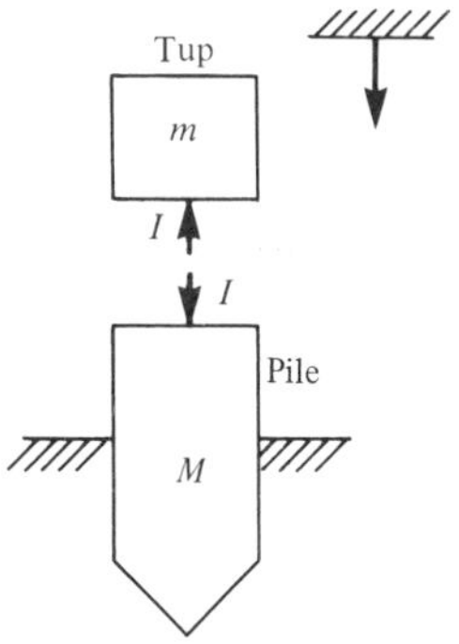

Figure 4.32 Pile driving: falling tup.

$$mu - mv = -I \qquad \text{(opposite to motion)}$$

where v is the velocity of the tup just before impact, and for the pile

$$Mu - 0 = I$$

Hence adding these two equations to eliminate I gives

$$mu - mv + Mu = 0$$

or

$$mv = (m + M)u$$

This states that the total momentum before impact is equal to the total momentum after impact. Solving for u gives

$$u = \frac{m}{m+M}v = \frac{900}{2100} \times 6.26 = 2.68 \text{ m/s}$$

At this stage the kinetic energy of pile and tup moving together is

$$T = \tfrac{1}{2} \times 2100 \times 2.68^2 = 7541.5 \text{ J}$$

(*Note:* The loss of KE as a result of the impact is $\frac{1}{2} \times 900 \times 6.26^2 - 7541.5 = 10\,092.9$ J.)

(c) Let R be the average resistance of the ground (see Figure 4.33) and x the penetration. Then by equation (4.17)

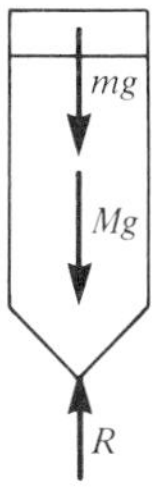

Figure 4.33 Pile driving: ground penetration.

$$[(m + M)g - R]x = 0 - \tfrac{1}{2}(m + M)u^2$$

Hence

$$R = (m + M)\left(\frac{u^2}{2x} + g\right)$$

$$= 2100\left(\frac{2.68^2}{2 \times 0.11} + 9.81\right) = 89\,160 \text{ N}$$

EXAMPLE 4.8

An aircraft on a level flight increases its speed from 750 km/h to 900 km/h in 12 s by igniting a rocket that produces a constant thrust of 45 kN. Calculate the average drag of the aircraft whose mass is 5000 kg during that time.

SOLUTION

Let T be the thrust of the rocket, R be the average drag during the time Δt, and v_1 and v_2 be the initial and final velocities of the aircraft at time t and $t + \Delta t$ respectively. The resultant thrust on the aircraft is $(T - R)$ and by equation (4.18)

$$mv_2 - mv_1 = \int_t^{t+\Delta t} (T - R)\,\mathrm{d}t$$

Solution Cont.

Since T is constant and R is an average value, it follows that

$$mv_2 - mv_1 = T\Delta t - R\Delta t$$

Solving for R yields

$$R = \frac{T\Delta t - m(v_2 - v_1)}{\Delta t}$$

or

$$R = T - \frac{m(v_2 - v_1)}{\Delta t}$$

$$= 45 \times 10^3 - \frac{5000}{12}\left(\frac{900 - 750}{3.6}\right)$$

$$= 17\,361 \text{ N}$$

4.6.1 **Rocket motion**

To illustrate the momentum equation further let us consider the motion of a rocket. Let M be the mass and v the velocity at time t. The rocket is burning fuel at the rate m kg/s and ejecting it with a velocity u relative to the rocket.

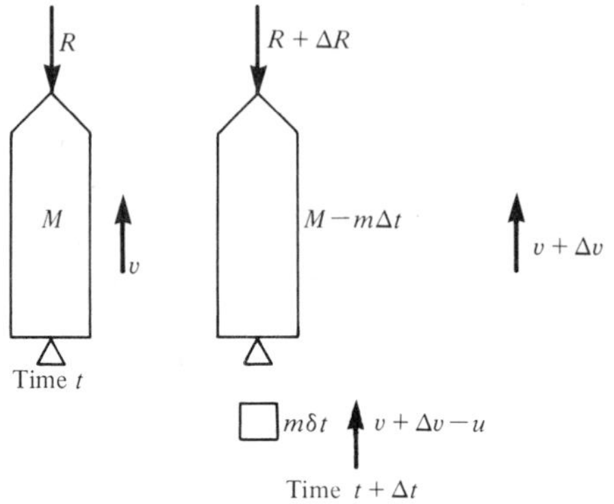

Figure 4.34 Rocket motion.

To obtain the equation of motion of the rocket at any instant in time t, we consider the situation at time $t + \Delta t$ as shown in Figure 4.34.

Let p represent the momentum. The momentum at time t is

$$p = Mv$$

and at time $t + \Delta t$

$$p + \Delta p = (M - m\Delta t)(v + \Delta v) + m\Delta t(v + \Delta v - u)$$

Hence the change in momentum Δp in a time Δt is

$$\Delta p = M\Delta v - mu\Delta t$$

If R is the average resistance to the motion during that time then

$$\Delta p = -R\Delta t$$

where the minus sign indicates that R opposes the motion. Thus

$$-R\Delta t = M\Delta v - mu\Delta t$$

Dividing by Δt and letting $\Delta t \rightarrow 0$ yields

$$M\frac{dv}{dt} = mu - R$$

If M_0 was the mass at time $t = 0$, it follows that

$$(M_0 - mt)\frac{dv}{dt} = mu - R \qquad (4.19)$$

This is the equation for the motion of the rocket and we see that the thrust is due entirely to the exhaust gases. Exhaust velocities can be very large, e.g. 2500 m/s.

To obtain the velocity–time relationship of the rocket we can separate the variables in equation (4.19) and integrate giving

$$\int \mathrm{d}v = \int \frac{mu}{M_0 - mt}\,\mathrm{d}t - \int \frac{R}{M_0 - mt}\,\mathrm{d}t + \text{constant}$$

or

$$v = -u \ln (M_0 - mt) - \int \frac{R}{M_0 - mt}\,\mathrm{d}t + \text{constant}$$

If R is due to gravity, then, neglecting the variation of g with height, $R = (M_0 - mt)g$, and we have

$$v = -u \ln (M_0 - mt) - gt + \text{constant}$$

If $v = 0$ at $t = 0$, constant $= u \ln M_0$. Hence

$$v = u \ln\left(\frac{M_0}{M_0 - mt}\right) - gt$$

FLUID FLOW 4.7

As a further application of the change in linear momentum principle, let us consider the flow of a fluid past a stationary and moving vane.

Figure 4.35(a) shows a stationary wedge-shaped vane which splits equally a jet of fluid issued from a nozzle. Let v be the velocity of the jet as it reaches the vane, ρ the density of the fluid and A the cross-sectional area of the jet.

Figure 4.35(b) shows the free body diagram of the fluid that passes over the top surface of the vane; f_x and f_y are the resultant forces exerted on the fluid by the vane.

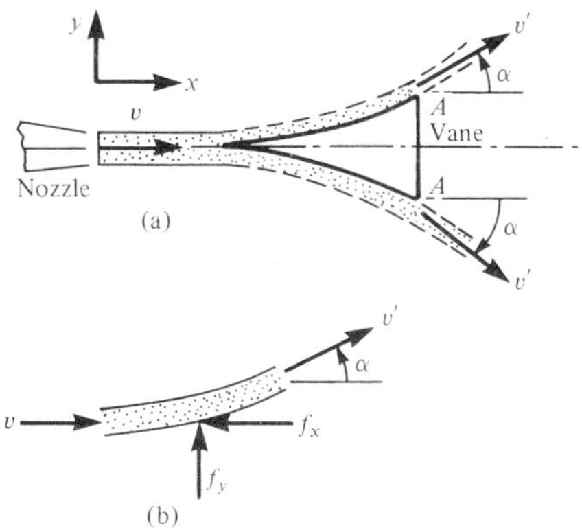

Figure 4.35 Fluid flow past a stationary vane.

In the absence of friction the speed v' of the jet as it leaves the vane must be equal to v.

According to Newton's second law,

$$\frac{\mathrm{d}}{\mathrm{d}t}(m\mathbf{v}) = \mathbf{R}$$

This is a vector equation, i.e. the rate of change of linear momentum is equal to the resultant force. If we consider a short time interval Δt we may write

$$\Delta(m\mathbf{v}) = \mathbf{R}\Delta t$$

and with m constant we have

$$m(\mathbf{v}_2 - \mathbf{v}_1) = \mathbf{R}\Delta t \tag{4.20}$$

where $\mathbf{v}_1$ and $\mathbf{v}_2$ are the initial and final velocities respectively. We now apply this equation to the fluid passing over the top surface of the vane.

The mass of fluid on each side of the vane whose momentum is being changed is one-half of the fluid issuing from the nozzle:

$$\begin{aligned} m &= \text{volume} \times \text{density} \times \text{time interval} \\ &= \tfrac{1}{2}(Av)\rho\Delta t = \tfrac{1}{2}\rho A v \Delta t \end{aligned}$$

Considering the change in the velocity in the x-direction we have the absolute velocities

$$\begin{aligned} v_{2x} &= v \cos \alpha \\ v_{1x} &= v \end{aligned}$$

so that

$$v_{2x} - v_{1x} = v(\cos \alpha - 1)$$

Applying equation (4.20) gives

$$\tfrac{1}{2}\rho A v^2 \Delta t(\cos \alpha - 1) = -f_x \Delta t$$

Therefore

$$f_x = \tfrac{1}{2}\rho A v^2(1 - \cos \alpha)$$

Similarly in the y-direction

$$\begin{aligned} v_{2y} &= \pm v \sin \alpha \\ v_{1y} &= 0 \end{aligned}$$

Hence

$$\tfrac{1}{2}\rho A v^2 \Delta t \sin \alpha = \pm f_y \Delta t$$

Therefore

$$f_y = \tfrac{1}{2}\rho A v^2 \sin \alpha$$

It follows that for the whole vane

$$F_x = 2f_x$$

Hence

$$F_x = \rho A v^2(1 - \cos \alpha)$$

and (because of symmetry)

$$F_y = f_y - f_y = 0$$

Suppose now that the vane is moving to the right with an absolute velocity u, as in a hydraulic turbine such as a Pelton wheel (Figure 4.16). Then, neglecting frictional forces, the fluid enters and leaves tangentially to the vane with a velocity $(v - u)$ relative to the vane as shown in the velocity diagram in Figure 4.36. The absolute velocities of the fluid at entry and exit are equal to v, the jet velocity; they are also equal to the vector sum of the velocity of the vane and the velocity of the fluid relative to the vane. In this case the mass of fluid reaching the vane in a time Δt is

$$m = \rho A(v - u)\Delta t$$

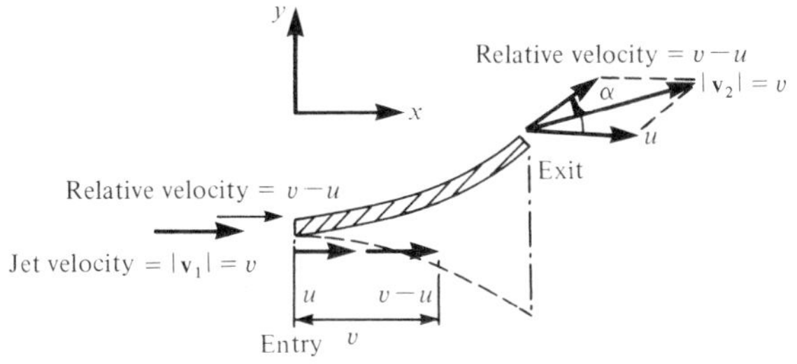

Figure 4.36 Fluid flow past a moving vane.

The absolute velocities in the x-direction are:

$$v_{1x} = v \qquad \text{at entry}$$
$$v_{2x} = u + (v - u)\cos\alpha \qquad \text{at exit}$$

Hence

$$\begin{aligned} v_{2x} - v_{1x} &= u + (v - u)\cos\alpha - v \\ &= (v - u)(\cos\alpha - 1) \end{aligned}$$

Application of equation (4.20) yields:

$$F_x = \rho A(v - u)^2(\cos\alpha - 1) \tag{4.21}$$

for the force on the fluid, and by Newton's third law the force on the vane is

$$F_{\text{vane}} = -F_x = \rho A(v - u)^2(1 - \cos\alpha)$$

The effect of friction between the vane and the fluid would be to reduce the velocity v of the fluid at exit from the vane.

EXAMPLE 4.9

A Pelton wheel is supplied with water from a reservoir under a head of 120 m and the buckets deflect the water through an angle of 165°. If the runner of 1 m diameter at the buckets rotates at 400 rev/min, calculate the power available at the shaft given that the jet diameter is 100 mm and neglecting frictional losses. The water density is 1000 kg/m^3.

SOLUTION

Jet velocity

$$\begin{aligned} v &= \sqrt{2gh} = \sqrt{2 \times 9.81 \times 120} \\ &= 48.52 \text{ m/s} \quad \text{(as in example 4.6)} \end{aligned}$$

Velocity of the buckets

$$u = \omega R = \frac{2\pi \times 400}{60} \times 0.5 = 20.94 \text{ m/s}$$

Solution Cont.

Cross-sectional area of the jet

$$A = \frac{\pi}{4} \times 0.1^2 = 0.0079 \text{ m}^2$$

Mass of water reaching the buckets per unit time is

$$\text{mass flow} = \rho A(v - u)$$
$$= 1000 \times 0.0079 \times (48.52 - 20.94)$$
$$= 216.6 \text{ kg/s}$$

Force on the buckets

$$F_x = 216.6\,(48.52 - 20.94)\,(1 - \cos 165°)$$
$$= 11\,745 \text{ N}$$

Power

$$P = F_x u$$
$$= 11\,745 \times 20.94$$
$$= 246 \text{ kW}$$

EXAMPLE 4.10

Figure 4.37 shows one of the blades of a single-row impulse turbine. The absolute velocity v_1 of the gases leaving the nozzle is at an angle α to the direction of motion of the blade. The inlet and outlet blade angles are β_1 and β_2 respectively. Draw the velocity diagrams for inlet and outlet and use the data given below to calculate: (a) the whirl velocity (change in the absolute velocity of the gases in the direction of motion), (b) the power of the turbine wheel, (c) the axial thrust, and (d) the efficiency of blading.
Data: $v_1 = 500$ m/s; $\alpha = 20°$; $\beta_1 = 29°$; $\beta_2 = 20°$; speed of rotation of the turbine wheel, $N = 3000$ rev/min; mean diameter of the wheel, $D = 1$ m; mass flow, $m = 5$ kg/s; blade friction factor, 0.85.

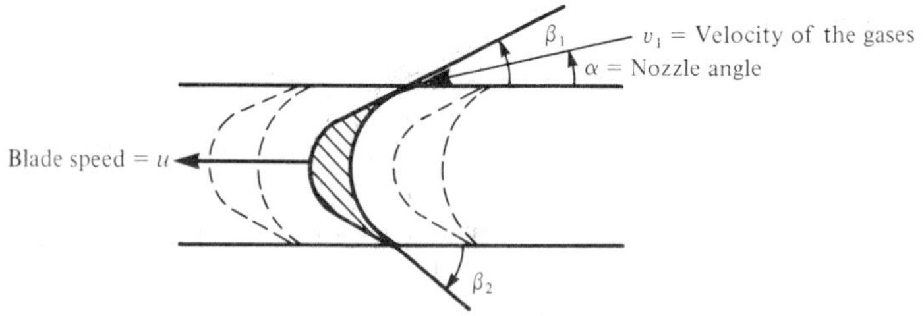

Figure 4.37 Blade of impulse turbine of example 4.10.

SOLUTION

Referring to Figure 4.38 we have

$$u_1 \sin \beta_1 = v_1 \sin \alpha$$

and therefore

$$u_1 = v_1 \frac{\sin \alpha}{\sin \beta_1} = \frac{500 \times \sin 20°}{\sin 29°}$$
$$= 353 \text{ m/s}$$

$$u_2 = k u_1 = 0.85 \times 353 = 300 \text{ m/s}$$

$$u = \frac{2\pi N D}{2 \times 60} = \frac{2\pi \times 3000}{2 \times 60} = 157 \text{ m/s}$$

Solution Cont.

(a) Whirl velocity

$$v_w = u_1 \cos \beta_1 + u_2 \cos \beta_2$$
$$= 353 \cos 29° + 300 \cos 20° = 591 \text{ m/s}$$

(b) Let F_b be the force on the blade. Then from the impulse–momentum equation we have, in the direction of motion,

$$F_b = m(v_2 - v_1) = m v_w$$
$$= 5 \times 591 = 2955 \text{ N}$$

Power is

$$F_b u = 2955 \times 157$$
$$= 464 \times 10^3 \text{ W} \quad \text{or } 464 \text{ kW}$$

Solution Cont. **Solution Cont.**

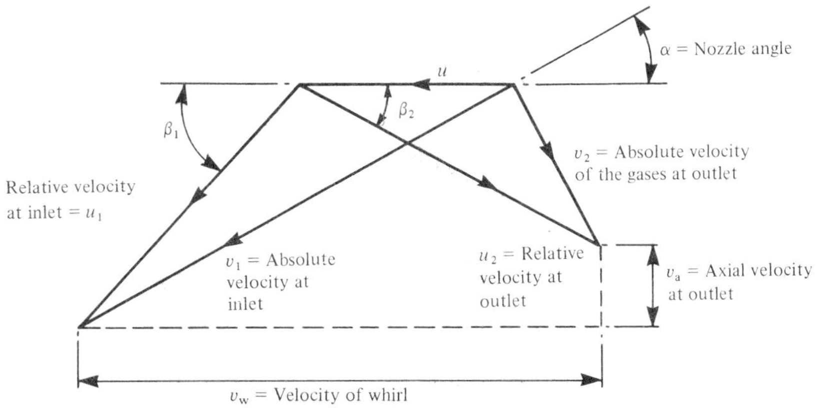

Figure 4.38 Velocity diagram for inlet and outlet conditions for example 4.10.

(c) Axial thrust is change in the absolute velocity in the axial direction × mass flow. Therefore

$$\begin{aligned} v_a &= u_1 \sin \beta_1 - u_2 \sin \beta_2 \\ &= 353 \sin 29° - 300 \sin 20° \\ &= 69 \text{ m/s} \end{aligned}$$

Hence axial thrust

$$m v_a = 5 \times 69 = 345 \text{ N}$$

(d) Efficiency η is

$$\begin{aligned} \eta &= \frac{\text{power out}}{\text{power in}} = \frac{F_b u}{\frac{1}{2} m v_1^2} \\ &= \frac{464 \times 10^3}{\frac{1}{2} \times 5 \times 500^2} \\ &= 0.74 \text{ or } 74\% \end{aligned}$$

The reader should note that since m is the mass flow, the term $\frac{1}{2}mv_1^{\,2}$ is the rate of change of the kinetic energy, i.e. the power in.

IMPACT 4.8

4.8.1 Conservation of momentum

The state of rest or motion of bodies is often altered as a result of the sudden application of forces that act over short time intervals. Familiar examples are the collisions of the balls on a snooker table and the coupling of railway wagons in a marshalling yard.

Let us go back for a moment to Newton's third law: *Action and reaction between two bodies are equal and opposite.* Suppose that a body A exerts a force on body B, then accordingly body B will exert an equal force on body A but of opposite direction. Expressed mathematically,

$$\mathbf{F}_{BA} = -\mathbf{F}_{AB}$$

Consider now the interaction of two bodies A and B of masses m_A and m_B respectively, e.g. the snooker balls or the railway wagons. By Newton's second law we have

$$\frac{d}{dt}(m_B \mathbf{v}_B) = -\frac{d}{dt}(m_A \mathbf{v}_A)$$

since $\mathbf{F}_{BA} = -\mathbf{F}_{AB}$ or

$$\frac{d}{dt}(m_B\mathbf{v}_B + m_A\mathbf{v}_A) = 0$$

Since the product mass × velocity is the momentum, by definition, this equation tells us that

$$m_B\mathbf{v}_B + m_A\mathbf{v}_A = \text{constant} \tag{4.22}$$

i.e. the total momentum is conserved if no external forces act on the system, i.e. if the system is isolated. Since equation (4.22) is a vector equation, it follows that there is "conservation of linear momentum in any direction".

To solve the impact or collision problems completely we need to know something of the nature of the bodies involved. When two bodies collide they will either lock together (such as the coupling of railway wagons) or separate (as in the case of the snooker balls). Newton carried out experiments with metal, cork and glass balls and defined a coefficient of restitution e such that

$$\frac{\text{relative velocity of the spheres after impact}}{\text{relative velocity of the spheres before impact}} = -e$$

Hence if u_1 and u_2 are the velocities of two balls of masses m_1 and m_2 respectively before impact and v_1 and v_2 their respective velocities after impact, then

$$-e = \frac{v_2 - v_1}{u_2 - u_1} \qquad \text{or} \qquad e = \frac{v_2 - v_1}{u_1 - u_2}$$

The coefficient of restitution e depends on the materials: $e = 1$ for elastic impact, which is true for hard bodies such as steel balls; $e = 0$ for plastic impacts or for bodies locking at impact; $0 < e < 1$ for all other cases.

The nature of the impact of bodies is quite complicated, and for a detailed explanation the reader should consult more advanced texts on dynamics, such as those mentioned in the bibliography at the end of this text.

4.8.2 **Loss of kinetic energy during impact**

When two bodies collide and move on, there is a loss of kinetic energy. Let us consider the particular situation when two railway wagons collide, couple and move on together.

Let m_1 be the mass of the first wagon moving with a speed v_1 and m_2 the mass of the second wagon whose speed is v_2, both moving on the same horizontal track. If $v_1 > v_2$ the first wagon will collide with the second and once coupled by a special device the two will move on together at a speed v.

By equation (4.22) the total momentum is conserved so that

$$m_1v_1 + m_2v_2 = (m_1 + m_2)v$$

Solving for v yields

$$v = \frac{m_1v_1 + m_2v_2}{m_1 + m_2}$$

and the loss of kinetic energy ΔT will be given by

$$\Delta T = -\left[\tfrac{1}{2}(m_1 + m_2)v^2 - (\tfrac{1}{2}m_1 v_1{}^2 + \tfrac{1}{2}m_2 v_2{}^2)\right]$$
$$= \frac{\tfrac{1}{2}m_1 m_2}{m_1 + m_2}(v_1 - v_2)^2$$

on substituting for v.

If the two wagons or any two bodies do not move on together it can be shown that

$$\Delta T = \frac{\tfrac{1}{2}m_1 m_2 (1 - e^2)(v_1 - v_2)^2}{m_1 + m_2}$$

We leave the proof as an exercise for the reader. This shows that if the collision is perfectly elastic $\Delta T = 0$, i.e. there is no energy loss since $e = 1$.

EXAMPLE 4.11

During a shunting operation two railway wagons of mass 25 t and 15 t moving along a straight and level track at speeds of 5 km/h and 2 km/h, respectively, collide, lock and move on together; each pair of buffers has a stiffness of 2.4×10^5 N/m (one pair per wagon). Calculate (a) the common velocity after impact and the loss of kinetic energy, and (b) the maximum compression in each pair of buffer springs and the force exerted between the wagons.

SOLUTION

Conservation of momentum gives

$$25 \times 10^3 \times 5/3.6 + 15 \times 10^3 \times 2/3.6 = (25 + 15) \times 10^3 v$$

Hence the common velocity after impact is

$$v = \frac{25 \times 5 + 15 \times 2}{40} = 3.875 \text{ km/h}$$

(*Note:* The factor 3.6, although not necessary in this case, is to convert km/h to m/s.)

KE before impact

$$T_1 = \tfrac{1}{2} \times 25 \times 10^3 \left(\frac{5}{3.6}\right)^2 + \tfrac{1}{2} \times 15 \times 10^3 \left(\frac{2}{3.6}\right)^2$$
$$= 26.43 \times 10^3 \text{ J}$$

KE after impact

$$T_2 = \tfrac{1}{2} \times 40 \times 10^3 \left(\frac{3.875}{3.6}\right)^2 = 23.17 \times 10^3 \text{ J}$$

Loss of KE

$$\Delta T = (26.43 - 23.17) \times 10^3 = 3260 \text{ J}$$

This loss will appear as strain energy in the buffers. If x is the deflection of each pair of buffers then

$$2 \times \tfrac{1}{2}Kx^2 = \Delta T$$

where K is the stiffness of each pair of buffers. Hence

$$x = \sqrt{\frac{\Delta T}{K}} = \sqrt{\frac{3260}{2.4 \times 10^5}}$$
$$= 0.117 \text{ m} = 117 \text{ mm}$$

The force F between the wagons is equal to Kx; therefore

$$F = 2.4 \times 10^5 \times 0.117 = 28 \text{ kN}$$

EXERCISES

4.1 A car of mass 1250 kg is travelling at 120 km/h round a bend of 275 m radius. The road is banked at 12° to the horizontal. Calculate the normal reaction, the friction force and hence the minimum coefficient of friction between the road and the tyres if there is no slip.

4.2 The power developed by the locomotive of a fast train of total mass 515 t is 6 MW at the maximum speed of 270 km/h. The rolling resistance is 0.5% of its weight. If the total resistance is of the form $A + Bv^2$, calculate the value of B. Calculate also the tractive effort of the locomotive for an initial acceleration of 0.35 m/s² starting from rest.

4.3 The tractive effort of a locomotive of mass 60 t is given by:

$$T = \begin{cases} 125 \times 10^3 \text{ N} & \text{for } 0 \leqslant v \leqslant 75 \text{ km/h} \\ K/v \text{ N} & \text{for } v \geqslant 75 \text{ km/h} \end{cases}$$

When coupled to a train of mass 240 t the total resistance is given by

$$R = 4750 + kv^2 \text{ N}$$

If this train has a maximum speed of 200 km/h on a level and straight track, calculate (a) the maximum acceleration, (b) the time taken to reach 175 km/h, (c) the distance travelled to reach that same speed, and (d) the maximum speed up an incline of 1 in 150.

4.4 Using the data given in Figure 4.13, estimate the time taken for a 700 t train to reach 120 km/h on a level track, starting from rest, and the distance travelled. The resistance characteristic of the train is given by

$$A + Bv^2$$

where A is the constant resistive force term $= 55$ N/t, B is the drag coefficient, and v is the speed.

4.5 A motor car of mass 1300 kg, with an engine developing a tractive effort of 1700 N, can travel at a speed of 160 km/h on a level road. The resistance to motion due to windage and road drag varies as the square of speed. Calculate the time taken for the speed of the car to rise from 72 km/h to 120 km/h up an incline of 1 in 20 when the tractive effort is kept at 1700 N. Calculate also the power developed by the engine at 120 km/h if the transmission efficiency is 82.5%.

4.6 A vehicle has a mass of 1500 kg; its resistance to motion is given by $R = 300 + 54v$ N for speeds up to 30 m/s and $R = 300 + 1.8v^2$ N for speeds above 30 m/s, where v is the speed in m/s. The prime mover of this vehicle develops a tractive effort given by $T = 6000 - 64.8v$ N. Calculate the distance covered from rest if the vehicle is to reach a speed of 140 km/h up an incline of 1 in 50. Calculate also the maximum speed on a level track.

4.7 An electrically driven car of 750 kg has a resistance to motion of $1.025v^2$ N, where v is the speed in m/s. The electric motor develops a constant power of 55 kW at any speed but 20% of this power is dissipated in the transmission system. Neglecting the small rolling resistance calculate: (a) the maximum speed of the car on a straight and level road, (b) the maximum speed up an incline of 1 in 10 (an approximate value will be sufficient), and (c) the tension in the tow-bar when the car is pulling a trailer of 450 kg up the incline at the instant when the speed is 55 km/h. The trailer has a resistance of $1.25v^2$.

4.8 A goods wagon of 80 t is moving along a horizontal track at 3 km/h in a marshalling yard. A second wagon of 60 t, moving at 5 km/h on the same track and in the same direction as the first, reaches it and the two are coupled without rebound by an automatic device. Calculate (a) the common speed of the two coupled wagons, and (b) the loss of energy due to the coupling operation.

4.9 A buffer has a stiffness given by $K_1 = 0.25 \times 10^6$ N/m for compressions up to 200 mm and $K_2 = 0.65 \times 10^6$ N/m for compressions above 200 mm. Such a buffer is used to bring to rest a railway truck of 25 t moving at 4 km/h. If the rolling resistance is 0.3% of the weight of the truck, calculate the compression of the buffer (assuming no rebound).

4.10 A railway truck is at rest at the bottom of an incline of 1 in 70. A second truck of equal weight starts from rest at a point 305 m up the incline, and is allowed to run down under gravity. The trucks collide at the bottom of the incline and the coefficient of restitution is 0.2. Calculate how far each truck travels along the level if the frictional resistance for each truck is 0.7% of the weight on both the incline and the level. Where the level meets the incline, the rails are slightly curved, each in a vertical plane, so that there is no vertical impact, and at the instant the collision takes place both trucks are on the level.

4.11 A railway truck of 45 t travelling at 2.5 km/h is brought to rest in a distance of 650 mm by a pneumatic buffer. Initially the piston in the cylinder is at a distance of 750 mm from the closed end and the pressure is 1 bar. Calculate (a) the coefficient of rolling friction, neglecting the friction in the cylinder, and (b) the pressure in the cylinder at the instant the truck is brought to rest. The diameter of the cylinder is 200 mm. The law inside the cylinder is pressure $\times$ volume = constant.

4.12 A rocket has an initial mass of 80 t and a mass at burn-out of 20 t. It burns fuel at the rate of 780 kg/s and ejects it at a relative velocity of 2500 m/s. If this rocket is to be launched vertically calculate: (a) its initial acceleration, (b) its acceleration at burn-out, and (c) its thrust. Air resistance and variation in gravity may be neglected.

4.13 Calculate the velocity of the rocket in exercise 4.12 at burn-out and the height reached, neglecting drag and the variation in gravity. (It can be shown that the results are about 15–20% too high when these effects are neglected.)

4.14 Figure 4.37 shows part of a mechanism in which a collar slides on a vertical rod. Its motion is controlled by a spring of stiffness K. In the rest position at A the spring is unstretched and has a length L. In that position a device releases the collar of mass m which then falls under gravity. Derive an expression for its velocity as it reaches its lowest position at B, a distance S from A, neglecting friction. If friction is taken into account what would be the new expression for the velocity at B?

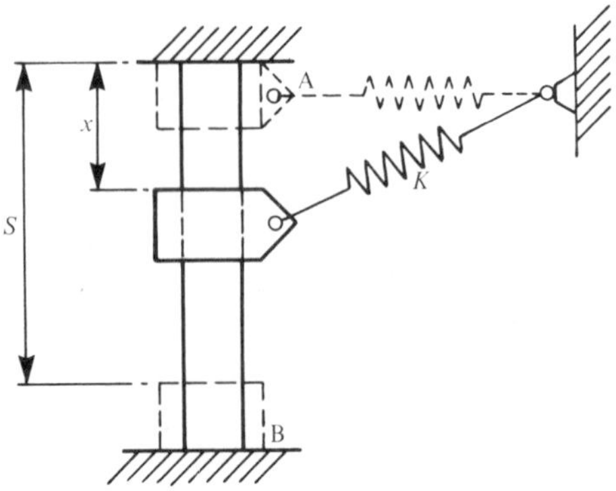

Figure 4.39

4.15 An archer shoots an arrow of mass m with an initial velocity u at an angle α to the horizontal. For small velocities the resistance to motion may be taken to be proportional to the velocity and in the direction of the velocity vector, hence $R = kv$. Derive expressions for the x and y coordinates of the arrow as functions of time. If $k = 0.01$, $m = 0.15$ kg, $u = 60$ m/s and $\alpha = 15°$, at what distance from the archer will the arrow land, neglecting the height of the archer?

4.16 Packages are being transferred from a horizontal conveyor on to a loading bay at E by means of the chute ABCDE shown in Figure 4.40. Portion CD of the chute consists of a number of small rollers which offer no resistance to the motion of the packages. Assuming a 10% energy loss as the packages are transferred at A and using the given data, calculate the minimum length $l = \text{DE}$ to ensure that the packages are brought to rest at E.

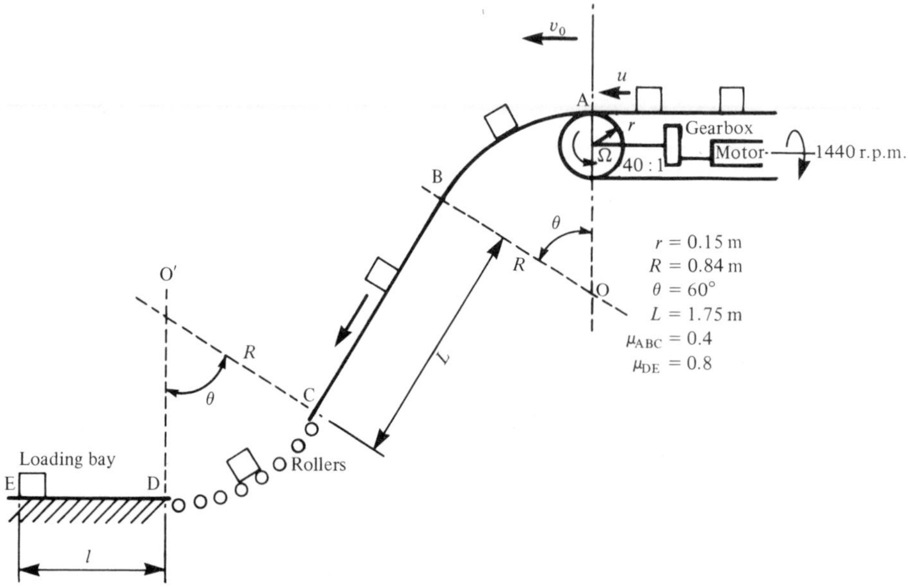

Figure 4.40

(*Note:* Part of the solution involves a differential equation of the type

$$\frac{dy}{dx} + Py = Q$$

(where P and Q are functions of x only or constants), whose analytical solution is

$$y = e^{-\int P\,dx}\left(\int Qe^{P\,dx}\,dx + C\right)$$

Alternatively a numerical solution may be preferred.)

5

Kinetics of Rigid Bodies

5.1 EQUATIONS OF MOTION

In the previous chapter we considered the motion of bodies whose sizes were not relevant to the situations under discussion. We were therefore able to regard these bodies as particles. In many situations in practice, however, size is important as in, for example, the motion of the connecting rod of an engine, the armature of an electric motor, the rotor of a gas turbine, the gears of a reduction gearbox, a car on its suspension or an aircraft during an aerobatic display.

In this chapter we shall confine our analysis to a study of the motion of rigid bodies in a plane, i.e. in two dimensions. We shall, however, consider gyroscopic motion in its simplest form, and its importance in certain practical situations, and shall demonstrate that the motion of a rigid body is made up of simultaneous translation and rotation, and that the equations of motion take very simple forms.

Figure 5.1 shows a rigid body of any shape moving in the xy-plane under the action of N externally applied forces, $P_1, P_2, \ldots, P_N$. G is the centre of mass with coordinates $\bar{x}$ and $\bar{y}$ relative to a Newtonian reference frame Ox, Oy. Q is a particle of mass δm with coordinates x and y relative to the centre of mass. The reader is reminded that the centre of mass of a system of particles* is given by

$$\bar{x} = \frac{\sum \delta m x_j}{M} \qquad \bar{y} = \frac{\sum \delta m y_j}{M} \qquad (5.1)$$

where x_j and y_j are the coordinates of a particle relative to xOy and $M = \sum \delta m$ is the total mass.

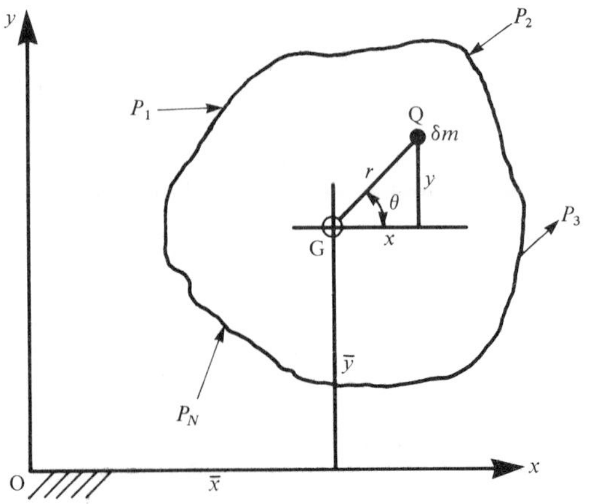

Figure 5.1 Plane motion of a rigid body.

*For a rigid body $\bar{x} = \frac{1}{M}\int x \, dm$ and $\bar{y} = \frac{1}{M}\int y \, dm$.

The particle at Q is subjected to forces due to the external forces on the body and to internal forces between particles in the body. Let X_e and Y_e be the contribution of the external forces, X_i and Y_i the resultants of the internal forces acting at Q. The position of the particle is $\bar{x}+x$ parallel to the x-axis and $\bar{y}+y$ parallel to the y-axis. By Newton's second law

$$\delta m(\ddot{\bar{x}}+\ddot{x}) = X_e + X_i$$
$$\delta m(\ddot{\bar{y}}+\ddot{y}) = Y_e + Y_i$$

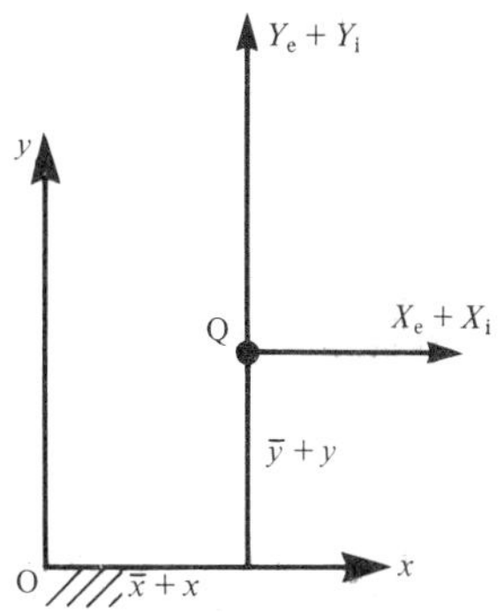

Figure 5.2 Forces acting at a point Q of a rigid body.

For all the particles of the body it follows that

$$\sum\delta m(\ddot{\bar{x}}+\ddot{x}) = \sum X_e + \sum X_i$$
$$\sum\delta m(\ddot{\bar{y}}+\ddot{y}) = \sum Y_e + \sum Y_i$$

or

$$(\sum\delta m)\ddot{\bar{x}} + \sum\delta m\ddot{x} = \sum X_e = X \tag{5.2}$$

$$(\sum\delta m)\ddot{\bar{y}} + \sum\delta m\ddot{y} = \sum Y_e = Y \tag{5.3}$$

noting that $\sum X_i = \sum Y_i = 0$, since internal forces occur in pairs and are equal and opposite by Newton's third law.

We also note that

$$\ddot{\bar{x}}\sum\delta m = M\ddot{\bar{x}}$$

and

$$\ddot{\bar{y}}\sum\delta m = M\ddot{\bar{y}}$$

because for a rigid body every particle must have the same acceleration as that of the centre of mass G. Furthermore

$$\sum\delta m\ddot{x} = \sum\delta m\ddot{y} = 0$$

because

$$\frac{d^2}{dt^2}(\sum\delta mx) = \frac{d^2}{dt^2}(\sum\delta my) = 0$$

by the definition of the centre of mass. Hence equations (5.2) and (5.3) become

$$\begin{aligned} M\ddot{\bar{x}} &= X \\ M\ddot{\bar{y}} &= Y \end{aligned} \tag{5.4}$$

X and Y are the resultants of the components of the external forces parallel to the x- and y-axes respectively. Thus equation (5.4) tells us that as far as translation is concerned the rigid body behaves as if it were a particle of mass M at G with all the external forces acting through G. These equations apply for any collection of particles or rigid bodies connected together. They also apply for a flexible body, a portion of gas or any other system provided that the forces X and Y are the totals of all the forces applied from outside the boundary defining the system.

The external forces will in general have a turning effect on the body, causing it to rotate in the plane. Consider an axis perpendicular to the x,y-plane and passing through an arbitrary point P as shown in Figure 5.3. P may be anywhere inside or outside the body but stationary relative to it. The particle at Q has absolute coordinates $x_P + x_1$ and $y_P + y_1$ and the forces acting on it are as shown in Figure 5.2.

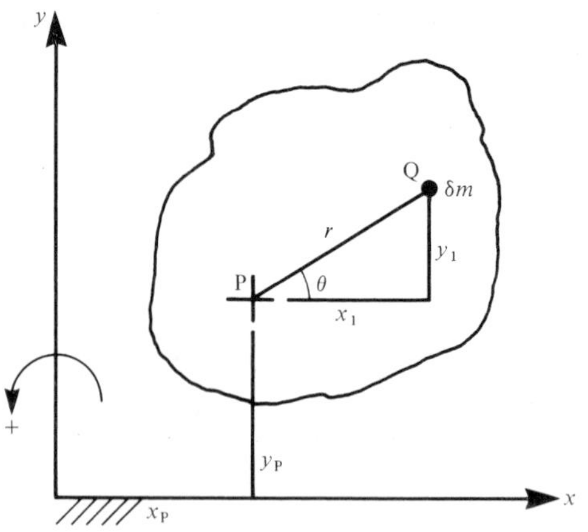

Figure 5.3 Axis through an arbitrary point P of a rigid body.

By Newton's second law

$$\delta m(\ddot{x}_P + \ddot{x}_1) = X_e + X_i$$
$$\delta m(\ddot{y}_P + \ddot{y}_1) = Y_e + Y_i$$

The moment about P of the forces is given by

$$\delta M_P = (Y_e + Y_i)x_1 - (X_e + X_i)y_1$$

taking anticlockwise moments as positive. Hence the total moment of the forces about P is

$$M_P = \sum Y_e x_1 - \sum X_e y_1$$

(since the moment of the internal forces is equal to zero by Newton's third law). It follows then that

$$M_P = \sum[\delta m(\ddot{y}_P + \ddot{y}_1)]x_1 - \sum[\delta m(\ddot{x}_P + \ddot{x}_1)]y_1 \tag{5.5}$$

If the coordinates of P relative to the centre of mass G are X_G and Y_G then $x_1 = x_G + x$ and $y_1 = y_G + y$. Hence

$$\ddot{x}_1 = \ddot{x}_G + \ddot{x} \qquad \ddot{y}_1 = \ddot{y}_G + \ddot{y}$$

Expanding equation (5.5) and substituting for $x_1, \ddot{x}_1, y_1$ and $\ddot{y}_1$ yields

$$M_P = \ddot{y}_P M x_G - \ddot{x}_P M y_G + \frac{d}{dt}\sum \delta m(x_1\dot{y}_1 - y_1\dot{x}_1) \tag{5.6}$$

To evaluate the last term we use the polar coordinates (r, θ) shown in Figure 5.3 so that

$$x_1 = r\cos\theta \qquad \text{and} \qquad y_1 = r\sin\theta$$

Differentiating gives $\dot{x}_1 = -(r\sin\theta)\dot{\theta}$ and $\dot{y}_1 = (r\cos\theta)\dot{\theta}$ and substituting in equation (5.6) leads to

$$M_P = I_P\ddot{\theta} + (\ddot{y}_P M x_G - \ddot{x}_P M y_G) \tag{5.7}$$

where $I_P = \sum r^2\delta m$ is the moment of inertia of the body about an axis through P and $\ddot{\theta}$ is the angular acceleration of the body.

Equation (5.7) is quite general since P is any point we care to choose. Thus P can also be a fixed point, a point moving with constant velocity or the centre of mass G. If P is the centre of mass, then $\ddot{x}_G = \ddot{y}_G = 0$, and the equation becomes simplified to

$$M_G = I_G\ddot{\theta} \tag{5.8}$$

where I_G is the moment of inertia of the body about an axis through G, perpendicular to the xy-plane.

The motion of a rigid body is completely determined by the following equations:

$$M\ddot{\bar{x}} = X \qquad (5.9a)$$

$$M\ddot{\bar{y}} = Y \qquad (5.9b)$$

$$I_G\ddot{\theta} = M_G \qquad (5.9c)$$

The first two of these represent the total of all the forces applied from outside, and the last represents the total moment of these forces about an axis through G.

If a body is constrained to rotate about a fixed axis P, the moment equation becomes

$$I_P\ddot{\theta} = M_P \qquad \text{or} \qquad (I_G + Mh^2)\ddot{\theta} = M_P$$

where h is the distance between the axes through P and G.

In deriving the third equation in (5.9) we defined the moment of inertia I as

$$I = \sum \delta m r^2$$

I is a property of a given body and its value for the more common shapes is given in Appendix A.4. The moment of inertia is sometimes expressed in terms of the *radius of gyration, k,* and the mass M of the body, so that

$$I = Mk^2$$

This is equivalent to regarding the mass M as being concentrated at a distance k from the axis.

5.1.1 Connected rigid bodies

We frequently encounter rigid bodies that are connected together and moving as a result of forces applied to them; mechanisms are typical examples of such bodies since they are made up of rigid links connected together.

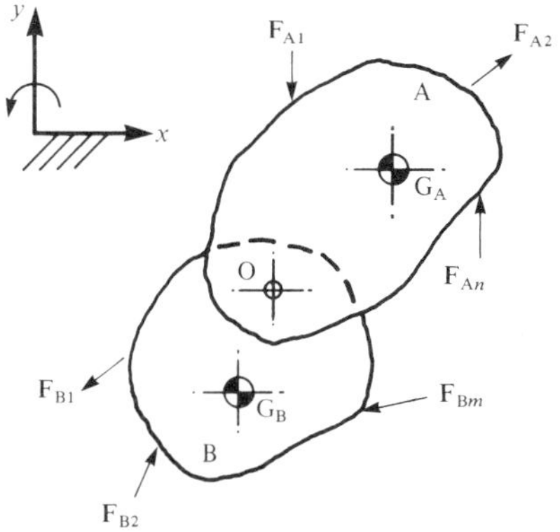

Figure 5.4 Connected rigid bodies.

Figure 5.4 shows two bodies A and B connected together by means of a pin at O. G_A and G_B are the centres of mass and each body is subjected to a number of externally applied forces: $F_{A1}, F_{A2}, \ldots, F_{An}$ on body A and $F_{B1}, F_{B2}, \ldots, F_{Bm}$ on body B as shown. To analyse the motion it is best to consider each body in turn and to introduce unknown reactions F_x and F_y at the pin O (Figure 5.5).

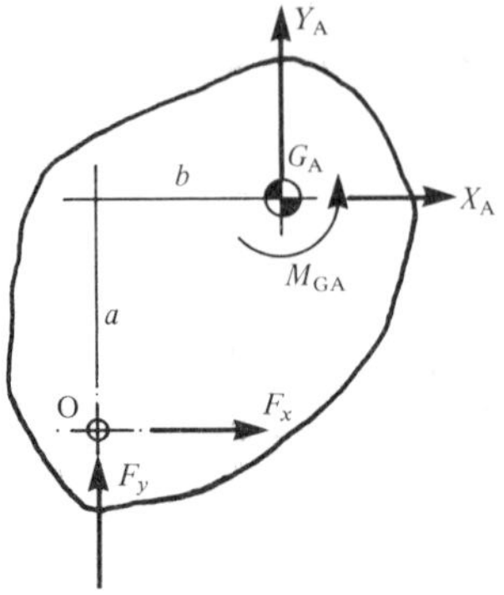

Figure 5.5 Free body diagram for rigid body A.

Applying equation (5.9) yields for body A:

$$(F_{A1} + F_{A2} + \ldots + F_{An})_x + F_x = m_A \ddot{x}_{GA}$$

Similarly

$$(F_{A1} + F_{A2} + \ldots + F_{An})_y + F_y = m_A \ddot{y}_{GA}$$

These equations may be expressed as follows:

$$X_A + F_x = m_A \dot{u}_A$$

and

$$Y_A + F_y = m_A \dot{v}_A$$

where X_A and Y_A are the resultants of the external forces in the x- and y-directions acting through the centre of mass, and $\dot{u}_A$ and $\dot{v}_A$ are the accelerations of the centre of mass in the x- and y-directions respectively.

For the moment equation we have:

$$M_{GA} + F_x a - F_y b = I_{GA} \alpha_A$$

where M_{GA} is the moment about G_A of the external forces, I_{GA} is the moment of inertia of body A about an axis through its centre of mass G_A, and α_A is the angular acceleration of A.

Applying equation (5.9) to body B we find (Figure 5.6):

$$X_B - F_x = m_B \dot{u}_B$$
$$Y_B - F_y = m_B \dot{v}_B$$
$$M_{GB} + F_x c - F_y d = I_{GB} \alpha_B$$

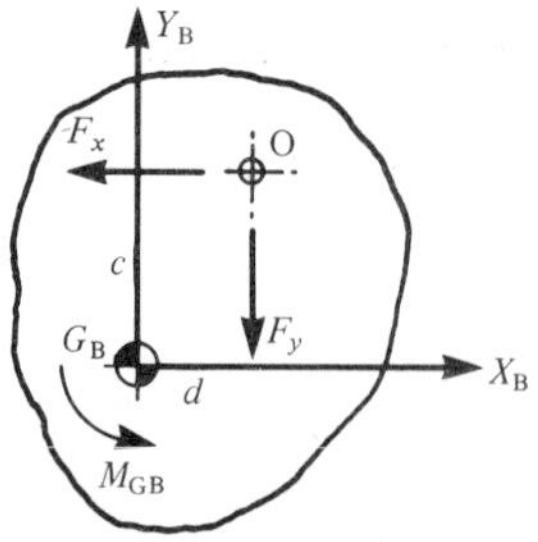

Figure 5.6 Free body diagram for rigid body B.

There are eight unknowns, namely F_x, F_y, $\dot{u}_A$, $\dot{v}_A$, $\dot{u}_B$, $\dot{v}_B$, α_A, α_B, and only six equations. We therefore need two more equations in order to solve for all eight unknowns. We can use the fact that there is a constraint at O. Point O has the same acceleration in both bodies so that we can write

$$\ddot{x}_{OA} = \ddot{x}_{OB} \quad \text{and} \quad \ddot{y}_{OA} = \ddot{y}_{OB}$$

But

$$\ddot{x}_{OA} = \dot{u}_A + a\alpha_A$$

and

$$\ddot{x}_{OB} = \dot{u}_B - c\alpha_B$$

Hence

$$\dot{u}_A + a\alpha_A = \dot{u}_B - c\alpha_B$$

Similarly

$$\dot{v}_A - b\alpha_A = \dot{v}_B + d\alpha_B$$

where the sign of the coordinates a, b, c and d is significant.

The last two equations are the relationships necessary to enable us to solve for all the unknowns.

As an illustration of the dynamics of connected rigid bodies consider the case of the four-bar linkage shown in Figure 5.7. C_i is the input torque and C_o the load torque, G_1, G_2 and G_3 are the centres of mass of the links 1 (AB), 2 (BC) and 3 (CD) of mass m_1, m_2 and m_3 respectively. I_1, I_2 and I_3 are their moments of inertia about an axis through their respective centres of mass.

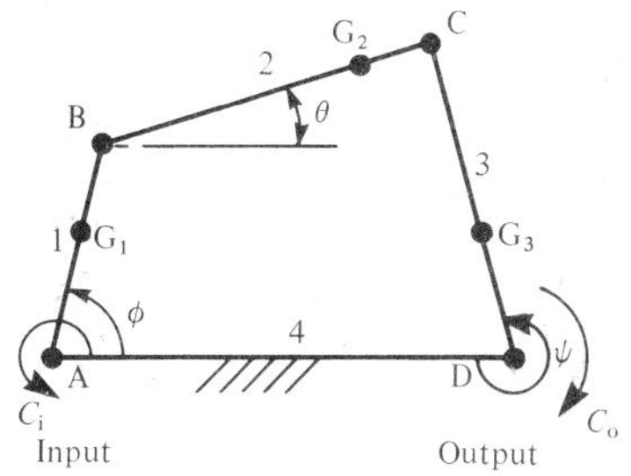

Figure 5.7 Four-bar linkage.

From a practical point of view we need to know how thick each link should be, how big to make the pins at A, B, C and D, and what power will be needed to drive the mechanism. In operation the input torque has to overcome the output torque or load demand as well as the "inertia forces" due to the accelerations of the links, i.e. the $m\ddot{x}$, $m\ddot{y}$ and $I\alpha$ terms.

Forces will therefore be set up in each link, and to evaluate them we need to consider each link in turn as a free body; thus Figure 5.8 shows the free body diagram for each link. In link 1 there will be reactions X and Y at A, forces X_1 and Y_1 at the pin B, and the weight $W_1 = m_1 g$ acting at G_1. At B on link 2 forces X_1 and Y_1 will be present opposite to those at A in accordance with Newton's third law. There will also be forces X_2 and Y_2 at C and the weight $W_2 = m_2 g$ acting at G_2. Similarly, reactions X_2, Y_2, X_3 and Y_3, and the weight $W_3 = m_3 g$ are present in link 3.

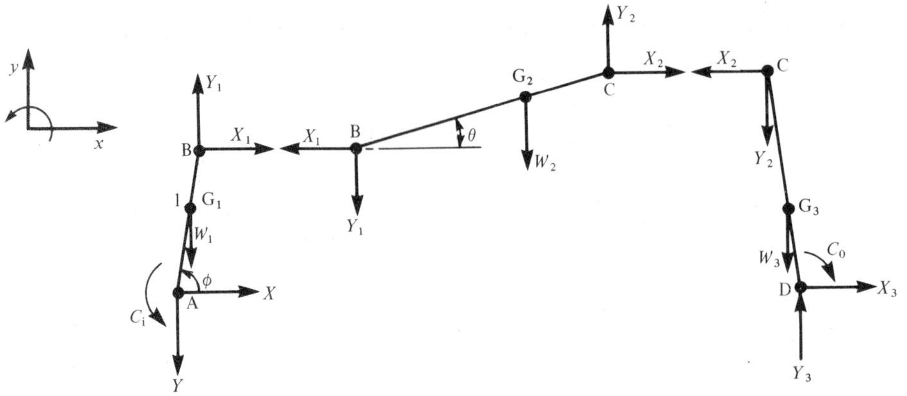

Figure 5.8 Free body diagrams for each link of four-bar linkage.

We can now write down three equations of motion for each link, two for translation and one for rotation. Applying equation (5.9) to link 1 we have

$$X + X_1 = m_1\ddot{x}_1$$
$$Y_1 - Y - W_1 = m_1\ddot{y}_1$$
$$Y_1 a \cos\phi - X_1 a \sin\phi - W_1 a_1 \cos\phi + C_i = I_A\ddot{\phi}$$

where $a = \text{AB}$, $a_1 = \text{AG}_1$ and $I_A = I_{G_1} + m_1 a_1^2$. For convenience the moments of the forces have been taken about A since A is a fixed point in this case.

Similar equations will be obtained for links 2 and 3. For link 2 the moments of the forces must be taken about the centre of mass G_2, whereas for link 3 the moments can be taken about a fixed point, D, as was done for link 1.

In this way we shall obtain nine equations of motion to solve for the 11 unknowns: X, Y, X_1, Y_1, X_2, Y_2, X_3, Y_3, $\ddot{\theta}$, $\ddot{\psi}$, C_i. The other two equations required to solve for all unknowns are obtained from the kinematics of the linkage; they are

$$a \cos\phi + b \cos\theta + c \cos\psi = d$$

and

$$a \sin\phi + b \sin\theta + c \sin\psi = 0$$

These are equations (3.11) and (3.12). From these two equations we can solve for the derivatives of θ and ψ as a function of the input speed $\dot{\phi}$, which is usually constant in practice.

In some mechanisms the actual weights of the links are small compared with the "inertia forces" and may be omitted in the equations of motion. The following are further examples of connected rigid bodies.

EXAMPLE 5.1

A car of mass M is driven at the rear wheels by a tractive force P. The centre of mass is at a height h above the road and at a distance l_1 behind the front wheel axis. The wheelbase is L. Calculate the reaction

Example Cont.

under each wheel if the total drag of the car is assumed to act through the centre of mass. Calculate also the angular acceleration of the rear wheels if I is the moment of inertia of the axle assembly.

SOLUTION

Figure 5.9 shows the free body diagram for the car. Let $l_2 = L - l_1$ be the distance of G from the rear wheel axis; D is the drag.

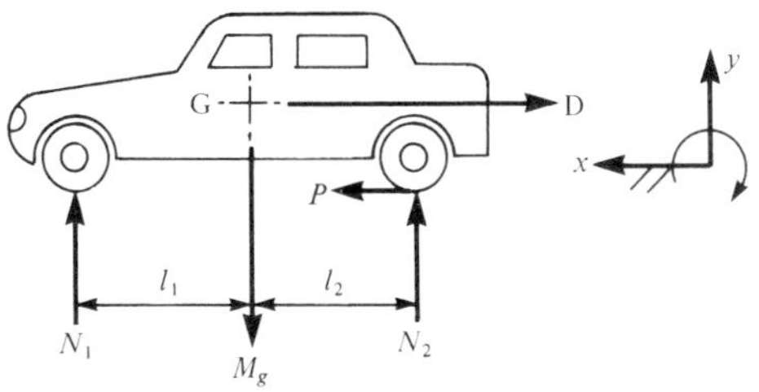

Figure 5.9 Car of example 5.1.

(a) From (5.9) we have for the equations of translation:

$$P - D = M\ddot{x}$$
$$N_1 + N_2 - Mg = \ddot{y} = 0$$

since there is no acceleration in the y-direction.

(b) For the equation of rotation we have, taking moments about G,

$$Ph + N_1 l_1 - N_2 l_2 = \ddot{\theta} = 0$$

since there is no rotation of the car.

From the second equation, solving for N_2 gives

$$N_2 = Mg - N_1$$

Substituting in the third equation and solving for N_1 then yields

$$N_1 = \frac{Mgl_2 - Ph}{l_1 + l_2} = \frac{Mgl_2 - Ph}{L}$$

Hence from the second equation, solving for N_2 yields

$$N_2 = \frac{Mgl_1 + Ph}{l_1 + l_2} = \frac{Mgl_1 + Ph}{L}$$

Thus while the car is accelerating the reaction is increased under the rear wheels but decreased under the front wheels, the amount in each case being Ph/L.

Solution Cont.

If the friction coefficient between the tyres and the road is μ then $P/N_2 \leqslant \mu$ for no skidding to occur.

Figure 5.10 shows a free body diagram for the rear wheels; X and Y are the forces from the car body, C is the driving couple from the engine and mg the weight of the rear wheels.

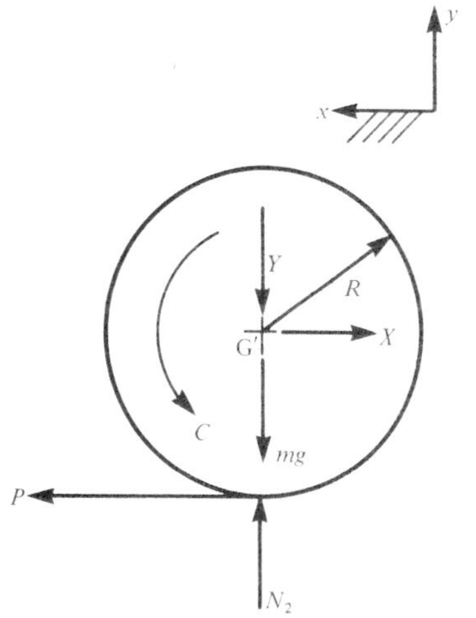

Figure 5.10 Free body diagram for rear wheel of car.

Applying the equations for rotation about the centre of mass G′, which eliminates the unknown reactions X and Y, yields

$$C - PR = I\dot{\omega}$$

where R is the rolling radius. Hence

$$\dot{\omega} = \frac{C - PR}{I}$$

I is the moment of inertia of the wheels, and if I is very small then $P \simeq C/R$, i.e. most of the engine torque is available to accelerate the car. Accelerations $\ddot{x}$ and $\dot{\omega}$ are related by the equation $\ddot{x} = R\dot{\omega}$ provided there is no slippage between the wheels and the road.

EXAMPLE 5.2

The rocket shown in Figure 5.11 has a total mass of 25 t and is propelled by two engines each providing a thrust T of 250 kN at an angle θ of 2° to the axis of the rocket. If one rocket fails to operate at launch, calculate the accelerations of the rocket. The rocket may be assumed to be a slender rod 25 m long.

Example Cont.

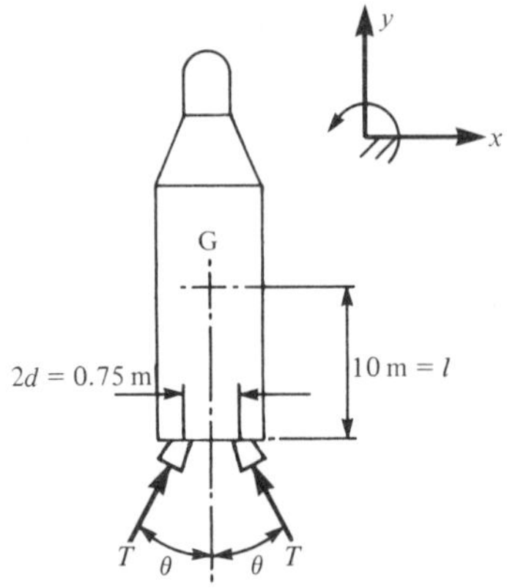

Figure 5.11 Rocket of example 5.2.

SOLUTION

Let us assume that the right-hand rocket fails. Applying equations (5.9) gives

$$T\cos\theta - mg = m\ddot{y}$$
$$T\sin\theta = m\ddot{x}$$
$$(T\cos\theta)d - (T\sin\theta)l = I_G\alpha$$

where α is the angular acceleration. For a slender rod, $I_G = \frac{1}{12}mL^2$. Hence

$$I_G = \frac{1}{12} \times 25 \times 10^3 \times 25^2$$
$$= 1.302 \times 10^6 \text{ kg m}^2$$

From the first equation

$$\ddot{y} = \frac{T\cos\theta}{m} - g$$
$$= \frac{250\cos 2°}{25} - 9.81$$
$$= 0.184 \text{ m/s}^2$$

From the second equation

$$\ddot{x} = \frac{T\sin\theta}{m}$$
$$= \frac{250\sin 2°}{25}$$
$$= 0.349 \text{ m/s}^2$$

From the third equation

$$\alpha = \frac{250 \times 10^3}{1.302 \times 10^6}(\cos 2° \times 0.375 - \sin 2° \times 10)$$
$$= 4.95 \times 10^{-3} \text{ rad/s}^2$$

EXAMPLE 5.3

A torque T is applied to the pinion of a geared system. The pinion of moment of inertia I_1 and pitch radius R_1 meshes with a wheel of moment of inertia I_2 and pitch radius R_2. Calculate the acceleration of the system.

SOLUTION

Figure 5.12 shows the two gears. Let α_1 and α_2 be the accelerations of the pinion and wheel respectively. At the contact point A where two teeth meet, let P be the tangential force exerted by the pinion on the wheel as shown; then by Newton's third law P will also act on the pinion but in the opposite direction.

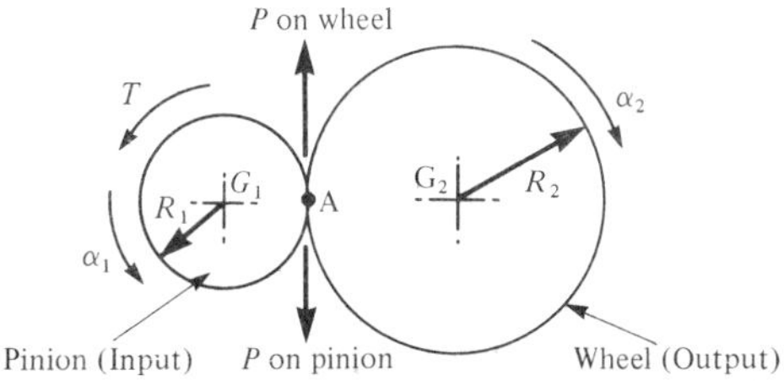

Figure 5.12 Two gears.

This system is one in pure rotation about fixed axes G_1 and G_2, and applying the moment equation to each in turn gives for the pinion

$$T - PR_1 = I_1\alpha_1$$

and for the wheel

$$PR_2 = I_2\alpha_2$$

There is also a relationship between α_1 and α_2 since

Solution Cont.

the linear acceleration of the point A is the same for pinion and wheel; hence

$$\alpha_1 R_1 = \alpha_2 R_2$$

Solving for P and substituting in the first equation gives

$$I_1\alpha_1 = T - I_2\alpha_2\frac{R_1}{R_2} = T - I_2\left(\frac{R_1}{R_2}\right)^2\alpha_1$$

Solving for α_1 then yields

$$\alpha_1 = \frac{T}{I_1 + I_2(R_1/R_2)^2} = \frac{T}{I_e}$$

where $I_e = I_1 + I_2/G^2$ is the equivalent moment of inertia of the system as seen by the input. It is sometimes called the reflected inertia. R_2/R_1 is the gear ratio G. G is usually expressed in terms of the number of teeth; thus if the pinion has N_1 teeth and the wheel N_2 teeth then

$$G = \frac{R_2}{R_1} = \frac{N_2}{N_1}$$

Similarly the acceleration of the wheel

$$\alpha_2 = \frac{TG}{I'_e}$$

where $I'_e = I_1 G^2 + I_2$.

KINETIC ENERGY 5.2

Consider a rigid body moving in the xy-plane under the action of external forces $P_1, P_2, \ldots, P_N$ as shown in Figure 5.13. Let a particle of mass δm at Q whose coordinates are x and y have velocities $\dot{x}$ and $\dot{y}$ as shown. The kinetic energy δT of that particle is

$$\delta T = \tfrac{1}{2}\delta m(\dot{x}^2 + \dot{y}^2) \tag{5.10}$$

If $\bar{x}$ and $\bar{y}$ are the coordinates of the centre of mass G and r and θ the polar coordinates of Q relative to G, then we have

$$x = \bar{x} + r\cos\theta$$

and

$$y = \bar{y} + r\sin\theta$$

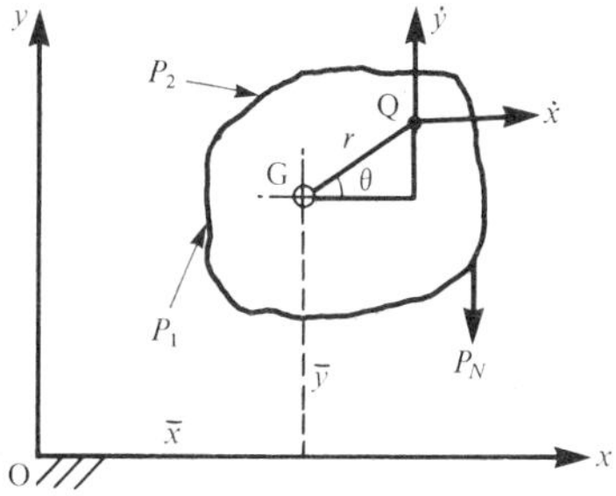

Figure 5.13 Sketch for finding the kinetic energy of a rigid body.

Hence by differentiating with respect to time the velocities are

$$\dot{x} = \dot{\bar{x}} - (r \sin\theta)\dot{\theta} \qquad \dot{y} = \dot{\bar{y}} + (r\cos\theta)\dot{\theta} \tag{5.11}$$

where $\dot{\theta} = \omega$ is the angular velocity of the body; it follows that

$$\dot{x}^2 = \dot{\bar{x}}^2 + (r^2 \sin^2\theta)\omega^2 - (2\dot{\bar{x}} r \sin\theta)\omega$$

and

$$\dot{y}^2 = \dot{\bar{y}}^2 + (r^2 \cos^2\theta)\omega^2 - (2\dot{\bar{y}} r \cos\theta)\omega$$

Substituting in (5.10) and summing for the whole body gives

$$T = \tfrac{1}{2}\sum\delta m(\dot{\bar{x}}^2 + \dot{\bar{y}}^2) + \tfrac{1}{2}\sum\delta m r^2\omega^2 - \tfrac{1}{2}\sum 2\dot{\bar{x}}\omega r(\sin\theta)\delta m + \tfrac{1}{2}\sum 2\dot{\bar{y}}\omega r(\cos\theta)\delta m$$

or

$$T = \tfrac{1}{2}\sum\delta m(\dot{\bar{x}}^2 + \dot{\bar{y}}^2) + \tfrac{1}{2}\omega^2\sum\delta m r^2 - \dot{\bar{x}}\omega\sum\delta m r\sin\theta + \dot{\bar{y}}\omega\sum\delta m r\cos\theta$$

The last two terms are equal to zero, by definition of the centre of mass. Hence the total kinetic energy of the body is given by

$$T = \tfrac{1}{2}Mv^2 + \tfrac{1}{2}I_G\omega^2 \tag{5.12}$$

where $v = \sqrt{\dot{\bar{x}}^2 + \dot{\bar{y}}^2}$ is the velocity of translation. We notice, therefore, that the kinetic energy is made up of energy due to translation and energy due to rotation.

5.2.1 Application to geared systems

There are many cases in practice where it is necessary to transmit power to a load via a *converter* in order to effect an increase or a decrease in speed, and to modify the torque characteristic of the prime mover as seen by the load. For example, to set a car in motion we select a low gear so that a greater torque is available at the driving wheels. Converters take various forms but a common one conists of a number of gears suitably arranged.

Figure 5.14 shows such a system, consisting of two gears. The driver has a moment of inertia I_1 and rotates with angular velocity ω_1, while the driven gear of moment of inertia I_2 rotates with angular velocity ω_2. This system is equivalent to a simpler one consisting of a rotor of moment of inertia I_{e1} rotating at ω_1 or to a rotor of moment of inertia I_{e2} rotating at ω_2.

Considering the first case, if the two systems are equivalent their kinetic energies must be the same. Hence

$$\tfrac{1}{2}I_{e1}\omega_1^2 = \tfrac{1}{2}I_1\omega_1^2 + \tfrac{1}{2}I_2\omega_2^2 \tag{5.13}$$

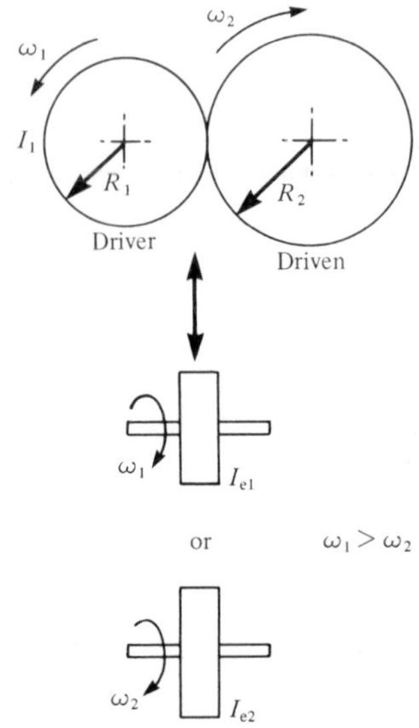

Figure 5.14 Sketch for finding the kinetic energy of two gears.

but

$$\omega_1 R_1 = \omega_2 R_2 \qquad \text{or} \qquad \omega_2 = \omega_1 \frac{R_1}{R_2}$$

If N_1 and N_2 are the numbers of teeth, then the gear ratio

$$G = \frac{R_2}{R_1} = \frac{N_2}{N_1}$$

and

$$\omega_2 = \omega_1/G$$

Substituting in (5.13) gives

$$I_{e1} = I_1 + I_2/G^2$$

as seen by the input (driver). Similarly for the second case,

$$I_{e2} = I_1 G^2 + I_2$$

as seen by the output (load).

In a compound geared train such as the one shown in Figure 5.15, if G_1 and G_2 are the gear ratios then

$$I_{e2} = I_2 + I_3/G_2^{\,2} \qquad \omega_1 > \omega_3$$

as seen by the intermediate shaft, and

$$I_{e1} = I_1 + I_{e2}/G_1^{\,2}$$

as seen by the input shaft, or

$$I_{e1} = I_1 + I_2/G_1^{\,2}\, I_3/G_1^{\,2}G_2^{\,2}$$

Alternatively the equivalent moment of inertia at the output shaft is

$$I_{e3} = I_1 G_1^{\,2} G_2^{\,2} + I_2 G_2^{\,2} + I_3 \qquad (5.14)$$

The output speed is

$$\omega_3 = \omega_1/G_1 G_2.$$

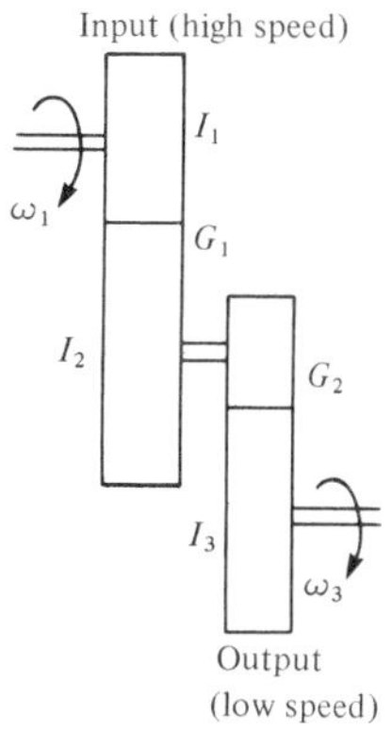

Figure 5.15 Compound gears.

In practice the input shaft is connected to the output of a prime mover and the output of the geared system is connected to a load, e.g. a pump, a fan, a propeller, the wheels of a car etc. If I_P is the moment of inertia of the prime mover, I_L that of the load and G the overall gear ratio, then the equivalent moment of inertia referred to the prime mover shaft is

$$I_{eP} = I_P + I_e + I_L/G^2 \qquad (5.15)$$

where I_e is the equivalent moment of inertia of the geared system, which may be simple or compound, i.e. a simple reduction or a multiple reduction.

If α_P is the angular acceleration of the system and T the torque applied then, applying equation (5.9) for a body rotating about a fixed axis, we have

$$\alpha_P = T/I_{eP}$$

EXAMPLE 5.4

Figure 5.16 shows the essential elements for a lift: a prime mover (an electric motor in this case) drives a drum through a double reduction gearbox. The lift cage is connected to the drum via a steel cable. The counterweight normally fitted to balance the empty cage has been omitted in this example. If the acceleration of the cage is limited to 0.1g and to a maximum speed of 0.35 m/s, calculate the power of the prime mover using the given data. The mechanical efficiency of the prime mover is 97% and that of the geared system 98%.

Example Cont.

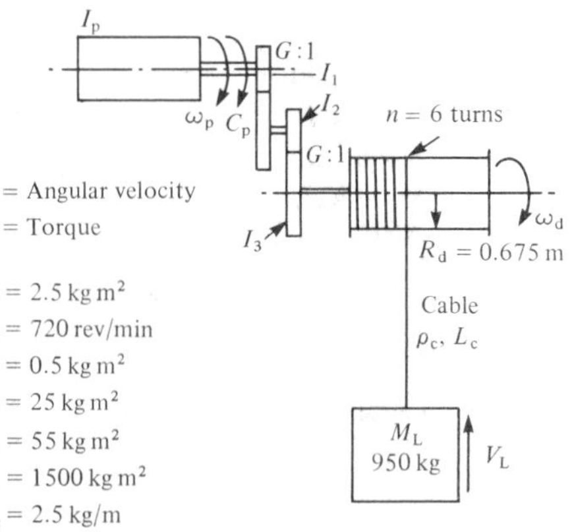

Figure 5.16 Elements of a lift.

SOLUTION

Assuming the gears to be identical, the gear ratio for each is G so that

$$\omega_p = \omega_d G^2$$

but

$$\omega_p = \frac{2\pi \times 720}{60} = 75.4 \text{ rad/s}$$

and

$$\omega_d = \frac{v_L}{R_d} = \frac{0.35}{0.675} = 0.519 \text{ rad/s}$$

Hence

$$G = \sqrt{75.4/0.519} = 12.05$$

Since the moment of inertia of a concentrated mass m at a distance l from an axis is ml^2, it follows that the moment of inertia of the cable about the drum axis is

$$I_c = \rho_c L_c R_d^2 + 2\pi R_d \rho_c n R_d^2$$
$$= R_d^2 \rho_c (L_c + 2\pi n R_d)$$

where n is the number of turns on the drum. Hence

$$I_c = 0.675^2 \times 2.5(75 + 2\pi \times 6 \times 0.675)$$
$$= 114.4 \text{ kg m}^2$$

and the moment of inertia of the lift about the drum axis is

$$I_L = M_L R_d^2 = 950 \times 0.675^2 = 432.8 \text{ kg m}^2$$

Solution Cont.

Hence the total moment of inertia about the drum axis is

$$I = I_d + I_c + I_L + I_3$$
$$= 1500 + 114.4 + 432.8 + 55$$
$$= 2102.2 \text{ kg m}^2$$

The moment of inertia referred to the intermediate shaft is

$$I_{e2} = I_2 + I/G^2$$
$$= 25 + 2102.2/12.05^2$$
$$= 39.48 \text{ kg m}^2$$

The moment of inertia referred to the input shaft is

$$I_{ep} = I_p + I_1 + I_{e2}/G^2$$
$$= 2.5 + 0.5 + 39.48/12.05^2$$
$$= 3.27 \text{ kg m}^2$$

For a constant acceleration of 0.1g = 0.981 m/s² the angular acceleration of the drum is

$$\alpha_d = \frac{0.981}{0.675} = 1.45 \text{ rad/s}^2$$

Hence the acceleration at the prime mover shaft will be

$$\alpha_p = 1.45 \times G^2 = 1.45 \times 12.05^2$$
$$= 210.54 \text{ rad/s}^2$$

The torque required consists of two parts: (a) the torque to accelerate the system given by $I_{ep}\alpha_p$ and

Solution Cont.

(b) the torque to overcome the weight of the cage given by $M_L g R_d / G^2$; hence the need for a counterweight. Thus the total torque C_p is given by

$$C_p = 3.27 \times 210.54 + 950 \times 9.81 \times 0.675/12.05^2$$
$$= 688.47 + 43.32 = 731.79 \text{ N m}$$

Solution Cont.

The work done by a couple is defined as the product of the torque and the angular displacement, i.e. $U = C\theta$ (see section 5.2.2), and the power, $P = \mathrm{d}U/\mathrm{d}t = C\omega$. Hence with an overall efficiency $\eta = 0.97 \times 0.98 = 0.95$, the power required P is

$$P = C_p\omega_p/\eta = 731.79 \times 75.4/0.95$$
$$= 58 \text{ kW}$$

Figure 5.17 shows the geared system, referred to as an *actuator,* used in the space shuttle *Orbiter* to operate the linkages of the payload bay doors (see section 3.9). The actuator consists of two 400 Hz, 115 V three-phase motors, rotating at about 11 000 rev/min. Each motor drives through a differential, a torque limiter and spur gears to provide the required output torque and rotational rate. The actuator output torques vary from 2.11 N m to 2528 N m and gear ratios vary from approximately 250:1 to 32 000:1.

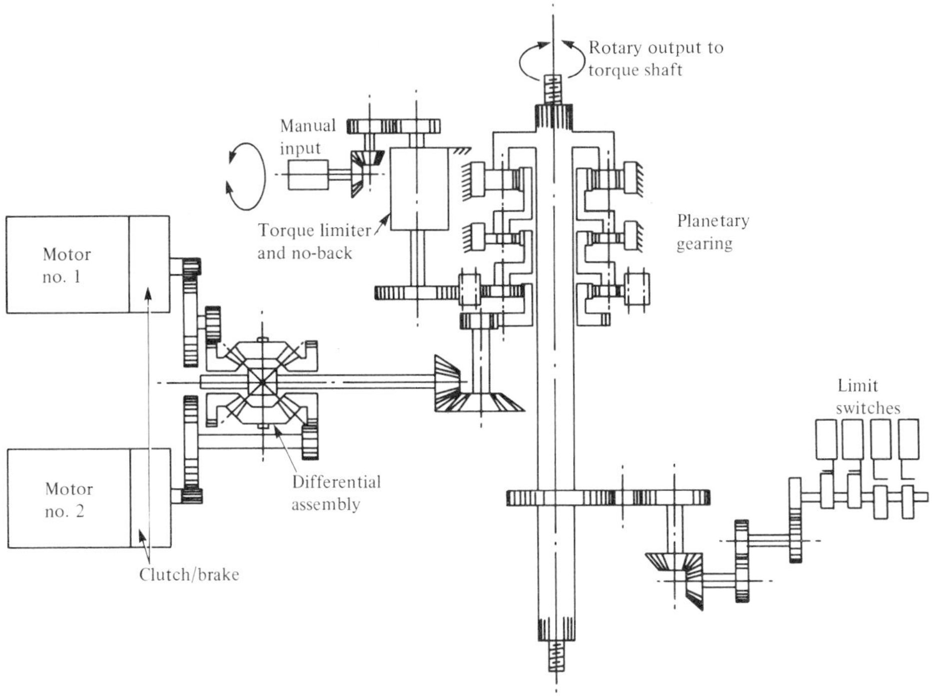

Figure 5.17 Typical actuator (schematic) of space shuttle *Orbiter.*

5.2.2 **Work and power**

Consider pure rotation of a rigid body as a result of a torque C applied to it. Let it rotate by an amount $\Delta\theta$ in a time Δt. Then the work done ΔU is defined to be

$$\Delta U = C\Delta\theta \text{ N m or J}$$

and the total work done U will be

$$U = U\int C \, d\theta \tag{5.16}$$

If the body is rotating about an axis through the centre of mass G, we know from equation (5.9) that

$$I_G \alpha = C$$

or

$$I_G \omega \frac{d\omega}{d\theta} = C$$

Separating the variables and integrating between θ_1 and θ_2 yields

$$I_G \int_{\omega_1}^{\omega_2} \omega \, d\omega = \int_{\theta_1}^{\theta_2} C \, d\theta$$

or

$$\tfrac{1}{2} I_G \omega_2^2 - \tfrac{1}{2} I_G \omega_1^2 = \int_{\theta_1}^{\theta_2} C \, d\theta \tag{5.17}$$

Hence the change in rotational kinetic energy is equal to the work done by the resultant couple or torque or moment about G of the external forces on the body.

Thus we may write more simply

$$U_{1\to 2} = \Delta T_{1\to 2}$$

$$\text{work} = \text{change in KE}$$

Power is defined in a previous chapter is the rate of change of work. Hence

$$P = \frac{dU}{dt} = \frac{d}{dt}(C\theta) = C\omega \qquad \omega = \frac{d\theta}{dt}$$

It is also equal to the rate of increase of KE, thus

$$P = \frac{d}{dt}(\tfrac{1}{2} I\omega^2) = I\omega\frac{d\omega}{dt} = I\omega\alpha = C\omega \tag{5.18}$$

We should realise that the torque C is in many cases the resultant of a number of torques acting on the system, i.e. driving torques and friction torques.

In the case of a rigid body in translation and rotation, such as that shown in Figure 5.1, the work–energy equation for a displacement from some position 1 to another position 2 becomes

$$\int_{1\to 2} X \, dx + \int_{1\to 2} Y \, dy + \int_{1\to 2} C \, d\theta = \tfrac{1}{2} M u^2 + \tfrac{1}{2} M v^2 + \tfrac{1}{2} I \omega^2$$

where u and v are the velocities of the centre of mass G in the x- and y-directions respectively.

EXAMPLE 5.5

Power from an electric motor running at 1400 rev/min is transmitted by a "Vee" belt from a pulley of 120 mm mean diameter to a pulley of 325 mm mean diameter, the centre distance between them being 475 mm. The angle of the groove is 40° and the coefficient of friction is 0.35. If the tension in the belt is limited to 450 N calculate (a) the power transmitted, neglecting the mass of the belt, and (b) the power transmitted, taking into account the mass of the belt, which is 0.2 kg/m.

SOLUTION

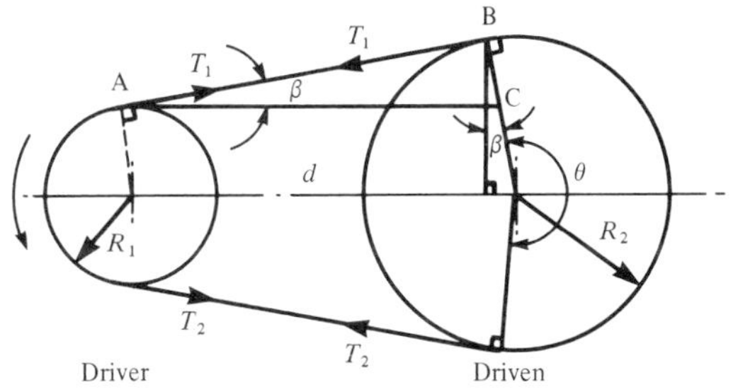

Figure 5.18 Power transmission using pulleys and belt.

We must first determine the angle of lap θ. Referring to Figure 5.18 we have

$$\frac{BC}{AC} = \sin\beta$$

i.e.

$$\frac{R_2 - R_1}{d} = \sin\beta = \sin\left(\frac{\theta}{2} - 90°\right)$$
$$= \cos\frac{\theta}{2}$$

Hence

$$\cos\frac{\theta}{2} = \frac{325 - 120}{2 \times 475} = 0.22$$

which means that $\theta = 155°$ or 2.706 rad. Referring to section 4.2.4, we have the following:

(a) Neglecting the mass of the belt,

$$\mu' = 0.35/\sin 20° = 1.023$$

Hence

$$\frac{T_1}{T_2} = e^{1.023 \times 2.706} = 15.93$$

Since $T_1 \ngtr 450$ N we find

$$T_2 = 450/15.93 = 28.25 \text{ N}$$
$$\omega = \frac{2\pi \times 1400}{60}$$
$$= 146.6 \text{ rad/s}$$

$$\text{Power transmitted} = (T_1 - T_2)R\omega$$
$$= (450 - 28.25) \times 0.06 \times 146.6$$
$$= 3.71 \text{ kW}$$

(b) Including the mass of the belt,

$$\rho\omega^2R^2 = 0.2 \times 146.6^2 \times 0.06^2 = 15.48 \text{ N}$$

Taking the mass of the belt into account we find

$$\frac{T_1 - 15.48}{T_2 - 15.48} = 15.93$$

Solving for T_2 yields

$$T_2 = \frac{450 - 15.48}{15.93} + 15.48 = 42.76 \text{ N}$$

$$\text{Power transmitted} = (T_1 - T_2)R\omega$$
$$= (450 - 42.76) \times 0.06 \times 146.6$$
$$= 3.58 \text{ kW}$$

a reduction of 3.5%.

5.2.3 The flywheel

As an important illustration of the work–energy equation (5.17) we propose to consider the need for a flywheel in machines.

The flywheel in its simplest form consists of a heavy disc rotating at a particular speed. It has two important practical applications:

(1) As a source of power. Vehicles powered by the energy stored in flywheels have been used successfully, particularly in Germany and Switzerland, e.g. public transport vehicles. France recently introduced a stand-by generator set which uses the energy stored in a flywheel. To reduce frictional losses in these applications the flywheel runs in an atmosphere of helium or hydrogen.

The proposed trolley buses of San Francisco shown in Figure 5.19 are an example of the flywheel as a source of power. These buses will use the energy stored in a 1500 kg flywheel rotating at 12 000 rev/min to transport 80 passengers from one end of the town to the other (a distance of 10 km). At one terminus M/D1 acting as a motor will transform electrical energy picked up from the overhead wires to kinetic energy of the flywheel. When the electrical supply is disconnected the stored energy is used to drive M/D1, working as a dynamo, to supply electrical energy to M/D2, working as a motor, to drive the wheels. During braking and when going downhill M/D2 works as a dynamo and supplies current to M/D1, now a motor, to increase the kinetic energy of the flywheel. With this process two-thirds of the energy required to climb hills is recovered when going downhill. The overall efficiency of this system is close to 70%.

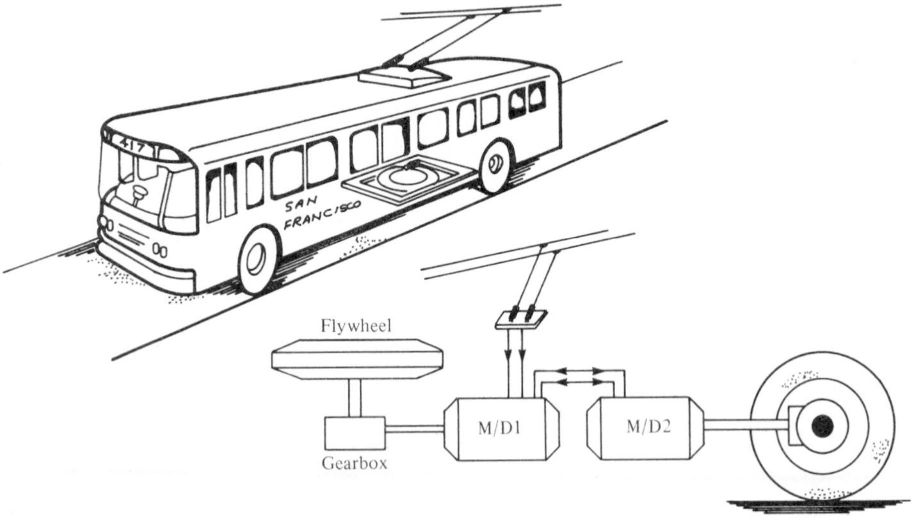

Figure 5.19 San Francisco trolley bus and flywheel system.

(2) As a means of controlling the speed fluctuations in prime movers and/or loads.

It is this latter aspect that we shall consider in what follows.

In case (2) the flywheel is a device used to store energy during part of the cycle of a machine and to give up energy during the other part of the cycle. It is in fact a reservoir of energy, the level of which fluctuates according to demand.

An examination of the elements of a car, for example, will reveal a flywheel usually positioned between the engine and the gearbox. Similarly we shall find a flywheel in punching machines, and the turntable of a record player acts as a flywheel to ensure a constant speed.

To assess the need for a flywheel let us consider a typical system consisting of a prime mover driving a load as shown diagrammatically in Figure 5.20.

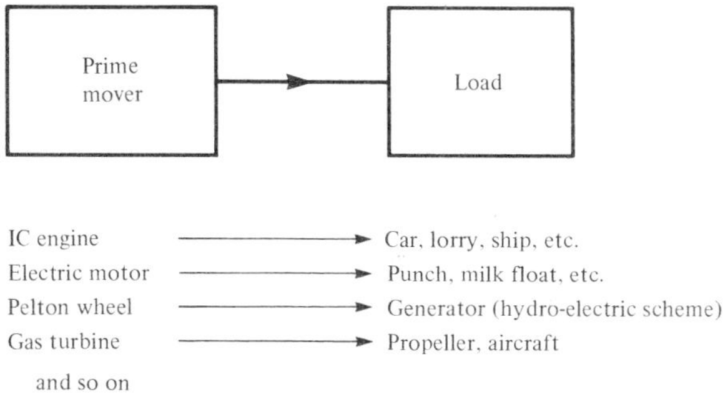

Figure 5.20 Typical systems of prime movers and loads.

The prime mover and the load have their own characteristics during one cycle of operation. A diesel engine delivers a torque that is constantly fluctuating whereas that of a DC shunt-wound electric motor is practically constant. A punching machine requires a variable torque whereas a centrifugal pump working against a constant head requires a constant torque.

When a prime mover is coupled to a load there will be times when the torque exceeds that demanded by the load, and other times when it will fall short. Consequently the mean speed of such a system will fluctuate, and the magnitude of the fluctuations will depend on the inertia of the system. From a practical point of view they can be unacceptably large, and so to limit them, and thereby improve performance, a flywheel is introduced into the system, usually between the prime mover and the load.

The flywheel takes the form of a heavy metal disc and in many designs the bulk of its mass is concentrated at the rim, for reasons that will become apparent later.

To illustrate the way the torque delivered by a prime mover varies during one cycle of operation, we shall consider the case of a single-cylinder four-stroke engine. The torque delivered by such an engine while rotating at a mean speed ω_0 is shown, together with the corresponding speed fluctuation during the cycle, in Figure 5.21. The speed ω_0 is in fact the matching point discussed in section 4.3, when the engine is driving a particular load.

An examination of the torque T versus crank angle θ shows that the torque fluctuates considerably during one cycle of operation. In this case one cycle is 720° or two revolutions of the crankshaft.

The torque delivered by the engine is equivalent to a mean torque T_m given by

$$T_m = \frac{1}{\theta_2 - \theta_1}\int_{\theta_1}^{\theta_2} T\,d\theta = \frac{1}{4\pi}\int_0^{4\pi} T\,d\theta \qquad (5.19)$$

and this must be equal to the mean torque demanded by the load at ω_0.

Consider two points during the cycle, one at R and one at E. At R the load demand is PR $(= T_m)$ but the torque available is $-$RQ, i.e. there is a deficiency in the torque at PQ, and consequently, since $T = I\dot{\omega}$ (where I is the moment of inertia of the system, load and prime mover) it follows that the speed of the system will decrease.

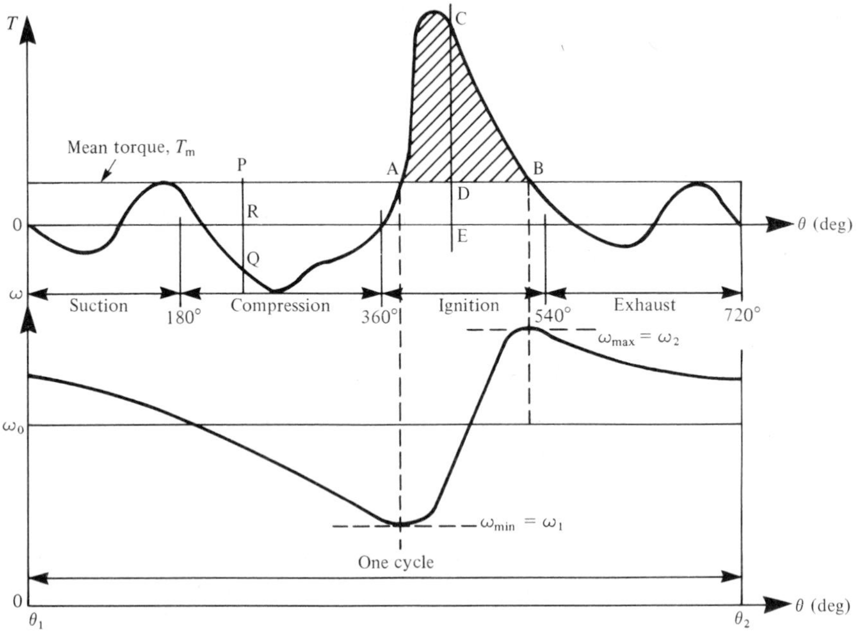

Figure 5.21 Torque delivered by an engine, compared with speed of rotation.

At E the torque demand is DE ($= T_m$) and the torque available is CE. Hence there is an excess torque CD, and the speed will increase. Looking at the entire cycle we see that the speed will have some minimum value ω_1 at A and a maximum value ω_2 at B. This speed fluctuation about the mean value ω_0 will occur during every cycle, and since ω_0 is usually hundreds of revolutions per minute this fluctuation takes place in a very short space of time.

We see, therefore, from the T versus θ relationship that between A and B there is an excess torque, and hence an excess amount of work or energy. This energy can be stored until it is needed by a flywheel, which is a rotating device having a large moment of inertia compared with that of the prime mover and load.

The excess energy ΔE at any instant is given by

$$\Delta E = \int_A^B (T - T_m)\,d\theta$$

$$= \tfrac{1}{2}I(\omega_2^2 - \omega_1^2)$$

by equation (5.17). If the speed fluctuation is small compared with ω_0 (as it usually is in practice), then we may write

$$\omega_0 \simeq (\omega_1 + \omega_2)/2$$

so that

$$\Delta E = \Delta T = I(\omega_2 - \omega_1)(\omega_1 + \omega_2)/2$$

$$= I\omega_0(\omega_2 - \omega_1)$$

$$= I\omega_0\Delta\omega$$

Let K_s be the coefficient of fluctuation of speed defined by

$$K_s = \frac{\omega_2 - \omega_1}{\omega_0} = \frac{\Delta\omega}{\omega_0}$$

then

$$\Delta E = K_s I \omega_0^2 \qquad (5.20)$$

The design of the flywheel is based on acceptable values for the coefficient of fluctuation of speed. Typical values are given below:

agricultural machines	$K_s = 0.05\ (\pm 2.5\%)$
weaving machines	$K_s = 0.01\text{–}0.02$
generators	$K_s = 0.006\ (\pm 0.3\%)$

If I_s is the moment of inertia of the system (prime mover plus load) and I_f is the moment of inertia of the flywheel, then I in (5.20) is

$$I = I_f + I_s$$

Hence for a given prime mover–load system rotating with angular speed ω_0, and with a specified coefficient of fluctuation K_s, the required moment of inertia is obtained from

$$I_f + I_s = \frac{\Delta E}{K_s \omega_0^2} \quad \text{or} \quad I_f = \frac{\Delta E}{K_s \omega_0^2} - I_s \qquad (5.21)$$

The torque diagram may consist of many loops above and below the mean torque, in which case it is best to tabulate the energy in each loop and hence calculate the excess energy ΔE over the complete cycle.

EXAMPLE 5.6

A press is driven by an electric motor delivering a constant torque. The stroke of the tool is 150 mm and it travels 50 mm in forming the workpiece, during which time the force exerted is constant and 20.4 kJ of work is done. The maximum speed of the flywheel measured at its radius of gyration is 30 m/s and it is specified that this should not fall below 27 m/s during the operation of the press. Calculate the mass of the flywheel and the force exerted by the tool.

SOLUTION

Figure 5.22 illustrates the cycle; the area OABE represents the work done by the motor and CC′D′D the work required for the formation of the workpiece. Hence the work done per cycle is 20 400 J. The mean torque is

$$OA = T_m$$
$$= \frac{20\,400}{\theta_0}\ \text{N m}$$

where θ_0 is the angle turned through by the motor in one cycle. The mean speed is

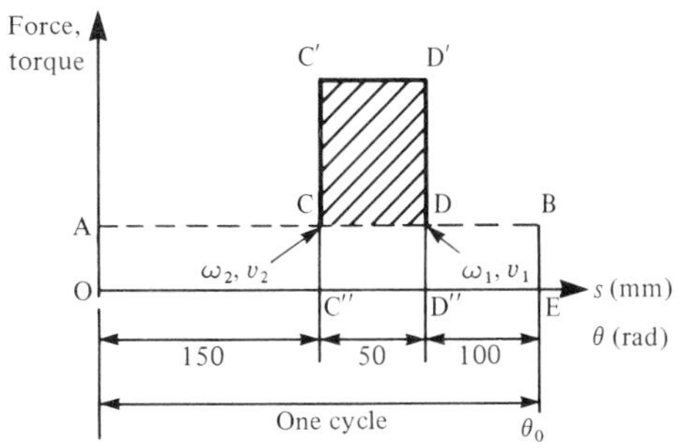

Figure 5.22 Use of the flywheel: the press of example 5.6.

Solution Cont.

$$v_0 = \frac{v_1 + v_2}{2} = \frac{30 + 27}{2} = 28.5 \text{ m/s}$$

The maximum speed occurs at C just before the forming operation and the minimum speed occurs at D at the end of the operation. The force exerted by the tool during the forming operation is 20 400/0.05 = 408 kN.

The work done by the motor between C and D, i.e. during 50/300 = 1/6 of the cycle, is given by

$$U_{CD} = \frac{\theta_0}{6} T_m = 20\,400/6 = 3400 \text{ J}$$
$$= 3.4 \text{ kJ}$$

Hence the net work,

$$\Delta E = -(20.4 - 3.4) = -17 \text{ kJ}$$

It is negative since the demand exceeds that available.

Solution Cont.

$$\Delta E = \tfrac{1}{2}I(\omega_2^2 - \omega_1^2)$$
$$= \tfrac{1}{2}Mk^2(\omega_2 + \omega_1)(\omega_2 - \omega_1)$$

where $\omega_0 = (\omega_2 + \omega_1)/2$ and $\Delta\omega = \omega_2 - \omega_1$. But radius of gyration. Hence

$$\Delta E = M(k\omega_0)(k\Delta\omega)$$

where $\omega_0 = (\omega_2 + \omega_1)/2$ and $\Delta\omega = \omega_2 - \omega_1$. But $k\omega_0 = 28.5$ m/s and $k\Delta\omega = 3$ m/s, since the mass can be considered to be concentrated at a radius k. Thus solving for M yields

$$M = \frac{17\,000}{28.5 \times 3} = 198.8 \text{ kg}$$

(*Note:* The deficiency in energy, area CC′D′D, is equal to the surplus energy, area OACC″ + area DBED″. The latter is

$$T_m \frac{5\theta_0}{6} = \frac{20\,400}{\theta_0} \times \frac{5\theta_0}{6} = 17\,000 \text{ J} = 17 \text{ kJ})$$

5.2.4 **Impulse and momentum**

Consider once again equations (5.9)

$$M\ddot{\bar{x}} = X$$
$$M\ddot{\bar{y}} = Y$$
$$I_G\ddot{\theta} = M_G \text{ or } C$$

Replacing the accelerations by dv_x/dt, dv_y/dt and $d\omega/dt$ respectively, separating the variables and integrating yields

$$Mv_{x2} - Mv_{x1} = \int_{t_1}^{t_2} X\,dt$$
$$Mv_{y2} - Mv_{y1} = \int_{t_1}^{t_2} Y\,dt \qquad (5.22)$$
$$I_G\omega_2 - I_G\omega_1 = \int_{t_1}^{t_2} C\,dt$$

For the motion of translation we see that the change in linear momentum is equal to the linear impulse, as it is for the motion of a particle.

For rotation, the product $I\omega$ is defined as the angular momentum and $\int C\,dt$ as the angular impulse, so that the change in the angular momentum is equal to the angular impulse. To carry out the integration C must be a constant or a known function of time.

The three equations of motion for a rigid body can be written in the form

$$X = \frac{\mathrm{d}}{\mathrm{d}t}(Mv_x) = \frac{\mathrm{d}}{\mathrm{d}t}(P_x)$$
$$Y = \frac{\mathrm{d}}{\mathrm{d}t}(Mv_y) = \frac{\mathrm{d}}{\mathrm{d}t}(P_y) \quad (5.23)$$
$$C = \frac{\mathrm{d}}{\mathrm{d}t}(I_G\omega) = \frac{\mathrm{d}}{\mathrm{d}t}(H)$$

where H is the angular momentum $I\omega$.

EXAMPLE 5.7

The drum of a winch in an overhead travelling crane lifts a 350 kg load from rest to a speed of 0.3 m/s in 1.5 s under a constant torque from an electric motor through a 95 to 1 reduction. The drum has a radius of 0.2 m and a moment of inertia of 45 kg m^2. Calculate the torque required at the drum and hence at the motor, neglecting friction.

SOLUTION

This problem is best solved by a direct application of the angular momentum equation.

The moment of inertia at the drum axis is given by

$$I = I_d + MR^2$$

where M is the mass of the load, R the radius of the drum and I_d the moment of inertia of the drum. If C_d is the torque at the drum then by equation (5.22)

$$I\omega_2 - I\omega_1 = \int_0^t (C_d - MgR)\,\mathrm{d}t$$

Here Mg is the weight of the load, ω_2 is the final angular velocity of the drum, and $\omega_1 = 0$ its initial angular velocity. Since the torque is constant we have

$$I\omega_2 = (C_d - MgR)t \quad (5.24)$$

Solving for C_d gives

$$C_d = \frac{I\omega_2}{t} + MgR$$
$$= \frac{(45 + 350 \times 0.2^2)}{1.5} \times \frac{0.3}{0.2} + 350 \times 9.81 \times 0.2$$
$$= 745 \text{ N m}$$

and the motor torque

$$C_p = 745/95 = 7.84 \text{ N m}$$

Equation (5.24) could have been obtained by considering the drum and load separately and applying the linear momentum equation to the load and the angular momentum equation to the drum. Each equation would contain the tension in the cable and by elimination equation (5.24) would result.

GYROSCOPIC EFFECTS 5.3

5.3.1 Gyroscopic equation

Although we are not studying the motion of a rigid body in space in this chapter we will consider a special case which does not require an advanced knowledge of dynamics. It concerns the simple application of gyroscopic motion to a variety of engineering problems.

The reader is asked to accept the fact that moments, like forces, can be treated as vector quantities, with magnitude and direction, and that angular velocity, like velocity, may similarly be treated as a vector quantity. Furthermore, moments and angular velocities can be represented by directed arrows in accordance with the right-hand, or corkscrew, rule.

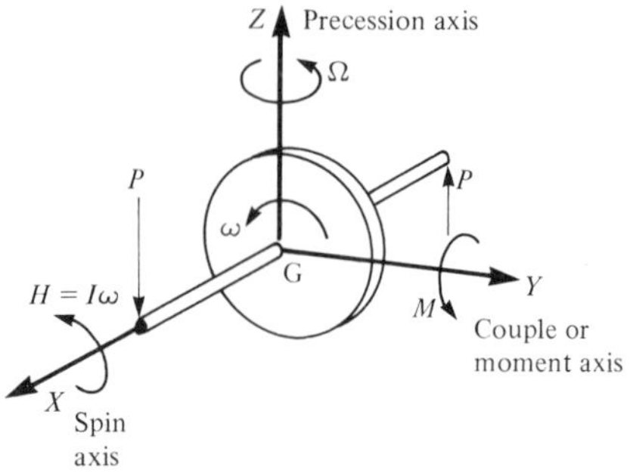

Figure 5.23 The gyroscope.

Figure 5.23 shows a simple gyroscope consisting of a disc rotating with an angular velocity ω about an axis GX through its centre of mass G. If I is the moment of inertia about GX then the angular momentum vector **H**, of magnitude $I\omega$, is directed along GX.

When a moment of magnitude M is applied to the disc by the two equal and opposite forces P, for example, then we find that the disc will rotate about the axis GZ with an angular velocity $\boldsymbol{\Omega}$. This motion is referred to as precession. In practice this can be observed if the disc is mounted in such a way that it is free to take up any position. This is achieved by mounting it in gimbals.

Thus we have three mutually perpendicular axes: GX the angular momentum axis, called the spin axis; the couple or moment axis GY; and the precession axis GZ.

To explain this strange behaviour we will consider two positions of the disc, one at time t and another one at time $t + \Delta t$ and use the angular momentum equation. Let M be the external moment applied, H the angular momentum and $\boldsymbol{\Omega}$ the precession rate. The momentum equation (5.23) states that

$$M = \frac{\mathrm{d}}{\mathrm{d}t}(H) = \frac{\mathrm{d}}{\mathrm{d}t}(I\omega)$$

We can rewrite this equation for a small interval of time Δt as follows

$$M\Delta t = \Delta(I\omega)$$

i.e. the angular impulse is equal to the change in angular momentum. Referring to Figure 5.24, which is a plan view of the disc, then at time t the angular momentum $I\omega$ is along GX; at time $t + \Delta t$ the spin axis has moved through an angle $\Delta\phi$ about GZ into the position shown. Hence the change in the angular momentum $\Delta H = \Delta(I\omega)$ is a vector at right angles to the spin axis, so that this change $\Delta H = I\omega\Delta\phi$. But $\Delta\phi$ is a small angle and since $M\Delta t = I\omega\Delta\phi$ it follows that dividing by Δt and letting $\Delta t \to 0$ we find

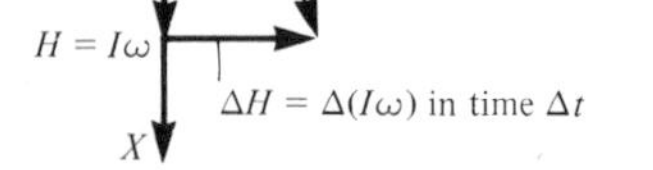

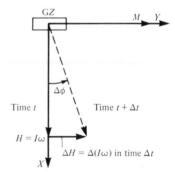

Figure 5.24 Precession.

$$M = I\omega\frac{\mathrm{d}\phi}{\mathrm{d}t} = I\omega\Omega \tag{5.25}$$

where $\boldsymbol{\Omega}$ is the precession rate and M is referred to as the gyroscopic moment or gyroscopic couple.

5.3.2 **Effects of precession in practice**

The reader will no doubt be aware that the gyroscope is used extensively in navigation because once spinning at a high speed (10 000 to 20 000 rev/min) the rotor of the gyroscope will maintain a given orientation in space. In actual fact the gyroscope drifts a little because of friction and lack of complete balance, and has to be reset after a certain time. For precision gyroscopes typical values of the drift rate and rotor eccentricity are 0.1°/h and 2×10^{-5} mm respectively.

One other important aspect of precession is its effect on the bearings of machines and behaviour of vehicles. For example, when a ship is moving in a circular path, the rotors of the turbines are forced to precess, and thereby incline the ship so that the bow is raised when turning to one side, and lowered when turning to the other. The bearings of the turbines will also be affected, because there will be greater pressure on some than on others.

Consider a car with a fore-and-aft engine on a bend as shown in Figure 5.25. Let v be the velocity, and ω the angular velocity of the engine, whose moment of inertia is I, rotating clockwise when viewed from the rear, and let R be the radius of the bend. The procedure to work out the effect of precession on the car is as follows:

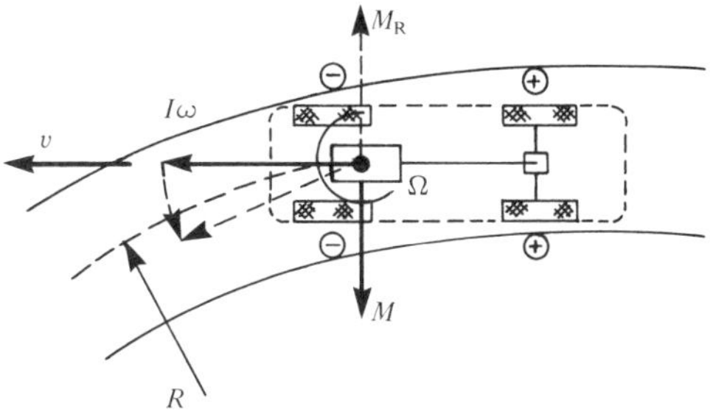

Figure 5.25 Car with fore-and-aft engine on a bend.

(1) Draw the vector $I\omega$.

(2) Since the direction taken is known, Ω is also known and is equal to v/R.

(3) If the rotor were free to precess the moment M to be applied would be as shown; the direction is easily obtained by drawing the change in $I\omega$ which takes place in the direction of Ω.

(4) Since the rotor is not in fact free, but forced to precess, it reacts against M by an equal and opposite moment M_R. This moment acts on the bearings of the engine and, hence, is transmitted to the car, increasing the pressure on the rear wheels and decreasing it on the front wheels.

If the car had a transverse engine rotating anticlockwise when viewed from the near side and making a left-hand bend the reader should verify that the pressure will increase on the offside wheels, in other words the car would tilt to the right and add to the inertia force due to the centripetal acceleration as the car goes round the circular bend.

EXAMPLE 5.8

A rider and his motorbike have a total mass of 180 kg and are moving at 80 km/h on a left-hand bend of 75 m radius. The mass of each wheel is 11.5 kg concentrated at a radius of 0.3 m, the moment of inertia of the engine is 0.12 kg m^2 and the overall gear ratio is 4.5. Calculate the gyroscopic effect on bike and rider. The rolling radius of each wheel is 0.34 m.

SOLUTION

In this case the wheels constitute the rotors and can be lumped together. Taking into account the moment of inertia of the engine, the total moment of inertia of an "equivalent rotor" rotating at the speed of the wheels is

$$I = 2 \times 11.5 \times 0.3^2 + 4.5^2 \times 0.12$$
$$= 4.5 \text{ kg m}^2$$

The angular velocity of the "rotor",

$$\omega = \frac{80}{3.6} \times \frac{1}{0.34} = 65.36 \text{ rad/s}$$

The precession rate

$$\Omega = \frac{V}{R} = \frac{80}{3.6 \times 75} = 0.296 \text{ rad/s}$$

Hence the gyroscopic couple

$$M = 4.5 \times 65.36 \times 0.296 = 87 \text{ N m}$$

acting clockwise on the rider and bike when seen from the rear, i.e. it is an overturning moment which the sketch in Figure 5.26 demonstrates.

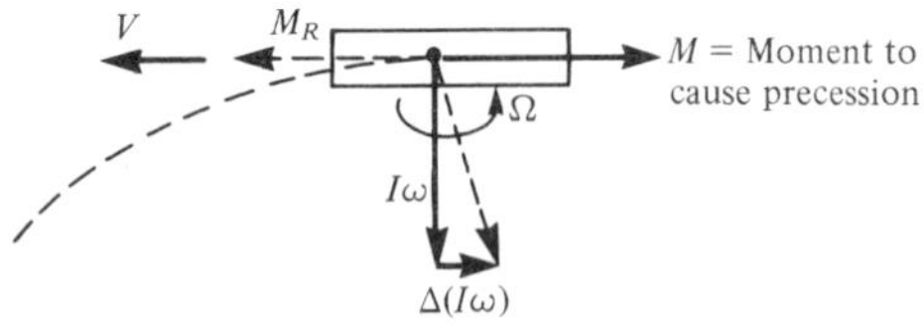

Figure 5.26 Overturning moment acting in example 5.8.

To this must be added the centripetal effect. If the height of the combined centre of mass is 0.70 m above the road and the rider cannot tilt the machine more than 40° inwards calculate the maximum allowable speed.

Figure 5.27 shows the free body diagram. F is the force inwards created by friction between the wheel and the road surface, N the normal reaction and Mg the weight. Taking moments about G,

$$Fh \cos \alpha - Nh \sin \alpha = 0$$

Solution Cont.

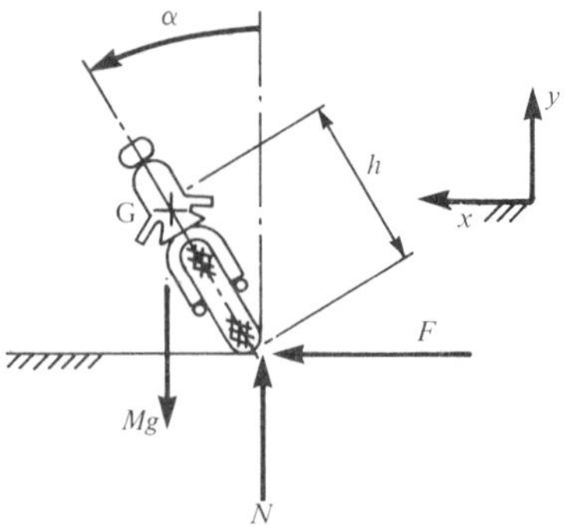

Figure 5.27 Free body diagram for motorbike and rider of example 5.8.

since $\ddot{\alpha} = 0$. Resolving the forces vertically,

$$N - Mg = 0$$

since $\ddot{y} = 0$.

Because the rider and bike are on a curved path

$$F = m\ddot{x} = \frac{Mv^2}{R}$$

where v is the allowable speed. Hence substituting in the moment equation and adding the gyroscopic couple M_G we have

$$M\frac{hv^2}{R} \cos \alpha + M_G = Mgh \sin \alpha$$

But

$$M_G = I\omega\Omega = I\frac{v}{r}\frac{v}{R} = \frac{Iv^2}{rR}$$

where r is the rolling radius of the wheel. Substituting in the above equation and solving for v gives

$$v = \sqrt{\frac{MghR \sin \alpha}{Mh \cos \alpha + I/r}}$$

$$= \sqrt{\frac{180 \times 9.81 \times 0.70 \times 75 \times \sin 40°}{180 \times 0.70 \times \cos 40° + 4.5/0.34}}$$

$$= 23 \text{ m/s or } 83.9 \text{ km/h}$$

The reader should verify that the gyroscopic couple is 13.7% of the centripetal couple.

EXERCISES

5.1 A flywheel of mass 1000 kg has a radius of gyration of 1.1 m. It is carried on a shaft 80 mm in diameter, at the circumference of which a constant tangential force of 1200 N opposes the rotation of the flywheel. If the flywheel is rotating at 120 rev/min, how long will it take to come to rest, and how many turns will it make in doing so?

5.2 A flywheel is supported on a shaft of radius r and the moment of inertia of the system is I about the shaft axis. A rope of negligible thickness is wound round the shaft and supports a mass M hanging vertically. Obtain an expression for the angular acceleration of the flywheel when its motion is opposed by a constant frictional couple C.

If the rope is released from the shaft after the flywheel has turned through an angle A from rest, and if the flywheel turns through a further angle B before it is brought to rest by the frictional couple, show that

$$C = \frac{IMgrA}{IA + (I + Mr^2)B}$$

5.3 A motorcycle engine develops a torque of 20 N m at 1800 rev/min. The speed reduction from the engine to the rear wheel is 9 to 1 in second gear and the efficiency of transmission is 88%. The mass of the machine and rider is 185 kg and the rolling and wind resistance at the corresponding road speed amounts to 90 N. The moment of inertia of the road wheels is 2.16 kg m^2 and of the engine parts is 0.08 kg m^2. The effective diameter of the driving wheel is 650 mm. Calculate the road speed and the acceleration of the motorcycle under the above conditions.

5.4 Figure 5.28 shows a truck being hauled up an incline with an acceleration a by means of a winch. Draw a free body diagram for each element of the system showing clearly all the forces. The truck has a mass M, the counterweight a mass m, the radius of the winch is R, the total resistance to the motion of the truck is F and the frictional torque at the bearings of the winch is f. If the winch provides a constant torque C, and has a moment of inertia I, show that the acceleration of the truck is given by

$$a = \frac{C - f + R(mg - F - Mg\sin\theta)}{I + R^2(M + m)}R$$

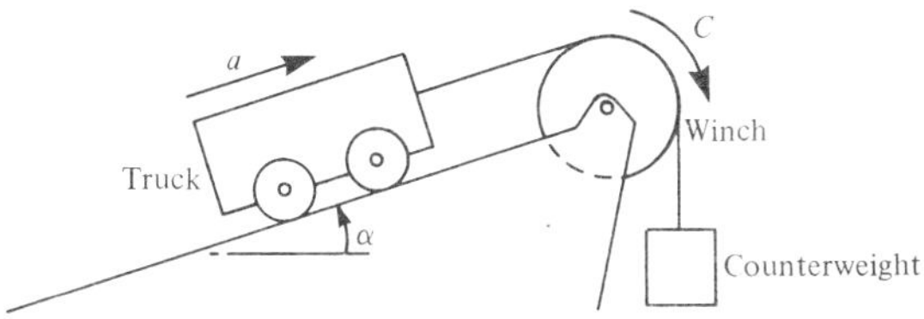

Figure 5.28

5.5 An electric motor drives a load through a 50:1 reduction gearbox. The torque developed by the motor is constant but that of the load is given by $40 + 23\omega_L$ N m, where ω_L is the speed of the load in rad/s. The moment of inertia of the motor is 0.005 kg m^2 and that of the load is 56 kg m^2, including an allowance for the gears. By considering motion at the motor shaft calculate the time taken for the system to reach full speed, if the overall efficiency is 65%. The motor is rated at 500 W at its full speed of 1425 rev/min.

5.6 Referring to exercise 5.5, calculate the time taken for the system to reach its full speed if a different motor is used whose torque available at the shaft is given by $2.75 - 0.003\,82\omega_{\text{motor}}$ N m.

5.7 A hoist used on a building site consists of a trolley running on inclined rails as shown in Figure 5.29; its platform AB carries a maximum load of 125 kg. The trolley is designed in such a way that the wheels are always in contact with the rails.

The trolley has a mass of 15 kg and its platform a mass of 7 kg; AB = 1 m. The trolley and its load are lifted by a motor driving a drum D through a double reduction.

The moments of inertia are: 0.075 kg m^2 for the motor, 2 kg m^2 for C and 12 kg m^2 for the drum D.

If the motor delivers a constant torque of 25 N m calculate (a) the acceleration of the loaded trolley, and (b) the bending moment at the root A of the platform, assuming that the weight is concentrated half-way along the platform.

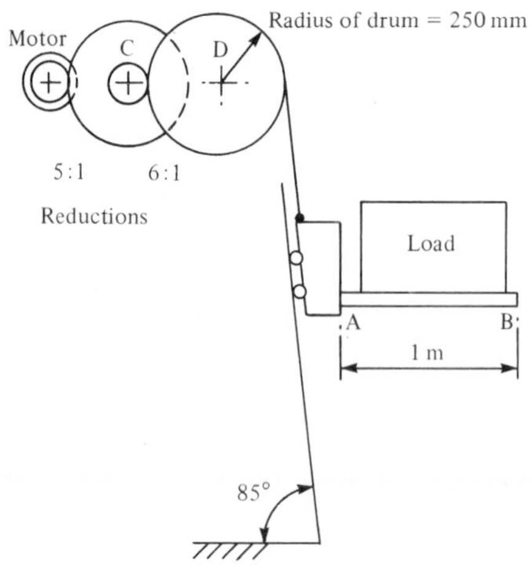

Figure 5.29

5.8 A car has a mass of 1250 kg; each of the four wheels has an effective diameter of 750 mm and a moment of inertia of 1.65 kg m^2. The rotating parts of the engine have a moment of inertia of 0.32 kg m^2. At the instant when the car is travelling at 25 km/h in second gear, which gives a 20:1 reduction, its acceleration is 3 m/s^2. Calculate the torque developed by the engine. The resistance to motion is $(200 + 0.45\,v^2)$ N where v is in m/s.

5.9 A prime mover delivers a mean torque of 150 N m at a mean speed of 1200 rev/min to a load. The energy fluctuations during one cycle measured above and below the mean torque line are: +400 J, −850 J, +800 J, −300 J, +200 J, −250 J. The prime mover and its load have a moment of inertia of 0.50 kg m^2. If the speed is to be maintained to ±2% of the mean, will a flywheel be required? If so what should its moment of inertia be? Calculate also the power delivered to the load.

5.10 The wheelbase of a car is 2.85 m, the height of the centre of mass is 0.6 m above the level of the road and the rear axle is 1.2 m behind the centre of mass. If the car is travelling along a level road at 50 km/h, calculate the minimum distance in which the car may be stopped when (a) the rear wheels are braked, (b) the front wheels are braked and (c) all the wheels are braked, given a coefficient of friction between the tyres and the road of (1) 0.1 and (2) 0.6. If N_1 and N_2 are the normal reactions between the ground and the front and rear wheels respectively, what is the ratio N_1/N_2 for each of these two values when four-wheel brakes are used?

5.11 A car with a fore-and-aft engine rounds a right-hand bend of 50 m radius at a speed of 100 km/h. Show on a diagram which wheel will have its pressure increased or decreased if the engine rotates at 3000 rev/min in a clockwise direction as seen from the front. The moment of inertia of the engine is 3.75 kg m^2 and the wheelbase is 2.75 m. Calculate the gyroscopic couple.

5.12 The wheels of a motorcycle have a moment of inertia of 2 kg m^2 and the engine parts a moment of inertia of 0.1 kg m^2. The axis of rotation of the engine crankshaft is parallel to that of the road wheels. If the gear ratio is 5:1, the diameter of the road wheels is 650 mm and the motorcycle rounds a bend of 30 m radius at a speed of 60 km/h, calculate the magnitude and direction of the gyroscopic couple.

5.13 The rotor of the turbine of a yacht rotates at 1200 rev/min. Its mass is 750 kg and its radius of gyration is 250 mm. If the yacht pitches with a maximum angular velocity of 1 rad/s, what gyroscopic couple will be transmitted to the hull? The turbine rotates clockwise when seen from the stern.

6

Introduction to Spatial Dynamics

6.1 ELEMENTS OF VECTOR CALCULUS

6.1.1 Position vector

Consider any point P in space relative to a fixed point O. To reach P we use a straight line **r** directed from O to P. This is the position vector. If we now take Cartesian axes O*xyz* we can develop the analysis using vector calculus (Figure 6.1). A vector may be expressed conveniently in terms of its components and the three unit vectors **i, j** and **k,** whose directions are those of the axes of the Cartesian frame of reference O*x*, O*y* and O*z*. If *x*, *y* and *z* are the directed lengths of the projections of the vector **r** on these axes, we then have the following vector equation

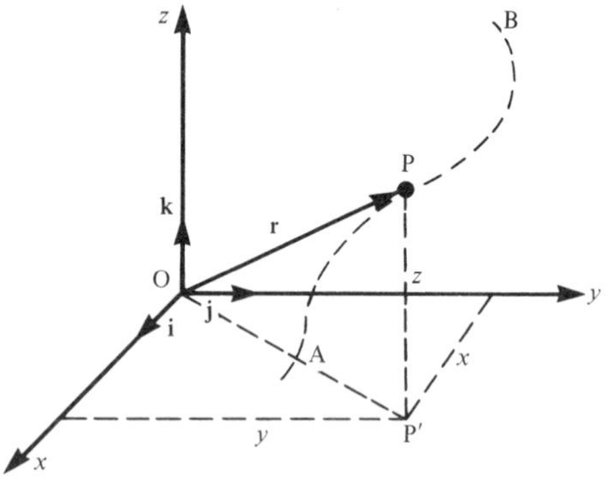

Figure 6.1 Position vector of a point in Cartesian coordinates.

$$\mathbf{r} = x\mathbf{i} + y\mathbf{j} + z\mathbf{k} \quad (6.1)$$

Furthermore if the particle is moving along the space curve AB, *x*, *y* and *z* must be functions of time, i.e.

$$x = x(t) \qquad y = y(t) \qquad z = z(t)$$

Hence the vector equation for the position of the particle at any instant may be written thus

$$\mathbf{r} = x(t)\mathbf{i} + y(t)\mathbf{j} + z(t)\mathbf{k}$$

The magnitude of the position vector **r**, denoted by $|\mathbf{r}|$ or simply r, is

$$r = \sqrt{x^2 + y^2 + z^2}$$

as can easily be verified by considering the length of the projection $(\mathrm{OP}')^2 = x^2 + y^2$: from the triangle OP′P,

$$r^2 = (\mathrm{OP}')^2 + z^2 = x^2 + y^2 + z^2$$

6.1.2 **Differentiation of a vector with respect to a scalar**

Let **A** be any vector representing a position, a displacement, a velocity, a force, etc., which is a function of any scalar quantity u, so that

$$\mathbf{A} = \mathbf{A}(u)$$

Then, as when calculating the derivative of scalar quantities, we find that as u increases to $u + \Delta u$,

$$\mathbf{A} + \Delta\mathbf{A} = \mathbf{A}(u + \Delta u)$$

so that the change $\Delta\mathbf{A}$ in **A**, which may be a change in magnitude or direction, or both, is given by

$$\Delta\mathbf{A} = \mathbf{A}(u + \Delta u) - \mathbf{A}(u)$$

and the average change is

$$\frac{\Delta\mathbf{A}}{\Delta u} = \frac{\mathbf{A}(u + \Delta u) - \mathbf{A}(u)}{\Delta u}$$

The derivative of **A** with respect to the scalar quantity u is defined to be

$$\frac{\mathrm{d}\mathbf{A}}{\mathrm{d}u} = \lim_{\Delta u \to 0} \frac{\mathbf{A}(u + \Delta u) - \mathbf{A}(u)}{\Delta u}$$

In dynamics the scalar quantity is usually the time t.

If the components of **A** are A_x, A_y and A_z in a Cartesian frame of reference, then

$$\mathbf{A} = A_x\mathbf{i} + A_y\mathbf{j} + A_z\mathbf{k}$$

Since **i**, **j** and **k** are constant unit vectors in fixed directions their derivatives are zero, and it follows that

$$\frac{\mathrm{d}\mathbf{A}}{\mathrm{d}u} = \lim_{\Delta u \to 0} \frac{(\mathrm{A}_x + \Delta A_x)\mathbf{i} + (\mathrm{A}_y + \Delta A_y)\mathbf{j} + (\mathrm{A}_z + \Delta A_z)\mathbf{k}}{\Delta u}$$

$$= \frac{\mathrm{d}A_x}{\mathrm{d}u}\mathbf{i} + \frac{\mathrm{d}A_y}{\mathrm{d}u}\mathbf{j} + \frac{\mathrm{d}A_z}{\mathrm{d}u}\mathbf{k} \qquad (6.2)$$

If **A** and **B** are two vectors it is easily verified from the above that the derivative of their sum is

$$\frac{\mathrm{d}}{\mathrm{d}u}(\mathbf{A} + \mathbf{B}) = \frac{\mathrm{d}\mathbf{A}}{\mathrm{d}u} + \frac{\mathrm{d}\mathbf{B}}{\mathrm{d}u}$$

This equation can be extended to any number of vectors.

6.1.3 **Velocity of a particle**

Consider a particle moving along the space curve AB, and suppose it started its journey at A; after a time t it is at P, having covered a distance s = AP along the curve, and its position vector is then $\mathbf{r}$ measured from the origin O of a Newtonian frame of reference with Cartesian axes xyz. At time $t + \Delta t$ it is at P′ after travelling a further distance Δs along the curve and its position vector is now $\mathbf{r} + \Delta\mathbf{r}$, and $\Delta\mathbf{r}$ represents the displacement of the particle in time Δt. Since $\mathbf{r}$ must be a function of the time t we can write

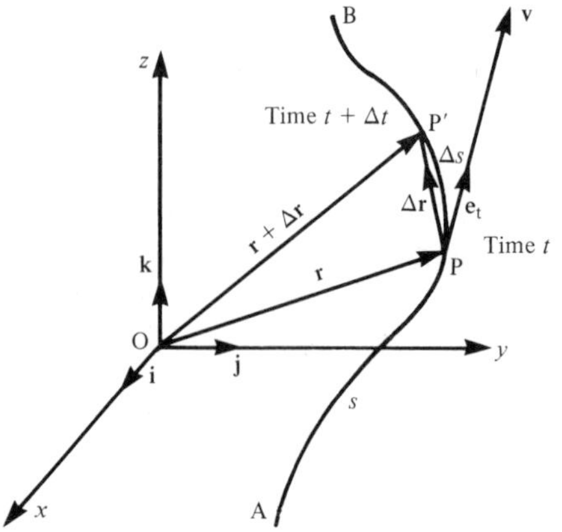

Figure 6.2 Velocity of a particle in Cartesian coordinates.

$$\Delta\mathbf{r} = \mathbf{r}(t + \Delta t) - \mathbf{r}(t)$$

and since velocity is the rate of change of displacement, it follows from section 6.1.2 that

$$\frac{d\mathbf{r}}{dt} = \lim_{\Delta t \to 0} \frac{\Delta r}{\Delta t} = \lim_{\Delta t \to 0} \frac{\mathbf{r}(t + \Delta t) - \mathbf{r}(t)}{\Delta t}$$

is the instantaneous velocity $\mathbf{v}$ of the particle at P, at time t, i.e.

$$\mathbf{v} = \frac{d\mathbf{r}}{dt} = \dot{\mathbf{r}} \tag{6.3}$$

Referring to Figure 6.2, we see that as Δt gets smaller and smaller, P′ gets closer and closer to P, and the vector $\Delta\mathbf{r}/\Delta t$ approaches the direction of the tangent to the curve at P; the velocity vector $\mathbf{v}$ is therefore always a tangent to the curve.

If

$$\mathbf{r} = x\mathbf{i} + y\mathbf{j} + z\mathbf{k}$$

then

$$\dot{\mathbf{r}} = \mathbf{v} = \dot{x}\mathbf{i} + \dot{y}\mathbf{j} + \dot{z}\mathbf{k} \tag{6.4}$$

and the magnitude of the velocity, the speed, is

$$v = \sqrt{\dot{x}^2 + \dot{y}^2 + \dot{z}^2}$$

We can express the velocity vector $\mathbf{v}$ in terms of the displacement s along the curve and a unit vector $\mathbf{e}_t$ tangential to the curve in the following way:

$$\frac{d\mathbf{r}}{dt} = \frac{d\mathbf{r}}{ds}\frac{ds}{dt}$$

where s is a scalar quantity and ds/dt is the speed of the particle at P. From Figure 6.2 we see that the ratio $\Delta\mathbf{r}/\Delta s$ approaches the value unity as Δt tends to zero, and becomes tangential to the curve at P; hence $d\mathbf{r}/ds = \mathbf{e}_t$, a unit vector along the tangent at P.

Thus the velocity vector **v** becomes

$$\mathbf{v} = \frac{ds}{dt}\mathbf{e}_t = \dot{s}\mathbf{e}_t \qquad (6.5)$$

6.1.4 Acceleration of a particle

Consider once again a particle moving along the space curve AB as shown in Figure 6.3. At time t the particle is at P and has a velocity **v**. At time $t + \Delta t$ it is at P′ and its velocity is $\mathbf{v} + \Delta\mathbf{v}$. The acceleration **a** of the particle is defined as the rate of change of velocity **v** with time. Hence

$$\mathbf{a} = \lim_{\Delta t \to 0} \frac{\Delta \mathbf{v}}{\Delta t} = \frac{d\mathbf{v}}{dt} = \dot{\mathbf{v}}$$

Since

$$\mathbf{v} = \dot{x}\mathbf{i} + \dot{y}\mathbf{j} + \dot{z}\mathbf{k}$$

from (6.4) it follows that

$$\mathbf{a} = \dot{\mathbf{v}} = \ddot{x}\mathbf{i} + \ddot{y}\mathbf{j} + \ddot{z}\mathbf{k}$$

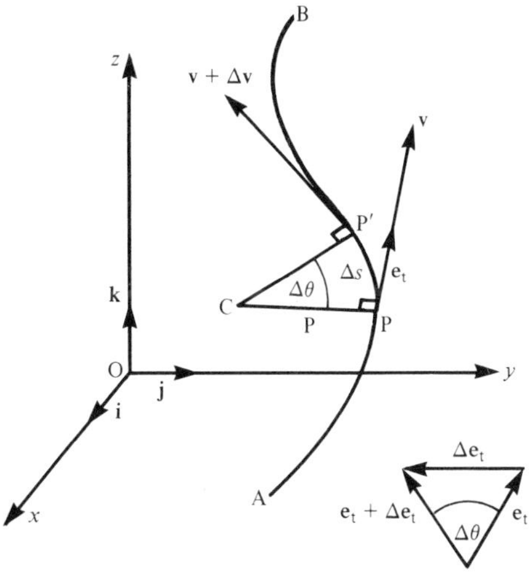

Figure 6.3 Acceleration of a particle in Cartesian coordinates.

It is frequently more convenient to express the acceleration in terms of the normal and tangential components. Consider the inset diagram in Figure 6.3 showing the change in the unit vector $\mathbf{e}_t$ as the particle moves from P to P′ in a time Δt. Let $\Delta\theta$ be the angle between the vectors $\mathbf{e}_t$ and $\mathbf{e}_t + \Delta\mathbf{e}_t$. The change in the magnitude of the unit vector is then

$$\Delta e_t = \left(1 \sin\frac{\Delta\theta}{2}\right) \times 2 \simeq \Delta\theta$$

Also we see that as Δt tends to zero the direction of $\Delta\mathbf{e}_t$ becomes perpendicular to the direction of $\mathbf{e}_t$, so that the derivative of $\mathbf{e}_t$ is

$$\frac{d\mathbf{e}_t}{dt} = \dot{\mathbf{e}}_t = \frac{d\theta}{dt}\mathbf{e}_n \qquad (6.6)$$

where $\mathbf{e}_n$ is a unit vector normal to the curve at P.

Since

$$\mathbf{v} = \dot{s}\mathbf{e}_t$$

differentiation with respect to time yields

$$\mathbf{a} = \dot{\mathbf{v}} = \ddot{s}\mathbf{e}_t + \dot{s}\dot{\mathbf{e}}_t = \ddot{s}\mathbf{e}_t + \dot{s}\frac{d\theta}{dt}\mathbf{e}_n \qquad (6.7)$$

But

$$\frac{d\theta}{dt} = \frac{d\theta}{ds}\frac{ds}{dt} = \frac{1}{\rho}v$$

where ρ is the radius of curvature of the curve at P. Hence

$$\mathbf{a} = \ddot{s}\mathbf{e}_t + \frac{v^2}{\rho}\mathbf{e}_n \tag{6.8}$$

where the first term is the tangential component of acceleration, and the second is the radial or centripetal acceleration directed towards the centre of curvature C.

6.1.5 **Velocity and acceleration of a particle in cylindrical coordinates**

The position of a particle P in space can also be conveniently represented by means of polar coordinates (r, θ) in the xy plane together with the coordinate z parallel to the z-axis, as shown in Figure 6.4. P′ is the projection of P in the xy plane, and its coordinates are r and θ, where $r = \mathrm{OP'}$ and θ is the angle between the x-axis and the radius r in the positive direction shown; z is the vertical distance P′P. Then r, θ and z are referred to as the cylindrical coordinates of P.

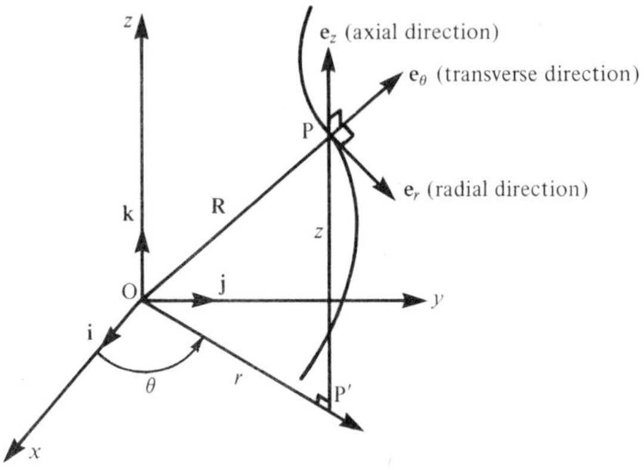

Figure 6.4 Position of a point in cylindrical coordinates.

It is useful to introduce a triad of unit vectors $\mathbf{e}_r$, $\mathbf{e}_\theta$ and $\mathbf{e}_z$ at P as shown, such that $\mathbf{e}_r$ is parallel to the direction of OP′, $\mathbf{e}_\theta$ is perpendicular to OP′ in the direction of θ and $\mathbf{e}_z$ is parallel to the z-axis, i.e. in an axial direction. The position of P is then

$$\mathbf{R} = r\mathbf{e}_r + z\mathbf{e}_z$$

Differentiating with respect to time yields the velocity v

$$\mathbf{v} = \dot{r}\mathbf{e}_r + r\dot{\mathbf{e}}_r + \dot{z}\mathbf{e}_z + z\dot{\mathbf{e}}_z$$

Since $\mathbf{e}_z$ does not change with time in either magnitude or direction, its derivative is zero. Also, by (6.6),

$$\dot{\mathbf{e}}_r = \frac{d\mathbf{e}_r}{d\theta}\frac{d\theta}{dt} = \dot{\theta}\mathbf{e}_\theta$$

Hence

$$\mathbf{v} = \dot{r}\mathbf{e}_r + r\dot{\theta}\mathbf{e}_\theta + \dot{z}\mathbf{e}_z \tag{6.9}$$

For the acceleration we differentiate equation (6.9) with respect to time, obtaining

$$\mathbf{a} = \dot{\mathbf{v}} = \ddot{r}\mathbf{e}_r + \dot{r}\dot{\mathbf{e}}_r + \dot{r}\dot{\theta}\mathbf{e}_\theta + r\ddot{\theta}\mathbf{e}_\theta + r\dot{\theta}\dot{\mathbf{e}}_\theta + \ddot{z}\mathbf{e}_z$$

But

$$\dot{\mathbf{e}}_\theta = \frac{d\dot{\mathbf{e}}_\theta}{d\theta}\frac{d\theta}{dt} = -\mathbf{e}_r\dot{\theta}$$

Hence

$$\mathbf{a} = (\ddot{r} - r\dot{\theta}^2)\mathbf{e}_r + (r\ddot{\theta} + 2\dot{r}\dot{\theta})\mathbf{e}_\theta + \ddot{z}\mathbf{e}_z \tag{6.10}$$

where the first term is the radial acceleration of P′ in the xy plane, the second term is the transverse acceleration of P′ in the xy plane and the third term is the axial acceleration of the particle. The first two terms together represent the accelerations of a particle at P′ in terms of its polar coordinates in the xy plane (see section 2.3.2).

It is sometimes useful to express the transverse acceleration of P′ as follows:

$$\frac{1}{r}\frac{d}{dt}(r^2\dot{\theta}) = r\ddot{\theta} + 2\dot{r}\dot{\theta}$$

6.1.6 **Velocity and acceleration of a particle in spherical coordinates**

The position of a particle P in space may also be defined by means of the position vector **R** and two angles ϕ and θ as shown in Figure 6.5. At P we erect a triad of unit vectors $\mathbf{e}_R$ in the direction of **R**, $\mathbf{e}_\theta$ tangential to the meridian plane OzP and $\mathbf{e}_\phi$ perpendicular to that plane.

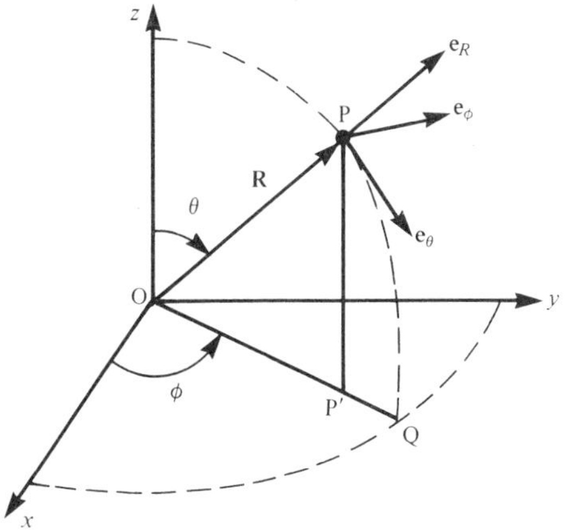

Figure 6.5 Position of a point in spherical coordinates.

Consider the small rotations $\Delta\theta$ and $\Delta\phi$, shown in Figure 6.6, that take place in a time Δt, and the resulting changes in the unit vectors $\Delta\mathbf{e}_R$, $\Delta\mathbf{e}_\theta$ and $\Delta\mathbf{e}_\phi$. From Figure 6.6(a) we have

$$\Delta\mathbf{e}_R = \Delta\theta\mathbf{e}_\theta$$

due to the rotation $\Delta\theta$, i.e. the change in the unit vector $\mathbf{e}_R$ is in the direction of the unit vector $\mathbf{e}_\theta$. Similarly

$$\Delta\mathbf{e}_\theta = -\Delta\theta\mathbf{e}_R$$

Since the magnitude of each vector is unity, from Figure 6.6(b) we have

$$\begin{aligned}\Delta\mathbf{e}_R &= (\sin\theta)\Delta\phi\mathbf{e}_\phi\\ \Delta\mathbf{e}_\theta &= (\cos\theta)\Delta\phi\mathbf{e}_\phi\\ \Delta\mathbf{e}_\phi &= -(\sin\theta)\Delta\phi\mathbf{e}_R\end{aligned}$$

due to the rotation $\Delta\phi$.

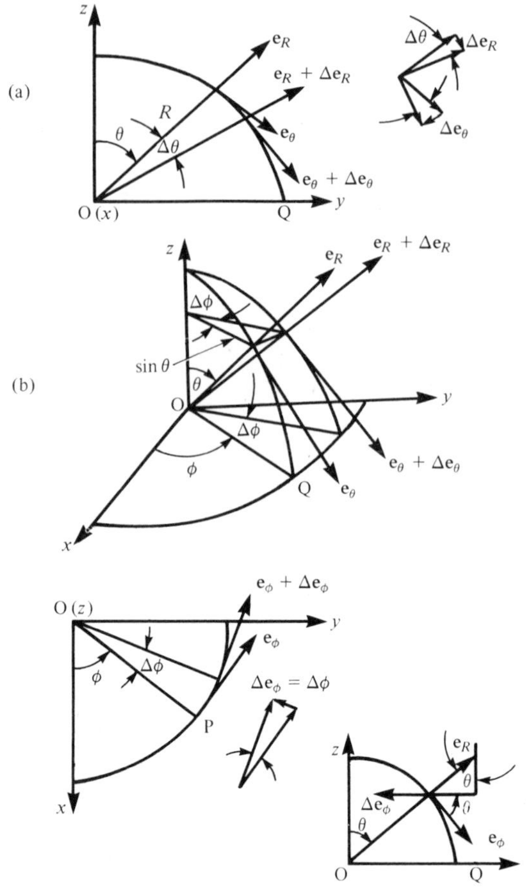

Figure 6.6 Velocity and acceleration of a point in spherical coordinates.

From Figure 6.6(c) we see that the change in the unit vector $\mathbf{e}_\phi$ is equal in magnitude to $\Delta\phi$ and in a direction parallel to the xOy plane and towards the xOz plane. Therefore

$$\begin{aligned}\Delta\mathbf{e}_\phi &= -\Delta\phi(\sin\theta)\mathbf{e}_R - \Delta\phi(\cos\theta)\mathbf{e}_\theta\\ \Delta\mathbf{e}_\theta &= -\Delta\theta\mathbf{e}_R + (\cos\theta)\Delta\phi\mathbf{e}_\phi\\ \Delta\mathbf{e}_R &= \Delta\theta\mathbf{e}_\theta + (\sin\theta)\Delta\phi\mathbf{e}_\phi\end{aligned}$$

Dividing each of these equations by Δt and proceeding to the limit we get the derivatives of each unit vector, i.e.

$$\begin{aligned}\dot{\mathbf{e}}_\phi &= -\dot\phi(\sin\theta)\mathbf{e}_R - \dot\phi(\cos\theta)\mathbf{e}_\theta\\ \dot{\mathbf{e}}_\theta &= -\dot\theta\mathbf{e}_R + \dot\phi(\cos\theta)\mathbf{e}_\phi\\ \dot{\mathbf{e}}_R &= \dot\theta\mathbf{e}_\theta + \dot\phi(\sin\theta)\mathbf{e}_\phi\end{aligned} \tag{6.11}$$

We can now obtain the velocity and acceleration of P in the directions of these unit vectors. Since

$$\mathbf{R} = R\mathbf{e}_R$$

differentiation yields for the velocity and acceleration

$$\begin{aligned} \mathbf{v} &= \dot{\mathbf{R}} = \dot{R}\mathbf{e}_R + R\dot{\mathbf{e}}_R \\ \mathbf{a} &= \ddot{\mathbf{R}} = \ddot{R}\mathbf{e}_R + 2\dot{R}\dot{\mathbf{e}}_R + R\ddot{\mathbf{e}}_R \end{aligned} \tag{6.12}$$

Substituting (6.11) in (6.12) yields

$$\mathbf{v} = \dot{R}\mathbf{e}_R + R\dot{\theta}\mathbf{e}_\theta + R\dot{\phi}(\sin\theta)\mathbf{e}_\phi \tag{6.13}$$

and

$$\begin{aligned} \mathbf{a} = {} & (\ddot{R} - R\dot{\theta}^2 - R\dot{\phi}^2\sin^2\theta)\mathbf{e}_R \\ & +(2\dot{R}\dot{\theta} + R\ddot{\theta} - R\dot{\phi}^2\sin\theta\cos\theta)\mathbf{e}_\theta \\ & + (2\dot{R}\dot{\phi}\sin\theta + 2R\dot{\theta}\dot{\phi}\cos\theta + R\ddot{\phi}\sin\theta)\mathbf{e}_\phi \end{aligned} \tag{6.14}$$

6.1.7 **Coordinate transformations**

Situations will arise when it will be necessary to transform displacements, velocities, accelerations or other quantities expressed in terms of the coordinates of a particular frame of reference into those of another frame of reference, e.g. from Cartesian to cylindrical, cylindrical to spherical, or spherical to Cartesian.

Consider, for example, the transformation of coordinates due to a rotation about the z-axis. Figure 6.7 shows two Cartesian frames of reference $Oxyz$ and $Ox'y'z'$; the two frames being coincident initially. Now let the xyz frame be rotated about the z-axis through an angle θ into the position $x'y'z'$. A particle at P whose coordinates in the xyz frame are (x, y, z) also has coordinates (x', y', z') in the $x'y'z'$ frame. Since the rotation is about the z-axis we must have $z' = z$. We now consider the point P′, the projection of P onto the xy and $x'y'$ planes, whose coordinates are (x, y) in the xy plane and $(x'y')$ in the

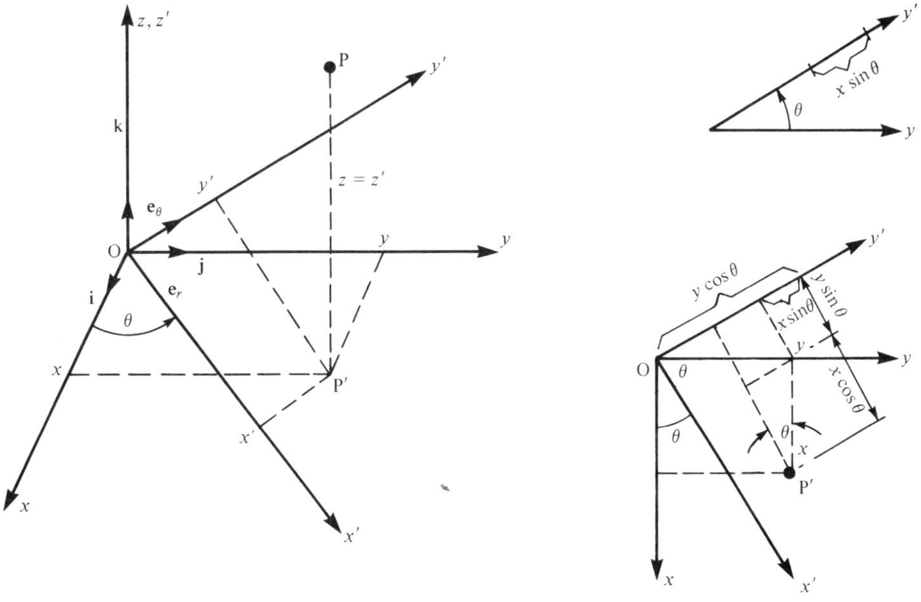

Figure 6.7 Coordinate transformation.

$x'y'$ plane. From the geometry of the inset diagram we have

$$\begin{aligned} x' &= x\cos\theta + y\sin\theta \\ y' &= -x\sin\theta + y\cos\theta \end{aligned} \tag{6.15}$$

Hence the coordinates of P in the $x'y'z'$ frame are

$$\begin{aligned} x' &= x\cos\theta + y\sin\theta \\ y' &= -x\sin\theta + y\cos\theta \\ z' &= z \end{aligned} \tag{6.16}$$

We can express these relationships more conveniently in matrix form thus

$$\begin{pmatrix} x' \\ y' \\ z' \end{pmatrix} = \begin{pmatrix} \cos\theta & \sin\theta & 0 \\ -\sin\theta & \cos\theta & 0 \\ 0 & 0 & 1 \end{pmatrix} \begin{pmatrix} x \\ y \\ z \end{pmatrix} \tag{6.17}$$

If we now consider the transformation from the $x'y'z'$ frame into the xyz frame we find

$$\begin{pmatrix} x \\ y \\ z \end{pmatrix} = \begin{pmatrix} \cos\theta & -\sin\theta & 0 \\ \sin\theta & \cos\theta & 0 \\ 0 & 0 & 1 \end{pmatrix} \begin{pmatrix} x' \\ y' \\ z' \end{pmatrix} \tag{6.18}$$

The two matrices are called the *transformation matrices.* Let $[T]$ be the transformation matrix in (6.17) and $[T']$ the transformation matrix in (6.18), then it is easy to verify that

$$[T'] = [T]^{-1}$$

If the position of a particle P has coordinates (r, θ, z) and (x, y, z) in cylindrical and Cartesian coordinates respectively, and the matrix for the transformation from Cartesian to cylindrical coordinates is $[T]$, then $[T']$ is that for the transformation from cylindrical to Cartesian coordinates.

Consider, for instance, the unit vectors **i**, **j** and **k** in the Cartesian frame, and $\mathbf{e}_r$, $\mathbf{e}_\theta$ and **k** in the cylindrical frame. Then from equation (6.13) we have

$$\begin{aligned} \mathbf{e}_r &= \mathbf{i}\cos\theta + \mathbf{j}\sin\theta \\ \mathbf{e}_\theta &= -\mathbf{i}\sin\theta + \mathbf{j}\cos\theta \\ \mathbf{e}_z &= \mathbf{k} \end{aligned}$$

Hence

$$\begin{pmatrix} \mathbf{e}_r \\ \mathbf{e}_\theta \\ \mathbf{e}_z \end{pmatrix} = [T] \begin{pmatrix} \mathbf{i} \\ \mathbf{j} \\ \mathbf{k} \end{pmatrix} \tag{6.19}$$

Furthermore if v_x, v_y and v_z are the velocities in Cartesian coordinates and v_r, v_θ and v_z its velocities in cylindrical coordinates, then

$$\begin{pmatrix} v_r \\ v_\theta \\ v_z \end{pmatrix} = [T] \begin{pmatrix} v_x \\ v_y \\ v_z \end{pmatrix} \tag{6.20}$$

EXAMPLE 6.1

The access to a multi-storey car park is from a spiral roadway of 3.5 m pitch and 7 m mean radius. A car enters it at a constant speed of 10 km/h, calculate its velocity components in Cartesian coordinates when it is two-thirds of the way to the first floor.

SOLUTION

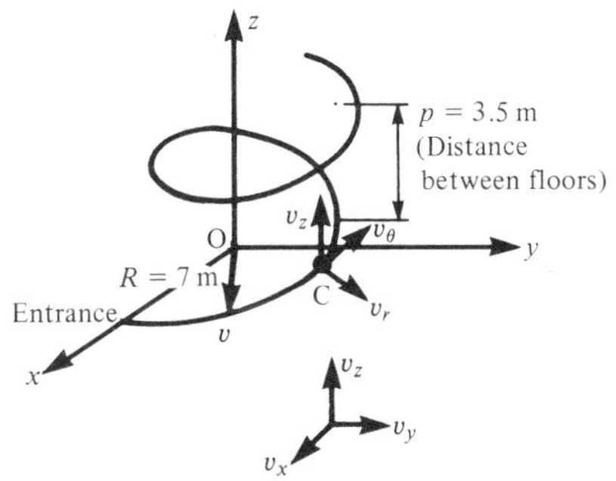

Figure 6.8 Ramp of multi-storey car park.

The diagram in Figure 6.8 shows the roadway and a Cartesian frame with origin on the axis of the spiral roadway. The velocity components of the car at any position C are as follows:

(a) In cylindrical coordinates:

$$v_r = 0 \quad \text{radially}$$

$$v_\theta = 10/3.6 = 2.77 \text{ m/s} \quad \text{tangentially}$$

$$v_z = z = \frac{p}{(2\pi R/v_\theta)} = \frac{3.5}{2\pi \times 7/2.77} = 0.057 \text{ m/s} \quad \text{axially}$$

(b) In Cartesian coordinates: v_x, v_y, v_z, such that, by equation (6.15),

$$\begin{pmatrix} v_x \\ v_y \\ v_z \end{pmatrix} = \begin{pmatrix} \cos\theta & -\sin\theta & 0 \\ \sin\theta & \cos\theta & 0 \\ 0 & 0 & 1 \end{pmatrix} \begin{pmatrix} v_r \\ v_\theta \\ v_z \end{pmatrix}$$

When the car is two-thirds of the way between the entrance and the first floor,

$$\theta = \tfrac{2}{3} \times 360 = 240°.$$

Hence

$$\begin{pmatrix} v_x \\ v_y \\ v_z \end{pmatrix} = \begin{pmatrix} -0.50 & +0.87 & 0 \\ -0.87 & -0.50 & 0 \\ 0 & 0 & 1 \end{pmatrix} \begin{pmatrix} 0 \\ 2.77 \\ 0.057 \end{pmatrix}$$

which yields

$$v_x = 0.87 \times 2.77 = 2.41 \text{ m/s}$$

$$v_y = -0.50 \times 2.77 = -1.385 \text{ m/s}$$

$$v_z = 0.057 \text{ m/s}$$

For transformation from cylindrical to spherical coordinates the transformation matrix can be shown to be

$$[T_s] = \begin{pmatrix} \sin\phi & 0 & \cos\phi \\ 0 & 1 & 0 \\ -\cos\phi & 0 & \sin\phi \end{pmatrix} \tag{6.21}$$

and for transformation from Cartesian to spherical coordinates it follows that the transformation matrix is

$$[T_{cs}] = [T_s][T] = \begin{pmatrix} \sin\phi\cos\theta & \sin\phi\sin\theta & \cos\phi \\ -\sin\theta & \cos\theta & 0 \\ -\cos\phi\cos\theta & -\cos\phi\sin\theta & \sin\phi \end{pmatrix} \tag{6.22}$$

EXAMPLE 6.2

A radar station at O is following an aircraft A whose velocity is 300 knots parallel to the yz plane and at an angle of 15° to the xy plane. At the instant where the Cartesian coordinates of the aircraft are as shown in Figure 6.9, calculate its position and velocities in spherical coordinates as measured by the radar. A radar would measure the elevation θ', the azimuth angle ϕ and the range R since its dish can pivot about the x- and z-axes.

Example Cont.

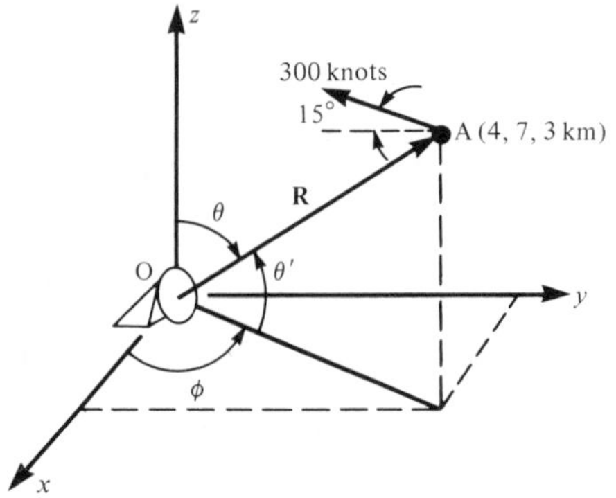

Figure 6.9 The tracking problem of example 6.2.

SOLUTION

From the data we have

$$
\begin{aligned}
R &= \sqrt{4^2 + 7^2 + 3^2} = 8.60 \text{ km} \\
\phi &= \arctan(7/4) = 60.26° \\
\theta &= 90 - \theta' = 90 - \arctan(3/\sqrt{4^2 + 7^2}) \\
&= 86.76°
\end{aligned}
$$

The transformation matrix (equation (6.22)) is

$$
[T_{cs}] = \begin{pmatrix} 0.495 & 0.867 & 0.057 \\ 0.868 & 0.496 & 0 \\ -0.028 & -0.049 & 0.998 \end{pmatrix}
$$

The velocity components of the aircraft in spherical coordinates are

$$
\begin{pmatrix} v_R \\ v_\phi \\ v_\theta \end{pmatrix} = [T_{cs}] \begin{pmatrix} v_x \\ v_y \\ v_z \end{pmatrix} = [T_{cs}] \begin{pmatrix} 0 \\ -289.778 \\ 77.646 \end{pmatrix}
$$

Solution Cont.

since

$$v_x = 0$$

and

$$
\begin{aligned}
v_y &= -300 \cos 15° = -289.778 \text{ knots} \\
v_z &= 300 \sin 15° = 77.646 \text{ knots}
\end{aligned}
$$

Substituting in the above equation yields

$$
\begin{aligned}
v_R &= 0.495 \times 0 + 0.867 \times -289.778 \\
&\quad + 0.057 \times 77.646 \\
&= -246.8 \text{ knots (to one d.p.)}
\end{aligned}
$$

The reader should verify that

$$v_\phi = -143.7 \text{ knots}$$

and

$$v_\theta = 91.7 \text{ knots}$$

6.1.8 **Scalar product of two vectors**

Let **A** and **B** be two vectors of magnitude A and B originating from point O as shown in Figure 6.10, and θ be the angle between their directions, measured positively in the sense of the rotation from **A** to **B**.

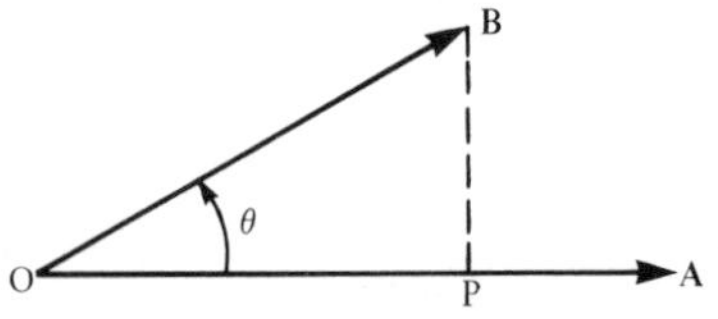

Figure 6.10 Scalar product.

The scalar product of the two vectors denoted by $\mathbf{A} \cdot \mathbf{B}$ (pronounced "A dot B") is defined by the equation

$$\mathbf{A} \cdot \mathbf{B} = AB \cos\theta \tag{6.23}$$

It is a scalar quantity and is measured by the projection of **B** on **A**. From this definition it follows that

$$\mathbf{B} \cdot \mathbf{A} = BA \cos(-\theta) = AB \cos\theta = \mathbf{A} \cdot \mathbf{B}$$

so that the order is immaterial, i.e. the scalar multiplication of vectors is commutative (see section 1.3.2).

If $90° < \theta < 270°$ the scalar product is negative and if $\theta = 90°$ the scalar product is zero.

For the fundamental unit vectors **i**, **j** and **k** we have

$$\mathbf{i} \cdot \mathbf{i} = \mathbf{j} \cdot \mathbf{j} = \mathbf{k} \cdot \mathbf{k} = 1 \tag{6.24}$$

and

$$\mathbf{i} \cdot \mathbf{j} = \mathbf{j} \cdot \mathbf{k} = \mathbf{k} \cdot \mathbf{i} = 0$$

If

$$\mathbf{A} = a_x\mathbf{i} + a_y\mathbf{j} + a_z\mathbf{k}$$

and

$$\mathbf{B} = b_x\mathbf{i} + b_y\mathbf{j} + b_z\mathbf{k}$$

then using equation (6.24) we get

$$\mathbf{A} \cdot \mathbf{B} = a_xb_x + a_yb_y + a_zb_z \tag{6.25}$$

It therefore follows that if $\mathbf{A} = \mathbf{B}$

$$\mathbf{A}^2 = a_x^2 + a_y^2 + a_z^2$$

If $\mathbf{A} \cdot \mathbf{B} = 0$, and $\mathbf{A} \neq 0$ and $\mathbf{B} \neq 0$ the two vectors are at right angles to each other.

6.1.9 **Vector product of two vectors**

Let **A** and **B** be two vectors of magnitudes A and B respectively and θ be the angle between them measured positively from **A** towards **B** as shown in Figure 6.11. The vector product $\mathbf{A} \wedge \mathbf{B}$ or $\mathbf{A} \times \mathbf{B}$, pronounced "A vector B" or "A cross B", is defined to be a vector whose magnitude is

$$AB \sin\theta \tag{6.26}$$

and whose direction is perpendicular to both vectors and whose sense is in accordance with the right-hand cork-screw rule.

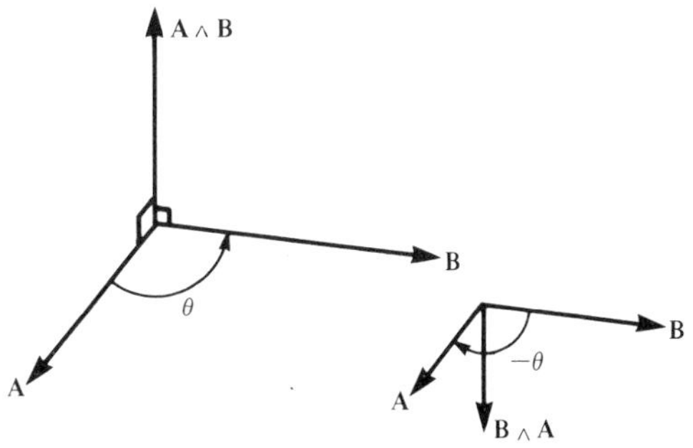

Figure 6.11 Vector product.

From this definition it follows that the vector multiplication of vectors is not commutative, since

$$BA \sin(-\theta) = -AB \sin\theta$$

Hence

$$\mathbf{B} \wedge \mathbf{A} = -\mathbf{A} \wedge \mathbf{B} \tag{6.27}$$

as illustrated in Figure 6.11.

When two vectors are parallel their vector product is zero, since $\sin\theta = 0$ or $\sin\pi = 0$. Conversely, if $\mathbf{A} \wedge \mathbf{B} = 0$ then either $\mathbf{A} = 0$ or $\mathbf{A}$ is parallel to $\mathbf{B}$. We should note that two vectors are parallel irrespective of sense if the lines representing them are parallel, thus $\mathbf{P}$ and $-\mathbf{P}$ are opposite but parallel vectors.

Let us now consider the vector products of the unit vectors **i**, **j** and **k**; from the definition we have:

$$\begin{aligned} &\mathbf{i} \wedge \mathbf{i} = \mathbf{j} \wedge \mathbf{j} = \mathbf{k} \wedge \mathbf{k} = 0 \\ &\mathbf{i} \wedge \mathbf{j} = \mathbf{k} \qquad \mathbf{j} \wedge \mathbf{k} = \mathbf{i} \qquad \mathbf{k} \wedge \mathbf{i} = \mathbf{j} \end{aligned} \tag{6.28}$$

Hence for two vectors **A** and **B** we have

$$\begin{aligned} \mathbf{A} \wedge \mathbf{B} &= (a_x\mathbf{i} + a_y\mathbf{j} + a_z\mathbf{k}) \wedge (b_x\mathbf{i} + b_y\mathbf{j} + b_z\mathbf{k}) \\ &= a_x\mathbf{i} \wedge (b_x\mathbf{i} + b_y\mathbf{j} + b_z\mathbf{k}) + a_y\mathbf{j} \wedge (b_x\mathbf{i} + b_y\mathbf{j} + b_z\mathbf{k}) \\ &\quad + a_z\mathbf{k} \wedge (b_x\mathbf{i} + b_y\mathbf{j} + b_z\mathbf{k}) \\ &= (a_yb_z - a_zb_y)\mathbf{i} + (a_zb_x - a_xb_z)\mathbf{j} + (a_xb_y - a_yb_x)\mathbf{k} \end{aligned}$$

using the results of (6.28) and assuming that vector multiplication is distributive, i.e. $\mathbf{A} \wedge (\mathbf{B} + \mathbf{C}) = \mathbf{A} \wedge \mathbf{B} + \mathbf{A} \wedge \mathbf{C}$; the above result can be represented more simply by means of a determinant, thus

$$\mathbf{A} \wedge \mathbf{B} = \begin{vmatrix} \mathbf{i} & \mathbf{j} & \mathbf{k} \\ a_x & a_y & a_z \\ b_x & b_y & b_z \end{vmatrix} \tag{6.29}$$

The last two rows are in the order of the terms of the product; from the properties of determinants, if these two rows are interchanged, the value of the determinant is unchanged but its sign is changed; thus $\mathbf{A} \wedge \mathbf{B} = -\mathbf{B} \wedge \mathbf{A}$.

6.1.10 **Application to mechanics**

(a) Work done by a force

A force acting on a particle is said to do work when the particle is displaced in a given direction, as discussed in section 4.4.1. The work done is a scalar quantity and is proportional to the force and the component of the displacement in the direction of the force.

If **P** and **s** are the force and the displacement respectively, included at an angle θ, the work done is

$$Ps\cos\theta = \mathbf{P} \cdot \mathbf{s}$$

Thus work is the scalar product of the force and the displacement. The work done is zero when **P** and s are perpendicular to each other.

If a particle is acted upon by a number of forces $\mathbf{P}_1, \mathbf{P}_2, \mathbf{P}_3, \ldots, \mathbf{P}_n$, it follows that during a displacement s of the particle, each force does work, i.e. $\mathbf{P}_1 \cdot \mathrm{s}, \mathbf{P}_2 \cdot \mathrm{s}, \ldots, \mathbf{P}_n \cdot \mathrm{s}$. Hence the total work done is

$$\sum_{1}^{n}(P \cdot \mathrm{s}) = \mathrm{s} \cdot (\sum P) = \mathrm{s} \cdot \mathbf{R}$$

where **R** is the resultant of the forces.

EXAMPLE 6.3

Two tugs are pulling a tanker in a harbour at a constant velocity of 1.5 knots, as shown in Figure 6.12. The cables make an angle of 12° with the direction of motion of the ship and the tension in each cable is 75 kN. Calculate the work done per second. (1 knot = 1.852 km/h.)

Example Cont.

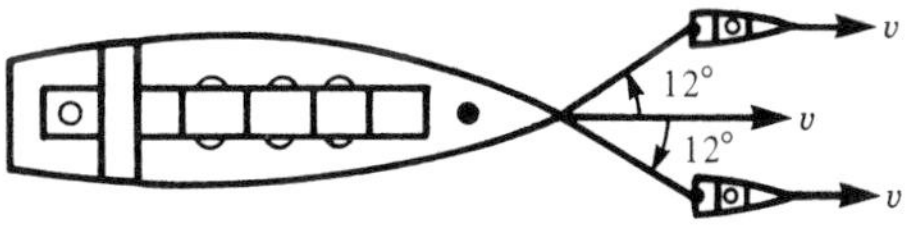

Figure 6.12 Sketch for example 6.3.

SOLUTION

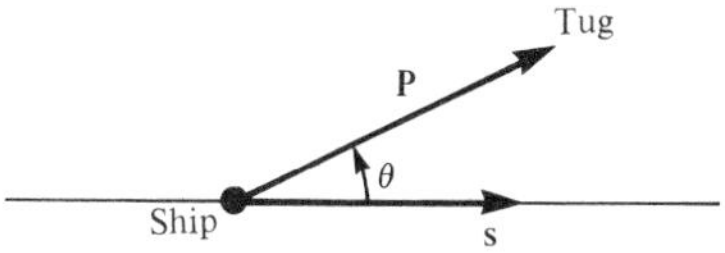

Figure 6.13 Application of scalar product in example 6.3.

Let **P** be the tension in each cable and s the displacement of the ship in a time t (Figure 6.13). From the definition of work U we have

$$U = \mathbf{P} \cdot \mathrm{s} = (P \cos \theta)s$$

Solution Cont.

The work done per second by each tug is

$$(\mathbf{P} \cdot \mathrm{s})/t = \mathbf{P} \cdot \frac{\mathrm{s}}{t} = \mathbf{P} \cdot \mathrm{v}$$

(t is a scalar) where v is the velocity. Hence the total work done per second is

$$2Pv \cos \theta = 2 \times 75 \times 10^3 \times 1.5 \times 1.852 \times \cos 12°/3.6$$

$$= 113.2 \times 10^3 \text{ J/s}$$

But J/s is the unit of power, the watt; it therefore follows that the power is also given by the scalar product of **P**, the force, and v, the velocity.

(b) Moment of a force

Consider a force **P** and AB its line of action as shown in Figure 6.14. Let O be any convenient point, and **R** the position vector of any point A on the line of action of the force from O. The moment **M** of the force about the point O is defined by the vector product

$$\mathbf{M} = \mathbf{R} \wedge \mathbf{P}$$

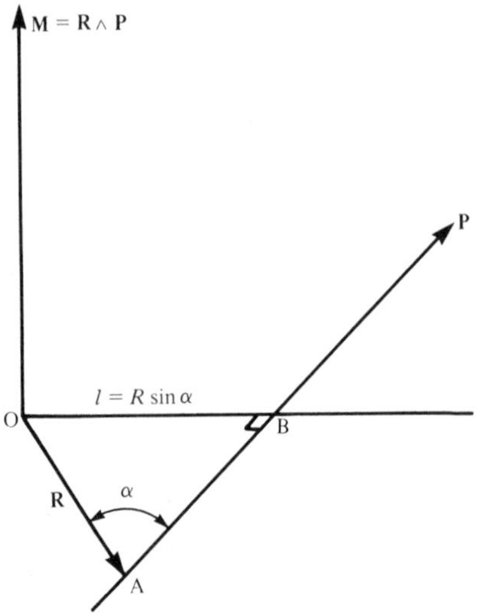

Figure 6.14 Moment of a force.

This vector is perpendicular to the plane of **R** and **P**, and therefore to the plane containing the line of action AB of the force and the point O. The magnitude of this moment is lP, where l is the length of the perpendicular OB to the line of action. Since $l = R \sin \alpha$, the magnitude of the moment is

$$RP \sin \alpha$$

α being the angle between the direction of the position vector and the line of action of the force.

If a number of forces $\mathbf{P}_1, \mathbf{P}_2, \ldots, \mathbf{P}_n$ act through the same point A, they have a resultant $\mathbf{Q} = \sum \mathbf{P}$. The moment of this resultant about O is

$$\begin{aligned} \mathbf{R} \wedge \mathbf{Q} &= \mathbf{R} \wedge (\mathbf{P}_1 + \mathbf{P}_2 + \ldots + \mathbf{P}_n) \\ &= \mathbf{R} \wedge \mathbf{P}_1 + \mathbf{R} \wedge \mathbf{P}_2 + \ldots + \mathbf{R} \wedge \mathbf{P}_n \end{aligned}$$

It is therefore equal to the vector sum of the moments of each force.

EXAMPLE 6.4

A force $\mathbf{P} = 250\mathbf{i} + 120\mathbf{j} + 300\mathbf{k}$ N is applied to a particle whose position vector is $\mathbf{R} = 2\mathbf{i} + \mathbf{j} + 3\mathbf{k}$ m. Calculate the moment of this force about each axis of a Cartesian frame of reference and the magnitude of the moment about the origin.

SOLUTION

Let **M** be the moment of this force about O, the origin of our Cartesian frame of reference (Figure 6.15). Since **M** is a vector we can write

$$\mathbf{M} = M_x\mathbf{i} + M_y\mathbf{j} + M_z\mathbf{k}$$

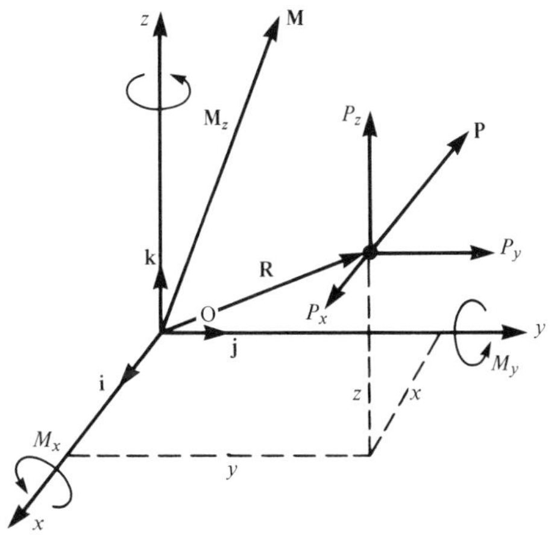

Figure 6.15 Calculating the moment of the force in example 6.4.

But by definition

$$\mathbf{M} = \mathbf{R} \wedge \mathbf{P}$$
$$= \begin{vmatrix} \mathbf{i} & \mathbf{j} & \mathbf{k} \\ x & y & z \\ P_x & P_y & P_z \end{vmatrix}$$
$$= (P_z y - P_y z)\mathbf{i} + (P_x z - P_z x)\mathbf{j} + (P_y x - P_x y)\mathbf{k}$$

by (6.29). Hence it follows that the moments about the axes are:

$$M_x = P_z y - P_y z = 300 \times 1 - 120 \times 3 = -60 \text{ N m}$$

Solution Cont.

$$M_y = P_x z - P_z x = 250 \times 3 - 300 \times 2 = 150 \text{ N m}$$
$$M_z = P_y x - P_x y = 120 \times 2 - 250 \times 1 = -10 \text{ N m}$$

The magnitude M of the moment about O is

$$M = \sqrt{M_x^2 + M_y^2 + M_z^2} = \sqrt{(-60)^2 + 150^2 + (-10)^2} = 161.86 \text{ N m}$$

The magnitude of the moment about O could also be obtained as follows: If **A** and **B** are two vectors of magnitude A and B respectively and θ the angle between them, it then follows from equations (6.23) and (6.25) that

$$\cos\theta = \frac{\mathbf{A} \cdot \mathbf{B}}{AB} = \frac{a_x b_x + a_y b_y + a_z b_z}{AB}$$

Thus in the above problem we can calculate the magnitude M of the moment by first calculating the angle θ between the position vector **R** and the force **P** and then evaluating $M = RP\sin\theta$. Hence we have

$$\theta = \arccos\left(\frac{250 \times 2 + 120 \times 1 + 300 \times 3}{\sqrt{2^2 + 1^2 + 3^2} \times \sqrt{250^2 + 120^2 + 300^2}}\right)$$
$$= 6.08°$$

where

$$\sqrt{2^2 + 1^2 + 3^2} = R = 3.74$$

and

$$\sqrt{250^2 + 120^2 + 300^2} = P = 408.53$$

$$M = 3.74 \times 408.53 \times \sin 6.08° = 161.86 \text{ N m}$$

as above.

6.1.11 **Vector triple product**

We shall encounter situations in dynamics where three vectors **A**, **B** and **C** occur as the product $\mathbf{A} \wedge (\mathbf{B} \wedge \mathbf{C})$. This is referred to as a *vector triple product,* and sometimes we may find it convenient to expand such a product into the following useful expression:

$$\mathbf{A} \wedge (\mathbf{B} \wedge \mathbf{C}) = (\mathbf{A} \cdot \mathbf{C})\mathbf{B} - (\mathbf{A} \cdot \mathbf{B})\mathbf{C} \tag{6.30}$$

To prove this equation we proceed thus:

$$\mathbf{A}\wedge(\mathbf{B}\wedge\mathbf{C}) = \begin{vmatrix} \mathbf{i} & \mathbf{j} & \mathbf{k} \\ A_x & A_y & A_z \\ (B_yC_z - B_zC_y) & (B_zC_x - B_xC_z) & (B_xC_y - B_yC_x) \end{vmatrix}$$

$$= \mathbf{i}[A_y(B_xC_y - B_yC_x) - A_z(B_zC_x - B_xC_z)] - \mathbf{j}[A_x(B_xC_y - \ldots \text{etc.}$$

$$= [\mathbf{i}B_x(A_xC_x + A_yC_y + A_zC_z) - \mathbf{i}C_x(A_xB_x + A_yB_y + A_zB_z)] + \ldots$$

$$= (\mathbf{A}\cdot\mathbf{C})(B_x\mathbf{i} + B_y\mathbf{j} + B_z\mathbf{k}) - (\mathbf{A}\cdot\mathbf{B})(C_x\mathbf{i} + C_y\mathbf{j} + C_z\mathbf{k})$$

Hence

$$\mathbf{A}\wedge(\mathbf{B}\wedge\mathbf{C}) = (\mathbf{A}\cdot\mathbf{C})\mathbf{B} - (\mathbf{A}\cdot\mathbf{B})\mathbf{C}$$

which is a vector perpendicular to the vector $\mathbf{B}\wedge\mathbf{C}$, in the plane of **B** and **C**.

6.2 KINEMATICS OF RIGID BODIES

6.2.1 Rotation about a fixed point: velocities

Consider a rigid body rotating about a fixed point A. Let ω be its angular velocity and AX the instantaneous axis of rotation as shown in Figure 6.16. The angular velocity may be represented by a vector $\boldsymbol{\omega}$ directed along AX in accordance with the right-hand rule, and if P is any point in the body whose position vector from A is **R** then its velocity $\mathbf{v}_{PA}$ is given by

$$\mathbf{v}_{PA} = \boldsymbol{\omega}\wedge\mathbf{R} \tag{6.31}$$

If M is the projection of P on AX, the velocity of P is $\omega\mathrm{MP} = \omega R\sin\theta$ at right angles to the plane AXP; this is in fact what the above vector product represents.

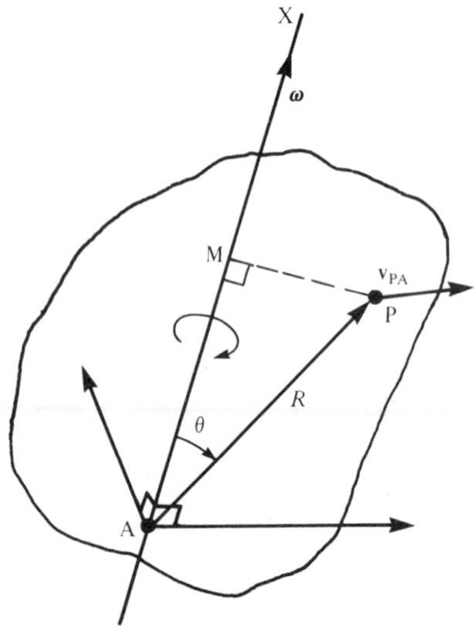

Figure 6.16 Rotation of a rigid body about a fixed point: velocity.

To show that angular velocities obey the rule for the addition of vectors, let the body have a number of angular velocities $\boldsymbol{\omega}_1, \boldsymbol{\omega}_2, \ldots$ about axes through A. Then if $\mathbf{v}_1, \mathbf{v}_2, \ldots$ are their contributions to the velocity **v** of the point P then

$$\mathbf{v} = \mathbf{v}_1 + \mathbf{v}_2 + \ldots = \boldsymbol{\omega}_1\wedge\mathbf{R} + \boldsymbol{\omega}_2\wedge\mathbf{R} + \ldots$$
$$= (\boldsymbol{\omega}_1 + \boldsymbol{\omega}_2 + \ldots)\wedge\mathbf{R} = \boldsymbol{\omega}\wedge\mathbf{R}$$

where $\omega_1 + \omega_2 + \ldots$ is the resultant of the angular velocities added vectorially.

The point A need not always be a fixed point, but can be a point moving with a velocity $\mathbf{v}_A$ relative to a Newtonian frame, whereupon the absolute velocity $\mathbf{v}$ of the point P is

$$\begin{aligned} \mathbf{v} &= \mathbf{v}_A + \boldsymbol{\omega} \wedge \mathbf{R} \\ &= \mathbf{v}_A + \mathbf{v}_{PA} \end{aligned} \tag{6.32}$$

where $\mathbf{v}_{PA}$ is the velocity of P relative to A and equals $\boldsymbol{\omega} \wedge \mathbf{R}$.

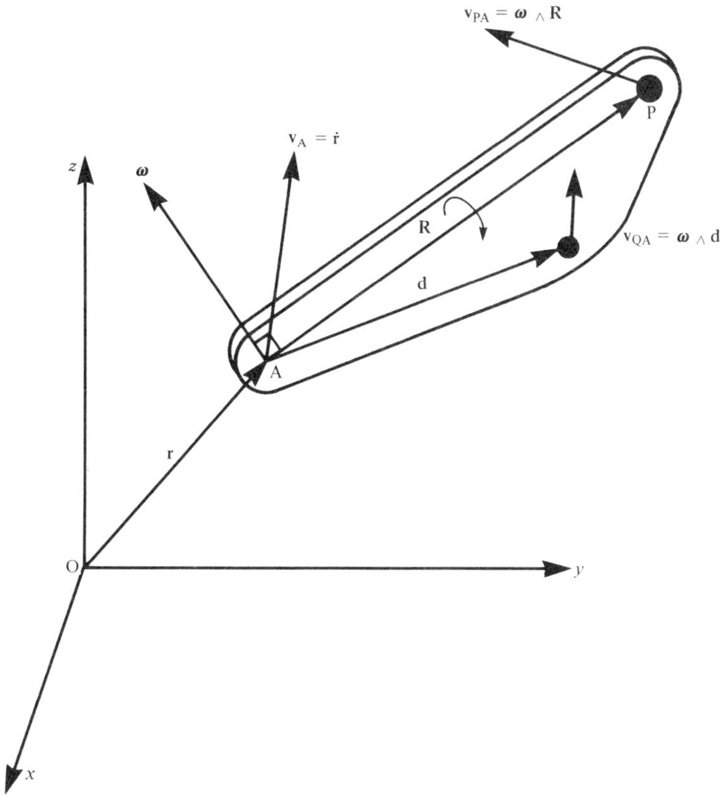

Figure 6.17 Rotation of a link in a spatial mechanism.

Equation (6.32) is illustrated in Figure 6.17 where the body might be one of the links in a spatial mechanism, for example, where A would, very likely, be a spherical joint. If Q is any other point of the link, as shown, then its velocity relative to *xyz* frame is

$$\begin{aligned} \mathbf{v}_Q &= \mathbf{v}_A + \mathbf{v}_{QA} \\ &= \mathbf{v}_A + \boldsymbol{\omega} \wedge \mathbf{d} \end{aligned}$$

where $\mathbf{d}$ is the position vector of Q from A.

EXAMPLE 6.5

If point A of the link in Figure 6.17 coincides with O, the origin of the *xyz* frame, and the link has an angular velocity $\boldsymbol{\omega} = \mathbf{i} + 1.5\mathbf{j} + 3\mathbf{k}$ rad/s, calculate

Example Cont.

the velocity components of point P given that $\mathbf{R} = 150\mathbf{i} + 125\mathbf{j} + 275\mathbf{k}$ mm.

SOLUTION

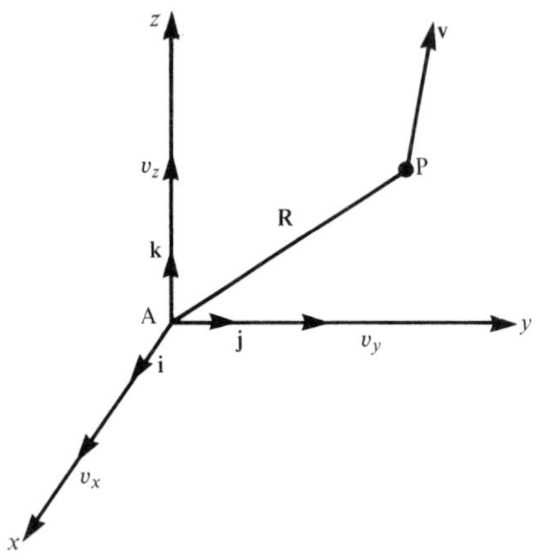

Figure 6.18 Velocity components of the link in Figure 6.17.

In this case $\mathbf{v}_A = 0$ and $\mathbf{v}_{PA} = \boldsymbol{\omega} \wedge \mathbf{R} = \mathbf{v}$ (say). Let $\boldsymbol{\omega} = \omega_x\mathbf{i} + \omega_y\mathbf{j} + \omega_z\mathbf{k}$ and $\mathbf{R} = x\mathbf{i} + y\mathbf{j} + z\mathbf{k}$ (Figure 6.18). Then

Solution Cont.

$$\boldsymbol{\omega} \wedge \mathbf{R} = \begin{vmatrix} \mathbf{i} & \mathbf{j} & \mathbf{k} \\ \omega_x & \omega_y & \omega_z \\ x & y & z \end{vmatrix}$$

by (6.29). Hence the components of $\mathbf{v}$ are

$$\begin{aligned} v_x &= z\omega_y - y\omega_z \\ &= 0.275 \times 1.5 - 0.125 \times 3 \\ &= 0.038 \text{ m/s} \end{aligned}$$

$$\begin{aligned} v_y &= x\omega_z - z\omega_x \\ &= 0.15 \times 3 - 0.275 \times 1 \\ &= 0.175 \text{ m/s} \end{aligned}$$

$$\begin{aligned} v_z &= y\omega_x - x\omega_y \\ &= 0.125 \times 1 - 0.15 \times 1.5 \\ &= -0.100 \text{ m/s} \end{aligned}$$

or

$$\mathbf{v}_{PA} = 0.038\mathbf{i} + 0.175\mathbf{j} - 0.100\mathbf{k}$$

6.2.2 **Rotation about a fixed point: accelerations**

The acceleration of any point of a rigid body is the time derivative of the velocity; thus referring to Figure 6.17 the acceleration $\mathbf{a}$ of P relative to the fixed frame xyz is

$$\mathbf{a} = \frac{d}{dt}(\mathbf{v}) = \frac{d}{dt}(\mathbf{v}_A + \boldsymbol{\omega} \wedge \mathbf{R})$$

Performing the differentiation yields

$$\mathbf{a} = \dot{\mathbf{v}}_A + \dot{\boldsymbol{\omega}} \wedge \mathbf{R} + \boldsymbol{\omega} \wedge \dot{\mathbf{R}}$$

but $\dot{\mathbf{R}}$ is the velocity of P relative to A. Hence

$$\dot{\mathbf{R}} = \boldsymbol{\omega} \wedge \mathbf{R}$$

by (6.31). So the acceleration is

$$\mathbf{a} = \mathbf{a}_A + \dot{\boldsymbol{\omega}} \wedge \mathbf{R} + \boldsymbol{\omega} \wedge (\boldsymbol{\omega} \wedge \mathbf{R}) \tag{6.33}$$

The first term is the acceleration of A. The second and third terms represent the acceleration of P relative to A: $\dot{\boldsymbol{\omega}} \wedge \mathbf{R}$ is the acceleration component perpendicular to the plane of $\dot{\boldsymbol{\omega}}$ and $\mathbf{R}$, and $\boldsymbol{\omega} \wedge (\boldsymbol{\omega} \wedge \mathbf{R})$ is the acceleration component perpendicular to $\boldsymbol{\omega}$ and in the plane of $\boldsymbol{\omega}$ and $\mathbf{R}$ (Figure 6.19). Also $\dot{\boldsymbol{\omega}}$ is the angular acceleration of the body; if the body rotates at constant angular velocity, $\dot{\boldsymbol{\omega}} = 0$ and $\dot{\boldsymbol{\omega}} \wedge \mathbf{R} = 0$.

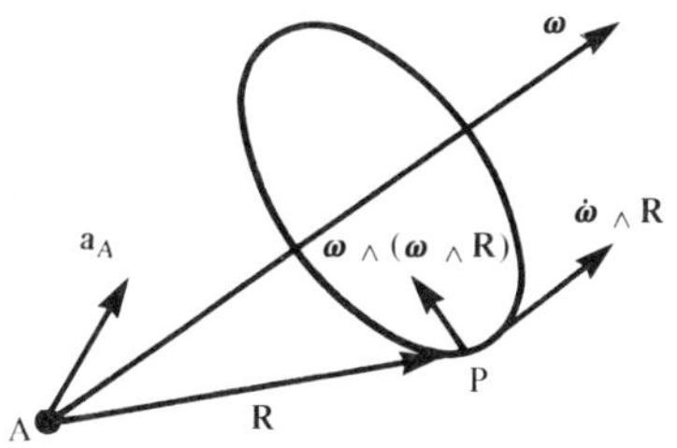

Figure 6.19 Rotation of a rigid body about a fixed point: acceleration.

As a simple illustration of the application of equations (6.32) and (6.33) consider the following example:

EXAMPLE 6.6

Two sliders A and B are constrained to move in slots at right angles to each other, as shown in Figure 6.20; and are connected by the rigid link AB of length 450 mm. At the instant when $\theta = 30°$ slider A is moving with a velocity of 0.6 m/s and an acceleration of 1.2 m/s^2 in the direction shown. Calculate the velocity and acceleration of the slider B at that instant and the angular velocity and acceleration of the link AB.

Example Cont.

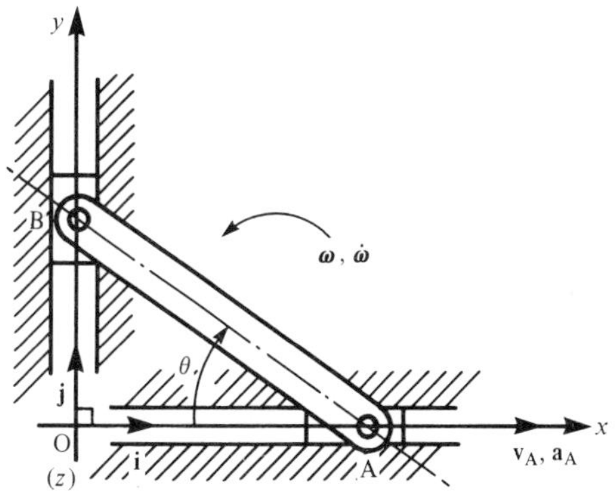

Figure 6.20 Sliders of example 6.6.

SOLUTION

We take the xOy frame of reference to coincide with the slots. The Oz axis is towards the reader. Let $\boldsymbol{\omega}$ and $\dot{\boldsymbol{\omega}} = \boldsymbol{\alpha}$ be respectively the angular velocity and angular acceleration of the link AB, and $\mathbf{v}_B$ and $\mathbf{a}_B$ be the velocity and acceleration of slider B.

We are given

$$\mathbf{v}_A = 0.6\mathbf{i} \qquad \mathbf{a}_A = 1.2\mathbf{i}$$

Also let

$$\mathbf{v}_B = v\mathbf{j} \qquad \mathbf{a}_B = a\mathbf{j}$$

and

$$\boldsymbol{\omega} = \omega\mathbf{k} \qquad \boldsymbol{\alpha} = \alpha\mathbf{k}$$

since the link is moving in the xy plane.

Solution Cont.

From equation (6.32) we have

$$\mathbf{v}_B = \mathbf{v}_A + \boldsymbol{\omega} \wedge \mathbf{R}$$

i.e.

$$\begin{aligned} v\mathbf{j} &= 0.6\mathbf{i} + \omega\mathbf{k} \wedge (-0.45 \cos 30° \, \mathbf{i} + 0.45 \sin 30° \, \mathbf{j}) \\ &= 0.6\mathbf{i} - 0.39\omega\mathbf{j} - 0.225\omega\mathbf{i} \end{aligned}$$

Hence, comparing the **i** and **j** components,

$$0 = 0.6 - 0.225\omega \qquad \omega = 2.67 \text{ rad/s}$$

and

$$v = -0.39 \times 2.67 \qquad v = 1.04 \text{ m/s}$$

Solution Cont.

From equation (6.33) we have

$$\mathbf{a}_B = \mathbf{a}_A + \boldsymbol{\alpha} \wedge \mathbf{R} + \boldsymbol{\omega} \wedge (\boldsymbol{\omega} \wedge \mathbf{R})$$

where $\boldsymbol{\omega}$ is the angular velocity and $\boldsymbol{\alpha}$ is the angular acceleration of the link.

Substituting numerical values yields

$$a\mathbf{j} = 1.2\mathbf{i} + \alpha\mathbf{k} \wedge (-0.39\mathbf{i} + 0.225\mathbf{j}) + 2.67\mathbf{k} \wedge [2.67\mathbf{k} \wedge (-0.39\mathbf{i} + 0.225\mathbf{j})]$$

$$= 1.2\mathbf{j} - 0.39\alpha\mathbf{j} - 0.225\alpha\mathbf{i} + 2.78\mathbf{i} - 1.604\mathbf{j}$$

$$= (3.98 - 0.225\alpha)\mathbf{i} - (0.39\alpha + 1.604)\mathbf{j}$$

Hence, comparing the i and j components,

$$\alpha = 3.98/0.225 = 17.69 \text{ rad/s}^2$$

and

$$a = -0.39 \times 17.69 - 1.604 = -8.5 \text{ m/s}^2$$

EXAMPLE 6.7

Let us consider now the situation where the sliders A and B are constrained to move in the slots shown in Figure 6.21. Slider B moves along the z-axis and slider A moves in the xy plane with the groove making an angle θ with the y-axis; hence the link has three-dimensional motion. If the slider A is moving with constant velocity $\mathbf{v}_A$, obtain expressions for the velocity and acceleration of the slider B and the angular velocity of the link AB at the instant when the coordinates of A and B are as shown.

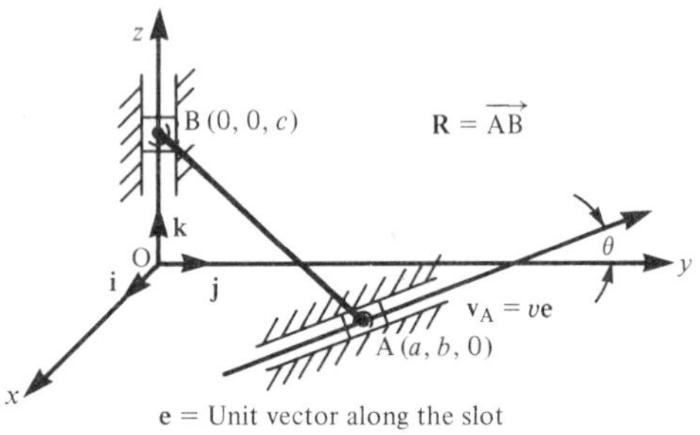

Figure 6.21 Sliders of example 6.7.

SOLUTION

(a) Velocity of slider B:

Let us first obtain the position vectors of A and B

$$\mathbf{R}_B = c\mathbf{k} \qquad \mathbf{R}_A = a\mathbf{i} + b\mathbf{j}$$

The position of B relative to A

$$\mathbf{R} = \mathbf{R}_B - \mathbf{R}_A = c\mathbf{k} - a\mathbf{i} - b\mathbf{j}$$

For the velocities we have

$$\mathbf{v}_B = v_B\mathbf{k} \qquad \mathbf{v}_A = v\mathbf{e} = -v\sin\theta\,\mathbf{i} + v\cos\theta\,\mathbf{j}$$

and the velocity of B relative to A is

$$\mathbf{v}_{BA} = \mathbf{v}_B - \mathbf{v}_A = v_B\mathbf{k} - v\sin\theta\,\mathbf{i} - v\cos\theta\,\mathbf{j}$$

To obtain the velocity of B we can make use of the fact that AB is rigid so that the velocity of B relative to A is perpendicular to AB. Hence applying the scalar product yields

$$\mathbf{v}_{BA} \cdot \mathbf{R} = 0$$

i.e.

$$(v_B\mathbf{k} + v\sin\theta\,\mathbf{i} - v\cos\theta\,\mathbf{j}) \cdot (c\mathbf{k} - a\mathbf{i} - b\mathbf{j}) = 0$$

Recalling that

$$\mathbf{i} \cdot \mathbf{i} = \mathbf{j} \cdot \mathbf{j} = \mathbf{k} \cdot \mathbf{k} = 1 \text{ and}$$

$$\mathbf{i} \cdot \mathbf{j} = \mathbf{j} \cdot \mathbf{k} = \mathbf{k} \cdot \mathbf{i} = 0$$

we obtain

$$v_Bc - va\sin\theta + vb\cos\theta = 0$$

Solving for v_B gives

$$v_B = \frac{a\sin\theta - b\cos\theta}{c}v$$

Solution Cont.

(b) Angular velocity of the link AB:

The velocity equation in terms of the angular velocity $\boldsymbol{\omega}$ of the link is

$$\mathbf{v}_B = \mathbf{v}_A + \boldsymbol{\omega} \wedge \mathbf{R}$$

Hence

$$\boldsymbol{\omega} \wedge \mathbf{R} = \mathbf{v}_B - \mathbf{v}_A = \mathbf{v}_{BA}$$

Let the components of $\boldsymbol{\omega}$ be ω_1 along Ox, ω_2 along Oy and ω_3 along Oz, so that the above equation becomes

$$(\omega_1\mathbf{i} + \omega_2\mathbf{j} + \omega_3\mathbf{k}) \wedge (c\mathbf{k} - a\mathbf{i} - b\mathbf{j}) = v_B\mathbf{k} - v \sin\theta\, \mathbf{i} - v \cos\theta\, \mathbf{j}$$

Expanding the vector product yields

$$(\omega_2 c + \omega_3 b)\mathbf{i} - (\omega_1 c + \omega_3 a)\mathbf{j} + (\omega_2 a - \omega_1 b)\mathbf{k} = v_B\mathbf{k} - v \sin\theta\, \mathbf{i} - v \cos\theta\, \mathbf{j}$$

It follows that

$$\omega_2 c + \omega_3 b = -v \sin\theta$$
$$\omega_1 c + \omega_3 a = v \cos\theta$$
$$\omega_2 a - \omega_1 b = v_B$$

Solution Cont.

Thus we have three linear equations in the three unknowns ω_1, ω_2 and ω_3, from which the angular velocity of the link is

$$\omega = \sqrt{\omega_1^2 + \omega_2^2 + \omega_3^2}$$

(c) Acceleration of the slider B:

The acceleration equation is

$$\mathbf{a}_B = \mathbf{a}_A + \dot{\boldsymbol{\omega}} \wedge \mathbf{R} + \boldsymbol{\omega} \wedge (\boldsymbol{\omega} \wedge \mathbf{R})$$

The acceleration term $\dot{\boldsymbol{\omega}} \wedge \mathbf{R}$ is perpendicular to the link, i.e. perpendicular to **R**. Hence we can eliminate it from the above equation by forming the scalar product with **R**. Thus

$$\mathbf{a}_B \cdot \mathbf{R} = \boldsymbol{\omega} \wedge (\boldsymbol{\omega} \wedge \mathbf{R}) \cdot \mathbf{R}$$

since $(\dot{\boldsymbol{\omega}} \wedge \mathbf{R}) \cdot \mathbf{R} = 0$ and $\mathbf{a}_A = 0$.

Knowing $\boldsymbol{\omega}$ from (b) we can easily solve the above equation for the acceleration $\mathbf{a}_B$ of B, where $\mathbf{a}_B = a_B\mathbf{k}$.

EXAMPLE 6.8

Figure 6.22 shows a link OP rotating at a constant angular velocity ω_1 about a vertical axis. At the same time it is elevated at a constant angular velocity ω_2 about a horizontal axis. Using the following data calculate (a) the angular velocity of the link, (b) the angular acceleration of the link, (c) the velocity of the point P, and (d) the acceleration of the point P. (Data: OP $= l =$ 1.25 m, $\omega_1 = 0.75$ rad/s, $\omega_2 = 0.4$ rad/s, $\theta = 60°$.)

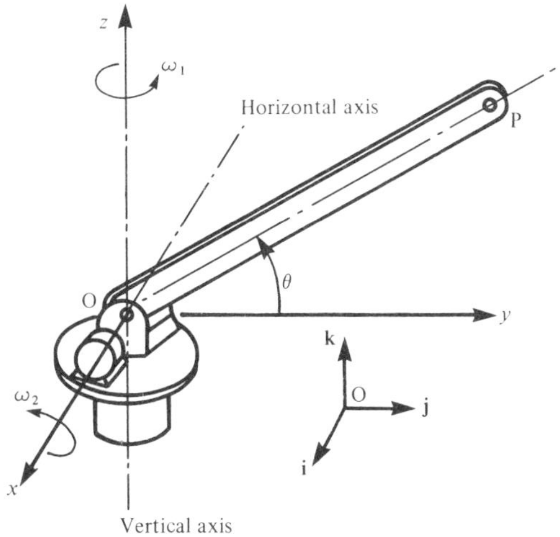

Figure 6.22 Link of example 6.8.

SOLUTION

At the instant considered the link is in the *yz* plane of the Newtonian frame of reference O*xyz* shown.

(a) By section 6.2.1 the angular velocity $\boldsymbol{\omega}$ of the link is

$$\begin{aligned}\boldsymbol{\omega} &= \boldsymbol{\omega}_1 + \boldsymbol{\omega}_2 \\ &= \omega_1\mathbf{k} + \omega_2\mathbf{i} = 0.75\mathbf{k} + 0.4\mathbf{i} \text{ rad/s}\end{aligned}$$

of magnitude

$$\omega = \sqrt{0.75^2 + 0.4^2} = 0.85 \text{ rad/s}$$

(b) Let $\boldsymbol{\alpha}$ be the angular acceleration of the link; then

$$\boldsymbol{\alpha} = \frac{\mathrm{d}}{\mathrm{d}t}(\boldsymbol{\omega}) = \frac{\mathrm{d}}{\mathrm{d}t}(\boldsymbol{\omega}_1 + \boldsymbol{\omega}_2)$$

Since $\boldsymbol{\omega}_1$ is constant in magnitude and direction, $\dot{\boldsymbol{\omega}}_1 = 0$. Hence

$$\boldsymbol{\alpha} = \dot{\boldsymbol{\omega}}_2$$

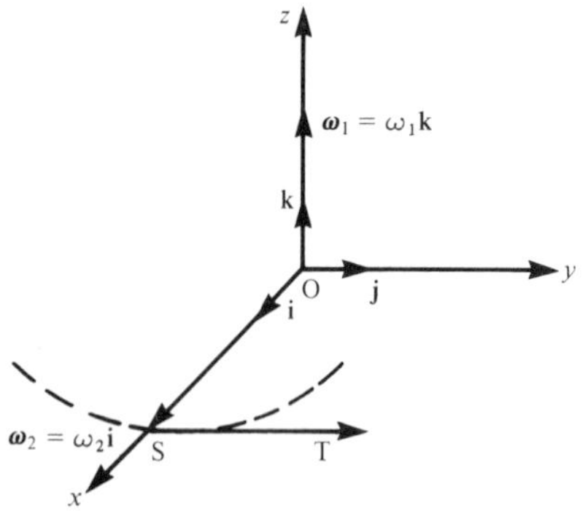

Figure 6.23 Vector diagram for example 6.8.

To calculate $\boldsymbol{\alpha}$ consider Figure 6.23: the tip of the vector $\boldsymbol{\omega}_2$ moves in a circle of radius $\boldsymbol{\omega}_2$ so that the change in this vector is a vector $\overrightarrow{\text{ST}}$ parallel to the *y*-axis as shown. Hence $\overrightarrow{\text{ST}}$ represents the angular acceleration $\boldsymbol{\alpha}$ of the link. Recalling the vector product $\mathbf{k} \wedge \mathbf{i} = \mathbf{j}$,

$$\alpha = \boldsymbol{\omega}_1 \wedge \boldsymbol{\omega}_2 = \omega_1\mathbf{k} \wedge \omega_2\mathbf{i} = \omega_1\omega_2\mathbf{j}$$

Solution Cont.

Hence

$$\alpha = \omega_1\omega_2 = 0.75 \times 0.4 = 0.3 \text{ rad/s}^2$$

(c) Let $\mathbf{R} = \overrightarrow{\text{OP}}$ be the position vector of P. Now

$$\begin{aligned}\mathbf{R} &= l\cos\theta\,\mathbf{j} + l\sin\theta\,\mathbf{k} \\ &= 1.25\cos 60^\circ\,\mathbf{j} + 1.25\sin 60^\circ\,\mathbf{k} \\ &= 0.625\mathbf{j} + 1.083\mathbf{k} \text{ m}\end{aligned}$$

The velocity $\mathbf{v}$ of P is given by equation (6.32); since $\mathbf{v}_\text{A} = 0$ we have

$$\mathbf{v} = \boldsymbol{\omega} \wedge \mathbf{R} = \begin{vmatrix} \mathbf{i} & \mathbf{j} & \mathbf{k} \\ 0.4 & 0 & 0.75 \\ 0 & 0.625 & 1.083 \end{vmatrix}$$

$$= -0.469\mathbf{i} - 0.433\mathbf{j} + 0.25\mathbf{k} \text{ m/s}$$

The magnitude of the velocity of P is

$$v = \sqrt{0.469^2 + 0.433^2 + 0.25^2} = 0.686 \text{ m/s}$$

(d) The acceleration of P is given by equation (6.33), and since here $\mathbf{a}_\text{A} = 0$ and $\dot{\boldsymbol{\omega}} \wedge \mathbf{R} = \boldsymbol{\alpha} \wedge \mathbf{R}$,

$$\begin{aligned}\mathbf{a} &= \boldsymbol{\alpha} \wedge \mathbf{R} + \boldsymbol{\omega} \wedge (\boldsymbol{\omega} \wedge \mathbf{R}) \\ &= \boldsymbol{\alpha} \wedge \mathbf{R} + \boldsymbol{\omega} \wedge \mathbf{v}\end{aligned}$$

Substituting numerical values yields

$$\mathbf{a} = \begin{vmatrix} \mathbf{i} & \mathbf{j} & \mathbf{k} \\ 0 & 0.3 & 0 \\ 0 & 0.625 & 1.083 \end{vmatrix} + \begin{vmatrix} \mathbf{i} & \mathbf{j} & \mathbf{k} \\ 0.4 & 0 & 0.75 \\ -0.469 & -0.433 & 0.25 \end{vmatrix}$$

$$\begin{aligned}&= 0.375\mathbf{i} + 0.325\mathbf{i} - 0.452\mathbf{j} - 0.173\mathbf{k} \\ &= 0.65\mathbf{i} - 0.452\mathbf{j} - 0.173\mathbf{k} \text{ m/s}^2\end{aligned}$$

of magnitude

$$a = \sqrt{0.65^2 + 0.452^2 + 0.173^2} = 0.81 \text{ m/s}^2$$

6.2.3 **Motion relative to moving coordinates**

When dealing with motion in space we shall come across problems that can be solved more efficiently by means of two sets of coordinates: one fixed, a Newtonian frame, and one fixed to the moving body and moving with it, e.g. an aeroplane or robotic device.

Consider, for example, the mechanism shown in Figure 6.24. A link OA rotates about OX whilst a cylinder AB connected to the arm OA is capable of rotation about an axis Ax through A. The end B connected to the piston rod can slide in or out, according to which side of the piston is under pressure. The whole system then rotates about a vertical axis OZ.

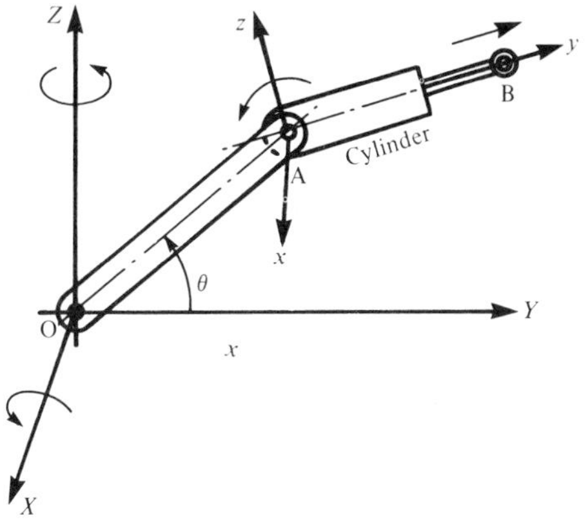

Figure 6.24 Motion with respect to moving coordinates.

To obtain the absolute velocity and acceleration of point B it is easier to do so with reference to a set of coordinates $Axyz$ fixed in the cylinder and moving with it and then to consider the motion of A relative to the fixed frame $OXYZ$.

Let us then derive general equations which will enable us to solve such problems by considering the motion in space of a point B as shown in Figure 6.25.

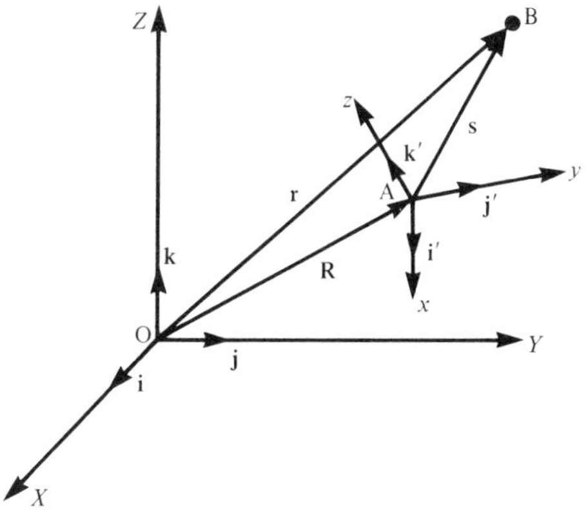

Figure 6.25 Vector diagram for the motion in Figure 6.24.

The position of B is fixed by means of the position vector **r** in the Newtonian frame XYZ, but its position can also be fixed by means of the position vector **R** from O to A, the origin of a moving frame of reference xyz, and the position vector s measured from A.

From the figure we have

$$\mathbf{r} = \mathbf{R} + \mathbf{s} \tag{6.34}$$

r and **R** may be expressed in terms of the unit vectors **i**, **j** and **k**, and **s** in terms of unit vectors **i**′, **j**′ and **k**′ in the moving coordinate system. We should note carefully that s is the position of B relative to the moving frame, i.e.

$$\mathbf{s} = x\mathbf{i}' + y\mathbf{j}' + z\mathbf{k}'$$

To obtain the velocity we differentiate equation (6.34) with respect to time:

$$\dot{\mathbf{r}} = \dot{\mathbf{R}} + \dot{\mathbf{s}} \tag{6.35}$$

But

$$\dot{\mathbf{s}} = (\dot{x}\mathbf{i}' + \dot{y}\mathbf{j}' + \dot{z}\mathbf{k}') + (x\dot{\mathbf{i}}' + y\dot{\mathbf{j}}' + z\dot{\mathbf{k}}') \tag{6.36}$$

where the first bracketed term is the velocity $\mathbf{v}_r$ of B as seen by an observer at A, i.e. the velocity of B relative to A so that $\mathbf{v}_r = \mathbf{v}_{BA}$, and the second bracketed term represents the effect of the rotation of the axes xyz.

If $\boldsymbol{\omega}$ is the angular velocity of the moving frame xyz with respect to the Newtonian frame, then $\dot{\mathbf{i}}'$, $\dot{\mathbf{j}}'$ and $\dot{\mathbf{k}}'$ are the rates of change of the unit vectors and are given by

$$\dot{\mathbf{i}}' = \boldsymbol{\omega} \wedge \mathbf{i}' \qquad \dot{\mathbf{j}}' = \boldsymbol{\omega} \wedge \mathbf{j}' \qquad \dot{\mathbf{k}}' = \boldsymbol{\omega} \wedge \mathbf{k}'$$

as for $\dot{\mathbf{R}} = \boldsymbol{\omega} \wedge \mathbf{R}$ in section 6.2.2.

It follows that

$$\begin{aligned} x\dot{\mathbf{i}}' + y\dot{\mathbf{j}}' + z\dot{\mathbf{k}}' &= x\boldsymbol{\omega} \wedge \mathbf{i}' + y\boldsymbol{\omega} \wedge \mathbf{j}' + z\boldsymbol{\omega} \wedge \mathbf{k}' \\ &= \boldsymbol{\omega} \wedge (x\mathbf{i}' + y\mathbf{j}' + z\mathbf{k}') \\ &= \boldsymbol{\omega} \wedge \mathbf{s} \end{aligned}$$

Hence

$$\dot{\mathbf{s}} = \mathbf{v}_r + \boldsymbol{\omega} \wedge \mathbf{s}$$

Substituting in (6.35) yields

$$\dot{\mathbf{r}} = \dot{\mathbf{R}} + \mathbf{v}_r + \boldsymbol{\omega} \wedge \mathbf{s} \tag{6.37}$$

To obtain the acceleration we differentiate equation (6.37) with respect to time:

$$\ddot{\mathbf{r}} = \ddot{\mathbf{R}} + \dot{\mathbf{v}}_r + \dot{\boldsymbol{\omega}} \wedge \mathbf{s} + \boldsymbol{\omega} \wedge \dot{\mathbf{s}} \tag{6.38}$$

But from (6.36)

$$\dot{\mathbf{v}}_r = (\ddot{x}\mathbf{i}' + \ddot{y}\mathbf{j}' + \ddot{z}\mathbf{k}') + (\dot{x}\dot{\mathbf{i}}' + \dot{y}\dot{\mathbf{j}}' + \dot{z}\dot{\mathbf{k}}') \tag{6.39}$$

where the first bracketed term is the acceleration $\mathbf{a}_r$ of B as seen by an observer at A, and the second bracketed term again represents the effect of the rotation of the moving axes xyz. But the second term of this equation is

$$\begin{aligned} \dot{x}(\boldsymbol{\omega} \wedge \mathbf{i}') + \dot{y}(\boldsymbol{\omega} \wedge \mathbf{j}') + \dot{z}(\boldsymbol{\omega} \wedge \mathbf{k}') &= \boldsymbol{\omega} \wedge (\dot{x}\mathbf{i}' + \dot{y}\mathbf{j}' + \dot{z}\mathbf{k}') \\ &= \boldsymbol{\omega} \wedge \mathbf{v}_r \end{aligned}$$

from (6.36). Substituting in equation (6.39) yields

$$\dot{\mathbf{v}}_r = \mathbf{a}_r + \boldsymbol{\omega} \wedge \mathbf{v}_r$$

and by substituting in equation (6.38) we obtain

$$\ddot{\mathbf{r}} = \ddot{\mathbf{R}} + \mathbf{a}_r + \boldsymbol{\omega} \wedge \mathbf{v}_r + \dot{\boldsymbol{\omega}} \wedge \mathbf{s} + \boldsymbol{\omega} \wedge (\mathbf{v}_r + \boldsymbol{\omega} \wedge \mathbf{s})$$

i.e.

$$\ddot{\mathbf{r}} = \ddot{\mathbf{R}} + \mathbf{a}_r + \dot{\boldsymbol{\omega}} \wedge \mathbf{s} + 2\boldsymbol{\omega} \wedge \mathbf{v}_r + \boldsymbol{\omega} \wedge (\boldsymbol{\omega} \wedge \mathbf{s}) \tag{6.40}$$

where $\ddot{\mathbf{R}}$ is the acceleration of the moving frame, $\mathbf{a}_r$ is the acceleration of B relative to the moving frame, $\dot{\boldsymbol{\omega}} \wedge \mathbf{s}$ is the effect of the angular acceleration of the moving frame, $2\boldsymbol{\omega} \wedge \mathbf{v}_r$ is the Coriolis acceleration, and $\boldsymbol{\omega} \wedge (\boldsymbol{\omega} \wedge \mathbf{s})$ is the centripetal acceleration.

If B is a point in a rigid body $\dot{\mathbf{v}}_r = \mathbf{a}_r = 0$ and $\mathbf{v}_r = 0$, and we get back to equations (6.32) and (6.33).

EXAMPLE 6.9

The cylinder shown in Figure 6.26 rotates at a constant angular velocity $\boldsymbol{\Omega}$ about a vertical axis OZ. At the same time it is being elevated at a constant angular velocity ω in a vertical plane whilst the piston rod is moving outwards with a constant velocity u.

Using the data given, calculate (a) the velocity of B, and (b) the acceleration of B. (Data: OB = 1.75 m, $u = 0.5$ m/s $\Omega = 0.75$ rad/s, $\omega = 0.4$ rad/s and $\theta = 60°$.)

Example Cont.

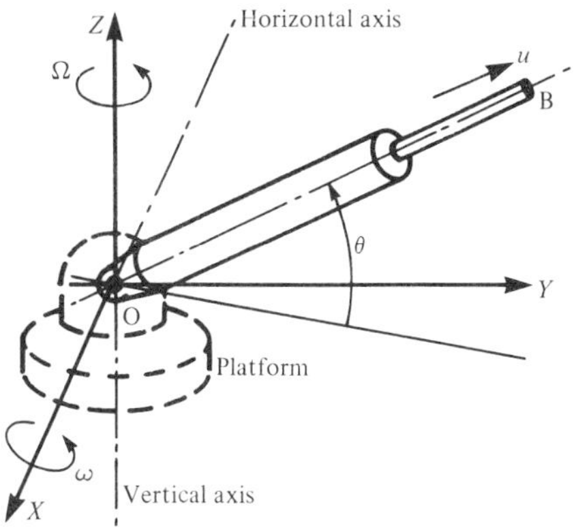

Figure 6.26 Cylinder of example 6.9.

SOLUTION

$$\mathbf{u} = 0.5 \cos 60° \, \mathbf{j} + 0.5 \sin 60° \, \mathbf{k}$$
$$= 0.25\mathbf{j} + 0.483\mathbf{k}$$

$$\mathbf{s} = 1.75 \cos 60° \, \mathbf{j} + 1.75 \sin 60° \, \mathbf{k}$$
$$= 0.875\mathbf{j} + 1.516\mathbf{k}$$

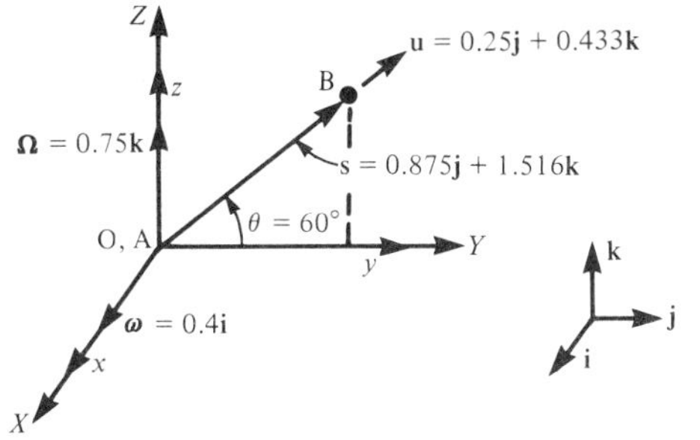

Figure 6.27 Vector diagram for example 6.9.

Let $OXYZ$ be a Newtonian frame of reference and $Axyz$ a frame attached to the rotating platform which supports the cylinder; A coincides with O.

The platform has an angular velocity $\boldsymbol{\Omega} = 0.75\mathbf{k}$ relative to the fixed frame $OXYZ$, and the cylinder an angular velocity $\boldsymbol{\omega} = 0.4\mathbf{i}$ relative to the supporting platform and hence to the rotating frame $Axyz$.

Solution Cont.

The two frames are coincident at the instant considered.

(a) Velocity of B (equation (6.37)):

Let s be the position vector of B. Then the absolute velocity $\mathbf{v}_B$ of B is given by

$$\mathbf{v}_B = \boldsymbol{\Omega} \wedge \mathbf{s} + \boldsymbol{\omega} \wedge \mathbf{s} + \mathbf{u}$$
$$= (\boldsymbol{\Omega} + \boldsymbol{\omega}) \wedge \mathbf{s} + \mathbf{u}$$
$$= (0.4\mathbf{i} + 0.75\mathbf{k}) \wedge (0.875\mathbf{j} + 1.516\mathbf{k})$$
$$+ 0.25\mathbf{j} + 0.433\mathbf{k}$$

Hence

$$\mathbf{v}_B = \begin{vmatrix} \mathbf{i} & \mathbf{j} & \mathbf{k} \\ 0.4 & 0 & 0.75 \\ 0 & 0.875 & 1.516 \end{vmatrix} + 0.25\mathbf{j} + 0.433\mathbf{k}$$

$$= \mathbf{i}(-0.875 \times 0.75) - \mathbf{j}(0.4 \times 1.516)$$
$$+ \mathbf{k}(0.4 \times 0.875) + 0.25\mathbf{j} + 0.433\mathbf{k}$$
$$= -0.656\mathbf{i} - 0.356\mathbf{j} + 0.783\mathbf{k}$$

The magnitude of $\mathbf{v}_B$ is

$$v_B = \sqrt{0.656^2 + 0.356^2 + 0.783^2}$$
$$= 1.083 \text{ m/s}$$

Solution Cont.

(b) Acceleration of B (equation (6.40)):

In this case $\ddot{\mathbf{R}} = \dot{\boldsymbol{\omega}} = 0$, since the origin of the moving frame coincides with that of the fixed frame, and the moving frame is not accelerating. Furthermore $\mathbf{a}_r = 0$ because B is moving with constant velocity $\mathbf{u}$.

It follows that the acceleration $\mathbf{a}_B$ of B is given by

$$\mathbf{a}_B = \boldsymbol{\Omega} \wedge (\boldsymbol{\Omega} \wedge \mathbf{s}) + \boldsymbol{\omega} \wedge (\boldsymbol{\omega} \wedge \mathbf{s}) + 2\boldsymbol{\Omega} \wedge (\boldsymbol{\omega} \wedge \mathbf{s} + \mathbf{u})$$

The vectors ω and s are perpendicular to each other so that

$$\boldsymbol{\omega} \wedge (\boldsymbol{\omega} \wedge \mathbf{s}) = -\omega^2 \mathbf{s}$$

Solution Cont.

Substituting numerical values yields

$$\begin{aligned}\mathbf{a}_B &= 0.75\mathbf{k} \wedge [0.75\mathbf{k} \wedge (0.875\mathbf{j} + 1.516\mathbf{k})] \\ &\quad - 0.4^2(0.875\mathbf{j} + 1.516\mathbf{k}) \\ &\quad + 2 \times 0.75\mathbf{k} \wedge [0.4\mathbf{i} \wedge (0.875\mathbf{j} \\ &\quad + 1.516\mathbf{k}) + 0.25\mathbf{j} + 0.438\mathbf{k}] \\ &= 0.75\mathbf{k} \wedge (-0.75 \times 0.875\mathbf{i}) - 0.140\mathbf{j} \\ &\quad - 0.243\mathbf{k} + 1.5\mathbf{k} \wedge (0.350\mathbf{k} - 0.606\mathbf{j} \\ &\quad + 0.25\mathbf{j} + 0.438\mathbf{k}) \\ &= -0.492\mathbf{j} - 0.140\mathbf{j} - 0.243\mathbf{k} + 0.909\mathbf{i} \\ &\quad -0.375\mathbf{i} \\ &= 0.534\mathbf{i} - 0.632\mathbf{j} - 0.243\mathbf{k}\end{aligned}$$

and

$$\begin{aligned}a_B &= \sqrt{0.534^2 + 0.632^2 + 0.243^2} \\ &= 0.862 \text{ m/s}^2\end{aligned}$$

ALTERNATIVE SOLUTION

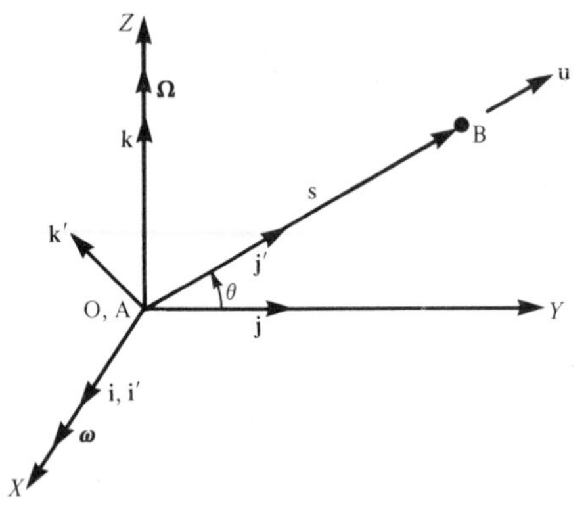

Figure 6.28 Alternative vector diagram for example 6.9.

Suppose we define a moving frame of reference fixed to the cylinder as shown in Figure 6.28, with unit vectors $\mathbf{i}'$, $\mathbf{j}'$ and $\mathbf{k}'$. The velocity of B relative to the rotating axes is $\mathbf{u} = u\mathbf{j}'$ where $u = |\mathbf{u}|$, i.e. the magnitude of $\mathbf{u}$. Also $\mathbf{s} = s\mathbf{j}'$.

Solution Cont.

The absolute velocity $\mathbf{v}_B$ of B is

$$\mathbf{v}_B = \boldsymbol{\omega} \wedge s\mathbf{j}' + \boldsymbol{\Omega} \wedge s\mathbf{j}' + u\mathbf{j}'$$

Before we can solve this equation we must express the unit vectors $\mathbf{i}'$, $\mathbf{j}'$ and $\mathbf{k}'$ as functions of $\mathbf{i}$, $\mathbf{j}$ and $\mathbf{k}$ in the fixed frame. We have

$$\begin{aligned}\mathbf{i}' &= \mathbf{i} \\ \mathbf{j}' &= \cos\theta\,\mathbf{j} + \sin\theta\,\mathbf{k} \\ \mathbf{k}' &= -\sin\theta\,\mathbf{j} + \cos\theta\,\mathbf{k}\end{aligned}$$

Substituting in the equation for $\mathbf{v}_B$ yields

$$\mathbf{v}_B = (\omega\mathbf{i} + \Omega\mathbf{k}) \wedge [s\cos\theta\,\mathbf{j} + s\sin\theta\,\mathbf{k} + u\cos\theta\,\mathbf{j} + u\sin\theta\,\mathbf{k}]$$

which is the equation previously obtained.

To obtain the acceleration we would proceed in a similar manner.

We shall encounter problems where the moving axes rotate relative to the fixed axes; it will then be necessary to relate the unit vectors along both sets of axes. This is done in the next section.

6.2.4 **Rotation of axes: Eulerian angles**

We saw in example 6.9 that by choosing a frame of reference that is moving with the body, in that case the cylinder, we needed a relationship between unit vectors in the moving frame and those in the fixed or Newtonian frame.

This orientation of axes fixed in the moving body (referred to as body axes) will occur quite frequently, e.g. in the gyroscopic stabilisation of a satellite spinning about its longitudinal axis, or in a robotic device where the movement of a "wrist" is referred to axes fixed to a "forearm" and then to a frame fixed to the ground.

As one illustration, consider three rotations of a moving set of axes xyz relative to a fixed set XYZ, the two sets being coincident initially. Now let us rotate the xyz axes about the z-axis through an angle ψ, and let $\mathbf{i}$, $\mathbf{j}$ and $\mathbf{k}$ be the unit vectors in the fixed system and $\mathbf{i}'$, $\mathbf{j}'$ and $\mathbf{k}'$ those in the moving system as shown in Figure 6.29. From the diagram we have

$$\begin{aligned} \mathbf{i}' &= \cos\psi\,\mathbf{i} + \sin\psi\,\mathbf{j} \\ \mathbf{j}' &= -\sin\psi\,\mathbf{i} + \cos\psi\,\mathbf{j} \\ \mathbf{k}' &= \mathbf{k} \end{aligned}$$

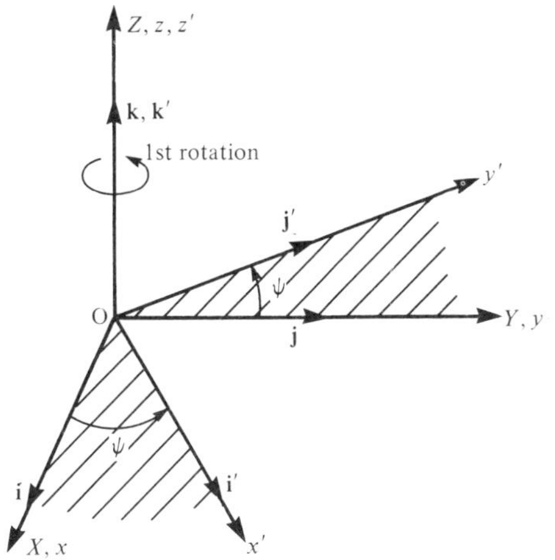

Figure 6.29 First rotation of axes, through ψ about z-axis.

This relationship may be expressed in matrix form thus

$$\begin{pmatrix} \mathbf{i}' \\ \mathbf{j}' \\ \mathbf{k}' \end{pmatrix} = \begin{pmatrix} \cos\psi & \sin\psi & 0 \\ -\sin\psi & \cos\psi & 0 \\ 0 & 0 & 1 \end{pmatrix} \begin{pmatrix} \mathbf{i} \\ \mathbf{j} \\ \mathbf{k} \end{pmatrix} \tag{6.41}$$

Let the $\mathbf{i}'$, $\mathbf{j}'$ and $\mathbf{k}'$ set now be rotated about the x'-axis through an angle θ as shown in Figure 6.30. We have

$$\begin{aligned} \mathbf{i}'' &= \mathbf{i}' \\ \mathbf{j}'' &= \cos\theta\,\mathbf{j}' + \sin\theta\,\mathbf{k}' \\ \mathbf{k}'' &= -\sin\theta\,\mathbf{j}' + \cos\theta\,\mathbf{k}' \end{aligned}$$

or in matrix form

$$\begin{pmatrix} \mathbf{i}'' \\ \mathbf{j}'' \\ \mathbf{k}'' \end{pmatrix} = \begin{pmatrix} 1 & 0 & 0 \\ 0 & \cos\theta & \sin\theta \\ 0 & -\sin\theta & \cos\theta \end{pmatrix} \begin{pmatrix} \mathbf{i}' \\ \mathbf{j}' \\ \mathbf{k}' \end{pmatrix} \tag{6.42}$$

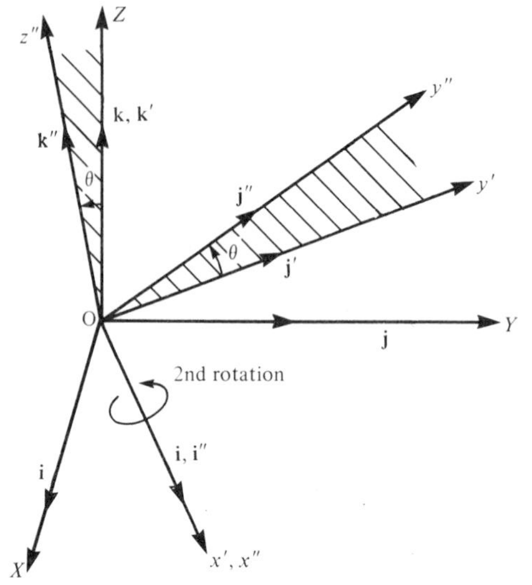

Figure 6.30 Second rotation of axes, through θ about x'-axis.

Combining equations (6.41) and (6.42) yields

$$\begin{pmatrix} \mathbf{i}'' \\ \mathbf{j}'' \\ \mathbf{k}'' \end{pmatrix} = \begin{pmatrix} 1 & 0 & 0 \\ 0 & \cos\theta & \sin\theta \\ 0 & -\sin\theta & \cos\theta \end{pmatrix} \begin{pmatrix} \cos\psi & \sin\psi & 0 \\ -\sin\psi & \cos\psi & 0 \\ 0 & 0 & 1 \end{pmatrix} \begin{pmatrix} \mathbf{i} \\ \mathbf{j} \\ \mathbf{k} \end{pmatrix}$$

i.e.

$$\begin{pmatrix} \mathbf{i}'' \\ \mathbf{j}'' \\ \mathbf{k}'' \end{pmatrix} = \begin{pmatrix} \cos\psi & \sin\psi & 0 \\ -\sin\psi\cos\theta & \cos\psi\cos\theta & \sin\theta \\ \sin\psi\sin\theta & -\cos\psi\sin\theta & \cos\theta \end{pmatrix} \begin{pmatrix} \mathbf{i} \\ \mathbf{j} \\ \mathbf{k} \end{pmatrix} \tag{6.43}$$

The last rotation is about the z''-axis through an angle ϕ as shown in Figure 6.31. This rotation is similar to the first, so that

$$\begin{aligned} \mathbf{i}''' &= \cos\phi\, \mathbf{i}'' + \sin\phi\, \mathbf{j}'' \\ \mathbf{j}''' &= -\sin\phi\, \mathbf{i}'' + \cos\phi\, \mathbf{j}'' \\ \mathbf{k}''' &= \mathbf{k}'' \end{aligned}$$

i.e.

$$\begin{pmatrix} \mathbf{i}''' \\ \mathbf{j}''' \\ \mathbf{k}''' \end{pmatrix} = \begin{pmatrix} \cos\phi & \sin\phi & 0 \\ -\sin\phi & \cos\phi & 0 \\ 0 & 0 & 1 \end{pmatrix} \begin{pmatrix} \mathbf{i}'' \\ \mathbf{j}'' \\ \mathbf{k}'' \end{pmatrix} \tag{6.44}$$

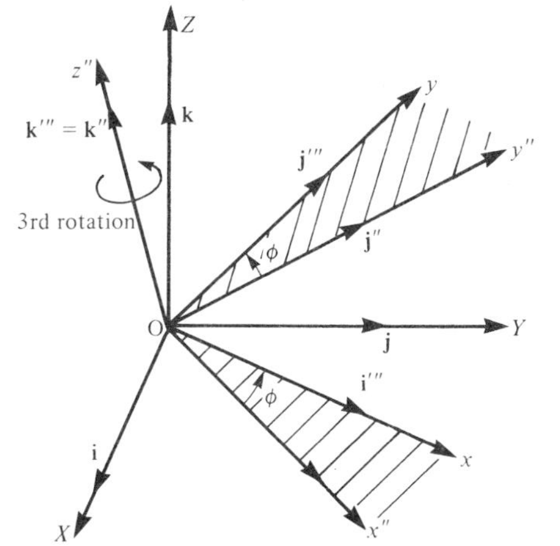

Figure 6.31 Third rotation of axes, through ϕ about z''-axis.

Hence after the three independent rotations *in the order* ψ, θ, ϕ we have

$$\begin{pmatrix} \mathbf{i}''' \\ \mathbf{j}''' \\ \mathbf{k}''' \end{pmatrix} = \begin{pmatrix} a_{11} & a_{12} & a_{13} \\ a_{21} & a_{22} & a_{23} \\ a_{31} & a_{32} & a_{33} \end{pmatrix} \begin{pmatrix} \mathbf{i} \\ \mathbf{j} \\ \mathbf{k} \end{pmatrix} \tag{6.45}$$

where

$$\begin{aligned}
a_{11} &= \cos\phi\cos\psi - \sin\phi\sin\psi\cos\theta \\
a_{12} &= \cos\phi\sin\psi + \sin\phi\cos\psi\cos\theta \\
a_{13} &= \sin\phi\sin\theta \\
a_{21} &= -\sin\phi\cos\psi - \cos\phi\sin\psi\cos\theta \\
a_{22} &= -\sin\phi\sin\psi + \cos\phi\cos\psi\cos\theta \\
a_{23} &= \cos\phi\sin\theta \\
a_{31} &= \sin\psi\sin\theta \\
a_{32} &= -\cos\psi\sin\theta \\
a_{33} &= \cos\theta
\end{aligned}$$

The three angles ψ, θ, ϕ are used to fix the orientation of a body in space relative to a fixed frame of reference; they are known as the *Eulerian angles,* after the Swiss mathematician Leonhard Euler (1707–83). If the order of the rotations is changed so will be the results, and it is therefore important to keep a record of the actual sequence; by convention the above sequence has been adopted as standard.

If x, y and z are the coordinates of a point P in a body relative to body-fixed axes x, y and z as shown in Figure 6.32, and X, Y and Z its coordinates relative to a fixed frame of reference, it can be shown, by proceeding in a way similar to that above, that

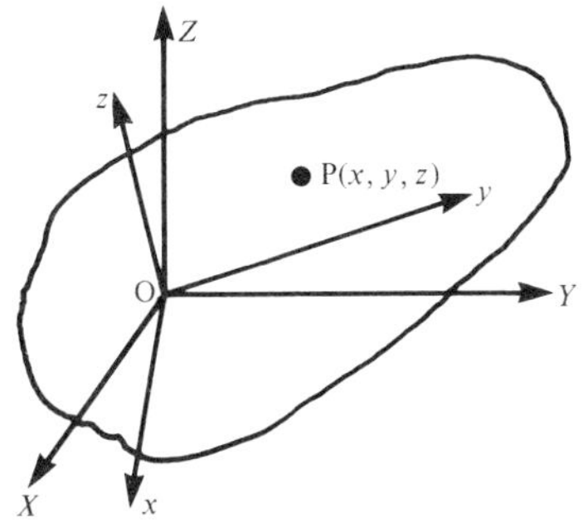

Figure 6.32 Fixed frame *XYZ* and body-fixed axes *xyz.*

$$\begin{pmatrix} X \\ Y \\ Z \end{pmatrix} = \underbrace{\begin{pmatrix} \cos\psi & -\sin\psi & 0 \\ \sin\psi & \cos\psi & 0 \\ 0 & 0 & 1 \end{pmatrix}}_{\text{first rotation}} \underbrace{\begin{pmatrix} 1 & 0 & 0 \\ 0 & \cos\theta & -\sin\theta \\ 0 & \sin\theta & \cos\theta \end{pmatrix}}_{\text{second rotation}}$$

$$\underbrace{\begin{pmatrix} \cos\phi & -\sin\phi & 0 \\ \sin\phi & \cos\phi & 0 \\ 0 & 0 & 1 \end{pmatrix}}_{\text{third rotation}} \begin{pmatrix} x \\ y \\ z \end{pmatrix} \tag{6.46}$$

The reader is strongly advised to verify this result.

6.3 ANGULAR MOMENTUM

6.3.1 Single particle

Consider a particle of mass m at A moving with a velocity $\mathbf{v}$ relative to a fixed frame of reference XYZ, a Newtonian frame, as shown in Figure 6.33. Its momentum $m\mathbf{v}$ is represented by the vector $\overrightarrow{AB}$ in the direction of the velocity. If we multiply this momentum vector by the perpendicular distance d to the origin O of our coordinate system, we obtain the moment of momentum or angular momentum of the particle with respect to that point.

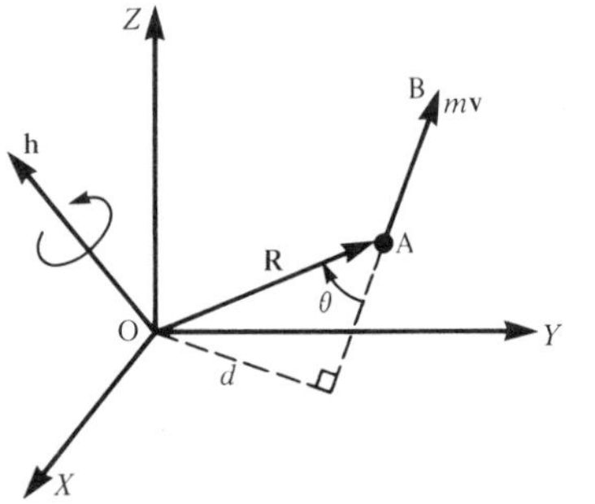

Figure 6.33 Angular momentum of a particle.

If $\mathbf{R}$ is the position vector of A, then $OA = |\mathbf{R}| = R$, and the magnitude h of the angular momentum is

$$h = R \sin\theta \, mv$$

Hence this angular momentum can be represented by a vector $\mathbf{h}$ perpendicular to the plane OAB and directed in accordance with the right-hand rule so that

$$\mathbf{h} = \mathbf{R} \wedge m\mathbf{v} \tag{6.47}$$

The rate of increase of the angular momentum is

$$\begin{aligned} \frac{\mathrm{d}}{\mathrm{d}t}(\mathbf{h}) &= \frac{\mathrm{d}}{\mathrm{d}t}(\mathbf{R} \wedge m\mathbf{v}) \\ &= \dot{\mathbf{R}} \wedge m\mathbf{v} + \mathbf{R} \wedge m\dot{\mathbf{v}} \end{aligned}$$

Since $\dot{\mathbf{R}} = \mathbf{v}$ it follows that

$$\frac{\mathrm{d}}{\mathrm{d}t}(\mathbf{h}) = \dot{\mathbf{h}} = \mathbf{R} \wedge m\dot{\mathbf{v}}$$

(because $\mathbf{v} \wedge \mathbf{v} = 0$), or

$$\dot{\mathbf{h}} = \mathbf{R} \wedge \mathbf{F} \tag{6.48}$$

where $\mathbf{F} = m\dot{\mathbf{v}}$ is the resultant force acting on the particle.

Thus the rate of increase of the angular momentum of the particle about O is equal to the moment about O of the resultant force on the particle. This is the principle of angular momentum.

In particular, if the resultant force has zero moment about O, the angular momentum about O remains constant and we have conservation of angular momentum for the particle. Since

$$\mathbf{R} = x\mathbf{i} + y\mathbf{j} + z\mathbf{k}$$

and

$$\mathbf{F} = F_x\mathbf{i} + F_y\mathbf{j} + F_z\mathbf{k}$$

equation (6.48) can always be reduced to three scalar equations for computational purposes.

6.3.2 **System of particles**

The angular momentum **H** about O of a system of particles is defined as the vector sum of the angular momenta of the separate particles about O. Thus we have

$$\mathbf{H} = \sum(\mathbf{R} \wedge m\mathbf{v})$$

and the rate of change of the angular momentum is

$$\frac{\mathrm{d}}{\mathrm{d}t}(\mathbf{H}) = \frac{\mathrm{d}}{\mathrm{d}t}\sum(\mathbf{R} \wedge m\mathbf{v}) = \sum\left(\frac{\mathrm{d}}{\mathrm{d}t}\mathbf{R} \wedge m\mathbf{v} + \mathbf{R} \wedge \frac{\mathrm{d}}{\mathrm{d}t}m\mathbf{v}\right)$$

Hence

$$\dot{\mathbf{H}} = \sum(\mathbf{R} \wedge m\dot{\mathbf{v}}) = \sum(\mathbf{R} \wedge \mathbf{F}) \qquad \text{since } \mathbf{v} \wedge m\mathbf{v} = 0$$

where **F** is the resultant force acting on the particle at **R**, i.e. at A in Figure 6.33. $\mathbf{R} \wedge \mathbf{F}$ is the moment of the force about O.

When the summation is carried out the internal actions are neglected because pairs of forces between particles are equal and opposite, and their moment about O is therefore zero.

If **M** is the moment about O of all the forces, then $\mathbf{M} = \sum(\mathbf{R} \wedge \mathbf{F})$ and so

$$\mathbf{M} = \dot{\mathbf{H}} \tag{6.49}$$

Equation (6.49) states that the moment about O of all the external forces acting on the system of particles is equal to the rate of change of the angular momentum about O.

We now propose to investigate equation (6.49) by introducing the centre of mass of the system of particles. Let us write equation (6.49) explicitly thus:

$$(\mathbf{R} \wedge \mathbf{F}) = \frac{\mathrm{d}}{\mathrm{d}t}\sum(\mathbf{R} \wedge m\mathbf{v}) \tag{6.49a}$$

Let $\mathbf{R}_\mathrm{G}$ be the position vector of the centre of mass G, and s be the position vector of a particle from the centre of mass. Substituting for **R** in equation (6.49a) we obtain

$$\mathbf{H} = \sum[(\mathbf{R}_\mathrm{G} + \mathbf{s}) \wedge m\mathbf{v}]$$

$$= \mathbf{R}_\mathrm{G} \wedge \sum m\mathbf{v} + \sum(\mathbf{s} \wedge m\mathbf{v})$$

The second term of this expression is the moment of momentum of the system of particles about the centre of mass G. Let this be denoted by $\mathbf{H}_G$. Then

$$\mathbf{H} = \mathbf{H}_G + \mathbf{R}_G \wedge \sum m\mathbf{v}$$

Differentiating yields

$$\dot{\mathbf{H}} = \dot{\mathbf{H}}_G + \dot{\mathbf{R}}_G \wedge \sum m\mathbf{v} + \mathbf{R}_G \wedge \frac{\mathrm{d}}{\mathrm{d}t}\left(\sum m\mathbf{v}\right) \tag{6.49b}$$

But by the definition of the centre of mass, $\dot{\mathbf{R}}_G \sum m = \sum m\mathbf{v}$. It therefore follows that the vector product $\dot{\mathbf{R}}_G \wedge \sum m\mathbf{v} = 0$. Hence equation (6.49b) becomes

$$\dot{\mathbf{H}} = \dot{\mathbf{H}}_G + \mathbf{R}_G \wedge \frac{\mathrm{d}}{\mathrm{d}t}\left(\sum m\mathbf{v}\right)$$

Since

$$\frac{\mathrm{d}}{\mathrm{d}t}\left(\sum m\mathbf{v}\right) = \sum \mathbf{F}$$

it follows that

$$\dot{\mathbf{H}} = \dot{\mathbf{H}}_G + \mathbf{R}_G \wedge \sum \mathbf{F} \tag{6.49c}$$

The resultant moment of the external forces is equal to

$$\mathbf{M} = \sum(\mathbf{R} \wedge \mathbf{F}) = \sum[(\mathbf{R}_G + \mathbf{s}) \wedge \mathbf{F}]$$

Let $\mathbf{M}_G = \sum(\mathbf{s} \wedge \mathbf{F})$ be the moment of the external forces about the centre of mass G, so that

$$\mathbf{M} = \mathbf{R}_G \wedge \sum \mathbf{F} + \mathbf{M}_G \tag{6.49d}$$

Comparing equations (6.49c) and (6.49d) it then follows that

$$\mathbf{M}_G = \dot{\mathbf{H}}_G \tag{6.50}$$

This result states that the rate of change of the angular momentum about the centre of mass of the system is equal to the total moment of the external forces about the centre of mass. This important equation is true whether the centre of mass is accelerating or not. Any other point selected must be at rest in a Newtonian frame.

6.3.3 **Rigid body**

A rigid body is a system consisting of an infinite number of particles such that the distances between them remain constant, and the equations derived in the previous section will also apply here. The expressions for the angular momentum of a rigid body are, however, different.

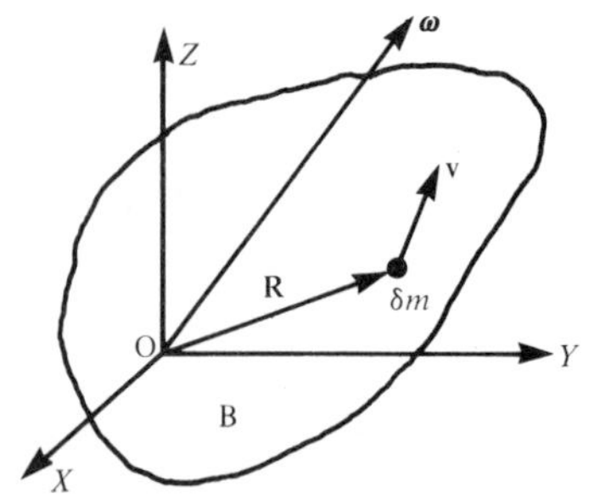

Figure 6.34 Angular momentum of a rigid body.

Consider the body B shown in Figure 6.34 and an element of mass δm at a distance $\mathbf{R}$ from O, the origin of a fixed frame of reference. Let $\mathbf{v}$ be the velocity of the element and $\boldsymbol{\omega}$ be the angular velocity of the body. Then by the definition of angular momentum we have for this element of mass

$$\delta \mathbf{H} = \mathbf{R} \wedge \delta m \mathbf{v}$$

and for the whole body

$$\mathbf{H} = \int (\mathbf{R} \wedge \mathbf{v})\, \mathrm{d}m$$

Since

$$\begin{aligned} \mathbf{v} &= \boldsymbol{\omega} \wedge \mathbf{R} \\ \mathbf{H} &= \int \mathbf{R} \wedge (\boldsymbol{\omega} \wedge \mathbf{R})\, \mathrm{d}m \\ &= \int [(\mathbf{R} \cdot \mathbf{R})\boldsymbol{\omega} - (\mathbf{R} \cdot \boldsymbol{\omega})\mathbf{R}]\, \mathrm{d}m \qquad (6.51) \end{aligned}$$

by equation (6.30).

Equation (6.51) is not very useful as it stands. Let

$$\mathbf{R} = x\mathbf{i} + y\mathbf{j} + z\mathbf{k}$$

and

$$\boldsymbol{\omega} = \omega_x \mathbf{i} + \omega_y \mathbf{j} + \omega_z \mathbf{k}$$

Substituting in (6.51) yields

$$\begin{aligned} \mathbf{H} = & \int [(y^2 + z^2)\omega_x - yx\omega_y - zx\omega_z]\, \mathrm{d}m\, \mathbf{i} \\ & + \int [(-xy\omega_x) + (x^2 + z^2)\omega_y - zy\omega_z]\, \mathrm{d}m\, \mathbf{j} \\ & + \int [(-xz\omega_x) - yz\omega_z + (x^2 + y^2)\omega_z]\, \mathrm{d}m\, \mathbf{k} \end{aligned}$$

But $\omega_x, \omega_y, \omega_z$ are common factors and can therefore be taken out of the integration sign; we then have

$$\begin{aligned} \mathbf{H} = & (I_{xx}\omega_x - I_{xy}\omega_y - I_{zx}\omega_z)\, \mathbf{i} \\ & + (-I_{xy}\omega_x - I_{yy}\omega_y - I_{zy}\omega_z)\, \mathbf{j} \\ & + (-I_{xz}\omega_x - I_{yz}\omega_y - I_{zz}\omega_z)\, \mathbf{k} \end{aligned}$$

or, expressed in matrix form,

$$\begin{pmatrix} H_x \\ H_y \\ H_z \end{pmatrix} = \begin{pmatrix} I_{xx} & -I_{yx} & -I_{zx} \\ -I_{xy} & I_{yy} & -I_{zy} \\ -I_{xz} & -I_{yz} & I_{zz} \end{pmatrix} \begin{pmatrix} \omega_x \\ \omega_y \\ \omega_z \end{pmatrix} \qquad (6.52)$$

where

$$\begin{aligned} I_{xx} &= \int (y^2 + z^2)\, \mathrm{d}m \\ I_{yy} &= \int (x^2 + z^2)\, \mathrm{d}m \\ I_{zz} &= \int (x^2 + y^2)\, \mathrm{d}m \end{aligned}$$

which are the moments of inertia of the body about the axes OX, OY, OZ, and

$$\begin{aligned} I_{yx} &= I_{xy} = \int xy\, \mathrm{d}m \\ I_{zy} &= I_{yz} = \int yz\, \mathrm{d}m \\ I_{xz} &= I_{zx} = \int xz\, \mathrm{d}m \end{aligned}$$

which are the *products of inertia* of the body. (These can be either positive or negative.) The moments and products of inertia are physical properties of the body.

Equation (6.52) is sometimes written thus

$$\mathbf{H} = \mathbf{I}\boldsymbol{\omega} \tag{6.53}$$

where **I** is called the *inertia tensor* of the body. The 3 × 3 matrix is a particular way of expressing this tensor.

The principal axes of the body are those on which the products of inertia vanish, and if the coordinate axes, say 1, 2 and 3, coincide with these, then

$$\mathbf{I} = \begin{pmatrix} I_{11} & 0 & 0 \\ 0 & I_{22} & 0 \\ 0 & 0 & I_{33} \end{pmatrix}$$

where I_{11}, I_{22} and I_{33} are principal moments of inertia of the body.

The angular momentum thus becomes

$$\mathbf{H} = I_{11}\mathbf{i} + I_{22}\mathbf{j} + I_{33}\mathbf{k}$$

6.3.4 Motion of a rigid body in space: Euler's equations

(a) Rate of change of a vector: rotating frame of reference

Let **i**, **j** and **k** be three unit vectors in a Cartesian frame of reference that rotates with an angular velocity $\boldsymbol{\omega}$ relative to a fixed reference frame, i.e. a Newtonian frame.

Any vector **R** may be expressed in terms of these unit vectors, so that

$$\mathbf{R} = R_x\mathbf{i} + R_y\mathbf{j} + R_z\mathbf{k}$$

Let us now obtain the rate of change $\mathrm{d}\mathbf{R}/\mathrm{d}t$ of this vector as seen by an observer in the Newtonian frame.

Differentiating **R** with respect to time gives

$$\frac{\mathrm{d}\mathbf{R}}{\mathrm{d}t} = (\dot{R}_x\mathbf{i} + \dot{R}_y\mathbf{j} + \dot{R}_z\mathbf{k}) + (R_x\dot{\mathbf{i}} + R_y\dot{\mathbf{j}} + R_z\dot{\mathbf{k}})$$

where the first bracketed term is the rate of change of **R** referred, to the moving frame, and the second bracketed term represents the effect of the rotation of the frame. Since **i**, **j** and **k** are vectors fixed in the rotating frame, they have the same angular velocity ω. Considering the vector **i**, for instance, we may regard it as the position vector of a particle P relative to an origin O, i.e. the origin of **i**. Then $\dot{\mathbf{i}}$ is the velocity of P relative to O, and by equation (6.31)

$$\dot{\mathbf{i}} = \boldsymbol{\omega}\wedge\mathbf{i}$$

Similarly for **j** and **k**

$$\dot{\mathbf{j}} = \boldsymbol{\omega}\wedge\mathbf{j} \qquad \dot{\mathbf{k}} = \boldsymbol{\omega}\wedge\mathbf{k}$$

Substituting in the expression for $\mathrm{d}\mathbf{R}/\mathrm{d}t$ yields

$$\frac{\mathrm{d}\mathbf{R}}{\mathrm{d}t} = \frac{\partial\mathbf{R}}{\partial t} + \boldsymbol{\omega}\wedge\mathbf{R} \tag{6.54}$$

where

$$\frac{\partial \mathbf{R}}{\partial t} = \dot{R}_x\mathbf{i} + \dot{R}_y\mathbf{j} + \dot{R}_z\mathbf{k}$$

and the symbol $\partial\mathbf{R}/\partial t$ is used here to denote the time derivative of **R** when the unit vectors are held fixed. Thus $\partial\mathbf{R}/\partial t$ is the rate of change of **R** as seen by an observer in the rotating frame and the term $\boldsymbol{\omega} \wedge \mathbf{R}$ is due to the rotation of the frame.

We may apply equation (6.54) to any vector in a rotating frame, such as velocity, acceleration, angular momentum, etc.

(b) Euler's equations of motion

Consider a rigid body moving in space under the action of a number of external forces $\mathbf{F}_1, \mathbf{F}_2, \ldots, \mathbf{F}_n$ whose resultant is **F** as shown in Figure 6.35.

Let xyz be a set of body-fixed axes whose origin is at the centre of mass G and $\boldsymbol{\omega}$ be the angular velocity of the body, and hence of the frame. Then $\boldsymbol{\omega}$ may be expressed thus:

$$\boldsymbol{\omega} = p\mathbf{i} + q\mathbf{j} + r\mathbf{k}$$

where p, q and r are the components of the angular velocity along the x-, y- and z-axes respectively and **i**, **j** and **k** are unit vectors along those axes.

If **H** is the angular momentum about G, then by equation (6.53)

$$\mathbf{H} = \mathbf{I}\boldsymbol{\omega}$$

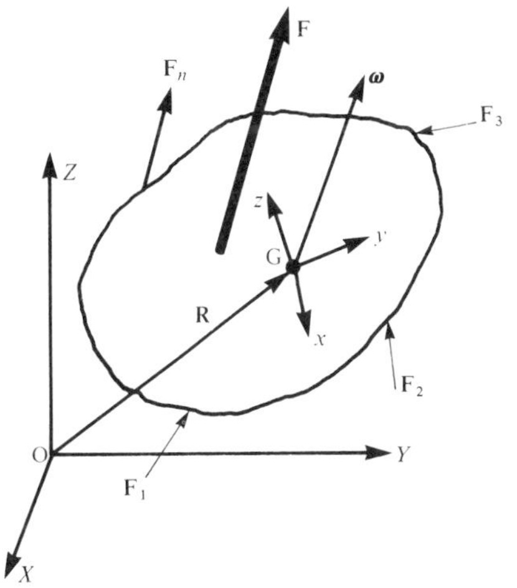

Figure 6.35 Motion of a rigid body caused by external forces: deriving Euler's equations.

And if **M** is the resultant external moment about G then by equation (6.50)

$$\mathbf{M} = \dot{\mathbf{H}} = \frac{d}{dt}(\mathbf{I}\boldsymbol{\omega}) \tag{6.55}$$

Carrying out the differentiation as in equation (6.54) we have

$$\begin{aligned}\dot{\mathbf{H}} &= \frac{\partial \mathbf{H}}{\partial t} + \boldsymbol{\omega} \wedge \mathbf{H} \\ &= \dot{H}_x\mathbf{i} + \dot{H}_y\mathbf{j} + \dot{H}_z\mathbf{k} + \boldsymbol{\omega} \wedge \mathbf{H}\end{aligned} \tag{6.56}$$

And expressing **M** in terms of its components it follows that

$$\begin{aligned}M_x &= \dot{H}_x - rH_y + qH_z \\ M_y &= \dot{H}_y - pH_z + rH_x \\ M_z &= \dot{H}_z - qH_x + pH_y\end{aligned} \tag{6.57}$$

These equations can be simplified by choosing the body-fixed axes xyz to coincide with the principal axes of the body, whereupon the products of inertia are zero and the equations (6.57) become

$$\begin{aligned} M_x &= A\dot{p} - (B - C)qr \\ M_y &= B\dot{q} - (C - A)rp \\ M_z &= C\dot{r} - (A - B)pq \end{aligned} \qquad (6.58)$$

which are Euler's equations of motion for a rigid body rotating about its centre of mass. In the above equations the principal moments of inertia are:

$$A = I_{xx} \qquad B = I_{yy} \qquad C = I_{zz}$$

To obtain the general motion of a rigid body in space we need to consider the total effect of the forces acting on the body. If **F** is the resultant of the external forces then by Newton's second law we have

$$\mathbf{F} = m\mathbf{a}$$

where **a** is the acceleration relative to a Newtonian frame and m is the mass of the body. If we now resolve **a** and **F** along the xyz body-fixed axes with origin at the centre of mass, then by equation (6.54)

$$\mathbf{a} = \frac{\partial \mathbf{v}}{\partial t} + \boldsymbol{\omega} \wedge \mathbf{v}$$

where

$$\mathbf{v} = v_x\mathbf{i} + v_y\mathbf{j} + v_z\mathbf{k}$$

is the velocity of the centre of mass. Substituting for **a** in the above equation of motion we have

$$\begin{aligned} F_x &= m(\dot{v}_x + v_z q - v_y r) \\ F_y &= m(\dot{v}_y + v_x r - v_z p) \\ F_z &= m(\dot{v}_z + v_y p - v_x q) \end{aligned} \qquad (6.59)$$

These six scalar equations (6.58) and (6.59) are sufficient to determine the motion of a body in space. Euler's equations have shortcomings in that the integrals of p, q and r do not give the orientation of the body, and in order to overcome this the Eulerian angles (section 6.2.4) are introduced. Nevertheless equations (6.58) are adequate to solve a large number of practical problems.

The following points should be borne in mind in the application of Euler's equations:

(a) The origin is the centre of mass of the rigid body or a fixed point.

(b) Axes xyz are fixed in the body, and referred to as body-fixed axes with origin at the centre of mass.

(c) Axes xyz are the principal axes of the body.

(d) p, q and r are the components of the absolute angular velocity $\boldsymbol{\omega}$ of the body.

(e) A, B and C are the principal moments of inertia of the body about the x-, y- and z-axes respectively.

(f) M_x, M_y and M_z are the moments of the external forces about the x-, y- and z-axes respectively.

EXAMPLE 6.10

Figure 6.36 shows a space vehicle during a coasting phase. In this case it is not subjected to any external forces and we wish to investigate its motion about its centre of mass.

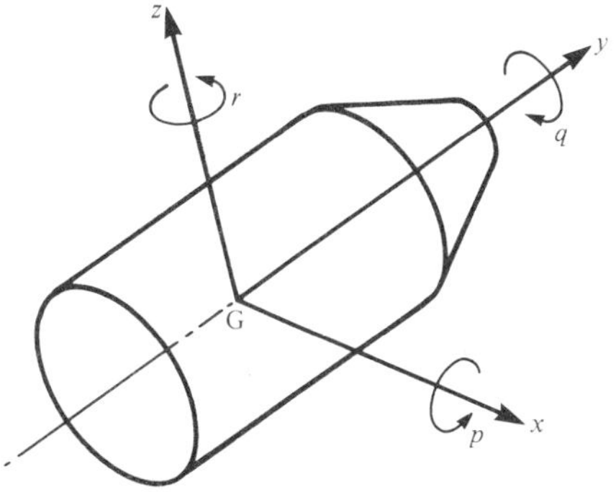

Figure 6.36 Space vehicle of example 6.10.

SOLUTION

The vehicle in this instance is a solid of revolution which has symmetry about the y-axis, so that $A = C$, i.e. $I_{xx} = I_{zz}$. Substitution in Euler's equations yields

$$0 = A\dot{p} - (B - A)qr$$
$$0 = A\dot{q}$$
$$0 = A\dot{r} - (A - B)pq$$

From the second equation we find

$$q = \text{constant}$$

which means that the body is spinning about the y-axis at a steady rate.

To simplify the remaining equations let

$$k = \frac{A - B}{A}q$$

Substituting in these equations we get

$$\dot{p} + kr = 0$$
$$\dot{r} - kp = 0$$

Multiplying the first of these equations by p and the second by r, and adding yields

$$p\dot{p} + r\dot{r} = 0$$

Integrating we have

$$p^2 + r^2 = \text{constant}$$

The angular velocity of the body has magnitude

$$\omega = \sqrt{p^2 + r^2 + q^2}$$

Since no external moments act on the body, the angular momentum vector **H** is constant and its component in the xz plane is, by equation (6.5.2),

$$A(p\mathbf{i} + r\mathbf{k})$$

EXAMPLE 6.11

During a manoeuvre in a harbour the ship shown in outline in Figure 6.37 is turning about a vertical axis through O at an angular velocity Ω and an angular acceleration $\dot{\Omega}$. At that instant a generator is started and its angular velocity and acceleration about its shaft are ω and $\dot{\omega}$ respectively.

Example Cont.

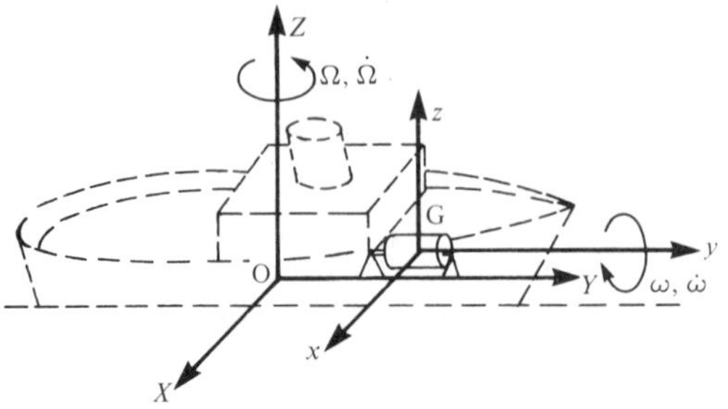

Figure 6.37 Manoeuvring ship.

Obtain an expression for the bearing reactions as a result of this manoeuvre if the bearings which support the shaft of the rotor of the generator are a distance d apart.

SOLUTION

Let XYZ be a Newtonian frame of reference and xyz the body-fixed axes in the rotor as shown in Figure 6.37. In order to obtain the components of the moment **M** parallel to the Newtonian frame, let us consider this problem when the xyz axes are parallel to XYZ.

The angular velocity $\boldsymbol{\omega}$ in Euler's equations is

$$\boldsymbol{\omega} = \omega \mathbf{j} + \Omega \mathbf{k}$$

and the angular acceleration of the rotor is

$$\begin{aligned}\dot{\boldsymbol{\omega}} &= \dot{\Omega}\mathbf{k} + \dot{\omega}\mathbf{j} + \Omega\mathbf{k} \wedge \omega\mathbf{j} \\ &= \dot{\Omega}\mathbf{k} + \dot{\omega}\mathbf{j} - \Omega\omega\mathbf{i}\end{aligned}$$

Hence the components p, q and r of the angular velocity and the angular acceleration components $\dot{p}$, $\dot{q}$ and $\dot{r}$ are:

$$\begin{aligned} p &= 0 & \dot{p} &= -\Omega\omega \\ q &= \omega & \dot{q} &= \dot{\omega} \\ r &= \Omega & \dot{r} &= \dot{\Omega} \end{aligned}$$

Solution Cont.

Substituting in Euler's equations (6.58), we get

$$\begin{aligned} M_x &= A(-\omega\Omega) - (B - C)\omega\Omega \\ M_y &= B\dot{\omega} - (C - A) \times 0 \\ M_z &= C\dot{\Omega} - (A - B) \times 0 \end{aligned}$$

Since $A = B$ these equations become

$$\begin{aligned} M_x &= -B\omega\Omega \\ M_y &= B\dot{\omega} \\ M_z &= C\dot{\Omega} \end{aligned}$$

Hence

$$\mathbf{M} = -B\omega\Omega\mathbf{i} + B\dot{\omega}\mathbf{j} + C\dot{\Omega}\mathbf{k}$$

and the bearing reactions **R** will be

$$\mathbf{R} = -\frac{B\omega\Omega}{d}\mathbf{i} + \frac{B\dot{\omega}}{d}\mathbf{j} + \frac{C\dot{\Omega}}{d}\mathbf{k}$$

If $\dot{\omega} = \dot{\Omega} = 0$, the bearing reactions are

$$\mathbf{R} = -\frac{B\omega\Omega}{d}\mathbf{i}$$

of magnitude $B\omega\Omega/d$, which the reader will recognise as the gyroscopic effect discussed in Chapter 5.

EXAMPLE 6.12

The two-bladed propeller of a light aircraft (Figure 6.38) rotates about its shaft axis Oz with constant speed ω; its moment of inertia is I about that axis.

Example Cont.

The aircraft makes a turn to the left about the vertical axis Oy at a constant angular velocity Ω; the y-axis remains vertical. A moment M that acts on the

Example Cont.

propeller is supported by bending of the shaft whilst a moment M_{Oz} is supported by torsion of the shaft. Obtain expressions for these two moments as functions of the angle θ between the propeller and an axis Ox perpendicular to Oy and Oz. O is the centre of the propeller. If $I = 8.25$ kg m^2, $\Omega = 0.1$ rad/s and the propeller rotates at 2500 rev/min, calculate the maximum values of the two moments.

SOLUTION

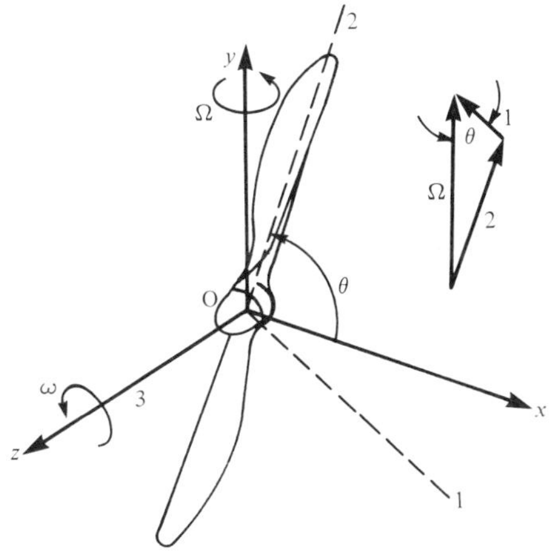

Figure 6.38 Two-bladed propeller of example 6.12.

Applying Euler's equations we have

$$I_1\dot{\omega}_1 - (I_2 - I_3)\omega_2\omega_3 = M_1$$
$$I_2\dot{\omega}_2 - (I_3 - I_1)\omega_1\omega_3 = M_2$$
$$I_3\dot{\omega}_3 - (I_1 - I_2)\omega_1\omega_2 = M_3$$

where 1, 2 and 3 refer to the principal axes.

In this case

$$I_1 = I_3 = I \qquad I_2 = 0$$
$$\omega_1 = -\Omega\cos\theta \qquad \omega_2 = \Omega\sin\theta$$
$$\omega_3 = \omega = \dot{\theta}$$

so that

$$\dot{\omega}_1 = \Omega\sin\theta\,\dot{\theta} = \Omega\omega\sin\theta$$
$$\dot{\omega}_2 = \Omega\cos\theta\,\dot{\theta} = \Omega\omega\cos\theta$$
$$\dot{\omega}_2 = 0$$

Substituting in the first of Euler's equations yields

$$I\Omega\omega\sin\theta + I\Omega\omega\sin\theta = M_1$$

or

$$M_1 = 2I\Omega\omega\sin\theta$$

This is the bending moment. Substituting in the second and third of Euler's equations yields

$$M_2 = 0$$

and

$$-I(-\Omega\cos\theta)(\Omega\sin\theta) = M_3$$

or

$$M_3 = \tfrac{1}{2}I\Omega^2\sin 2\theta$$

This is the torque on the shaft.

The maximum values are:

(a) bending moment

$$M_{1\,\max} = 2I\Omega\omega$$
$$= 2 \times 8.25 \times 0.1 \times \frac{2\pi \times 2500}{60}$$
$$= 432 \text{ N m}$$

(b) torque on the shaft

$$M_{3\,\max} = \tfrac{1}{2}I\Omega^2$$
$$= \tfrac{1}{2} \times 8.25 \times 0.1^2 = 0.04 \text{ N m}$$

EXAMPLE 6.13

Figure 6.39 shows a rig for testing equipment to be installed in an artificial satellite. It consists of a capsule that can rotate about an axis Oz fixed to a yoke which rotates about the axis OX perpendicular to OZ, with a constant angular velocity $\boldsymbol{\Omega}$. Calculate the magnitude of the maximum torque required about the X-axis when the capsule rotates at a constant speed ω, using the data given. The principal axes x, y and z are fixed to the capsule; OX, OY and OZ are fixed Cartesian axes. (Data: mass of the capsule = 75 kg, I_x = 2.5 kg m^2, $I_y = I_z$ = 7.5 kg m^2, Ω = 15 rad/s, ω = 35 rad/s.)

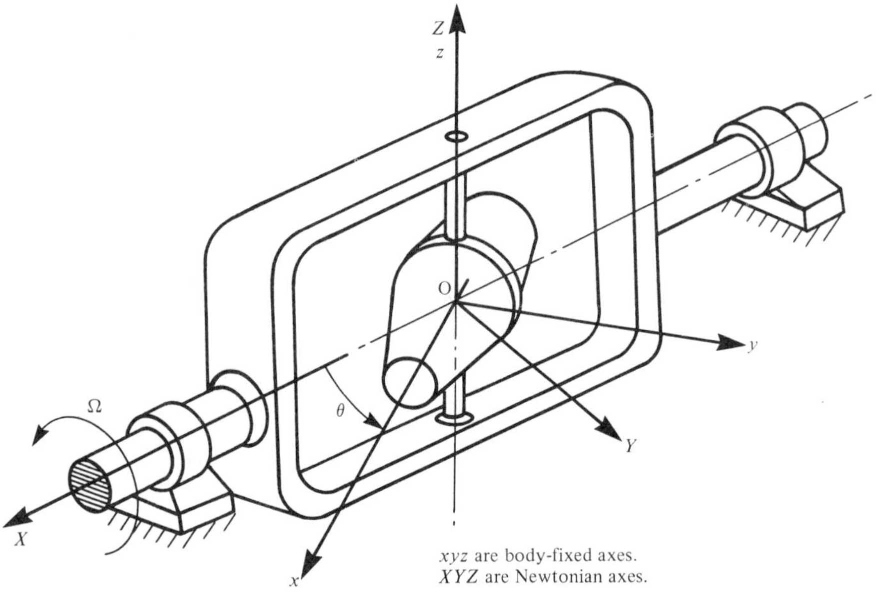

Figure 6.39 Testing rig of example 6.13.

SOLUTION

Let x, y and z be the principal axes of the capsule. Applying Euler's equations, we have

$$I_x\dot{\omega}_x - (I_y - I_z)\omega_y\omega_z = M_x$$
$$I_y\dot{\omega}_y - (I_z - I_x)\omega_z\omega_x = M_y$$
$$I_z\dot{\omega}_z - (I_x - I_y)\omega_x\omega_y = M_z$$

Referring to Figure 6.40, we have

$$\omega_x = \Omega\cos\theta \qquad \omega_y = -\Omega\sin\theta$$
$$\omega_z = \dot{\theta} = \omega$$
$$\dot{\omega}_x = -\Omega\sin\theta\,\dot{\theta} \qquad \dot{\omega}_y = -\Omega\cos\theta\,\dot{\theta}$$
$$\dot{\omega}_z = 0$$

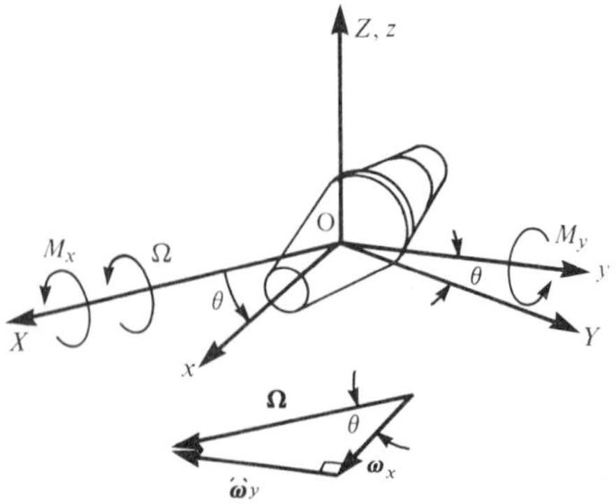

Figure 6.40 Axes for the testing rig.

Solution Cont.

Substituting in Euler's equations with $\dot{\theta} = \omega$,

$$\begin{aligned} M_x &= I_x(-\Omega\omega \sin\theta) - 0 \\ &= -I_x\Omega\omega \sin\theta \\ M_y &= I_y(-\Omega\omega\cos\theta) - (I_z - I_x)\Omega\omega\cos\theta \\ &= -\Omega\omega\cos\theta\,(I_y + I_z - I_x) \end{aligned}$$

M_z is not required for the purpose of calculating M:

$$\begin{aligned} M &= M_x\cos\theta - M_y\cos(90° - \theta) \\ &= M_x\cos\theta - M_y\sin\theta \end{aligned}$$

Therefore

$$\begin{aligned} M &= -I_x\Omega\omega\sin\theta\cos\theta \\ &\quad + \Omega\omega\cos\theta\,(I_y + I_z - I_x)\sin\theta \\ &= \tfrac{1}{2}\Omega\omega\sin 2\theta\,(-I_x + I_y + I_z - I_x) \\ &= \tfrac{1}{2}\Omega\omega(I_y + I_z - 2I_x)\sin 2\theta \\ &= 2625\sin 2\theta \end{aligned}$$

Thus

$$M_{\max} = 2625 \text{ N m}$$

EXERCISES

6.1 Given the two vectors

$$\mathbf{P} = 4\mathbf{i} - 3\mathbf{j} + 5\mathbf{k}$$

and

$$\mathbf{R} = \mathbf{i} + 2\mathbf{j} - 7\mathbf{k}$$

calculate (a) $\mathbf{P} \cdot \mathbf{R}$ and the angle between $\mathbf{P}$ and $\mathbf{R}$, and (b) $\mathbf{P} \wedge \mathbf{R}$.

6.2 Given the three vectors

$$\begin{aligned} \mathbf{P} &= \mathbf{i} + \mathbf{j} + \mathbf{k} \\ \mathbf{Q} &= 2\mathbf{i} - 3\mathbf{j} + 4\mathbf{k} \\ \mathbf{R} &= \mathbf{j} - 2\mathbf{k} \end{aligned}$$

calculate (a) $\mathbf{P} + \mathbf{Q} - \mathbf{R}$, (b) $\mathbf{P} \cdot (\mathbf{Q} + \mathbf{R})$ and $(\mathbf{P} + \mathbf{Q}) \cdot \mathbf{R}$, and (c) $\mathbf{P} \wedge (\mathbf{Q} \wedge \mathbf{R})$ and $(\mathbf{P} \wedge \mathbf{Q}) \wedge \mathbf{R}$.

6.3 Given the two vectors

$$\begin{aligned} \mathbf{P} &= \cos 15t\,\mathbf{i} + \sin 15t\,\mathbf{j} \\ \mathbf{R} &= 2t\mathbf{i} + 4t^2\mathbf{j} + t^3\mathbf{k} \end{aligned}$$

where t is the time, calculate (a) $\mathrm{d}\mathbf{P}/\mathrm{d}t \equiv \dot{\mathbf{P}}$ and $\dot{P}$, (b) $\mathrm{d}^2\mathbf{R}/\mathrm{d}t^2 \equiv \ddot{\mathbf{R}}$.

6.4 Calculate the values of b that will result in the vectors

$$\mathbf{P} = \mathbf{i} + 2\mathbf{j} + b\mathbf{k}$$

and

$$\mathbf{R} = b\mathbf{i} - 3\mathbf{j} + 5b\mathbf{k}$$

being perpendicular to each other.

6.5 The velocity of a boat relative to the water is represented by $3\mathbf{i} + 4\mathbf{j}$ knots, and that of the water relative to the bank is $\mathbf{i} - 3\mathbf{j}$ knots. Calculate the velocity of the boat relative to the bank if **i** and **j** represent east and north directions respectively.

6.6 Three forces acting on a particle have magnitudes 5, 3 and 1 kN and act in the directions of the vectors (0.6, 0.2, 0.3), (0.3, −0.2, 0.6) and (−0.2, −0.3, −0.6) m respectively. These remain constant while the particle moves from the point A (0.2, −0.1, −0.3) to the point B (0.5, −0.1, 0.1) m. Calculate the work done by the forces.

6.7 A rigid body is rotating with an angular velocity of 40 rad/s about an axis of direction (0, 0.3, −0.1) passing through the point A (0.1, 0.3, −0.1) m. Calculate the velocity at the point P (0.4, −0.2, 0.1) m in magnitude and direction.

6.8 A rigid body is rotating about the fixed point (300, −100, −200) mm with an angular velocity of 500 rad/s, the axis of rotation being in the direction of (200, 100, −200) mm. Calculate the velocities of points on the body whose positions are (400, 100, 0) mm and (300, 200, 100) mm.

6.9 A particle, of mass 15 kg, whose position at a particular instant is (500, 400, 100) mm, is moving with a velocity of $27\mathbf{i} + 21\mathbf{j} + 12\mathbf{k}$ m/s. Calculate the angular momentum about the origin.

6.10 The crank A_0A of the planar four-bar mechanism shown in Figure 6.41 rotates at a constant angular velocity of 50 rad/s anticlockwise. Using vector methods calculate (a) the velocity of the points A on A_0A and B on AB, (b) the angular velocity of the coupler AB and of the follower BB_0, and (c) the angular acceleration of BB_0 and of AB.

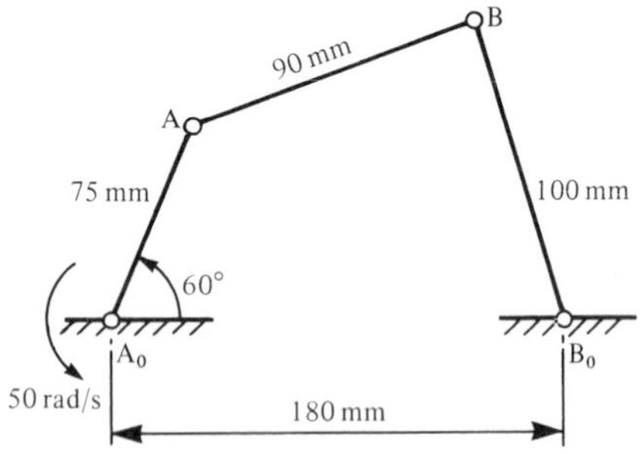

Figure 6.41

6.11 Sliders A and B are constrained to move in the guides G_1 and G_2 shown in Figure 6.42. G_1 is in the xz plane at an angle of 30° to the x-axis, and G_2 is in the xy plane at an angle of 15° to the y-axis. The two sliders are connected together by means of ball and socket joints to the rigid rod AB. If the velocity of A is 2 m/s in the direction shown, calculate the velocity of B at the instant when the coordinates at A are (105, 0, 170) mm and those of B are (120, 240, 0) mm. Calculate also the angular velocity of AB.

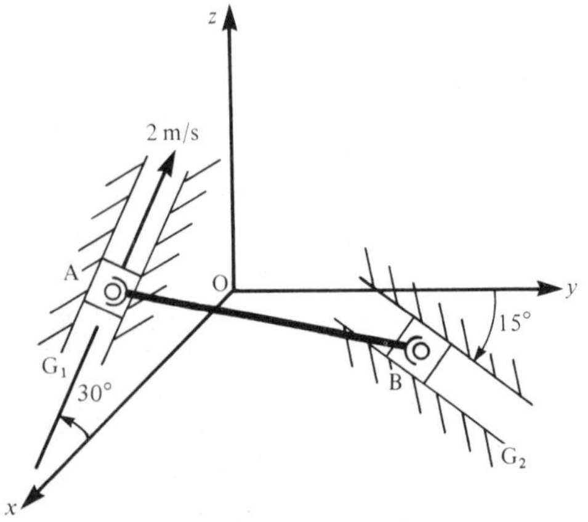

Figure 6.42

6.12 Figure 6.43(a) shows a spatial four-bar linkage where the input crank A_0A rotates in the xz plane about the y-axis at a constant angular velocity ω rad/s. The output crank B_0B rotates in the yz plane about an axis parallel to the x-axis and at a distance d from A_0. The cranks are connected by ball-and-socket joints at A and B to the rigid rod AB. Using the data given show that $\psi = 10.9°$ is one solution when $\phi = 60°$ and hence calculate the angular velocity $\mathbf{\Omega}$ rad/s of the output link B_0B. (Data: $A_0A = 127$ mm, $AB = 508$ mm, $B_0B = 254$ mm, $A_0B_0 = 508$ mm and $\omega = 35$ rad/s.)

(*Hint:* Refer to Figure 6.43(b) and represent each link by the vectors shown so that $\mathbf{a} + \mathbf{b} = \mathbf{c} + \mathbf{d}$.)

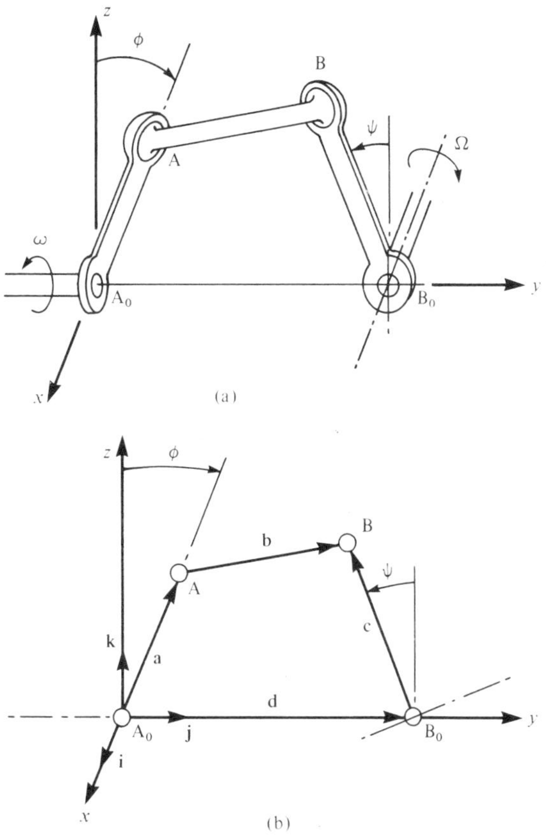

Figure 6.43

6.13 A single-stage turbine consists of a uniform thin disc rigidly fixed at the mid-span of a light uniform shaft. The disc has a diameter of 450 mm and a mass of 25 kg; it is out of true and makes an angle of 0.5° with a plane at right angles to the axis of the shaft. Calculate the couple acting on the bearings which support the shaft when the latter rotates at 15 000 rev/min. Use Euler's equations.

6.14 Figure 6.44 shows one of the four-bladed propellers of a ship. It rotates at a constant speed $\mathbf{\Omega}$ about the axis Ox and its principal moments of inertia are 2000 kg m^2 and 350 kg m^2. The ship is turning to port with a constant angular velocity ω about a vertical axis. Using Euler's equations calculate the resulting maximum bending and twisting moments on the shaft when the propeller rotates at 120 rev/min and the ship is turning at the rate of 0.3 rad/s.

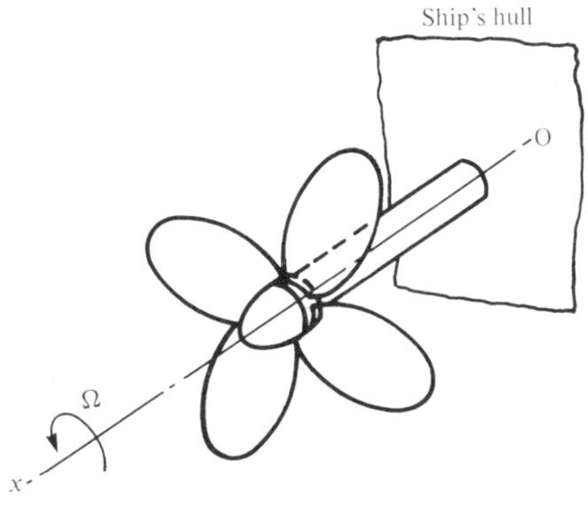

Figure 6.44

7

Introduction to Vibrations

7.1 INTRODUCTION

The essential elements of a vibrating mechanical system are a *mass* and a *spring.* Both of these elements are capable of storing energy, and the periodic transfer of kinetic energy from the mass to potential energy in the spring and vice versa constitutes the vibration. The spring is characterised by its stiffness, that is the force exerted per unit extension.

Normally, some energy is lost in the vibration either through friction or viscous forces or in other ways. Such losses are referred to as *damping,* and in an isolated mass–spring system they will cause any periodic motion initially present to decay progressively as the total energy in the system decreases.

In order to have a sustained vibration in a mass–spring system with damping, the system must be acted upon by an external fluctuating force, often referred to as the *exciting force* or excitation. In certain circumstances, the energy necessary for sustained vibration may be fed into the system in other ways. Systems that vibrate without the application of a fluctuating external force are called *self-excited.*

As an example of a system that is capable of vibrating, consider a machine sitting on a pad of rubber. The machine is capable of vibrating in many ways; for example, it could rock from side to side or twist about a vertical axis. This is because we have chosen an example having many degrees of freedom. The number of degrees of freedom of a system is the minimum number of coordinates that will completely define the positions of the moving parts of the system. The different ways in which the machine can vibrate are called modes. The number of possible modes of vibration is the same as the number of degrees of freedom, in this case six.

Probably the most important motion or mode of vibration will be a vertical oscillation of the machine. The parameters that are relevant to a discussion of this vertical oscillatory motion are the ones mentioned above: namely, the mass of the machine, the stiffness of the spring (which in this example is the rubber pad), the damping in the system (which would arise from energy losses in the rubber pad) and any fluctuating forces acting on the machine. Fluctuating forces would result, for example, from unbalanced rotating components.

An electric motor driving a flywheel through a flexible coupling is an example of a torsional vibrating system. The parameters in this torsional system corresponding to mass and stiffness are the moments of inertia of the motor armature and flywheel and the torsional stiffness of the coupling, which is the torque per unit angle of twist.

The twisting oscillation of the flywheel relative to the armature of the motor could be excited by fluctuations of motor torque and would be superimposed on the steady rotation.

PERIODIC MOTION 7.2

7.2.1 Sinusoidal motion

Before discussing how systems vibrate, it is desirable to consider how the periodic variation of a quantity can be described. We shall take displacement to be the quantity under consideration and denote by x its value at a time t. Everything about displacement in this section, however, will apply equally well to other variable quantities such as acceleration and force.

Figure 7.1 shows a sinusoidal or simple harmonic motion and indicates the amplitude x_0 and period τ of the motion. If the period is measured in seconds, the frequency of the motion f in hertz (Hz, cycles per second) is given by

$$f = \frac{1}{\tau} \tag{7.1}$$

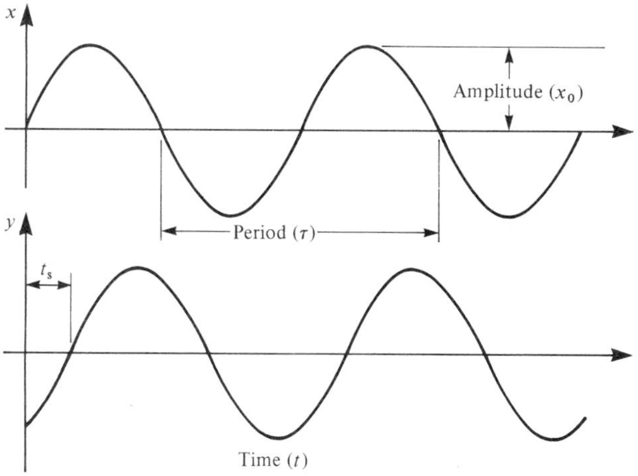

Figure 7.1 Simple harmonic or sinusoidal motion.

Although frequency is usually measured in hertz, this would require the motion to be written as

$$x = x_0 \sin 2\pi ft$$

since the angle must increase by 2π radians every cycle. To avoid the factor 2π, it is normal in calculations to use the circular frequency ω measured in radians per second, where

$$\omega = 2\pi f \tag{7.2}$$

The motion can then be written as

$$x = x_0 \sin \omega t$$

Also shown in Figure 7.1 is a second sinusoidal motion at the same frequency, but shifted along the time axis. This can be written as

$$y = y_0 \sin(\omega t - \theta)$$

where θ is called the phase angle or phase shift between the two motions; x is said to lead y, or y to lag x. If t_s is the time shift between the motions, then

$$\theta = 2\pi \frac{t_s}{\tau} \tag{7.3}$$

If x is differentiated with respect to time we get the following:

displacement

$$x = x_0 \sin \omega t \tag{7.4a}$$

velocity

$$\frac{dx}{dt} = \omega x_0 \cos \omega t = \omega x_0 \sin\left(\omega t + \frac{\pi}{2}\right) \tag{7.4b}$$

acceleration

$$\frac{d^2x}{dt^2} = -\omega^2 x_0 \sin \omega t = \omega^2 x_0 \sin(\omega t + \pi) \tag{7.4c}$$

It can be seen that the acceleration of a vibrating body is π radians, or 180°, out of phase with its displacement.

7.3 AN IDEALISED SYSTEM

Rather than discuss any one particular practical example of a vibrating system, we shall consider a simple mass–spring system that is representative of a wide range of practical systems. It is shown in Figure 7.2. The mass is a rigid body, which can move only vertically, and the spring has a constant stiffness, i.e. the spring force is proportional to the deflection. The damping is represented by a dashpot which exerts a force proportional to velocity. This form of damping simplifies the analysis of a system and if, as is usual, the damping is small, the results obtained agree closely with practice even though energy losses may arise in other ways.

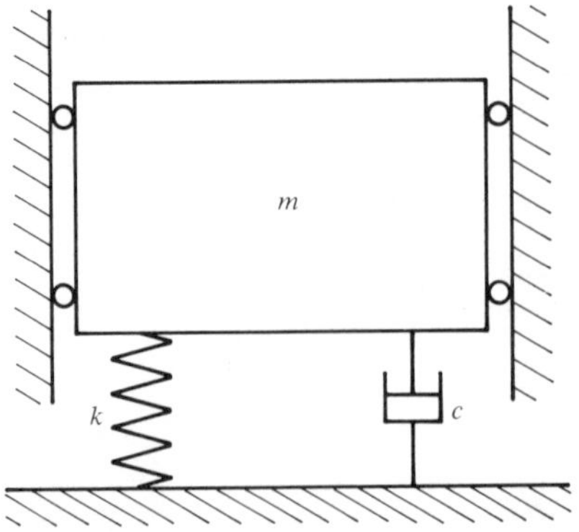

Figure 7.2 An idealised vibrating system with one degree of freedom.

In the system that has been described, the mass, spring stiffness and damping constant (see below) do not vary with displacement or velocity. Such a system is called linear, and its motion under the action of a number of sinusoidally varying forces is simply the sum of the motions that would result from each force acting independently. For this reason, only a pure sinusoidally exciting force is considered in the following sections.

The following numerical quantities will be needed: the mass, m; the spring stiffness, k, given by

$$k = \frac{\text{spring force}}{\text{spring deflection}}$$

the damping constant, c, given by

$$c = \frac{\text{damping force}}{\text{velocity}}$$

and the external force, $F_0 \sin \omega t$, causing the vibration. If the mass is in kilograms (kg), the spring stiffness should be measured in newtons per metre (N/m) and the damping constant in newton seconds per metre (N s/m).

FREE UNDAMPED VIBRATIONS: NATURAL FREQUENCY 7.4

Suppose the mass–spring system described in the previous section has no external force acting on it and damping is so small that we can neglect it. Suppose also that it is disturbed initially, by a blow, for example, or simply displaced from its equilibrium by some amount and released. The resulting motion will be a vibration at some frequency f_n, which we can derive by applying Newton's second law to the displaced position of the system.

Consider the mass at any instant in time when its displacement is x from the equilibrium position, of the system as shown in Figure 7.3. The free body diagram shows the forces acting on the mass: the restoring force $k(x + \delta_s)$ exerted by the spring, and the weight mg. Here δ_s is the static deflection when the mass is initially placed on the spring. By Newton's second law we have

$$\begin{aligned} m\ddot{x} &= -k(x + \delta_s) + mg \\ &= -kx - k\delta_s + mg \end{aligned}$$

But $mg = k\delta_s$, since at the equilibrium position the spring force balances the weight. Hence

$$m\ddot{x} + kx = 0 \qquad (7.5)$$

or

$$\ddot{x} + \frac{k}{m}x = 0$$

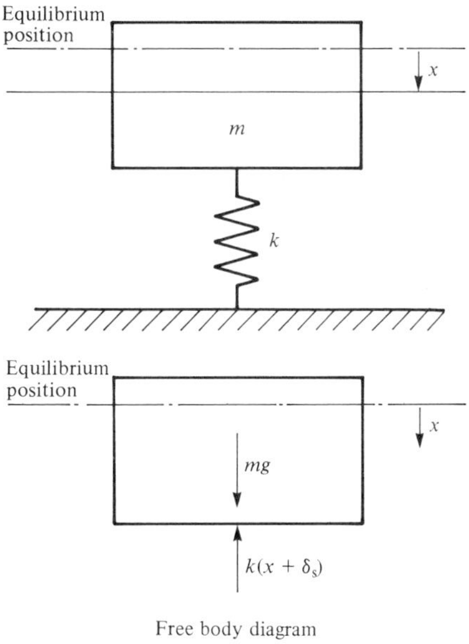

Figure 7.3 Free undamped vibration.

This equation is a second-order differential equation with constant coefficients. Let us assume for its solution that

$$x = e^{rt}$$

Then

$$\dot{x} = re^{rt}$$

and

$$\ddot{x} = r^2e^{rt}$$

Substituting in (7.5) yields

$$e^{rt}\left(r^2 + \frac{k}{m}\right) = 0$$

Hence

$$r = \pm j\sqrt{\frac{k}{m}}$$

where $j = \sqrt{-1}$, and the solution is

$$x = a\cos\left(\sqrt{\frac{k}{m}}t\right) + b\sin\left(\sqrt{\frac{k}{m}}t\right)$$

Two constants are required since the equation is of the second order. We can also write the solution in the following forms:

$$x = C\cos(\omega_n t + \phi) \qquad \text{or} \qquad x = C\sin(\omega_n t - \alpha) \tag{7.6}$$

Comparing with section 7.2.1 we see that the motion is simple harmonic at a frequency $\omega_n = \sqrt{(k/m)}$; ω_n is called the natural frequency of the system.

The constants C and ϕ or α are obtained from the initial conditions. For example, if we initially displaced the mass by an amount A and released it, then when $t = 0$, $x = A$ and $\dot{x} = 0$ (the velocity is zero when we let go of the mass after displacing it by an amount A), so that

$$A = C\cos\phi$$

and

$$0 = C\sin\phi$$

since

$$\dot{x} = -C\omega_n\sin(\omega_n t + \phi)$$

Hence

$$\phi = 0 \qquad C = A$$

giving

$$x = A\cos\omega_n t \tag{7.7}$$

A is referred to as the amplitude and ω_n is the undamped natural frequency (rad/s).

The period τ(s) of the vibration, which is the time taken to complete one oscillation, is given by

$$\tau = \frac{2\pi}{\omega_n}$$

and the natural frequency (Hz) is given by

$$f_n = \frac{1}{\tau} = \frac{\omega_n}{2\pi}$$

FREE DAMPED VIBRATIONS 7.5

In all real systems energy is lost owing to internal or external friction, and therefore there is a gradual decrease in the amplitudes of vibration. Friction of the viscous type gives rise to forces approximately proportional to the velocity at low speeds and is fairly representative of many practical situations, as was mentioned in section 7.3.

The force is thus opposite to the velocity and is equal to $c\,dx/dt$ or $c\dot{x}$, where c is the damping constant.

Such a damped system was shown diagrammatically in Figure 7.2. If the system is displaced from its equilibrium position and released, it will oscillate, but the oscillations will gradually die out because of damping.

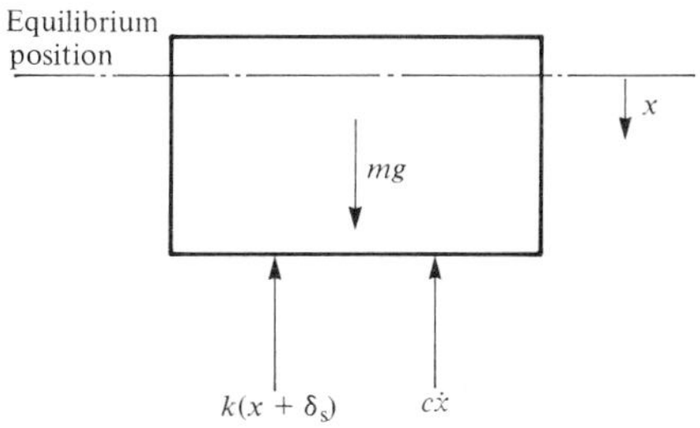

Figure 7.4 Free damped vibration.

Let x be the displacement from the equilibrium position at any instant t. The forces acting are as shown in the free body diagram (Figure 7.4). Applying Newton's second law, we have

$$m\ddot{x} = -k(x + \delta_s) - c\dot{x} + mg$$

or

$$m\ddot{x} + c\dot{x} + kx = 0 \tag{7.8}$$

since

$$k\delta_s = mg$$

We see from this equation that the motion of the mass will take place about its equilibrium position.

For the solution, let

$$x = e^{rt} \qquad \dot{x} = re^{rt} \qquad \ddot{x} = r^2e^{rt}$$

Substituting in (7.8) gives

$$mr^2 + cr + k = 0$$

a quadratic in r whose roots are

$$r = \frac{1}{2m}(-c \pm \sqrt{c^2 - 4mk}) \tag{7.9}$$

There are three cases to consider:

(1) $c^2 - 4mk > 0$,
(2) $c^2 - 4mk = 0$,
(3) $c^2 - 4mk < 0$.

Let us examine each case in turn.

Case (1): $c^2 > 4mk$
The solution of equation (7.8) is

$$x = Ae^{-r_1 t} + Be^{-r_2 t} \tag{7.10}$$

where

$$r_1 = -\frac{1}{2m}(c - \sqrt{c^2 - 4mk})$$

and

$$r_2 = -\frac{1}{2m}(c + \sqrt{c^2 - 4mk})$$

The two roots are real, the damping is large and no oscillations are possible. When the system is displaced from its equilibrium position it will return to it slowly as illustrated in Figure 7.5 (curve A). In this case the system is overdamped.

Case (2): $c^2 = 4mk$
Since $c^2 - 4mk = 0$, the two roots are equal so that $r_1 = r_2 = -c/2m$ and the solution of equation (7.8) is

$$x = e^{-ct/2m}(At + B)$$

When the system is displaced from its equilibrium position and released it returns to it fairly quickly but oscillations do not take place. This is shown in Figure 7.5 (curve B), and the damping in this case is referred to as critical.

Case (3): $c^2 < 4mk$
Since $c^2 - 4mk < 0$, the two roots are complex conjugates, i.e.

$$r_1 = -\frac{1}{2m}(c - j\sqrt{4mk - c^2})$$

and

$$r_2 = -\frac{1}{2m}(c + j\sqrt{4mk - c^2})$$

The solution of equation (7.8) is

$$x = e^{-ct/2m}(A \cos \omega_d t + B \sin \omega_d t) \quad (7.11)$$

where

$$\omega_d = \frac{1}{2m}\sqrt{4mk - c^2}$$

In this case, when the system is displaced from its equilibrium position and released, it oscillates about that position at a frequency ω_d, known as the damped natural frequency, as shown in Figure 7.5 (curve C), and the system is said to be lightly damped.

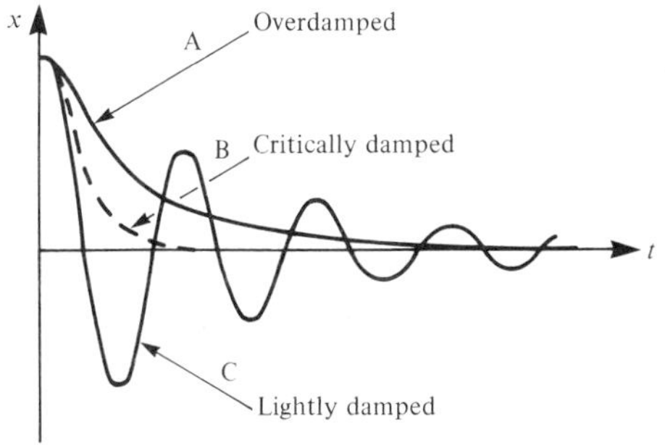

Figure 7.5 Effect of damping.

It is convenient in practice to express the amount of damping in a system by the ratio of the actual damping c to the critical damping from case (2):

$$c_c = 2\sqrt{mk}$$

Thus the damping ratio

$$\zeta = \frac{c}{2\sqrt{mk}}$$

It follows that

$$\omega_d = \omega_n\sqrt{1 - \zeta^2}$$

where

$$\omega_n = \sqrt{\frac{k}{m}}$$

and the solution for light damping is given by

$$x = A_0 e^{-\zeta\omega_n t} \cos(\omega_n\sqrt{1 - \zeta^2}\, t + \phi) \quad (7.12)$$

where A_0 and ϕ are constants that depend on the initial conditions.

EVALUATION OF THE DAMPING RATIO: LOGARITHMIC DECREMENT 7.6

The amount of damping in a system can be calculated from a recording of the free vibrations obtained as a result of an impulse or a blow applied to it. Such a recording is shown in Figure 7.6. A light beam carrying a heavy mass was struck and the subsequent displacement of the mass recorded on a storage oscilloscope. The envelope, i.e. the curve tangential to the oscillations, is the exponential part of equation (7.12).

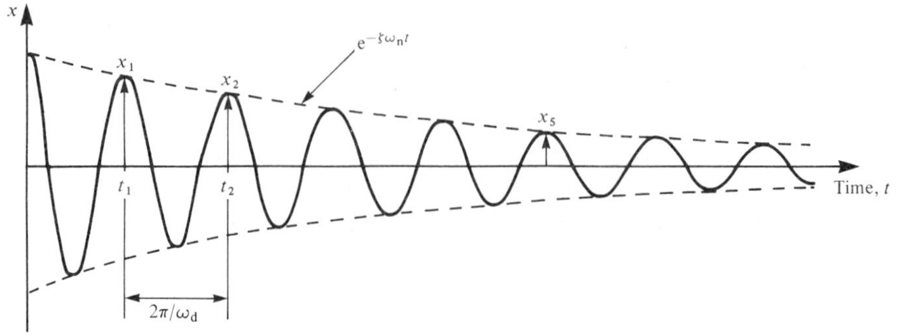

Figure 7.6 Vibration of a damped system: logarithmic decrement.

Consider two oscillations of amplitudes x_1 and x_2 at times t_1 and t_2 respectively. Then

$$t_2 - t_1 = 2\pi/\omega_d$$

and from equation (7.12) we have

$$x_1 = x_0 e^{-\zeta\omega_n t_1} \cos(\omega_d t_1 + \phi)$$

$$x_2 = x_0 e^{-\zeta\omega_n t_2} \cos(\omega_d t_2 + \phi)$$

Dividing yields

$$x_1/x_2 = \exp[\zeta\omega_n(t_2 - t_1)] = \exp(2\pi\zeta\omega_n/\omega_d) = \exp\left(2\pi\zeta/\sqrt{1-\zeta^2}\right)$$

the cosine terms being equal because of the relationship $t_2 - t_1 = 2\pi/\omega_d$. By taking logarithms on both sides we get

$$\ln(x_1/x_2) = 2\pi\zeta/\sqrt{1-\zeta^2}$$

But with light damping ζ is small so that

$$\ln(x_1/x_2) = 2\pi\zeta \tag{7.13}$$

The left-hand side of this equation is known as the *logarithmic decrement.*

Solving for ζ from equation (7.13) we find

$$\zeta = \frac{1}{2\pi}\ln\left(\frac{x_1}{x_2}\right) \tag{7.14}$$

In practice it is more accurate to calculate ζ by measuring n successive peaks so that

$$\zeta = \frac{1}{2\pi n}\ln\left(\frac{x_1}{x_n}\right)$$

Referring to the actual recording of Figure 7.6, the amplitudes were $x_1 = 13$ units, and $x_5 = 4$ units, after five oscillations. Hence the damping ratio is

$$\zeta = \frac{1}{2\pi \times 5}\ln\left(\frac{13}{4}\right) = 0.038$$

FORCED VIBRATIONS 7.7

7.7.1 Motion resulting from a periodically varying force

In general, the most important feature of a system capable of vibration is the way the system responds to a fluctuating applied force, and, in particular, the fact that very large amplitudes of vibration can occur if the frequency of the applied force is close to the natural frequency of the system, a condition referred to as *resonance.* In this section we consider in detail the motion of the mass–spring system described in section 7.3 when an external sinusoidal force is acting on it. Such motion is referred to as forced or steady-state motion to differentiate it from the free or transient motion described in section 7.4.

Figure 7.7(a) shows the spring–mass–damper system of section 7.3; only here the mass is subjected to a periodically varying force $F_0 \sin \omega t$ of amplitude F_0 and frequency ω. Let x be the displacement of the mass from its equilibrium position at any time t. The velocity is $\mathrm{d}x/\mathrm{d}t$ so that the force in the damper is $c\,\mathrm{d}x/\mathrm{d}t$ and the force exerted by the spring is kx as shown in the free body diagram (Figure 7.7(b)).

Applying Newton's second law, we have

$$m\frac{\mathrm{d}^2x}{\mathrm{d}t^2} = -kx - c\frac{\mathrm{d}x}{\mathrm{d}t} + F_0 \sin \omega t$$

or

$$m\ddot{x} + c\dot{x} + kx = F_0 \sin \omega t \qquad (7.15)$$

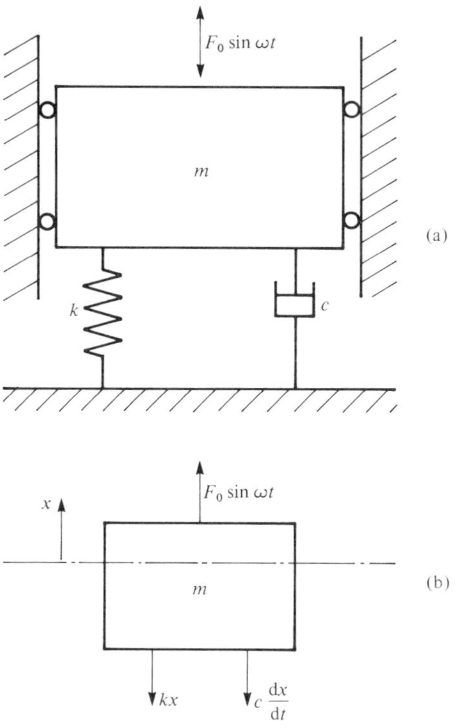

Figure 7.7 Periodically varying force causing vibrations.

It is shown in books on mathematics that the solution of this second-order differential equation with constant coefficients is given by

$$x = u + z$$

where z is the solution of the free damped vibration discussed in section 7.5, i.e. when there is no applied force, and u is a particular solution, which depends on the form of the excitation, $F_0 \sin \omega t$ in this case. We saw that the amplitudes of the free oscillations die out with time, and for this reason z is called the transient state; hence the solution of the above equation approaches $x = u$ as $t \to \infty$, referred to as the steady state.

The steady-state solution of the differential equation (7.15) is obtained by assuming a trial solution

$$x = A \sin \omega t + B \cos \omega t$$

or more conveniently

$$x = x_0 \sin(\omega t - \theta) \tag{7.16}$$

and finding x_0 and θ. Differentiating equation (7.16) with respect to time we have

$$\dot{x} = x_0\omega \cos(\omega t - \theta)$$
$$\ddot{x} = -x_0\omega^2 \sin(\omega t - \theta)$$

Substituting in equation (7.15) and expanding the $\cos(\omega t - \theta)$ and $\sin(\omega t - \theta)$ terms, we find

$$-mx_0\omega^2(\sin\omega t\cos\theta - \cos\omega t\sin\theta) + cx_0\omega(\cos\omega t\cos\theta + \sin\omega t\sin\theta)$$
$$+ kx_0(\sin\omega t\cos\theta - \cos\omega t\sin\theta) = F_0\sin\omega t$$

Equating the coefficients of $\cos\omega t$ on both sides of the equation gives

$$x_0\sin\theta\,(k - m\omega^2) = cx_0\omega\cos\theta$$

or

$$\tan\theta = \frac{c\omega}{k - m\omega^2} \tag{7.17}$$

and equating the coefficients of $\sin\omega t$ gives

$$x_0(k\cos\theta + c\omega\sin\theta - m\omega^2\cos\theta) = F_0 \tag{7.18}$$

But from Figure 7.8, showing $\tan\theta$ as in (7.17) we have

$$\sin\theta = \frac{c\omega}{\sqrt{(k - m\omega^2)^2 + c^2\omega^2}}$$

and

$$\cos\theta = \frac{k - m\omega^2}{\sqrt{(k - m\omega^2)^2 + c^2\omega^2}}$$

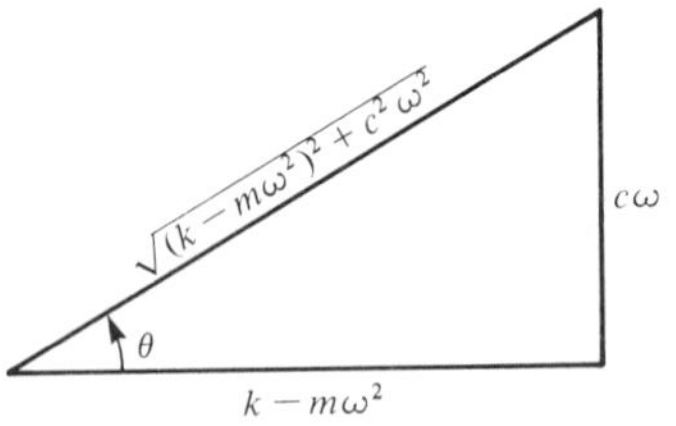

Figure 7.8 Evaluating $\sin\theta$ and $\cos\theta$ from $\tan\theta$.

Substituting in (7.18) yields

$$x_0 = \frac{F_0}{\sqrt{(k - m\omega^2)^2 + c^2\omega^2}} \tag{7.19}$$

When substituting for x_0 in equation (7.16) we note that the steady state is a sinusoidal vibration of the same frequency as the applied force $F_0\sin\omega t$, but its phase lags behind the phase of the applied force by the angle θ given by equation (7.17).

The amplitude x_0 of the motion will depend on both the amplitude and frequency of the applied force. Variations in the amplitude F_0 of the force will give directly proportional variations in the displacement amplitude. The effect of varying the frequency ω of the applied force, however, is more complicated and is shown in Figure 7.9.

In order to make the plot applicable for any values of mass m, spring stiffness k and damping constant c, the displacement amplitude x_0 is plotted as the amplitude ratio x_0/x_{st}, where x_{st} is the static amplitude, i.e. the amplitude when the frequency of the applied force is zero. At zero frequency the system is always in equilibrium so that the force in the spring will be equal to the applied force, giving

$$x_{st} = F_0/k$$

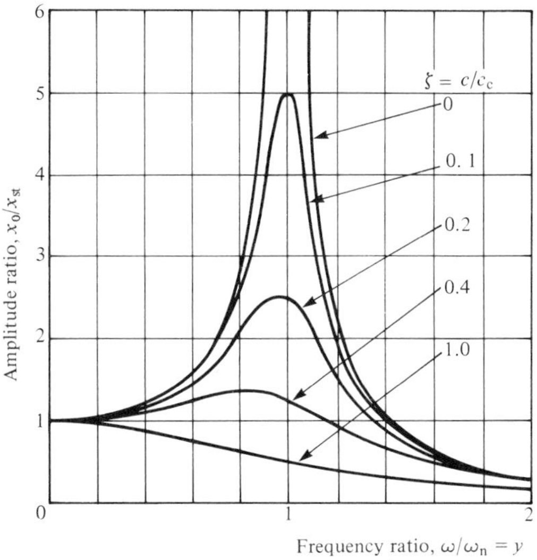

Figure 7.9 Response curves for a mass on a spring of constant stiffness with viscous damping.

Likewise the frequency ω of the applied force is plotted as the ratio $y = \omega/\omega_n$, where ω_n is the undamped natural frequency of the system given by

$$\omega_n = \sqrt{\frac{k}{m}}$$

as we saw in a previous section.

Figure 7.9 also shows the effect of damping. This is given as the ratio of the actual damping constant c in the system to the damping constant c_c that would be needed to make the system critically damped. Again from a previous section

$$c_c = 2\sqrt{mk}$$

and the damping ratio

$$\zeta = c/c_c$$

Taking k as a factor out of equations (7.19) and (7.17) and using the above relations we find

$$\frac{x_0}{x_{st}} = \frac{1}{\sqrt{(1 - y^2)^2 + 4\zeta^2 y^2}} \tag{7.20}$$

and

$$\theta = \arctan\left(\frac{2\zeta y}{1 - y^2}\right) \tag{7.21}$$

When plotted in this way, the curves shown in Figure 7.9 can be used to obtain the displacement amplitude for any values of force amplitude, force frequency, mass, stiffness and damping constant. The curves are called response curves and are worth considering in detail.

If the applied force is at zero frequency the displacement of the mass will always be such as to make the spring force equal to the applied force. The displacement will therefore be proportional to the force at any instant, so that the maximum displacement will occur at the instant when the force is at its maximum. In other words, the sinusoidally varying displacement is in phase with the sinusoidally varying force. The amplitude ratio, by definition, will be unity.

When the frequency of the force is very high, the system does not have time to respond, and so the displacement amplitude is very small. Under these circumstances the force in the spring is negligible; the applied force simply accelerates the mass. It follows, therefore, that it is the acceleration of the mass that is proportional to, and hence in phase with, the applied force. From equation (7.4c) the displacement of the mass will be 180° out of phase with its acceleration, and so exactly out of phase with the force.

Between the two extremes will be the case in which the frequency of the applied force is equal to the natural frequency of the system. As mentioned earlier, this condition is known as resonance, and it results in displacement amplitudes that are limited only by damping. It can be seen from Figure 7.9 that when damping is small compared with critical damping the amplitude near resonance is very large. In an undamped system the amplitude at resonance is theoretically infinite, but fortunately all practical systems include some damping, as was stated in section 7.5. It can be seen, however, that in lightly damped systems a small amount of additional damping can greatly reduce the amplitude of vibration near to resonance. Systems having damping equal to or greater than critical show no resonance peak in the response curve; the displacement amplitude gets steadily smaller as the frequency of the applied force is increased.

It has been seen that at low frequencies the displacement is in phase with the force, and that at high frequencies the displacement becomes 180° out of phase with the force. The variation in phase with frequency is plotted in Figure 7.10.

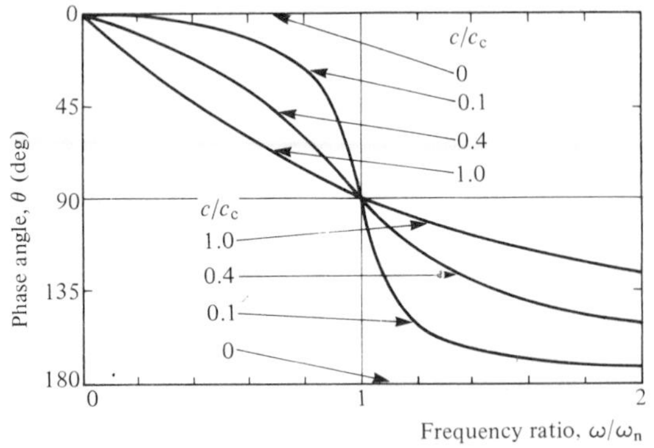

Figure 7.10 Phase angle by which the motion of the mass–spring system lags the applied force.

The complete solution of equation (7.15) including the transient is

$$x = A_0 e^{-\zeta\omega_n t} \cos(\omega_d t + \phi) + x_0 \sin(\omega t - \theta) \qquad \text{if } c < c_c$$

and

$$x = e^{-\zeta\omega_n t}(At + B) + x_0 \sin(\omega t - \theta) \qquad \text{if } c = c_c$$

This means that the motion described in section 7.5, namely a decaying oscillation at the natural frequency of the system, may be superimposed on the motions described in this section. The superimposition will occur if the steadily vibrating system is given an additional disturbance or if the amplitude of the applied sinusoidal force is rapidly changed, but it is not usually important because the free motion will die away leaving only the steady forced vibration. Its most common manifestation is the rapid reduction through resonance of the frequency of the applied force, occurring, for example, if rotating machinery on antivibration mounts is switched off and slowed down. After passing through resonance, the forced motion then has some free motion superimposed on it until the latter decays away. Just below resonance the force frequency will be only slightly lower than the natural frequency, and so the addition of the two motions will show beating effects. Figure 7.11 shows the motion of an out-of-balance rotor mounted on springs as it slows down.

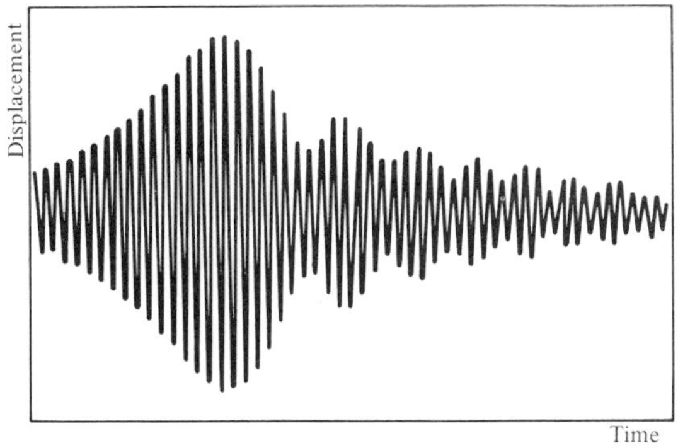

Figure 7.11 Motion of an unbalanced rotor mounted on springs as it slows down through resonance.

7.7.2 **Phasor diagrams**

The steady-state amplitude response of a spring–mass–damper system to an externally applied sinusoidal force and its phase lag may be more readily obtained from a diagram of the appropriate vectors. Such a diagram is known as a *phasor diagram.*

We saw in section 7.2.1 that a sinusoidal displacement $x = x_0 \sin \omega t$ has a velocity of $\omega x_0 \sin(\omega t + \pi/2)$ and an acceleration of $\omega^2 x_0 \sin(\omega t + \pi)$. If we consider the amplitudes of these quantities, namely x_0, ωx_0 and $\omega^2 x_0$ of the displacement, velocity and acceleration respectively, we can represent them by means of vectors rotating with angular velocity ω (phasors) as shown in Figure 7.12.

The instantaneous values of the displacement, velocity and acceleration are given by the perpendicular projections of the vectors on to the reference axis.

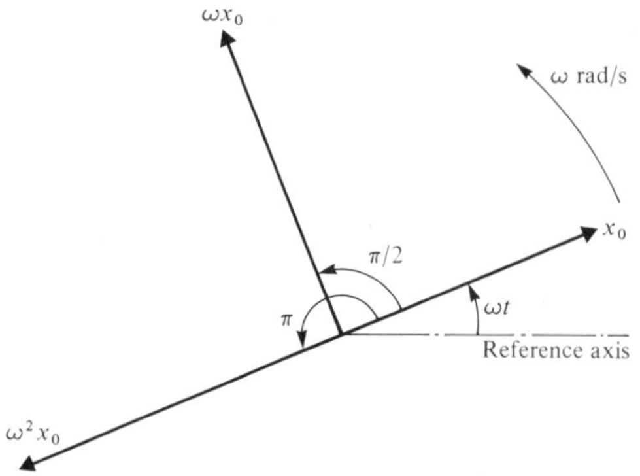

Figure 7.12 Representation of x_0, ωx_0 and $\omega^2 x_0$.

Equation (7.15) can be solved by means of such a diagram, as shown in Figure 7.13. On this diagram the force kx_0 in the spring is taken as the datum vector; the force $c\omega x_0$ in the damper and the inertia force $m\omega^2 x_0$ are then 90° and 180° respectively ahead of this vector. The closing vector F_0 is the external exciting force on the system and θ is the phase angle between excitation and the datum vector, i.e. the response.

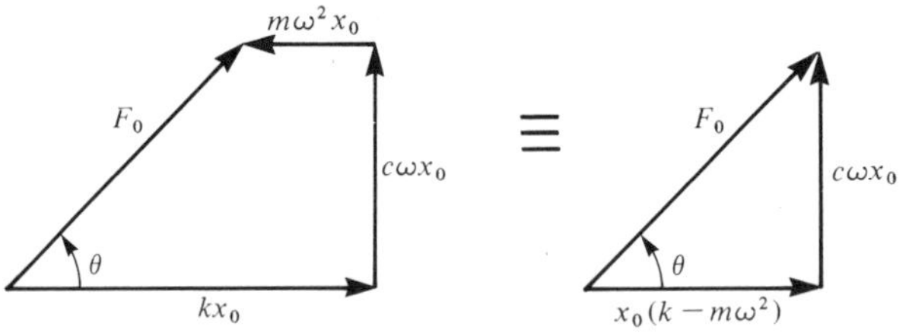

Figure 7.13 Phasor diagram for spring–mass–damper system.

By applying Pythagoras's theorem we readily obtain an expression for the amplitude x_0 and by trigonometry an expression for the phase angle θ leading to equations (7.17) and (7.19).

EXAMPLE 7.1

(a) A body of mass 15 kg is attached to two light springs in parallel as shown in Figure 7.14. If the spring stiffnesses are $k_1 = 2.5 \times 10^4$ N/m and $k_2 = 4 \times 10^4$ N/m, calculate the natural frequency of the system. (b) If the springs are then connected in series, what is the natural frequency of the system?

Example Cont.

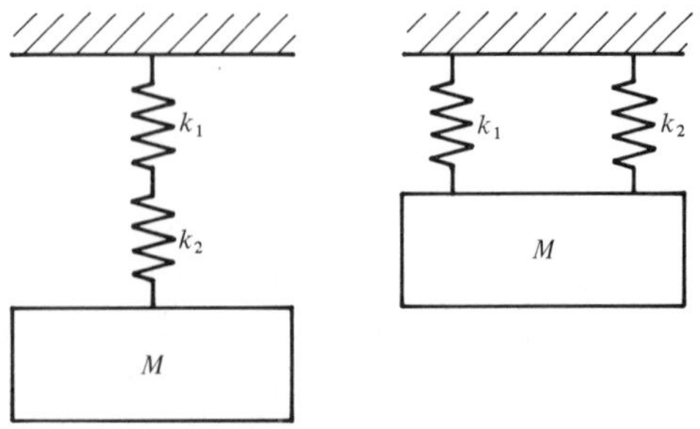

Figure 7.14 Springs and masses of example 7.1.

SOLUTION

(a) Springs in parallel:

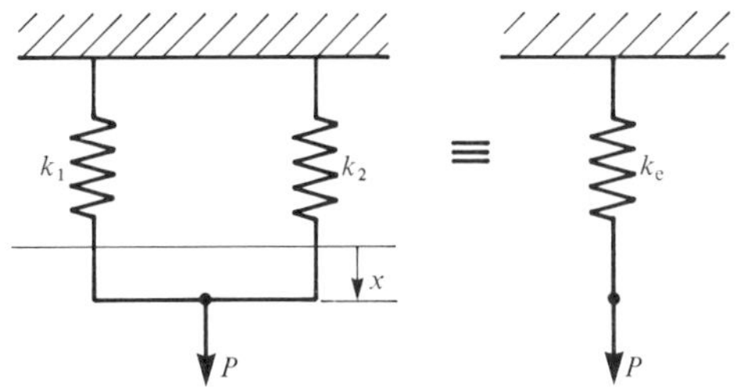

Figure 7.15 Equivalent diagram for springs in parallel.

Suppose we apply a force P to the springs and let x be the deflection. Then for equilibrium we must have:

$$k_1 x + k_2 x = P$$

Let us now replace the two springs by a single spring of stiffness k_e; then if k_e is such that under a load P its deflection is also x (Figure 7.15), we have

$$k_e x = P$$

Equating the above two equations we find

$$k_e = k_1 + k_2$$

and k_e is known as the equivalent stiffness.

The natural frequency of the system is

$$\omega_n = \sqrt{\frac{k_e}{M}} = \sqrt{\frac{(2.5 + 4) \times 10^4}{15}}$$

$$= 65.8 \text{ rad/s}$$

(b) Springs in series:

Let the deflections of the springs under the application of a force P be x_1 and x_2 as shown in Figure 7.16. Each spring is therefore subjected to the same load P so that

$$\frac{P}{k_1} = x_1 \quad \text{and} \quad \frac{P}{k_2} = x_2$$

Solution Cont.

If a spring of stiffness k_e has a deflection x when supporting the same load P, then

$$\frac{P}{k_e} = x$$

But

$$x = x_1 + x_2$$

Hence

$$\frac{P}{k_e} = \frac{P}{k_1} + \frac{P}{k_2}$$

or

$$\frac{1}{k_e} = \frac{1}{k_1} + \frac{1}{k_2}$$

so that

$$k_e = \frac{k_1 k_2}{k_1 + k_2}$$

and k_e is again the equivalent stiffness and the natural frequency of the system is

$$\omega_n = \sqrt{\frac{k_e}{M}} = \sqrt{\frac{2.5 \times 4 \times 10^8}{6.5 \times 10^3 \times 15}}$$

$$= 32 \text{ rad/s}$$

We therefore notice that when springs are placed in parallel the effective stiffness is increased, but when placed in series the effective stiffness is reduced.

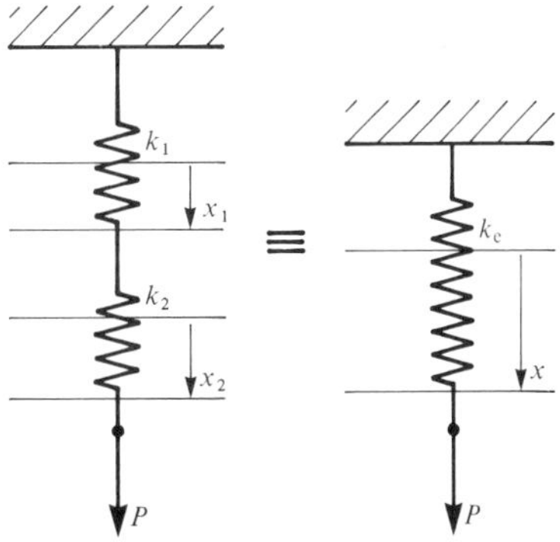

Figure 7.16 Equivalent diagram for springs in series.

EXAMPLE 7.2

Obtain an expression for the natural frequency of the system shown in Figure 7.17. OB is a rigid beam pivoted at O and supporting a mass M at B. The spring of stiffness k is pinned to the beam at A, a distance a from O.

Example Cont.

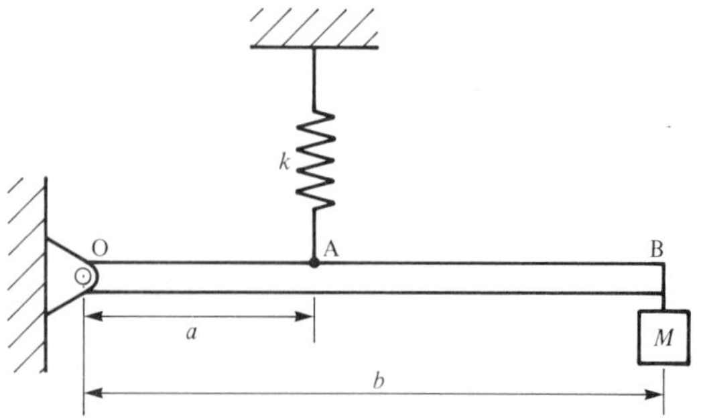

Figure 7.17 System of example 7.2.

SOLUTION

Let θ be the displacement of the beam from the equilibrium position. Then $a\theta$ is the deflection of the spring and $\ddot{\theta}$ the angular acceleration of the beam.

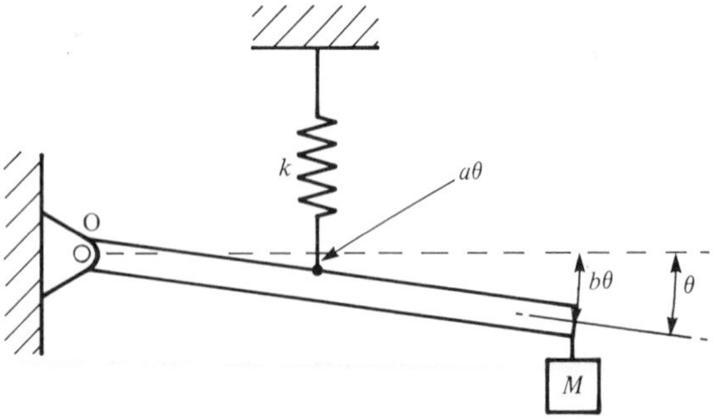

Figure 7.18 Equivalent system of example 7.2.

Solution Cont.

The restoring force exerted by the spring is $ka\theta$ upwards. Taking moments about O we have

$$(Mb\ddot{\theta})b = -(ka\theta)a$$

or

$$Mb^2\ddot{\theta} + ka^2\theta = 0$$

i.e.

$$\ddot{\theta} + \frac{k}{M}\left(\frac{a}{b}\right)^2\theta = 0$$

But this is the equation for simple harmonic motion; hence the natural frequency of the system is

$$\omega_n = \frac{a}{b}\sqrt{\frac{k}{M}} \text{ rad/s}$$

7.7.3 Vibrations caused by a rotating unbalance

One very common source of excitation in practice is the fact that many rotating machines are very seldom perfectly balanced. The rotors of electric motors, fans, centrifugal pumps and turbines are examples of such machines.

Figure 7.19 shows a machine constrained to move vertically, supported on springs and excited by unbalanced rotor R. The total mass of the machine is M, and the total stiffness k. Let us assume that there is some damping in the system which can be represented by a dashpot of constant c.

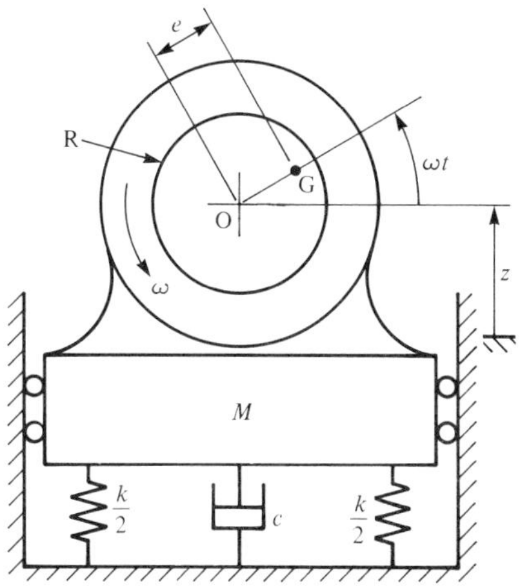

Figure 7.19 Vibrations caused by rotating unbalance.

If the rotor of mass m was perfectly balanced its centre of mass G would coincide with the geometric centre O which is in line with the axis of the bearings supporting the shaft of the rotor. Owing to imperfect balance, however, the centre of mass G is at a distance e from O; e is called the eccentricity.

If z is the displacement of the machine from the equilibrium position at any instant t, then the displacement of the rotor is given by

$$z + e \sin \omega t$$

By Newton's second law we have for the vertical motion of the machine

$$(M - m)\ddot{z} + m\frac{\mathrm{d}^2}{\mathrm{d}t^2}(z + e \sin \omega t) = -kz - c\dot{z}$$

Rearranging yields

$$M\ddot{z} + c\dot{z} + kz = me\omega^2 \sin \omega t \tag{7.22}$$

Comparing with equation (7.15), we observe that

$$F_0 = me\omega^2$$

Hence the steady-state displacement amplitude z_0 of the machine, from equation (7.19), is

$$z_0 = \frac{me\omega^2}{\sqrt{(k - M\omega^2)^2 + c^2\omega^2}} \tag{7.23}$$

The phase angle θ is given by equation (7.17)

$$\tan \theta = \frac{c\omega}{k - M\omega^2} \tag{7.24}$$

It is more convenient to express equations (7.23) and (7.24) in terms of the frequency ratio $y = \omega/\omega_n$ and the damping ratio ζ so that

$$\frac{M}{m}\frac{z_0}{e} = \frac{y^2}{\sqrt{(1 - y^2)^2 + 4\zeta^2 y^2}} \tag{7.25}$$

$$\tan \theta = \frac{2\zeta y}{1 - y^2} \tag{7.26}$$

Curves of Mz_0/me as a function of the frequency ratio y are shown in Figure 7.20 for different values of the damping ratio ζ.

When the speed of the rotor is low the machine moves very little, but as the speed increases, the amplitude takes on larger values until resonance is reached, i.e. when $y = 1$, where the speed of the rotor coincides with the natural frequency of the machine. At resonance the amplitude will reach dangerous values if the amount of damping in the system is small, a condition that must be avoided. At high speeds all the curves tend to Mz_0/me value of unity and damping has little effect. The displacement of the machine is then approximately 180° out of phase with the unbalance, in accordance with equation (7.26).

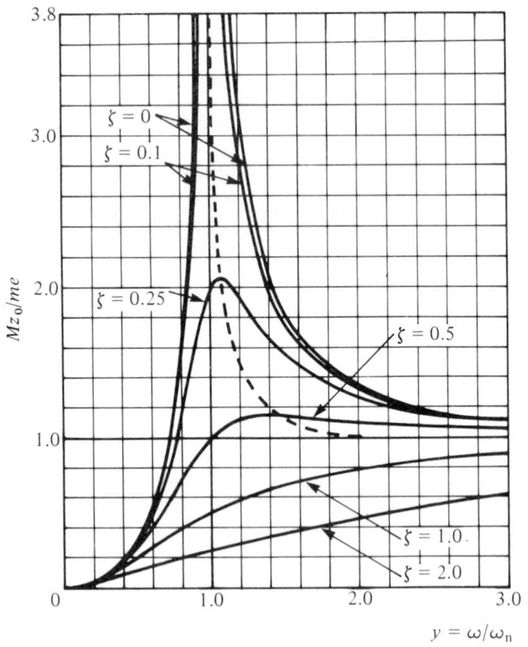

Figure 7.20 Curves of Mz_0/me as functions of frequency ratio.

7.8 VIBRATION ISOLATION

7.8.1 Introduction

An important aspect of forced vibration is transmission. When a mass is subjected to a disturbing force which varies with time, as shown in Figure 7.21, the supporting structure or surroundings S will evidently be subjected to a disturbing force also, because it is connected physically to the mass, usually by means of one or more mechanical elements: hard or soft springs, rubber mounts, etc. The magnitude of the force transmitted to the structure (i.e. the force felt by the structure) will not necessarily be equal to the disturbing force; it will depend on the system parameters: spring stiffness, mass, the amount of damping present and the value of the forcing frequency. An example of this type of transmitted force is that due to the action of a punching machine.

Similarly the motion of a supporting structure or floor S will be transmitted to any piece of equipment which it supports, as shown in Figure 7.23, and the magnitude of the transmitted motion (i.e. the motion that the equipment will have) will depend once again on the system parameters. An example of this kind of motion is the seismic disturbance of the floor of a laboratory which contains delicate measuring equipment such as chemical balances or microscopes.

It is, therefore, often desirable to prevent these forces or motions from reaching the supporting structures or surroundings, on the one hand, and some piece of equipment on the other, and we are thus led to study means of isolating these vibrations.

Hence the objectives of vibration isolation or vibration control are to eliminate these troublesome vibrations; there are two cases to be considered:

(1) The reduction of the vibrations caused by some piece of machinery transmitted to the surroundings; this type of isolation is referred to as *active isolation.*

(2) The prevention of the vibrations from the surroundings reaching some delicate piece of equipment; this type of isolation is referred to as *passive isolation.*

It follows, therefore, that effective vibration isolation or vibration control will depend very much on the selection of the elements, often called isolators, needed for this purpose. These elements will in general possess stiffness and damping which may or may not be constant; their mass will in most cases be small compared with the equipment or machine they support, and it can be neglected in calculations. At high frequencies, however, wave effects can occur in the isolators because of longitudinal standing waves, and under these conditions we cannot neglect the mass of the isolators.

7.8.2 **Transmissibility**

(a) Transmissibility without damping

In the case of active isolation the force to be isolated from the surroundings (supporting structure or foundations) is shown in Figure 7.21 for a system with one degree of freedom. It is assumed to be harmonic, so that $F(t) = F_0 \sin \omega t$, where F_0 is the maximum or peak value of the force and ω is the variable forcing frequency. This force acts on a piece of equipment of mass m supported on an isolator of constant stiffness k, and the complete system rests on the supporting structure S.

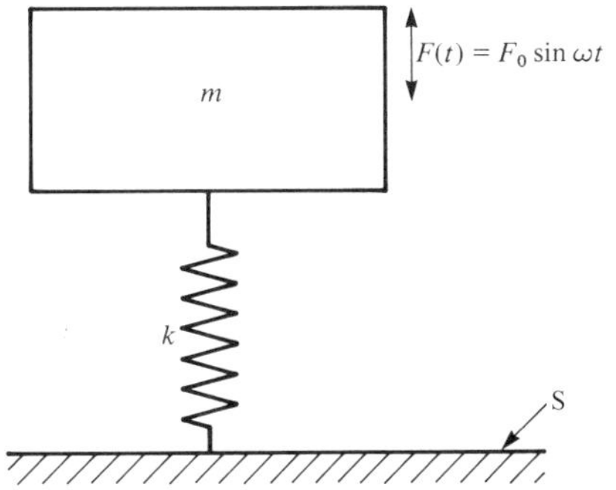

Figure 7.21 Mass subjected to a periodic disturbing force.

Let x be the displacement of the mass from the equilibrium position (Figure 7.22). By Newton's second law we have

$$m\ddot{x} = -kx + F_0 \sin \omega t$$

or

$$m\ddot{x} + kx = F_0 \sin \omega t$$

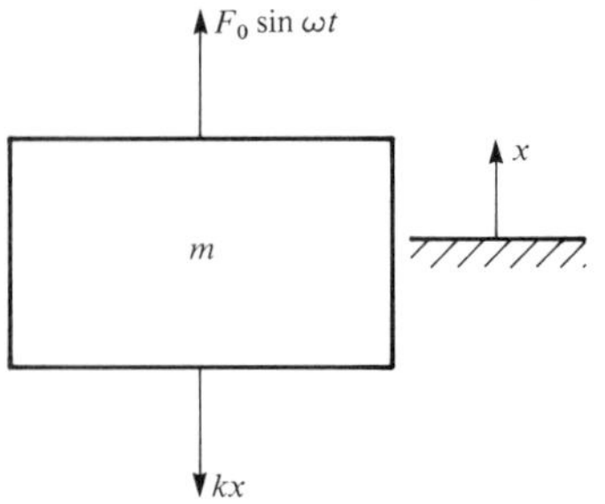

Figure 7.22 Displacement for Figure 7.21.

This equation is similar to equation (7.15), but with $c = 0$. The steady-state solution is

$$F_{\mathrm{T}} = \frac{F_0}{1 - (\omega/\omega_{\mathrm{n}})^2} \tag{7.27}$$

The force F_{T} is the force which the supporting structure feels at all times, and this force is transmitted by the isolator to the supporting structure, since it forms the only path between the mass and the structure, i.e. the disturbing force cannot be transmitted in any other way.

It is more convenient in practice to utilise non-dimensional terms, and the transmission factor or transmissibility T is defined as follows:

$$T = \frac{\text{maximum amplitude of the transmitted force}}{\text{maximum amplitude of the disturbing force}} = \frac{F_{\mathrm{T}}}{F_0}$$

It follows from equation (7.27) that

$$T = \frac{1}{1 - (\omega/\omega_{\mathrm{n}})^2} \tag{7.28}$$

The transmissibility is a measure of the force transmitted to the surroundings; it is also a measure of the degree of isolation provided by the isolator, here the spring. T is sometimes referred to as the active isolation factor.

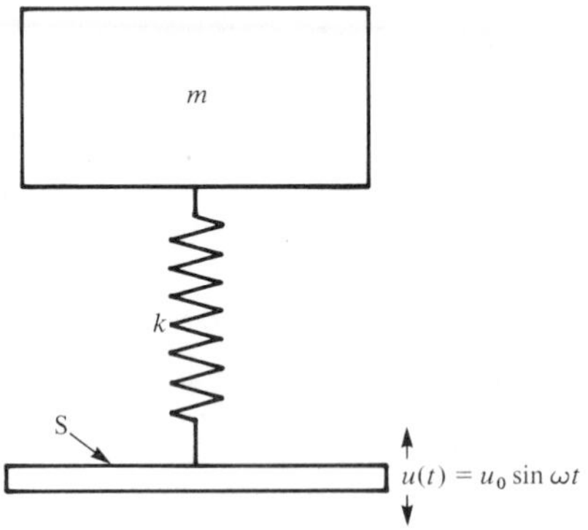

Figure 7.23 Seismic excitation of the mass–spring system.

In the case of passive isolation, let us suppose that a piece of equipment of mass m is to be isolated, by means of an isolator of constant stiffness k, from a supporting structure whose motion varies as $u(t)$; the system is shown in Figure 7.23. The motion of the supporting structure is assumed to be harmonic, so that $u(t) = u_0 \sin \omega t$.

Let x be the displacement of the mass (Figure 7.24). The extension of the spring is

$$x - u = x - u_0 \sin \omega t$$

and therefore exerted by the spring is

$$k(x - u_0 \sin \omega t)$$

Applying Newton's second law we have

$$m\ddot{x} = -k(x - u_0 \sin \omega t)$$

or

$$m\ddot{x} + kx = ku_0 \sin \omega t$$

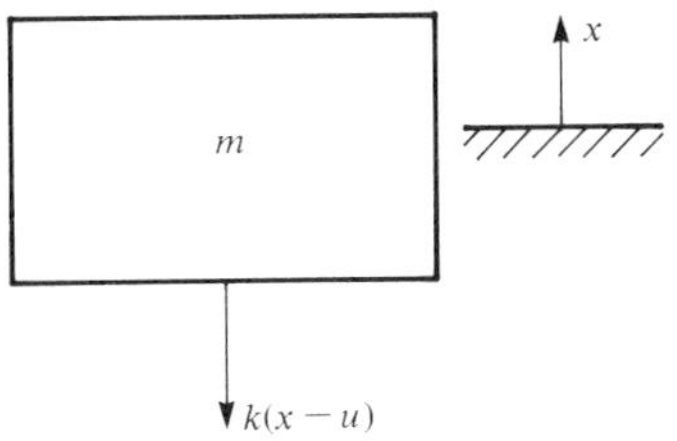

Figure 7.24 Displacement for Figure 7.23.

and the steady-state amplitude is

$$x_0 = \frac{u_0}{1 - (\omega/\omega_n)^2} \qquad (7.29)$$

The motion transmissibility T is defined as

$$T = \frac{\text{maximum value of the transmitted motion}}{\text{maximum value of the disturbing motion}} = \frac{x_0}{u_0}$$

It follows from equation (7.29) that

$$T = \frac{1}{1 - (\omega/\omega_n)^2} \qquad (7.30)$$

and in this case T is sometimes referred to as the passive isolation factor.

We see, therefore, that in both active and passive isolation, the transmissibility T is given by the same equation, and that it depends only on the frequency ratio (ω/ω_n), i.e. on the system parameters.

The transmissibility or isolation factor is of considerable importance in practice and it is of value to discuss it in more detail by considering Figure 7.25, which is a plot of equation (7.28) (or (7.30)). We notice that vibration isolation can only be achieved for values of the frequency ratio greater than about 1.5 ($\sqrt{2} = 1.414$ theoretically). Below this value there will be a magnification of the force or of the motion transmitted and this magnification will assume very large values in the neighbourhood of resonance, i.e. when $\omega = \omega_n$, the natural frequency of the system.

The force (or motion) transmitted will have the same value as the disturbing force (or motion) when the frequency ratio is either zero or 1.414. The second value corresponds to the crossover point, and the first value corresponds to a static condition or one in which the natural frequency ω_n of the system is always very much higher than the disturbing frequency, no matter what the value of the latter, i.e. when the isolator is extremely stiff; in the limit the "isolator" is solid, and the equipment rests directly on the structure, as does, for example, a turbo alternator set resting on a massive concrete block placed in the ground. The ground will always be subjected to any out-of-balance forces present in the turbo alternator set and therefore there will be no isolation. However, this absence of isolation may sometimes be more practical and more acceptable than using isolators, such as antivibration mountings.

Usually, though, it is desirable to be in the isolation region shown in Figure 7.25, and the degree of isolation depends on the particular application. As an example, in order to achieve an "isolation efficiency" of say 95%, which corresponds to a transmissibility of $(1 - 0.95) = 0.05$, the natural frequency of the system must be at least 4.5 times smaller than the disturbing frequency ω. For a given mass of equipment the required stiffness of the isolator is easily obtained, assuming that the disturbing force is at a fixed frequency.

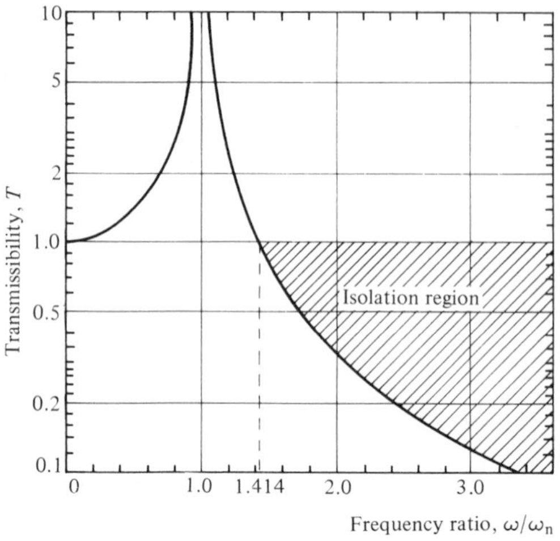

Figure 7.25 Transmissibility for zero damping.

If in a particular installation the disturbing frequency ω is not fixed but can vary between two extreme values, ω_1 and ω_2 (where $\omega_2 > \omega_1$), and we wish to ensure that there will be a reasonable degree of isolation within that range of frequencies, the only solution is to design the system parameters k and m such that the natural frequency is low enough to make the frequency ratio based on ω_1 greater than 1.5 at all times. However, a low natural frequency implies a low value for the stiffness, i.e. a soft spring and a large static deflection, and this aspect will need to be considered very carefully in the selection of the isolator to be used.

When the disturbing force (or motion) is non-harmonic, it is necessary to ensure that the frequency ratio (ω_1/ω_n) is greater than 1.5 for efficient isolation, ω_1 being the lowest frequency in the spectrum. The higher frequencies will not influence the efficiency of the isolation provided that the isolator is a linear one.

(b) Transmissibility with damping

Figure 7.25 is useful in the design of an isolator when there is no damping or when the damping is so small that it can be neglected, but if the damping is not negligible the transmissibility curve is greatly modified and the effect cannot be ignored.

When damping is present in a system, whatever the type (viscous, Coulomb or internal), a certain amount of energy is dissipated during each cycle of a vibration. As a result the amplitude of the single-degree-of-freedom system is likely to be reduced and infinite amplitudes at resonance cannot take place, although they may still be large enough to be dangerous. Damping, whether inherent in the system or deliberately introduced, will also have a profound influence on the value of the transmissibility and it is important to analyse the results. For simplicity we shall assume that our isolator can be represented by two linear elements in parallel, i.e. a spring of stiffness k and a damper (of the viscous type) of damping constant c as shown in Figure 7.26 for force transmission and motion transmission. We shall further assume that the force or the motion is harmonic.

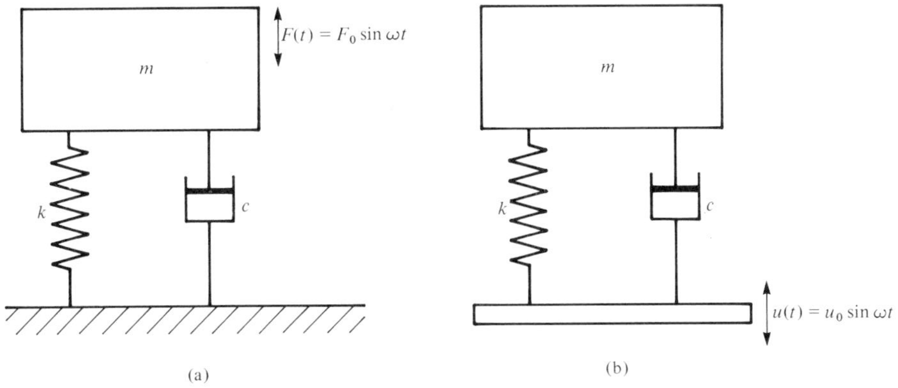

Figure 7.26 Viscously damped mass–spring systems: (a) force transmission; (b) motion transmission.

Let x_0 be the amplitude of the steady-state displacement of the mass m. Since the excitation is harmonic, the displacement or response of the mass will also be harmonic, as we saw previously. Its maximum velocity will therefore be ωx_0 and its maximum acceleration $\omega^2 x_0$. Hence we can construct the phasor diagram shown in Figure 7.27, taking the vector kx_0, the force in the spring, as datum.

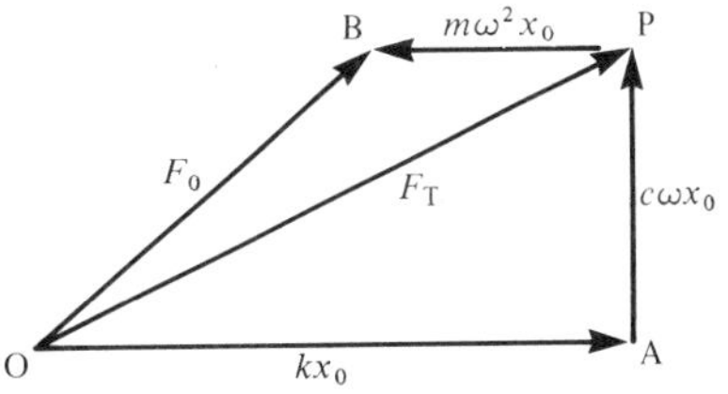

Figure 7.27 Phasor diagram for Figure 7.26.

The force F_T transmitted to the surroundings is given by the vector $\overrightarrow{OP}$, and therefore

$$F_T = x_0\sqrt{k^2 + c^2\omega^2}$$

But from OAPB (or from Figure 7.13) we have

$$x_0 = \frac{F_0}{\sqrt{(k - m\omega^2)^2 + c^2\omega^2}}$$

By definition the transmissibility T is

$$T = F_T/F_0$$

and therefore substituting in the above equation yields

$$F_T = \frac{F_0\sqrt{k^2 + c^2\omega^2}}{\sqrt{(k - m\omega^2)^2 + c^2\omega^2}} \tag{7.31}$$

or

$$T = \sqrt{\frac{1 + 4\zeta^2(\omega/\omega_n)^2}{(1 - (\omega/\omega_n)^2)^2 + 4\zeta^2(\omega/\omega_n)^2}} \tag{7.32}$$

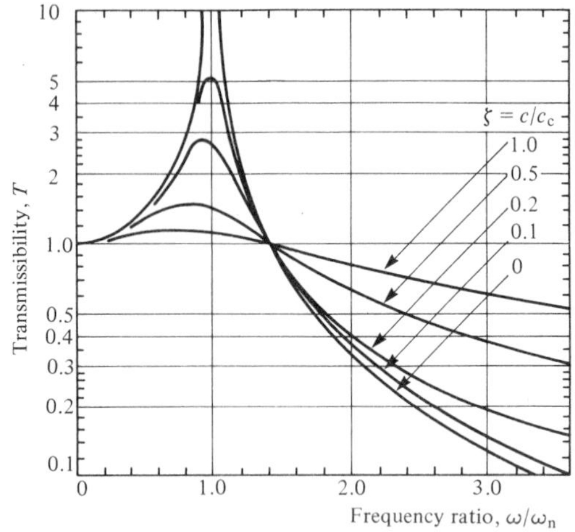

Figure 7.28 Influence of viscous damping on the value of the transmissibility.

Equation (7.32) is not easy to interpret and it is much simpler to study Figure 7.28, which is a plot of this equation for various values of the damping ratio. We observe once again that the transmissibility is less than unity for values of the frequency ratio greater than about 1.5. We notice, however, the following important features:

(1) When the frequency ratio is less than 1.5, damping is beneficial; the transmissibility at resonance is very much reduced and the greater the damping ratio the smaller the value of the transmissibility, although its value will never fall below unity. Damping is particularly beneficial in this region when, for instance, a machine has to be brought up to speed through the resonant frequency of the system, and run down through it. Damping is often more important in the latter process.

(2) When the frequency ratio is greater than 1.5, i.e. when it is in the isolation region, damping has an adverse effect. The greater the damping ratio the greater the value of the transmissibility and therefore the lower the isolation efficiency at a given frequency.

Figure 7.29 Diesel generator set on 10 isolators.

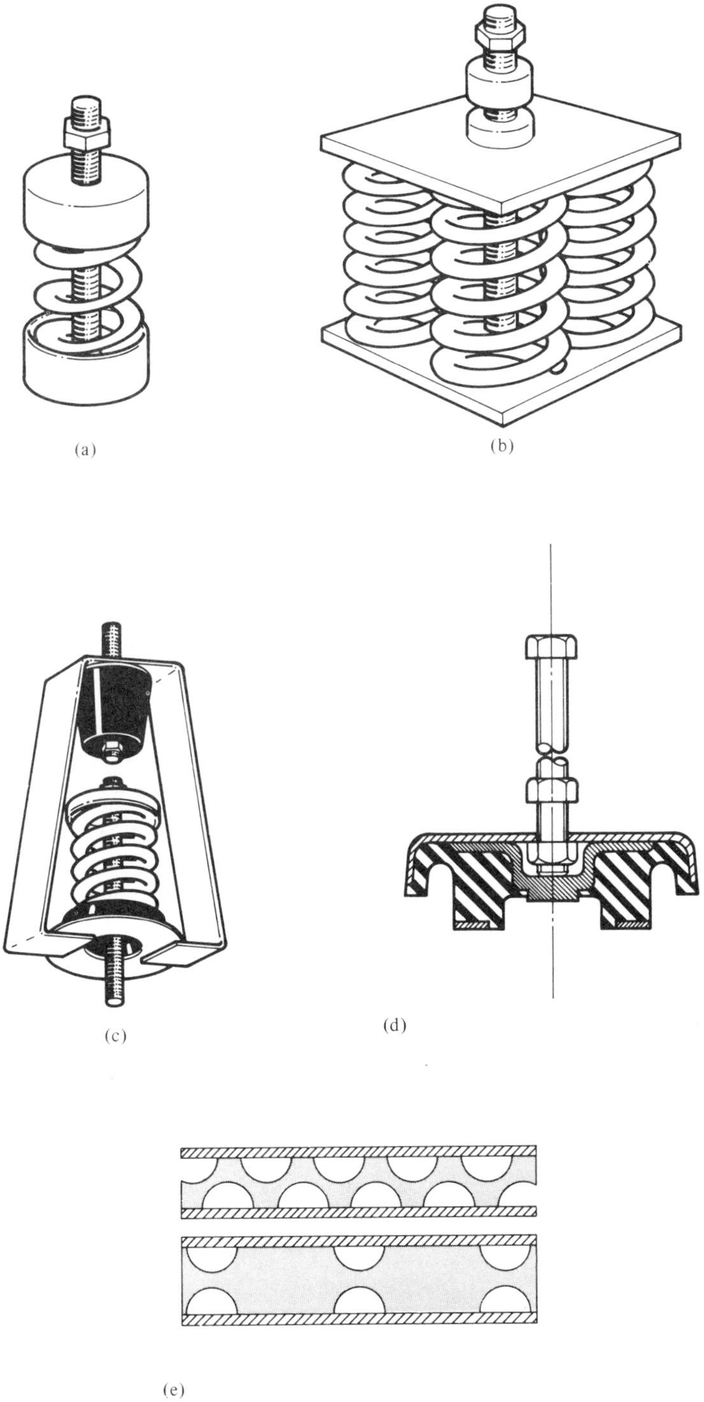

Figure 7.30 Commercially available isolators: (a) single-coil spring; (b) multiple springs; (c) hanger using a steel spring; (d) typical rubber isolator made of neoprene; (e) "TICO" pads comprising a moulded neoprene, fluted centre sandwiched between flat bonded cork support faces.

Careful consideration must be given to this effect when designing an isolation system. For example, if the frequency ratio is 2.5 and there is little damping, the isolation efficiency is about 80%. But if the damping ratio is increased to 0.2, the efficiency drops to about 72%, and a damping ratio of 0.5 lowers it further to about 54%, a very significant change. For the transmissibility to become as small as possible, whatever the value of the damping ratio, very large values of the frequency ratio, and therefore very soft isolators, would be necessary. However, these are not always desirable. Nevertheless, it is possible to design an isolator system with variable characteristics such that damping has the desired effect in both regions, i.e. a decreasing value of the damping as the frequency ratio increases.

(3) When the damping ratio lies between 0 and 0.1, the isolation region is hardly affected and equation (7.30) or Figure 7.25 can be used without introducing significant errors in the calculations.

(4) When the frequency ratio is less than about 0.25, damping has practically no influence on the transmissibility; however, it will always be greater than unity.

Figure 7.30 shows examples of commercially available isolators.

7.8.3 Force transmitted because of an unbalance

We should be aware that when an excitation is caused by an unbalance the actual force transmitted to the surroundings varies as the square of the frequency, and its magnitude F_T, as a function of the frequency ratio $y = \omega/\omega_n$, is given by

$$F_T = me\omega_n^2 y^2 \sqrt{\frac{1 + 4\zeta^2 y^2}{(1 - y^2)^2 + 4\zeta^2 y^2}} \tag{7.33}$$

The variation in the ratio $F_T/me\omega_n^2$ is shown in Figure 7.31 for various values of the damping ratio ζ.

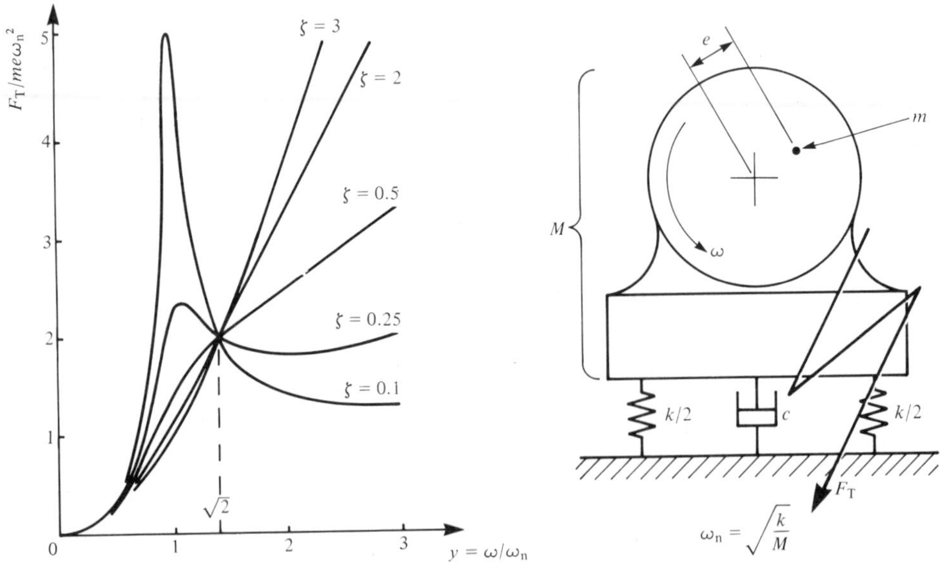

Figure 7.31 Force transmitted because of an unbalance (M is total mass and m is unbalanced mass).

EFFECTIVE MASS 7.9

In the previous sections the mass of the springs or isolators has been assumed to be small compared with the mass they support; in many cases such an assumption is valid, e.g. the diesel generator set shown in Figure 7.29. There are, however, installations where the mass of the spring must be taken into account. The following is an illustration of such a situation.

Machines are frequently supported on beams which make up floors in buildings. These beams have flexibility (inverse of stiffness) and it is necessary to take their mass into account. Let us then consider a beam simply supported at each end and carrying a machine of mass M, assumed to be a point load for simplicity, at its centre, as shown in Figure 7.32.

It is demonstrated in books on structures that the deflection y at a distance x from one of the supports of such a beam is given by

$$y = C(3L^2x - 4x^3)$$

where $C = W/48EI$, E is the modulus of elasticity, I is the second moment of area of the beam cross section and $W = Mg$ the weight of the machine.

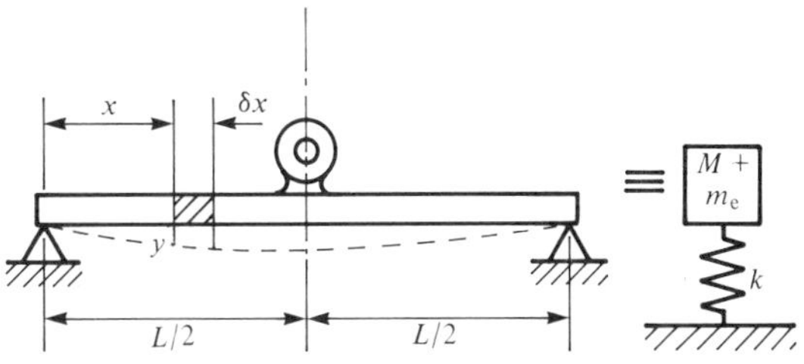

Figure 7.32 Loaded beam: effective mass.

The beam plus machine is then equivalent (neglecting damping) to our idealised spring-mass system of Figure 7.2, where the mass is equal to the mass of the machine together with a fraction, which we propose to calculate, of the mass of the beam.

Let us assume that during vibration the deflection of the beam is identical to the static deflection, so that the velocity of an element of mass δm will be $\dot{y} = y\omega_n$, where ω_n is the natural frequency of the loaded beam, the oscillations of the beam being assumed to be simple harmonic. If ρ is the mass per unit length of the beam, the mass of an element δx at a distance x from one support is $\delta m = \rho\delta x$, and its kinetic energy is

$$\tfrac{1}{2} \times \text{mass} \times (\text{velocity})^2 = \tfrac{1}{2}\rho\delta x\dot{y}^2 = \tfrac{1}{2}\rho\delta x y^2\omega_n^{\ 2}$$

The total kinetic energy T of the beam is then

$$T = 2 \times \tfrac{1}{2}\rho\omega_n^{\ 2}C^2 \int_0^{L/2} (3L^2x - 4x^3)^2\,dx$$

$$= 0.243\rho\omega_n^{\ 2}C^2L^7$$

If m_e is the effective mass of the beam then

$$\tfrac{1}{2}m_e\Delta_c^{\ 2}\omega_n^{\ 2} = 0.243\rho\omega_n^{\ 2}C^2L^7$$

where Δ_c is the deflection at the centre of the beam under a load W

$$\Delta_c = WL^3/48EI = CL^3$$

Hence

$$\tfrac{1}{2}m_e C^2 L^6 \omega_n^2 = 0.243\rho\omega_n^2 C^2 L^7$$

It follows that

$$m_e = 0.486\rho L$$

$$= 0.486 \times \text{mass of the beam}$$

This shows that practically one-half of the mass of the beam will have to be added to the mass of the machine that it supports.

The stiffness of the beam at its centre is

$$k = 48EI/L^3$$

and, therefore, the natural frequency of the beam plus machine is given by

$$\omega_n = \sqrt{\frac{k}{M + 0.486m_{beam}}}$$

EXAMPLE 7.3

It is proposed to instal a centrifugal pump bolted to a steel frame on four isolators as shown in Figure 7.33. The mass of the pump and its frame is 3500 kg; the pump impeller has a mass of 750 kg with an eccentricity of 1 mm and a speed of rotation of 960 rev/min. The isolators are to be positioned symmetrically about the centre of mass G at a distance of 0.45 m below it. The axis of rotation of the impeller is located at a distance of 0.15 m above G.

If a 90% isolation efficiency is to be achieved in the vertical direction, calculate the stiffness of each isolator. Assume that the isolators are identical and that the stiffness is the same in all directions, damping being neglected initially.

If the damping ratio of the isolators selected is 0.04 each, calculate the isolation efficiency and the value of the force transmitted.

Example Cont.

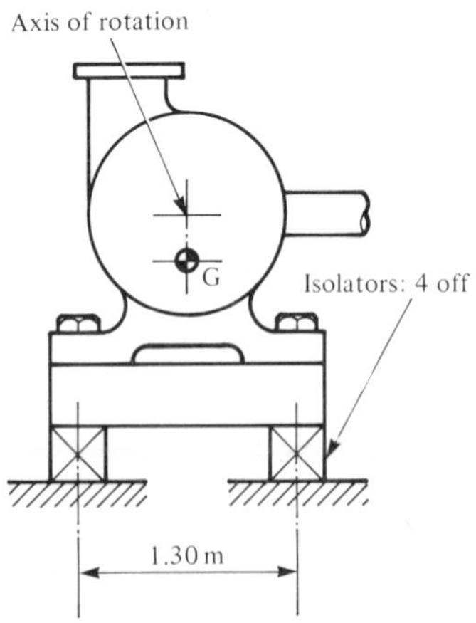

Figure 7.33 Unbalanced pump of example 7.3.

SOLUTION

The transmissibility is

$$T = (1 - \text{isolation efficiency}/100)$$

$$= (1 - 0.9) = 0.1$$

Solution Cont.

Neglecting damping we have, from equation (7.28)

$$T = \frac{1}{(\omega/\omega_n)^2 - 1} \qquad \text{since } \omega/\omega_n > 1$$

Solution Cont.

Solving for ω/ω_n yields

$$\frac{\omega}{\omega_n} = \sqrt{\frac{1}{T}+1} = \sqrt{11} = 3.32$$

But

$$\omega = \frac{2\pi \times 960}{60} = 100.5 \text{ rad/s}$$

Hence

$$\omega_n = 100.5/3.32 = 30.28 \text{ rad/s}$$

Since

$$\omega_n = \sqrt{4k/M}$$

where k is the stiffness of one isolator

$$k = \frac{M\omega_n^{\ 2}}{4} = \frac{3500 \times 30.28^2}{4}$$

$$= 0.8 \times 10^6 \text{ N/m}$$

Taking into account the damping in each isolator, the actual transmissibility will be

$$T = \sqrt{\frac{1 + 4\zeta^2(\omega/\omega_n)^2}{(1-(\omega/\omega_n)^2)^2 + 4\zeta^2(\omega/\omega_n)^2}}$$

by equation (7.32). Now $\zeta = 4 \times 0.04 = 0.16$, and ω/ω_n is unchanged. Hence

$$T = \sqrt{\frac{1 + 4 \times 0.16^2 \times 3.32^2}{(1-3.32^2)^2 + 4 \times 0.16^2 \times 3.32^2}}$$

$$= 0.145$$

The isolation efficiency I will now be

$$I = (1 - T) \times 100$$
$$= (1 - 0.145) \times 100$$
$$= 85.5\%$$

a reduction of 4.5%.

The out-of-balance force F_0 is given by

$$F_0 = me\omega^2 = 750 \times (1/1000) \times 100.5^2$$
$$= 7575.2 \text{ N}$$

The force transmitted will then be

$$F_T = F_0 T = 7575.2 \times 0.145 = 1098 \text{ N}$$

EXAMPLE 7.4

The diagram in Figure 7.34 shows a machine of total mass 550 kg bolted to the supporting floor at the centre. The floor consists of two parallel I-section beams each having a modulus of elasticity E of 210×10^9 N/m^2, a second moment of area I of 0.35×10^{-4} m^4 and a mass of 25 kg/m. Each beam is supported at the ends on thin expansion pads whose vertical stiffness is 4×10^6 N/m per pad. Calculate the natural frequency of the system, assuming the machine to be a point load. If the machine operates at 960 rev/min and has an unbalance of 0.05 kg m, calculate the force transmitted to the supporting walls. Damping is small enough to be negligible.

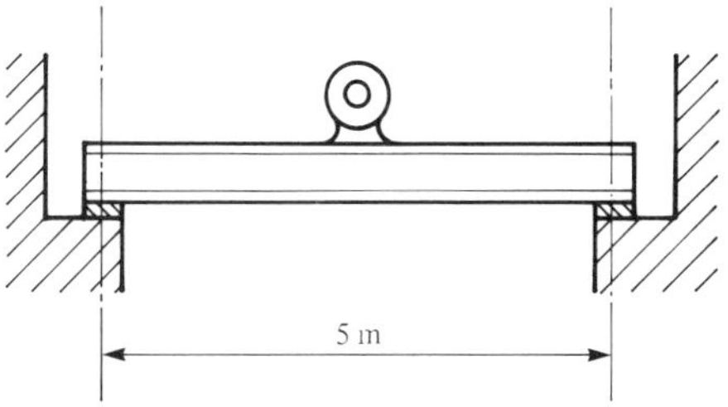

Figure 7.34 Machine and beam of example 7.4

SOLUTION

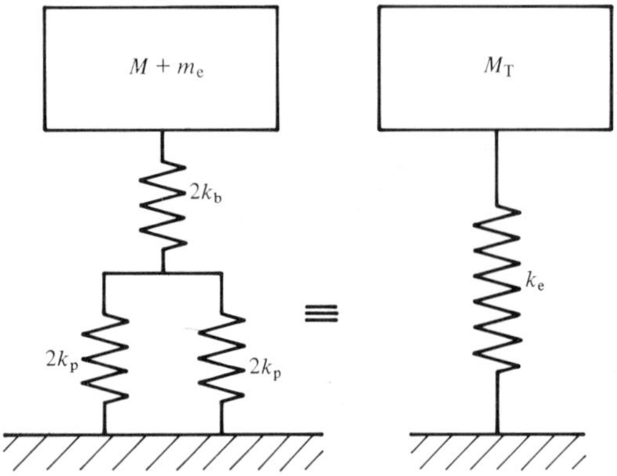

Figure 7.35 Equivalent system of example 7.4.

The actual system is equivalent to the one shown in Figure 7.35. Let M be the mass of the machine, m_e the equivalent mass of the beam, k_b the stiffness of each beam at the centre, k_p the stiffness of each pad, and k_e the stiffness of the equivalent system. Then

$$k_e = \frac{4k_p k}{4k_p + k}$$

where $k = 2k_b$. From section 7.9

$$k_b = 48EI/L^3$$
$$= 48 \times 210 \times 10^9 \times 0.35 \times 10^{-4}/5^3$$
$$= 2.83 \times 10^6 \text{ N/m}$$

Therefore

$$k = 5.66 \times 10^6 \text{ N/m}$$

Solution Cont.

$$k_e = 4 \times 4 \times 5.66 \times 10^{12}/(4 \times 4 \times 10^6 + 5.66 \times 10^6)$$
$$= 4.18 \times 10^6 \text{ N/m}$$

Total mass

$$M_T = 550 + 0.5 \times 25 \times 5 \times 2 = 550 + 125$$
$$= 675 \text{ kg}$$

Natural frequency of the equivalent system

$$\omega_n = \sqrt{\frac{k_e}{M_T}}$$
$$= \sqrt{\frac{4.18 \times 10^6}{675}} = 787 \text{ rad/s or } 12.5 \text{ Hz}$$

Excitation frequency is 960/60 = 16 Hz. Frequency ratio

$$y = \omega/\omega_n = 16/12.5 = 1.28$$

Amplitude of the excitation

$$me\omega^2 = 0.05 \times (2\pi \times 960/60)^2 = 505 \text{ N}$$

Since the damping can be neglected, the force transmitted, by equation (7.27), is

$$F_T = \frac{me\omega^2}{y^2 - 1} = \frac{505}{1.28^2 - 1} = 791 \text{ N}$$

In this situation there is amplification of the out-of-balance force, i.e. no isolation. In practice it is very probable that the machine would have to be mounted on isolators, a more complex model being required for analysis.

EXERCISES

7.1 A point has two simultaneous simple harmonic motions of the same frequency, $x_1 = a_1 \sin \omega t$ and $x_2 = a_2 \sin(\omega t + \phi)$. Show that the resulting motion $(x_1 + x_2)$ is simple harmonic at ω with amplitude $\sqrt{a_1^2 + a_2^2 + 2a_1a_2 \cos\phi}$ and phase angle $\arctan[a_2 \sin\phi/(a_1 + a_2 \cos\phi)]$. Sketch the two simple harmonic motions and their sum for $a_1 = 3$, $a_2 = 4$ and $\phi = 60°$.

7.2 A vibrating body is observed to take 4.3 s for 10 complete oscillations. Calculate the frequency in rad/s, cycles/s (Hz) and cycles/min. Calculate also the period.

7.3 For the spring systems shown in Figure 7.36, calculate the stiffness as measured at the point P, in the direction shown.

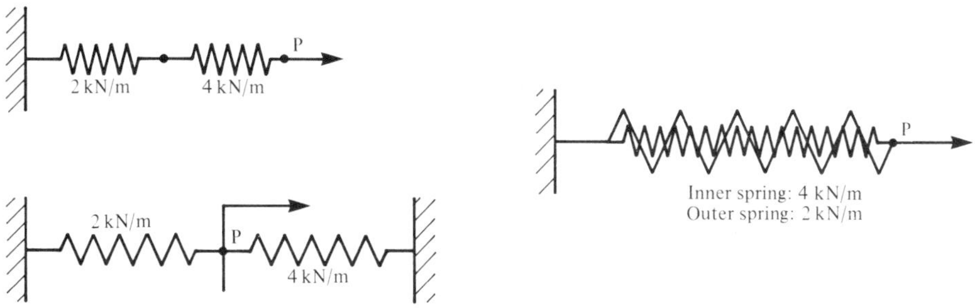

Figure 7.36

7.4 Calculate the stiffness of the system in Figure 7.37 measured at P. The crank AOP is assumed to be rigid.

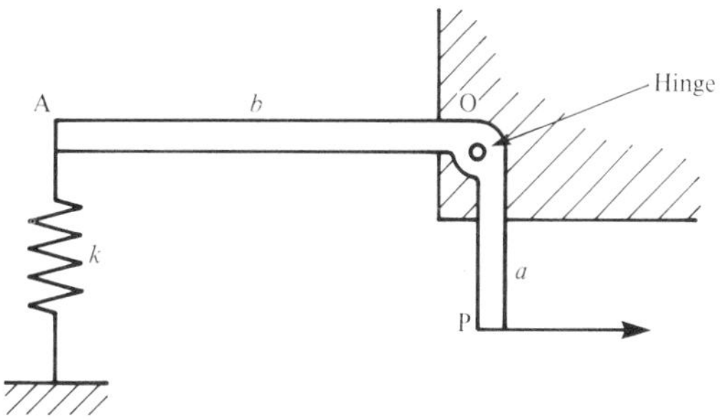

Figure 7.37

7.5 A steel wire is hung from the end of a steel cantilever beam (Figure 7.38). Calculate the vertical stiffness at the lower end of the wire. $E = 210 \times 10^9$ N/m^2.

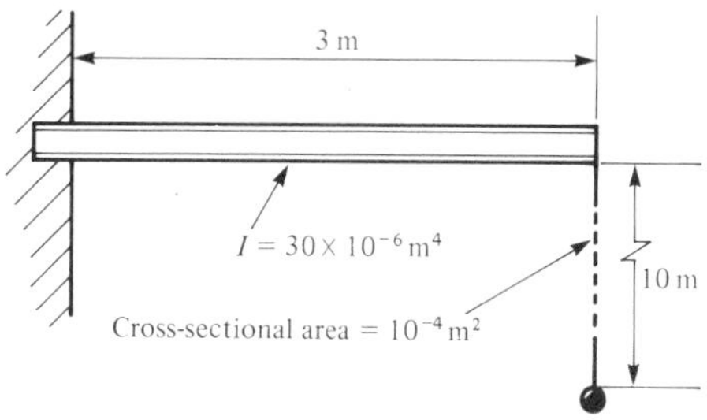

Figure 7.38

7.6 A mass of 1 kg is hung on a spring of stiffness 100 N/m, whose unstretched length is 0.3 m. While at rest in its equilibrium position it is given a knock which gives it a sudden upward velocity of 0.5 m/s. Sketch the graph of its distance from the spring support during the subsequent motion. What is the maximum value of the spring tension?

7.7 If a system produces a restoring force that is not proportional to the displacement, the stiffness measured at a particular displacement must be defined as (*change* in force) ÷ (*change* in displacement), i.e. dF/dx. A cylinder containing a gas is closed by a piston, of area A. Calculate the stiffness for small displacements of the piston around the point where the pressure and enclosed volume are p and V respectively. (Assume that motion takes place so slowly that the gas temperature is constant.)

7.8 An electric motor of mass 100 kg placed symmetrically on four identical springs compresses them by 14 mm (Figure 7.39). What is the frequency of free vertical vibration of the motor? If its radius of gyration is 0.08 m, what is the frequency of free angular oscillations about the centre of gravity?

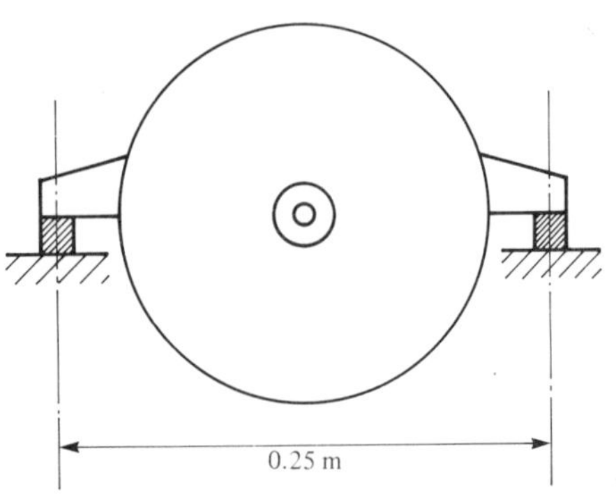

Figure 7.39

7.9 In a mass–spring–damper system, the spring stiffness is 20 kN/m and the damping constant is 0.8 kN s/m. The displacement of the mass from its equilibrium position is x. Draw the free body diagram for the following conditions: (a) $x = 0$, $\dot{x} = 1$ m/s; (b) $x = 0.1$ m, $\dot{x} = 0.5$ m/s; and (c) $x = 0.1$ m, $\dot{x} = -0.5$ m/s.

7.10 A damped oscillation is observed to be reduced by 80% in 5 s. What is the time constant? If there are 100 complete oscillations in this time, what is the logarithmic decrement of a complete cycle? Estimate the value of ζ.

7.11 For the system shown in Figure 7.40, obtain the differential equation of motion and so obtain expressions for the undamped natural frequency ω_n and the damping ratio ζ. The beam OA is rigid.

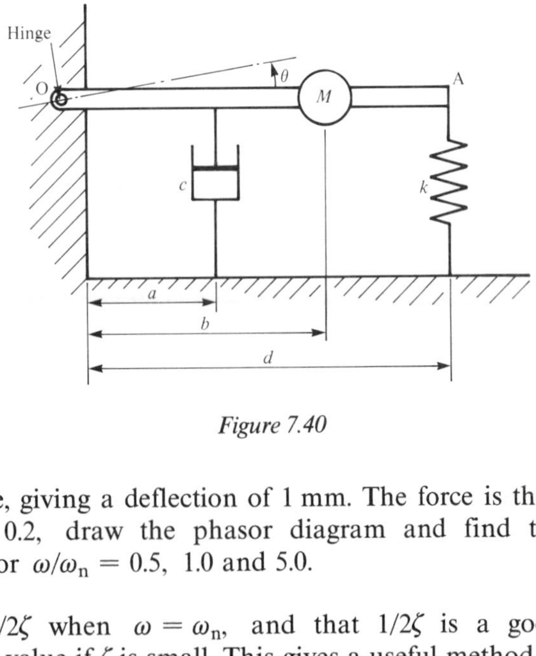

Figure 7.40

7.12 A steady force is applied to a machine, giving a deflection of 1 mm. The force is then varied sinusoidally. Given that $\zeta = 0.2$, draw the phasor diagram and find the amplitude and phase of the response for $\omega/\omega_n = 0.5$, 1.0 and 5.0.

7.13 Show that the amplitude ratio is $1/2\zeta$ when $\omega = \omega_n$, and that $1/2\zeta$ is a good approximation to the maximum (peak) value if ζ is small. This gives a useful method of estimating the damping ratio in practice. What is it for a system having a resonant amplitude ratio of 100?

7.14 A machine with a mass of 500 kg is on an elastic support with a static deflection of 2.5 mm. It is acted on by a vertical alternating force of 500 N at all frequencies. When the frequency coincides with the natural frequency of the system the amplitude of vibration is 6 mm. Calculate (a) the amount of damping present, (b) the amplitude of vibration when the machine is running at 700 cycles/min and (c) the transmissibility at that speed.

7.15 In a single-cylinder vertical engine, the piston displacement relative to the cylinder is given by:

$$x = 0.04(\cos \omega t + 0.4 \cos 2\omega t) \text{ m}$$

When the engine runs at 60 rad/s, calculate (a) the amplitude due to the primary force, i.e. at ω, (b) the amplitude due to the secondary force, i.e. at 2ω, (c) the maximum vibrational displacement of the engine, assuming that ϕ is 0 below resonance and π above resonance, and (d) the transmissibility.

The engine is supported by isolators of stiffness k and damping constant c. At what engine speeds will resonance occur? (Data: piston mass = 2 kg; spring stiffness, k = 64 kN/m; total engine mass = 100 kg; and damping constant, c = 1600 N m/s.)

Appendices

A.1 DERIVATIVES

Function	*Derivative*
x^n	nx^{n-1} $(n > 1$ if $x = 0)$
uv	$u(\mathrm{d}v/\mathrm{d}x) + v(\mathrm{d}u/\mathrm{d}x)$
u/v	$\dfrac{v(\mathrm{d}u/\mathrm{d}x) - u(\mathrm{d}v/\mathrm{d}x)}{v^2}$
$\sin ax$	$a \cos ax$
$\cos ax$	$-a \sin ax$
$\tan ax$	$a \sec^2 ax$
$\ln x$ (base e)	$\dfrac{1}{x}$
e^{ax}	$a\mathrm{e}^{ax}$
$f(u),\ u = g(x)$	$f'(u)g'(x)$

A.2 INTEGRALS

Function	*Integral*
x^n	$x^{n+1}/n + 1$ $(n \neq -1)$
$\dfrac{1}{x}$	$\ln x$ (base e)
e^{ax}	e^{ax}/a
$\sin x$	$-\cos x$
$\cos x$	$\sin x$
$1/(a + bx)$	$\dfrac{1}{b} \ln(a + bx)$
$x/(a + bx)$	$\dfrac{1}{b^2} [(a + bx) - a \ln(a + bx)]$

$1/(a + bx^2)$	$\dfrac{1}{\sqrt{ab}} \arctan\left(\sqrt{\dfrac{b}{a}}x\right)$	(a and $b > 0$)
$x/(a + bx^2)$	$\dfrac{1}{2b} \ln\,(a + bx^2)$	
$1/(a + bx + cx^2)$	$\dfrac{1}{\sqrt{4ac - b^2}} \arctan\left(\dfrac{2cx + b}{\sqrt{4ac - b^2}}\right)$	($4ac > b^2$)
$1/(a + bx + cx^2)$	$\dfrac{1}{\sqrt{b^2 - 4ac}} \ln\left(\dfrac{2cx + b - \sqrt{b^2 - 4ac}}{2cx + b + \sqrt{b^2 - 4ac}}\right)$	($4ac < b^2$)
$1/(a - bx^2)$	$\dfrac{1}{2\sqrt{ab}} \ln\left\lvert\dfrac{\sqrt{a} + \sqrt{b}x}{\sqrt{a} - \sqrt{b}x}\right\rvert = \dfrac{1}{\sqrt{ab}} \operatorname{artanh}\left(\sqrt{\dfrac{b}{a}}x\right)$	($a, b > 0$)
$x/(a + bx + cx^2)$	$\dfrac{1}{2c} \ln\,(a + bx + cx^2) - \dfrac{b}{2c}\displaystyle\int \dfrac{\mathrm{d}x}{a + bx + cx^2}$	

A.3 APPROXIMATE INTEGRATION

(a) *Simpson's rule* (quite accurate): If $y = f(x)$, range $x = a$ to $x = b$, divide the range $(b - a)$ into an *even* number of strips n, each of length h. Let $y_1, y_2, y_3, \ldots, y_{n+1}$ be the values of the function. Then

$$\int_a^b f(x)\,\mathrm{d}x \simeq \frac{h}{3}[y_1 + y_{n+1} + 4\sum(\text{even ordinates}) + 2\sum(\text{odd ordinates})]$$

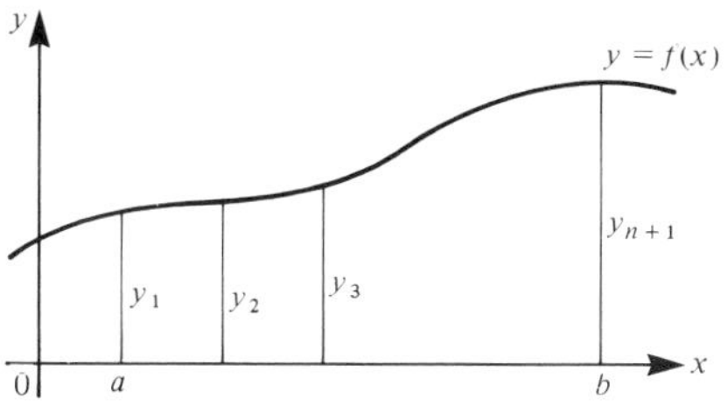

(b) *Trapezium rule* (less accurate): Divide the range $(b - a)$ into as many ordinates as required and equally spaced by an amount h. The greater the number of ordinates the better the accuracy. Then

$$\int_a^b f(x)\,\mathrm{d}x \simeq h[\tfrac{1}{2}(y_1 + y_{n+1} + y_2 + y_3 + \ldots + y_n]$$

A.4 MOMENTS OF INERTIA

(a) Concentrated mass m at radius R:

$$I = mR^2$$

(b) Cylinder of mass m, radius r, about a central axis:

$$I = \tfrac{1}{2}mr^2$$

(c) Disc of mass m, radius r, about an axis through the centre, perpendicular to the central axis:

$$I = \tfrac{1}{4}mr^2$$

(d) Rectangular block:

$$I_{11} = \tfrac{1}{12}m(a^2 + b^2)$$

$$I_{22} = \tfrac{1}{12}m(L^2 + b^2)$$

$$I_{33} = \tfrac{1}{12}m(a^2 + L^2)$$

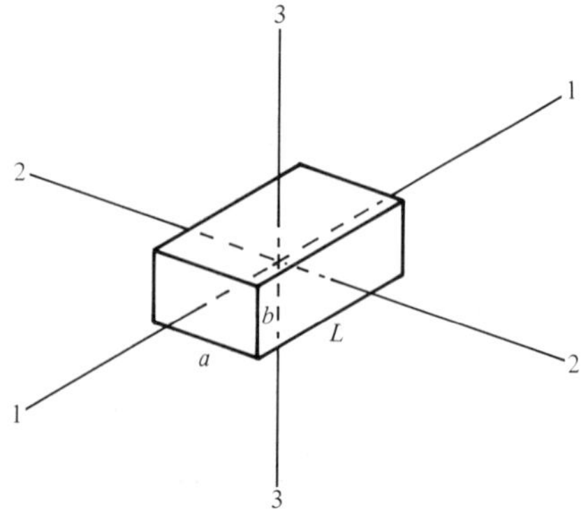

(e) Uniform thin rod of length L, mass m, about central axis:

$$I = \tfrac{1}{12}mL^2$$

about an axis through the end:

$$I = \tfrac{1}{3}mL^2$$

(f) *Parallel-axis theorem*: If I_G is the moment of inertia about an axis through the centre of mass G, I_O the moment of inertia about an axis through some point O and parallel to the axis through G and at a distance d, then

$$I_O = I_G + Md^2$$

where M is the mass of the body.

A.5 TRIGONOMETRY

$$\sin^2\theta + \cos^2\theta = 1$$

$$\tan^2\theta + 1 = \sec^2\theta$$

$$\sin(\theta \pm \alpha) = \sin\theta\cos\alpha \pm \cos\theta\sin\alpha$$

$$\cos(\theta \pm \alpha) = \cos\theta\cos\alpha \mp \sin\theta\sin\alpha$$

$$\sin\theta = \frac{2t}{1+t^2} \qquad \cos\theta = \frac{1-t^2}{1+t^2} \qquad t = \tan(\theta/2)$$

Cosine rule for triangles:

$$c^2 = a^2 + b^2 - 2ab\cos C$$

Sine rule for triangles:

$$\frac{a}{\sin A} = \frac{b}{\sin B} = \frac{c}{\sin C}$$

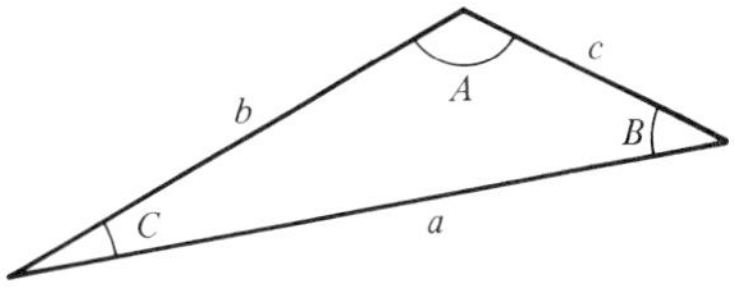

A.6 SOLUTION OF ALGEBRAIC EQUATIONS

(a) *Quadratic equation*:

$$ax^2 + bx + c = 0$$

The roots are

$$x = \frac{-b \pm \sqrt{b^2 - 4ac}}{2a}$$

For real roots we must have $b^2 > 4ac$.

(b) *Equation of the nth degree*, $n > 2$:

$$a_1x^n + a_2x^{n-1} + a_3x^{n-2} + \ldots + a_n = 0 \qquad \text{i.e. } f(x) = 0$$

If x_i is an approximation to one of the roots, a better value is given by the Newton–Raphson equation:

$$x_{i+1} = x_i - \frac{f(x_i)}{f'(x_i)}$$

A.7 FRICTION COEFFICIENTS (TYPICAL VALUES)

Surfaces in contact	μ_{static}	$\mu_{kinetic}$
steel on steel (dry)	0.6	0.4
steel on steel (greasy)	0.1	0.05
steel on bearing material (dry)	0.4	0.3
steel on bearing material (greasy)	0.1	0.07
steel on brass (dry)	0.5	0.4
brake lining on cast iron	0.4	0.3
rubber tyres on smooth road (dry)	0.9	0.8
Teflon on metal	0.04	0.04
metal on ice	-	0.02

A.8 COMMON SI UNITS

Quantity	*Name of unit*	*Symbol*
length	metre	m
mass	kilogram	kg
time	second	s
force	newton	N
energy/work	joule	J (= N m = kg m^2/s^2)
power	watt	W (= J s^{-1} = kg m^2/s^3)
pressure	pascal	Pa (= N m^{-2} = kg/m s^2)

1 hour (h) = 60 minutes (min) = 3600 s; 1 tonne (t) = 10^3 kg; 1 bar = 10^5 Pa.

Bibliography

Anand, D.K., and Cunnif, P.F., *Engineering mechanics* (*dynamics*) (Allyn and Bacon, 1984)

Beer, F.P., and Johnston, E.R., Jr, *Vector mechanics for engineers* (*dynamics*) (McGraw-Hill, 1972)

Beer, F.P., and Johnston, E.R., Jr, *Mechanics for engineers* (*dynamics*), 3rd Edn (McGraw-Hill, 1976)

Ginsberg, J.H., and Genin, J., *Dynamics*, 2nd Edn (Wiley, 1984)

Harrison, H.R., and Nettleton, T., *Principles of engineering mechanics* (Edward Arnold, 1978)

Hartenberg, R.S., and Denavit, J., *Kinematic synthesis of linkages* (McGraw-Hill, 1964)

Holmes, R., *The characteristics of mechanical engineering systems* (Pergamon Press, 1977)

Hrones, J.A., and Nelson, G.L., *Analysis of the four-bar linkage* (MIT–Wiley, 1951)

Meriam, S.L., *Engineering mechanics*, Vol. 2, *Dynamics* (Wiley, 1980)

Shames, I.H., *Engineering mechanics* (*statics and dynamics*) (Prentice Hall, 1970)

Smith,C.E., *Applied mechanics* (*dynamics*), 2nd Edn (Wiley, 1982)

Thomson, W.T., *Introduction to space dynamics* (Wiley, 1961)

Solutions

CHAPTER 1

1.1

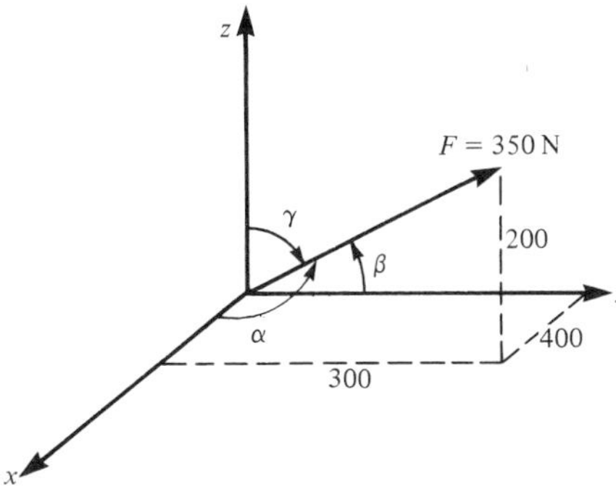

$$R = \sqrt{400^2 + 300^2 + 200^2} = 538.5$$

$$\cos\alpha = \frac{400}{538.5} = 0.7428$$

$$\cos\beta = \frac{300}{538.5} = 0.5571$$

$$\cos\gamma = \frac{200}{538.5} = 0.3714$$

Hence

$$F = F\cos\alpha\,\mathbf{i} + F\cos\beta\,\mathbf{j} + F\cos\gamma\,\mathbf{k}$$

$$= 350 \times 0.7428\mathbf{i} + 350 \times 0.5571\mathbf{j} + 350 \times 0.3714\mathbf{k}$$

$$= 260\mathbf{i} + 195\mathbf{j} + 130\mathbf{k}$$ ◀

1.2

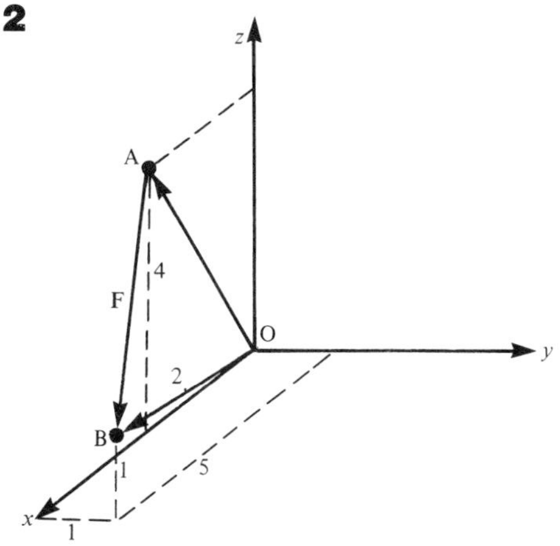

$$\mathbf{R} = \overrightarrow{AB} = \overrightarrow{OB} - \overrightarrow{OA} = (5\mathbf{i} + \mathbf{j} + \mathbf{k}) - (2\mathbf{i} + 4\mathbf{k}) = 3\mathbf{i} + \mathbf{j} - 3\mathbf{k}\ \text{m}$$

$$R = \sqrt{3^2 + 1^2 + 3^2} = 4.36\ \text{m}$$

$$\mathbf{F} = 2500 \times \frac{3}{4.36}\mathbf{i} + 2500 \times \frac{1}{4.36}\mathbf{j} - 2500 \times \frac{3}{4.36}\mathbf{k}$$

$$= 1720\mathbf{i} + 573.5\mathbf{j} - 1720\mathbf{k}\ \text{N}$$ ◀

The direction angles are:

$$\alpha = \arccos\left(\frac{3}{4.36}\right) = 46.52^\circ$$ ◀

$$\beta = \arccos\left(\frac{1}{4.36}\right) = 76.74^\circ$$ ◀

$$\gamma = \arccos\left(\frac{-3}{4.36}\right) = 133.48^\circ$$ ◀

$$\text{Acceleration } \mathbf{a} = \frac{\mathbf{F}}{m} = \frac{1720}{320}\mathbf{i} + \frac{573.5}{320}\mathbf{j} - \frac{1720}{320}\mathbf{k} = 5.38\mathbf{i} + 1.79\mathbf{j} - 5.38\mathbf{k}$$

Hence

$$a = \sqrt{5.38^2 + 1.79^2 + 5.38^2}$$
$$= 7.8 \text{ m/s}^2 \text{ in the directions } \alpha, \beta, \gamma$$ ◄

1.3

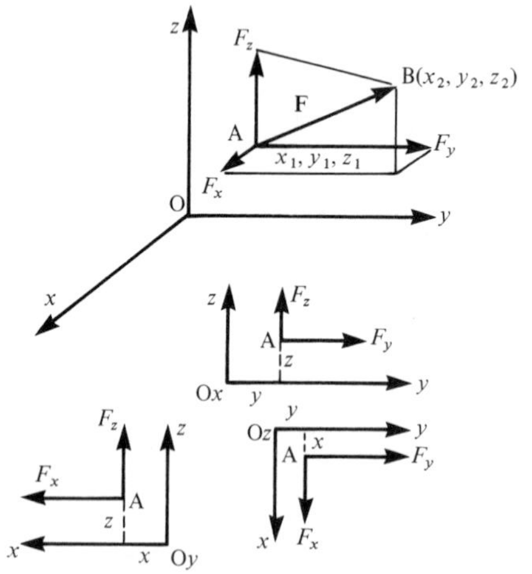

The lengths of the cuboid defined by F_x, F_y, F_z are:

$$\left.\begin{aligned} x_2 - x_1 &= X \\ y_2 - y_1 &= Y \\ z_2 - z_1 &= Z \end{aligned}\right\} \quad R = \sqrt{X^2 + Y^2 + Z^2}$$

Hence

$$F_x = \frac{X}{R}F, \quad F_y = \frac{Y}{R}F, \quad F_z = \frac{Z}{R}F.$$

Considering each plane in turn, we have for the moments about the axes

$$M_x = F_z y - F_y z$$ ◄
$$M_y = F_x z - F_z x$$ ◄
$$M_z = F_y x - F_x y$$ ◄

In the present case, $X = 3$, $Y = 1$, $Z = -3$, $R = 4.36$.

$$\therefore \quad F_x = 1720\text{ N}, \quad F_y = 573.5\text{ N}$$
$$F_z = -1720\text{ N (i.e. downwards)}$$

Also $x = 2, \quad y = 0, \quad z = 4.$

Hence

$$M_x = -1720 \times 0 - 573.5 \times 4 = -2294\text{ Nm}$$ ◄
$$M_y = 1720 \times 4 - (-1720) \times 2 = 10\,320\text{ Nm}$$ ◄
$$M_z = 573.5 \times 2 - 0 = 1147\text{ Nm}$$ ◄

1.4

$$\mathbf{e} = \frac{x\mathbf{i} + y\mathbf{j} + z\mathbf{k}}{\sqrt{x^2 + y^2 + z^2}}$$

where

$$x = 2 - 4 = -2, \quad y = 0 - 6 = -6$$
$$z = 10 - (-3) = 13$$

Hence

$$\sqrt{x^2 + y^2 + z^2} = \sqrt{2^2 + 6^2 + 13^2} = 14.46$$

and $\mathbf{e} = -0.138\mathbf{i} - 0.415\mathbf{j} + 0.899\mathbf{k}$ ◄

1.5

$$\mathbf{v} = 125\mathbf{i} + 210\mathbf{j} + 305\mathbf{k}\text{ mm/s}$$
$$\therefore \quad v = \sqrt{125^2 + 210^2 + 305^2} = 390.8\text{ mm/s}$$

Hence

$$\alpha = \arccos\left(\frac{125}{390.8}\right) = 71.3^\circ$$ ◄
$$\beta = \arccos\left(\frac{210}{390.8}\right) = 57.5^\circ$$ ◄
$$\gamma = \arccos\left(\frac{305}{390.8}\right) = 38.7^\circ$$ ◄

1.6

$$OA = \sqrt{2^2 + 2^2 + 3^2} = 4.123$$
$$OB = \sqrt{3^2 + 1^2 + 2^2} = 3.742$$
$$OC = \sqrt{4^2 + 0^2 + 5^2} = 6.403$$

$$\mathbf{T}_1 = \frac{2}{4.123}T_1\mathbf{i} + \frac{-2}{4.123}T_1\mathbf{j} + \frac{3}{4.123}T_1\mathbf{k}$$
$$= 0.485T_1\mathbf{i} - 0.485T_1\mathbf{j} + 0.728T_1\mathbf{k}$$

Similarly

$$\mathbf{T}_2 = 0.802T_2\mathbf{i} + 0.267T_2\mathbf{j} + 0.534T_2\mathbf{k}$$

and $\mathbf{T}_3 = -0.625T_3\mathbf{i} + 0 + 0.781T_3\mathbf{k}$

For equilibrium

$$\Sigma\mathbf{T} = 0 \quad \Rightarrow$$

along x-axis:

$$0.485T_1 + 0.802T_2 - 0.625T_3 = 0 \quad (1)$$

along y-axis:

$$-0.485T_1 + 0.267T_2 = 0 \quad (2)$$

along z-axis:

$$0.728T_1 + 0.534T_2 + 0.781T_3 = 1500 \times 9.81$$
$$= 14\,715\text{ N} \quad (3)$$

From (2)

$$T_1 = \frac{0.267}{0.485}T_2 = 0.551T_2$$

From (1)

$$(0.485 \times 0.551 + 0.802)\ T_2 = 0.625T_3$$

$$\Rightarrow \quad T_2 = 0.585T_3$$

From (3)

$$(0.728 \times 0.551 \times 0.585 + 0.534 \times 0.585 + 0.781)\ T_3 = 14\,715\text{ N}$$

Hence

$$T_1 = 3572\text{ N}, \quad T_2 = 6482\text{ N}$$ ◄

$$T_3 = 11\,080\text{ N}$$ ◄

1.7

Let F = force exerted by the ram; X, Y = the reactions at O, having a resultant $R = \sqrt{X^2 + Y^2}$; Mg = weight.

For equilibrium,

$$\Sigma\text{ forces} = 0$$

$$\Sigma\text{ moments about O} = 0$$

$$\Rightarrow \quad F\sin\beta + Y - Mg = 0$$

$$F\cos\beta + X = 0$$

$$Mg(b\cos\theta - a\sin\theta) + (F\cos\beta)(l\sin\theta) - (F\sin\beta)(l\cos\theta) = 0$$

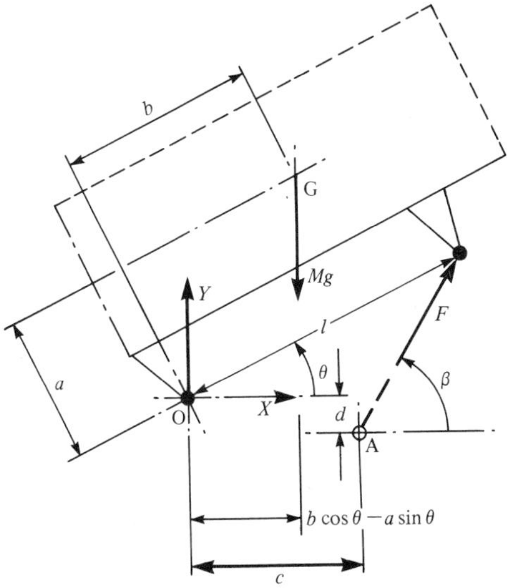

$$\tan\beta = \frac{l\sin\theta + d}{l\cos\theta - c}$$

$$b = 3.25/2 - 0.2 = 1.425\text{ m}$$

$$a = 1.25/2 + 0.3 = 0.925\text{ m}$$

$$l = 2.5\text{ m}, \quad d = 0.35\text{ m}, \quad c = 1.5\text{ m}$$

Solving for F, X and Y yields

$$F = Mg(b\cos\theta - a\sin\theta)/l\sin(\beta - \theta)$$

$$X = -F\cos\beta$$

$$Y = Mg - F\sin\beta$$

When $\theta = 0°$, $\beta = \arctan\left(\dfrac{d}{l - c}\right) = \arctan 0.35$ $= 19.29°$

$$F = 20 \times 10^3 \times 1.425/2.5\ \sin 19.29°$$

$$= 34.5\text{ kN}$$ ◄

$$X = -34.5\cos 19.29° = -32.6\text{ kN}$$

$$Y = (20 - 34.5\sin 19.29°) \times 10^3 = 8.6\text{ kN}$$

$$R = \sqrt{8.6^2 + 32.6^2} = 33.6\text{ kN}$$ ◄

Similarly, when $\theta = 30°$, $\beta = 67.43°$

$$F = 10.2\text{ kN}$$ ◄

$$X = -4.1\text{ kN}$$

$$Y = 10.6\text{ kN}$$

$$R = 11.4\text{ kN}$$ ◄

1.8

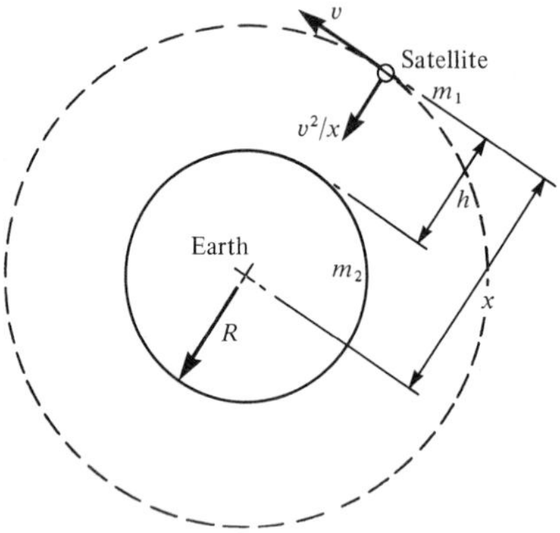

Let the speed be v. Then

$$\frac{v^2}{x} = \frac{g_0R^2}{(R+h)^2} = \frac{g_0R^2}{x^2}$$

$$\Rightarrow \quad v = R\sqrt{g_0/x}$$

$$= 6.371 \times 10^6 \times \sqrt{9.81/6.721 \times 10^6}$$

$$= 7697 \text{ m/s} \quad ◀$$

$$\text{Periodic time } \tau = 2\pi x/v = \frac{2\pi \times 6.721 \times 10^6}{7697 \times 3600}$$

$$= 1.524 \text{ h} = 91.44 \text{ min} \quad ◀$$

Alternatively

$$F = G\frac{m_1 m_2}{x^2};$$

$$F = m_1\frac{v^2}{x}$$

$$\Rightarrow \quad v = \sqrt{Gm_2/x}$$

$$v = \sqrt{\frac{6.67 \times 10^{-11} \times 5.976 \times 10^{24}}{6.271 \times 10^6}}$$

$$= 7701 \text{ m/s} \quad ◀$$

from which

$$\tau = 91.39 \text{ min} \quad ◀$$

CHAPTER 2

2.1 $v = \frac{150}{3.6} = 41.7\text{ m/s}$

$$a = \frac{3.25}{3.6} = 0.90\text{ m/s}^2$$

$$\frac{v^2}{R} = \frac{41.7^2}{750} = 2.32\text{ m/s}^2$$

$$\text{Total acceleration} = \sqrt{0.9^2 + 2.32^2} = 2.49\text{ m/s}^2$$

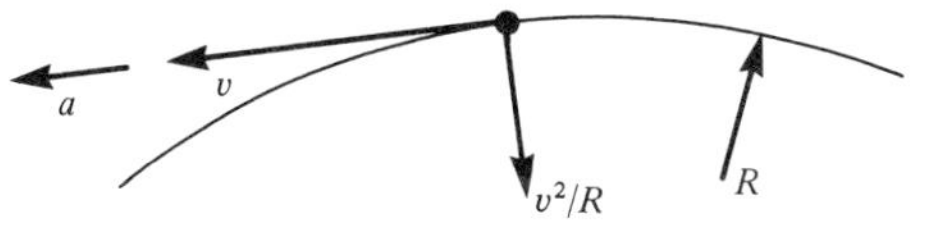

2.2 $a = -g$

i.e. $v\frac{dv}{dx} = -g \Leftrightarrow v\,dv = -g\,dx$

Integrating yields:

$$\tfrac{1}{2}v^2 = -gx + C$$

When $x = h$, $v = v_1$

$$\Rightarrow \quad C = \tfrac{1}{2}v_1^2 + gh$$

When $x = 0$, let $v = v_0$

$$\Rightarrow \quad v_0 = \sqrt{2gh + v_1^2} = \sqrt{2 \times 3.27 \times 10 + 7^2} = 10.7\text{ m/s}$$

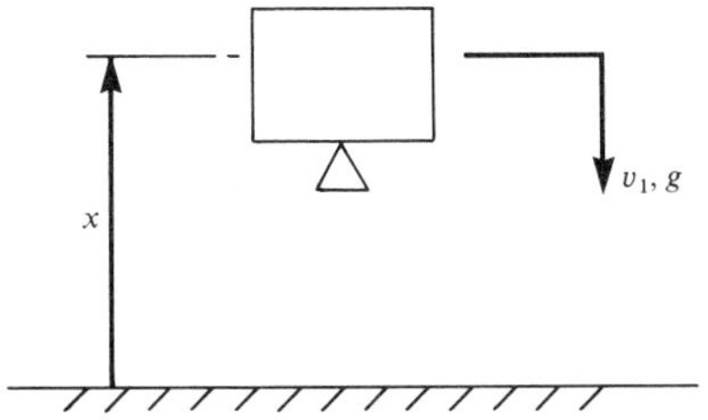

2.3

Let m = mass of the train. By Newton's second law, Σ forces = mass × acceleration. Hence

$$mv\frac{dv}{dx} = -k_1 mg - k_2 mgv^2$$

where $k_1 = 0.1$

and $mgk_2\left(\frac{100}{3.6}\right)^2 = 0.01mg$

$$\Rightarrow \quad k_2 = 1.3 \times 10^{-5}\text{ s}^2/\text{m}^2$$

(a) $$\int\frac{v\,dv}{k_1 + k_2v^2} = -gx + C$$

$$\therefore \quad \frac{1}{2k_2}\ln(k_1 + k_2v^2) = -gx + C$$

Let $v = v_0$ when $x = 0$. Then

$$C = \frac{1}{2k_2}\ln(k_1 + k_2v_0^2), \quad \text{so that}$$

$$x = \frac{1}{2k_2g}\ln\left(\frac{k_1 + k_2v_0^2}{k_1 + k_2v^2}\right)$$

When $v = 0$, the train has come to rest. Let the distance travelled then be X. Then

$$X = \frac{1}{2k_2g}\ln\left(1 + \frac{k_2}{k_1}v_0^2\right)$$

$$= \frac{1}{2 \times 1.3 \times 10^{-5} \times 9.81}\ln\left[1 + \frac{1.3 \times 10^{-5}}{0.1}\left(\frac{100}{3.6}\right)^2\right]$$

$$= 375\text{ m}$$

(b) $$\frac{dv}{dt} = -(k_1 + k_2v^2)g$$

$$\therefore \quad \int\frac{dv}{k_1 + k_2v^2} = -gt + C_1$$

When $t = 0$, $v = v_0$, and when $v = 0$, let $t = T$.

Hence the time to come to rest is

$$T = \frac{1}{g\sqrt{k_1k_2}}\arctan\left(\sqrt{\frac{k_2}{k_1}}\,v_0\right)$$

$$= \frac{1}{9.81\sqrt{0.1 \times 1.3 \times 10^{-5}}} \times \arctan\underbrace{\left(\sqrt{\frac{1.3 \times 10^{-5}}{0.1}} \times \frac{100}{3.6}\right)}_{\text{in radians!}}$$

$$= 27.4 \text{ s}$$ ◀

2.4

(a) After 1 minute,

$$H = vt \sin\alpha = \frac{225}{3.6} \times 60 \times \sin 15^\circ = 970 \text{ m}$$

Horizontal distance from radar is

$$s = X - vt\cos\alpha = 6000 - \frac{225}{3.6} \times 60 \times \cos 15^\circ$$

$$= 2378 \text{ m}$$

$$\text{Length of sight line } R = \sqrt{2378^2 + 970^2}$$

$$= 2568 \text{ m}$$ ◀

(b) At that instant,

$$\theta = \arctan\left(\frac{H}{s}\right) = \arctan\left(\frac{970}{2378}\right) = 22.2^\circ$$

$$\dot{R} = -v\cos\theta = -\frac{225}{3.6}\cos 22.2^\circ$$

$$= -57.9 \text{ m/s} \quad \text{(i.e. shortening)}$$ ◀

(c) $R\dot{\theta} = v\sin\theta \Rightarrow \dot{\theta} = \frac{v}{R}\sin\theta$. Hence

$$\theta = \frac{225/3.6}{2568} \times \sin 22.2^\circ = 0.009 \text{ rad/s}$$

$$= 0.52^\circ/\text{s}$$ ◀

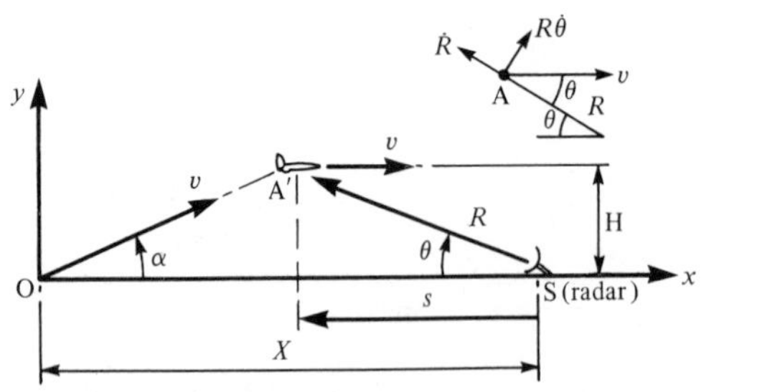

2.5

(a) Phase (1): $0 \leqslant t \leqslant t_1 = 6$ s

$$v_1 = \int_0^{t_1} a_1 \, dt = \int_0^6 3 \, dt = 3 \times 6 = 18 \text{ m/s}$$

Phase (2): $0 \leqslant T \leqslant 9$ s

$$v_2 = v_1 + \int_0^9 \left[1.75 + \left(\frac{3 - 1.75}{9}\right) T\right] dT$$

$$= 18 + 1.75 \times 9 + \frac{1.25}{9} \times \frac{9^2}{2} = 39.4 \text{ m/s}$$

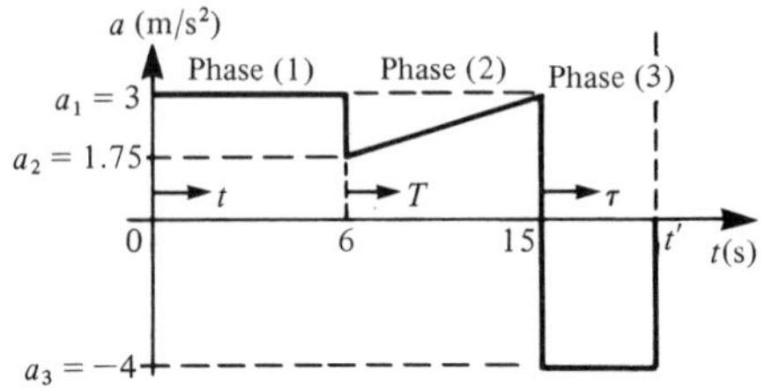

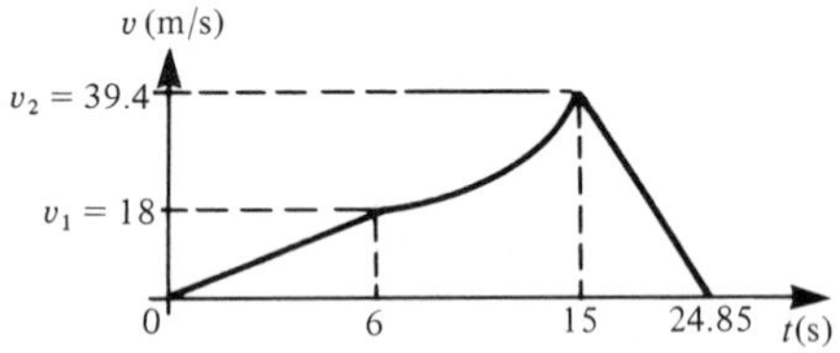

Phase (3): $0 \leqslant \tau \leqslant t'$

$$v = v_2 + \int_0^{\tau'} (-4) \, d\tau$$

When $\tau = \tau'$, $v = 0 \Rightarrow \tau' = \frac{39.4}{4} = 9.85$ s

$$\text{Total time } t' = 15 + 9.85 = 24.85 \text{ s}$$ ◀

(b) $\text{Total distance } s = \int_0^{t'} v \, dt = \left(\begin{array}{l}\text{area under the}\\ \text{velocity-time}\\ \text{graph}\end{array}\right)$

$$= \frac{18 \times 6}{2} + 18 \times 9 + \frac{1.75}{2} \times 9^2 + \frac{1.25}{9} \times \frac{9^3}{6}$$

$$+ \frac{39.4 \times 9.85}{2} = 497.7 \text{ m}$$ ◀

2.6

Let s = distance travelled = $\int v\,dt$

(i) Using the trapezium rule we have

$$s = \left(\frac{96}{2} + 0 + 36.0 + \ldots + 83.2 + 92\right) \times 0.5/3.6 = 120.1 \text{ m}$$

(ii) Using Simpson's rule we have

$$s = \frac{0.5}{3} \times \frac{1}{3.6}\left[\frac{19.2}{2} + 96 + 4(19.2 + 49.6 + 68 + 70.4 + 63.2 + 72 + 92) + 2(36 + 60.8 + 72 + 65.6 + 64.8 + 83.2)\right]$$

$$= 120.3 \text{ m}$$

During the slowing down phase,

$$v\frac{dv}{ds} = -a$$

$$\Rightarrow \quad \tfrac{1}{2}v^2 = -as + C$$

When $s = 0$,

$$v = v_0$$

$$\Rightarrow \quad C = \tfrac{1}{2}v_0^2.$$

When $v = 0$, the car has come to a standstill.

Hence

$$s = v_0^2/2a = \left(\frac{96}{3.6}\right)^2 \Big/ (2 \times 0.5 \times 9.81)$$

$$= 72.5 \text{ m}$$

2.7

Time interval $\Delta t = \Delta\theta/\omega = 5 \times 60/(2\pi \times 850 \times 57.3)$ $= 0.056$ s

θ (deg)	0		5	
y (mm)	0		0.43	
$v = \frac{\Delta y}{\Delta t} = \frac{\Delta y}{9.8 \times 10^{-4}}$ (m/s)		0.439		1.327
$a = \frac{\Delta v}{\Delta t}$ (m/s^2)	896		906	
θ (deg)	10		15	
y (mm)	1.73		3.78	
$v = \frac{\Delta y}{\Delta t} = \frac{\Delta y}{9.8 \times 10^{-4}}$ (m/s)		2.041		2.082
$a = \frac{\Delta v}{\Delta t}$ (m/s^2)	729		4.2	
θ (deg)	20		25	
y (mm)	5.82		7.59	
$v = \frac{\Delta y}{\Delta t} = \frac{\Delta y}{9.8 \times 10^{-4}}$ (m/s)		1.806		1.581
$a = \frac{\Delta v}{\Delta t}$ (m/s^2)	−282		−230	
θ (deg)	30		35	
y (mm)	9.14		10.41	
$v = \frac{\Delta y}{\Delta t} = \frac{\Delta y}{9.8 \times 10^{-4}}$ (m/s)		1.296		1.010
$a = \frac{\Delta v}{\Delta t}$ (m/s^2)	−291		−292	
θ (deg)	40		45	
y (mm)	11.4		12.12	
$v = \frac{\Delta y}{\Delta t} = \frac{\Delta y}{9.8 \times 10^{-4}}$ (m/s)		0.735		0.439
$a = \frac{\Delta v}{\Delta t}$ (m/s^2)	−281		−302	
θ (deg)	50		55	
y (mm)	12.55		12.70	
$v = \frac{\Delta y}{\Delta t} = \frac{\Delta y}{9.8 \times 10^{-4}}$ (m/s)		0.153		
$a = \frac{\Delta v}{\Delta t}$ (m/s^2)	−292			

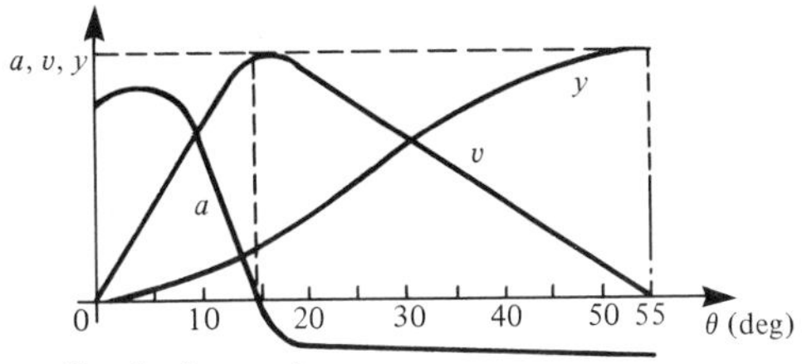

Sketch of y, v and a

2.8

$$v_1 = \frac{2\pi N}{60} \times R = \frac{2\pi \times 125}{60} \times 0.25$$

$$= 3.27 \text{ m/s}$$

$$v_2 = \frac{2\pi \times 125 \times 0.295}{60} = 3.86 \text{ m/s}$$

$$v_c = \sqrt{Rg} = \sqrt{0.25 \times 9.81} = 1.57 \text{ m/s}$$

Since v_1 and $v_2 > v_c$, the material leaves at A.

$\therefore \quad \theta = 0$

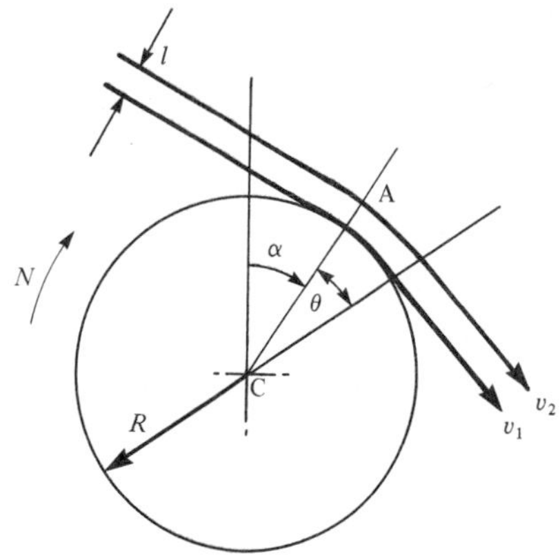

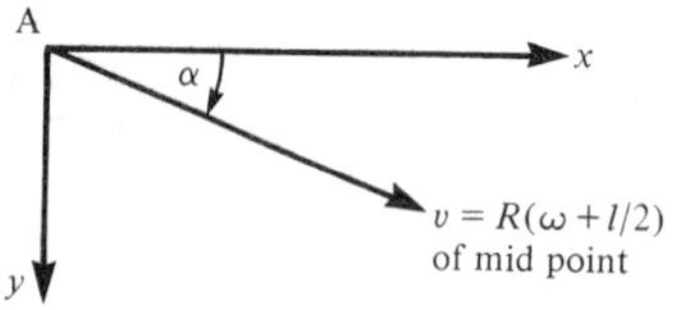

At any instant we have

$$\ddot{x} = 0$$

$$\therefore \quad v_x = \text{constant} = v\cos\alpha \qquad (1)$$

$$\ddot{y} = g$$

$$\therefore \quad \tfrac{1}{2}v_y^2 = gy + \text{constant} = gy + \tfrac{1}{2}v^2\sin^2\alpha$$

$$\text{or} \quad v_y = gt + v\sin\alpha \qquad (2)$$

Integrating equations (1) and (2) with respect to time yields $x = v\cos\alpha t$, $y = \frac{1}{2}gt^2 + v\sin\alpha t$.

If T is the time taken to reach the hopper level, then

$$gT^2 + 2vT\sin\alpha - 2(H + R'\cos\alpha) = 0$$

where

$$R' = R + l/2$$

But $v = 13.09\,(0.25 + 0.045/2) = 3.57$ m/s.

Hence $9.81T^2 + 1.85T - 5.55 = 0$, so that
$T = 0.66$ s

When $t = T$, $x = D$, so that

$$D = 3.57 \times \cos 15^\circ \times 0.66 = 2.28 \text{ m}$$ ◄

The minimum hopper width will be

$$d = v_2 T\cos\alpha - v_1 T\cos\alpha$$

$$= (3.86 - 3.27)\cos 15^\circ \times 0.66$$

$$= 0.38 \text{ m}$$ ◄

2.9

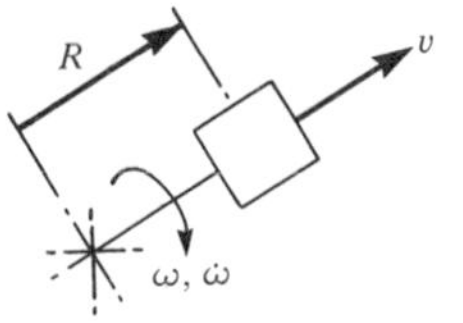

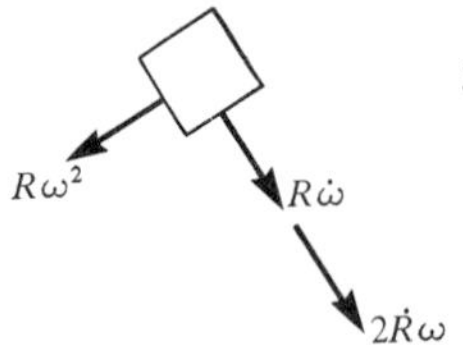

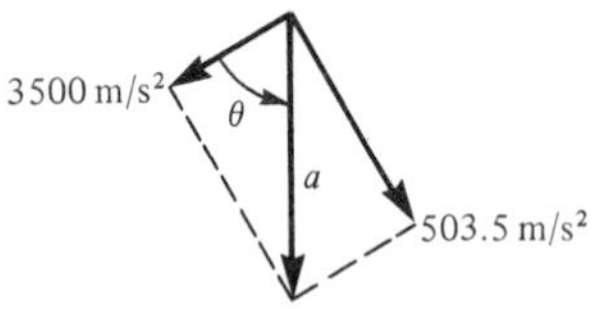

$$R\omega^2 = 0.35 \times 100^2 = 3500 \text{ m/s}^2$$

$$R\dot{\omega} = 0.35 \times 10 = 3.5 \text{ m/s}^2$$

$$2\dot{R}\omega = 2 \times 2.5 \times 100 = 500 \text{ m/s}^2$$

Total acceleration

$$a = \sqrt{3500^2 + 503.5^2} = 3536 \text{ m/s}^2$$ ◄

$$\text{at } \theta = \arctan\left(\frac{503.5}{3500}\right) = 8.19^\circ \text{ to the radius}$$ ◄

2.10

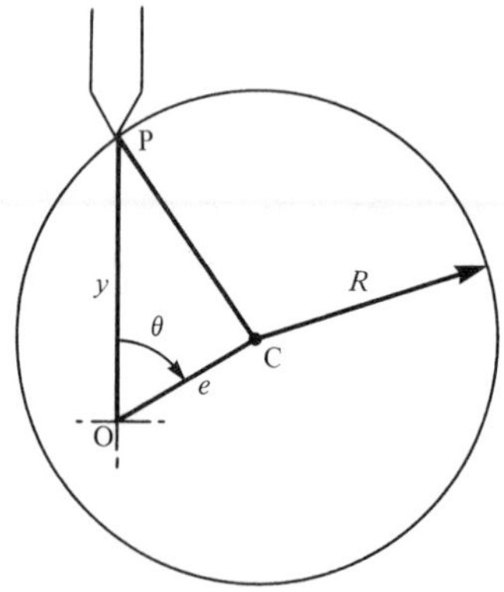

From the triangle OCP,

$$R^2 = y^2 + e^2 - 2ye\cos\theta$$

$$\Rightarrow \quad y^2 - 2ye\cos\theta - (R^2 - e^2) = 0$$

Solving for y yields

$$y = e\cos\theta + \sqrt{R^2 - e^2\sin^2\theta} \qquad (1)$$

Total travel $= 2e$ ◄

Differentiating (1) with respect to time gives for the velocity of P:

$$v_P = \dot{y} = -e\omega\left(\sin\theta + \frac{e\sin 2\theta}{2\sqrt{R^2 - e^2\sin^2\theta}}\right)$$

If e/R is small, then

$$v_P \simeq -e\omega\left(\sin\theta + \frac{e}{2R}\sin 2\theta\right)$$ ◀

The acceleration of P,

$$a_P = \dot{v}_P = -e\omega^2\left(\cos\theta + \frac{e}{R}\cos 2\theta\right)$$

$$\ddot{y}_{max} = -e\omega^2\left(1 + \frac{e}{R}\right)$$

$$= -0.015 \times \left(\frac{2\pi \times 720}{60}\right)^2\left(1 + \frac{15}{85}\right)$$

$$= 100.3 \text{ m/s}^2 = 10.2g$$ ◀

2.11

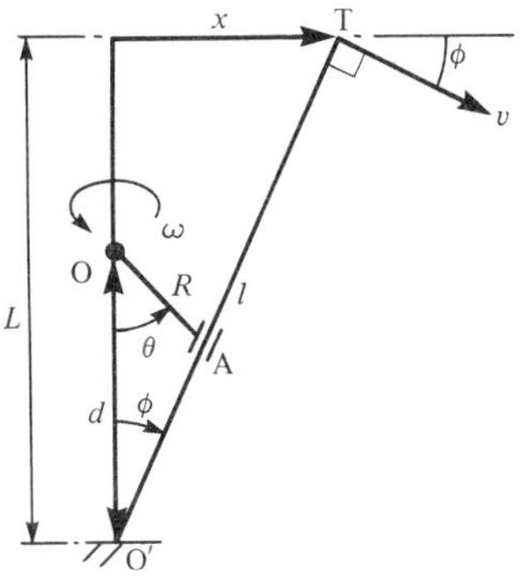

$$x = L\tan\phi$$

From ΔO′OA,

$$\tan\phi = \frac{R\sin\theta}{d - R\cos\theta}$$

$$\therefore \quad x = LR\frac{\sin\theta}{d - R\cos\theta}$$

Differentiating with respect to time yields

$$\dot{x} = LR\frac{(d - R\cos\theta)\cos\theta - \sin\theta(R\sin\theta)}{(d - R\cos\theta)^2}\dot{\theta}$$

$$= \frac{LR(d\cos\theta - R)}{(d - R\cos\theta)^2}\omega$$ ◀

Differentiating once more, we have

$$\ddot{x} = \frac{LR\omega^2}{(d - R\cos\theta)^4}\Big[(d - R\cos\theta)^2(-d\sin\theta) - 2(d - R\cos\theta)(R\sin\theta)(d\cos\theta - R)\Big]$$

and upon simplification we get

$$\ddot{x} = LR\omega^2\sin\theta(2R^2 - d^2 - dR\cos\theta)/(d - R\cos\theta)^3$$ ◀

2.12

Since $a = -\frac{dv}{dt} = -\frac{dv}{ds}$, the time elapsed is

$$T = \int_{v_1}^{v_2} -\frac{1}{a}\,dv$$

and distance travelled is

$$S = \int_{v_1}^{v_2} -\frac{v\,dv}{a}$$

v	7	6.5	6	5.5	5.0	4.5
$1/a$	23.8	24.4	25.0	27.0	30.3	37.0
v/a	166.6	158.6	150	148.5	151.5	166.5
v	4	3.5	3	2.5	2.0	1.5
$1/a$	43.5	52.6	66.7	83.3	100	125
v/a	174	184.1	200.1	208.25	200	
v	1.0					
$1/a$	147.9					
v/a						

Using the trapezium rule we have

$$S = 0.5\left(\frac{166.6 + 200}{2} + 158.6 + 150 + 148.5 + 151.5 + 166.5 + 174 + 184.1 + 200.1 + 208.25\right)$$

$$= 862 \text{ m}$$ ◀

$$T = 0.5\left(\frac{23.8 + 100}{2} + 24.4 + 25 + 27 + 30.3 + 37 + 43.5 + 52.6 + 66.7 + 83.3\right)$$

$$= 226 \text{ s}$$ ◀

2.13

$$T - kv^2 = m\ddot{x}$$

$$\Rightarrow \quad \ddot{x} = \frac{T}{m} - k'v^2 = a_p - k'v^2$$

At v_{max},

$$\ddot{x} = 0$$

$$\therefore \quad k' = \frac{a_p}{{v_{max}}^2} = \frac{4 \times 0.46}{(850/3.6)^2} = 3.30 \times 10^{-5} \blacktriangleleft$$

New maximum speed,

$$v_{1max} = \sqrt{\frac{a_p'}{k'}} = \sqrt{\frac{0.75 \times 4 \times 0.46}{3.30 \times 10^{-5}}} \times 3.6$$

$$= 736.2 \text{ km/h} \blacktriangleleft$$

$$\frac{dv}{dt} = a_p' - k'v^2$$

$$\Rightarrow \quad t = \int_{v_{max}}^{v_{1max}} \frac{dv}{a_p' - k'v^2}$$

$$= \frac{1}{2\sqrt{a_p'k'}} \ln\left|\frac{\sqrt{a_p'} + \sqrt{k'}\,v}{\sqrt{a_p'} - \sqrt{k'}\,v}\right|_{v_{max}}^{v_{1max}}$$

Hence

$$t = \frac{1}{2\sqrt{a_p'k'}}\left\{\ln\left|\frac{\sqrt{a_p'} + \sqrt{k'}\,v_{1max}}{\sqrt{a_p'} - \sqrt{k'}\,v_{1max}}\right| - \ln\left|\frac{\sqrt{a_p'} + \sqrt{k'}\,v_{max}}{\sqrt{a_p'} - \sqrt{k'}\,v_{max}}\right|\right\}$$

$$v_{max} = \frac{850}{3.6} = 236.1 \text{ m/s}$$

$$v_{1max} = \frac{736.2}{3.6} = 204.5 \text{ m/s}$$

$$a_p' = 0.75 \times 4 \times 0.46 = 1.38 \text{ m/s}^2$$

Substitution yields

$$t = \frac{1}{2\sqrt{1.38 \times 3.30 \times 10^{-5}}}\left\{\ln\left|\frac{\sqrt{1.38} + \sqrt{3.30 \times 10^{-5}} \times 204.5}{\sqrt{1.38} - \sqrt{3.30 \times 10^{-5}} \times 204.5}\right| - \ln\left|\frac{\sqrt{1.38} + \sqrt{3.30 \times 10^{-5}} \times 236.1}{\sqrt{1.38} - \sqrt{3.30 \times 10^{-5}} \times 236.1}\right|\right\}$$

$$= \frac{69.93}{60}(11.30 - 2.63) = 10.7 \text{ min} \blacktriangleleft$$

CHAPTER 3

3.1

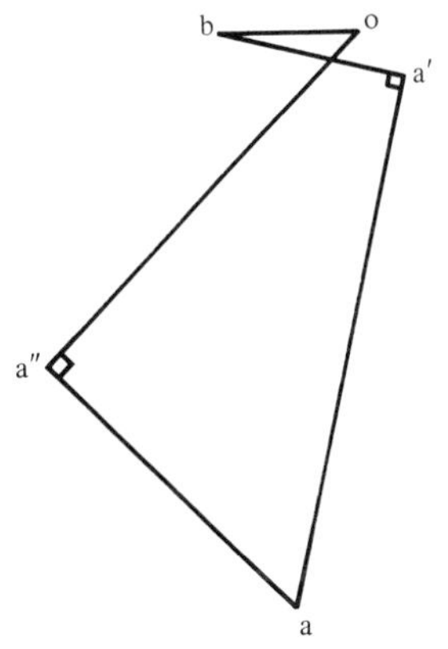

Graphically this is similar to example 3.1 in the text and gives $\omega_{OA} = 121$ rad/s.

Scales of $\frac{1}{5}$ full scale for the instantaneous centre method and 1 cm = 150 m/s^2 for the acceleration diagram will fit within an A4 sheet. The acceleration diagram should be as above.

With the above scale, aa$''$ = 5.9 cm, so that

$$\alpha = \frac{5.9 \times 150}{0.128} = 6910 \text{ m/s}^2 \curvearrowright$$

Analytically (see equation (3.27)), noting that $q = 0.128/0.32 = 0.4$):

$$v_B = -R\omega_{OA}\left(\sin\theta + \frac{q}{2}\sin 2\theta\right)$$

Hence

$$\dot{\omega}_{OA} = \frac{v_B}{-R\left(\sin\theta + \frac{q}{2}\sin 2\theta\right)}$$

$$= \frac{-15}{-0.128(\sin 50^\circ + 0.2\sin 100^\circ)}$$

$$= 121.7 \text{ rad/s} \blacktriangleleft$$

From equation (3.28),

$$\frac{\ddot{x}_B}{R} + \omega_{OA}^2(\cos\theta + q\cos 2\theta)$$

$$= -\dot{\omega}_{OA}\left(\sin\theta + \frac{q}{2}\sin 2\theta\right)$$

i.e. $$\frac{-250}{0.128} + 121.7^2(\cos 50^\circ + 0.4\cos 100^\circ)$$

$$= -\dot{\omega}_{OA}(\sin 50^\circ + 0.2\sin 100^\circ)$$

Solving for $\dot{\omega}_{OA}$, we get

$$\omega_{OA} = \frac{-6538.37}{\sin 50^\circ + 0.2\sin 100^\circ}$$

$$= 6790 \text{ rad/s}^2 \blacktriangleleft$$

(*Note*: This answer differs by 1.8% from that obtained by the graphical method. The latter could be improved by using a larger scale.)

3.2

By the instantaneous-centre method,

$$\frac{v_B}{IB} = \omega_{ABE} = \frac{v_E}{IE}$$

but $$v_B = \omega_{BC} \times BC$$

$$\therefore \quad \omega_{AB} = \omega_{BC} \times \frac{BC}{IB}$$

Hence

$$v_E = \omega_{BC} \times \frac{BC}{IB} \times IE \quad (1)$$

For the 50° position:

$$v_E = 0.08 \times \frac{20}{0.104 \times 4.00} \times 0.079 \times 400$$

From (1)

$$= 1.22 \text{ m/s} = 72.9 \text{ m/min} \blacktriangleleft$$

From the diagram,

$$v_{Ehor} = 67 \text{ m/min} \blacktriangleleft$$

For the 138° position:

$$v_E' = 0.08 \times \frac{20}{0.085 \times 400} \times 0.077 \times 400$$

from (1)

$$= 1.45 \text{ m/s} = 87 \text{ m/min} \blacktriangleleft$$

From the diagram,

$$v_{Ehor}' = 77 \text{ m/min} \blacktriangleleft$$

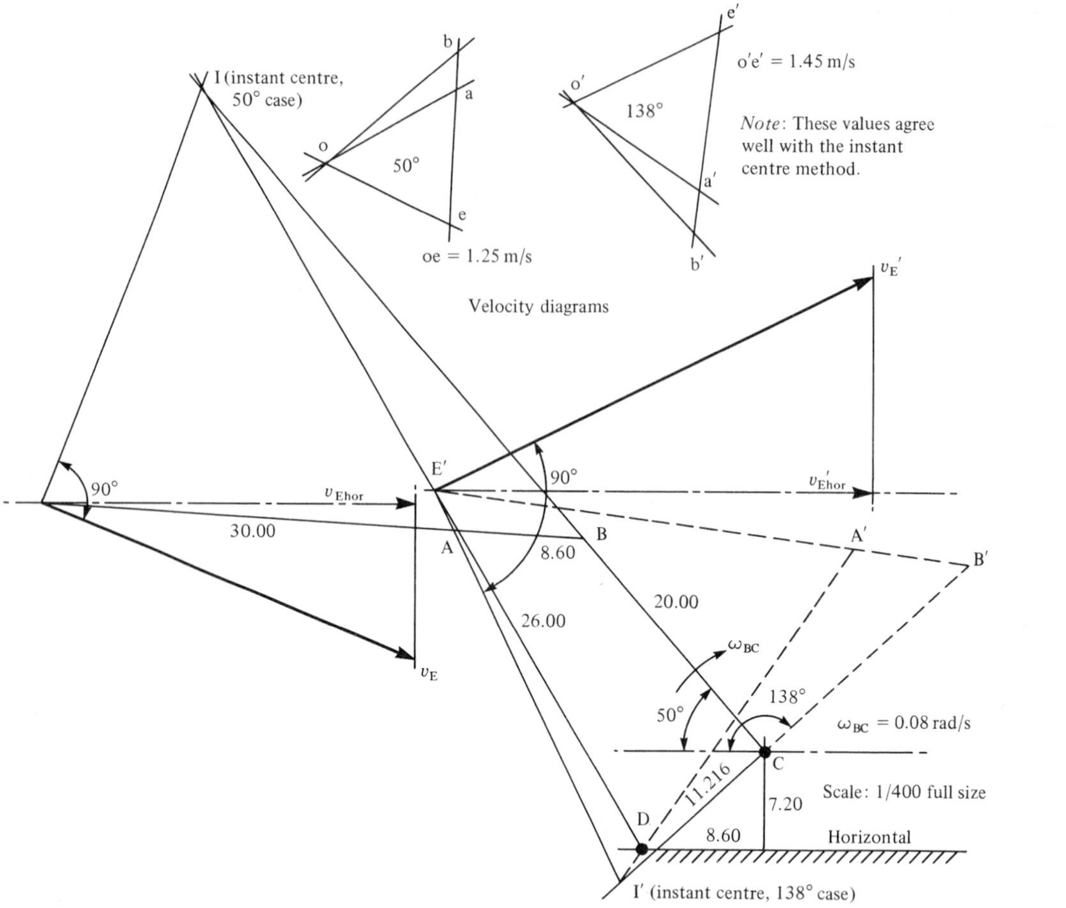

3.3

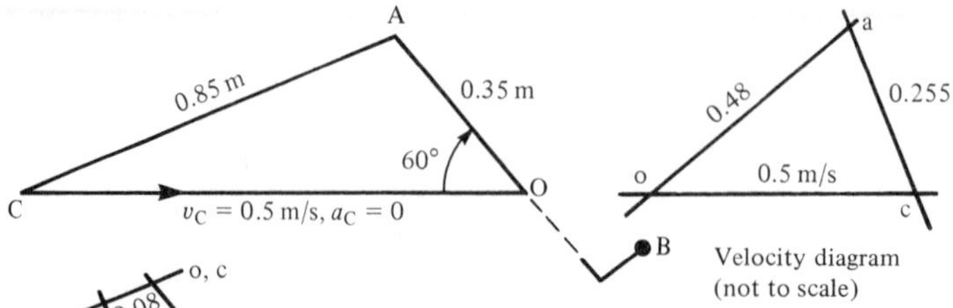

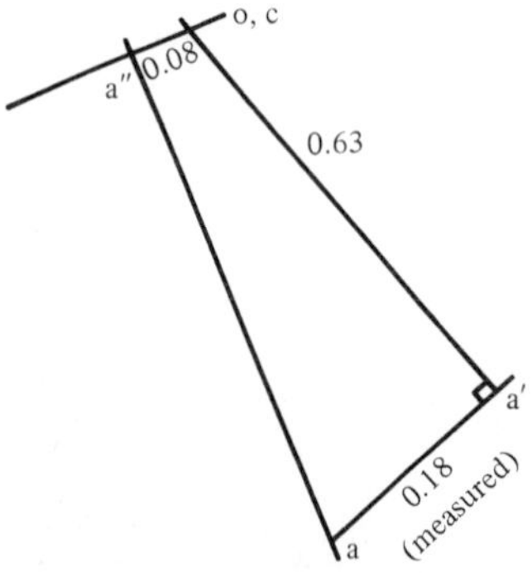

$\mathbf{a}_A = \mathbf{a}_C + \mathbf{a}_{AC}$

$\therefore\ \mathbf{a}_{An} + \mathbf{a}_{At} = \mathbf{a} + \mathbf{a}_{ACn} + \mathbf{a}_{ACt}$

Acceleration diagram
(not to scale)

$$\mathbf{v}_A = \mathbf{v}_C + \mathbf{v}_{AC}$$

To the scale of the diagram we find

$$oa = 0.47 \text{ m/s}$$

$$\omega_{OA} = \frac{oa}{OA} = \frac{0.48}{0.35} = 1.37 \text{ rad/s}$$

$$\mathbf{v}_B = \omega_{OA} \times OB = 1.37 \times 2.85$$
$$= 3.9 \text{ m/s} \quad ◀$$

$$\omega_{AC} = ac/AC = \frac{0.255}{0.85} = 0.3 \text{ rad/s} \circlearrowleft$$

$$a_{An} = \omega_{OA}^2 \times OA = 1.34^2 \times 0.35$$
$$= 0.63 \text{ m/s}^2 \searrow$$

$$a_{ACn} = \omega_{AC}^2 \times AC = 0.3^2 \times 0.85$$
$$= 0.08 \text{ m/s}^2 \swarrow$$

From the diagram,

$$\alpha_{OA} = \frac{aa'}{OA} = \frac{0.18}{0.35} = 0.51 \text{ rad/s}^2$$

$$a_{Bn} = \omega_{OA}^2 \times OB = 1.34^2 \times 2.85$$
$$= 5.12 \text{ m/s}^2$$

$$a_{Bt} = \alpha_{OA} \times OB = 0.51 \times 2.85$$
$$= 1.44 \text{ m/s}^2$$

Total acceleration of B,

$$a_B = \sqrt{a_{Bn}^2 + a_{Bt}^2} = \sqrt{5.12^2 + 1.44^2}$$
$$= 5.32 \text{ m/s}^2 \quad ◀$$

Analytically: Let $AC = l$, $OA = R$, $OB = d$.

$$q = \frac{R}{l} = \frac{0.35}{0.85} = 0.41 \text{ (small)}$$

Velocity

$$v_C = -R\omega\left(\sin\theta + \frac{q}{2}\sin 2\theta\right)$$

Acceleration

$$a_C = -R\omega^2(\cos\theta + q\cos 2\theta) - R\dot{\omega}\left(\sin\theta + \frac{q}{2}\sin 2\theta\right)$$

for $q < 1$

When $\theta = 60°$, to obtain the velocity,

$$-0.5 = -0.35\omega(\sin 60° + 0.205 \sin 120°)$$

$$\Rightarrow \quad \omega = 1.37 \text{ rad/s}$$

Hence

$$v_R = \omega OB = \omega d = 1.37 \times 2.85$$
$$= 3.9 \text{ m/s} \quad ◀$$

To obtain the acceleration,

$$0 = -1.37^2(\cos 60° + 0.41 \cos 120°) - \dot{\omega}(\sin 60° + 0.205 \sin 120°)$$

$$\Rightarrow \quad \dot{\omega} = -0.53 \text{ rad/s}^2$$

Hence

$$a_{Bt} = \dot{\omega}d = -0.53 \times 2.85 = -1.51 \text{ m/s}^2$$

$$a_{Bn} = \omega^2 d = 1.37^2 \times 2.85 = 5.35 \text{ m/s}^2$$

$$a_B = \sqrt{1.51^2 + 5.35^2} = 5.56 \text{ m/s}^2 \quad ◀$$

When $\theta = 35°$,

$$-0.5 = 0.35\omega_1(\sin 35° + 0.205 \sin 70°)$$

$$\Rightarrow \quad \omega_1 = 1.86 \text{ rad/s}$$

$$1.86^2(\cos 35° + 0.41 \cos 70°) = -\dot{\omega}_1(\sin 35° + 0.205 \sin 70°)$$

$$\Rightarrow \quad \dot{\omega}_1 = -4.33 \text{ rad/s}^2$$

$$a_{B1} = \sqrt{a_{Bt}^2 + a_{Bn}^2} = OB\sqrt{\dot{\omega}_1^2 + \omega_1^4}$$
$$= 2.85\sqrt{4.33^2 + 1.86^4} = 15.8 \text{ m/s}^2 \quad ◀$$

When $\theta = 135°$, in a similar way to the above we find

$$\omega_2 = 2.85 \text{ rad/s}$$

$$\dot{\omega}_2 = 11.44 \text{ rad/s}$$

and $$a_{B2} = 2.85\sqrt{11.44^2 + 2.85^4} = 40 \text{ m/s}^2 \quad ◀$$

3.4

$$v_B = \omega_{AB} \times AB$$
$$= \tfrac{1}{4} \times 432 = 108 \text{ mm/s}$$

$$v_G = dg = dh \times \frac{DG}{DH} = 120 \times \frac{990}{254}$$
$$= 468 \text{ mm/s} \quad ◀$$

$$\omega_{DG} = \frac{dh}{DH} = \frac{120}{254} = 0.47 \text{ rad/s} \quad ◀$$

$$\omega_{EF} = \frac{ef}{EF} = \frac{108}{229} = 0.47 \text{ rad/s}^2 \quad ◀$$

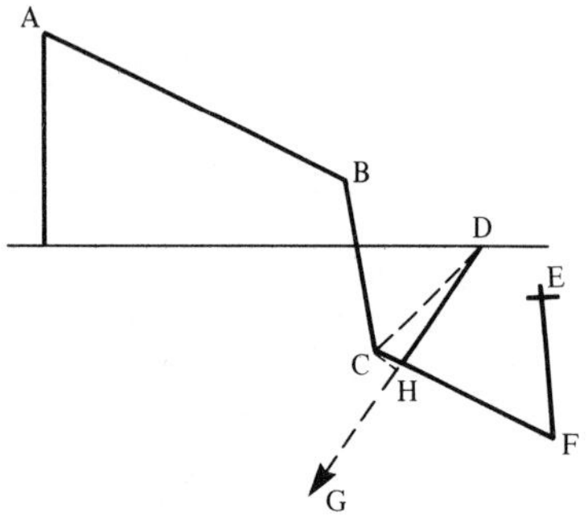

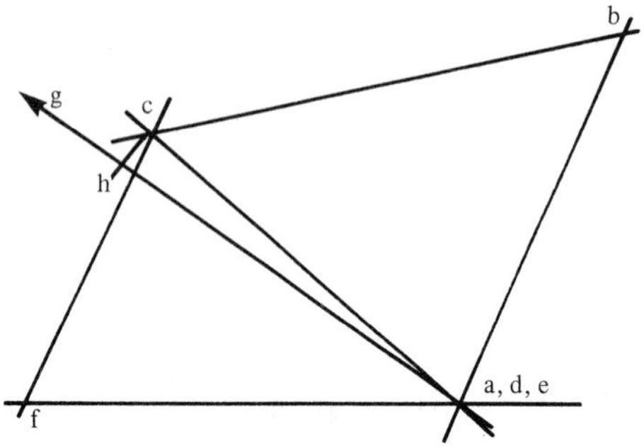

Velocity diagram (not to scale)

3.5

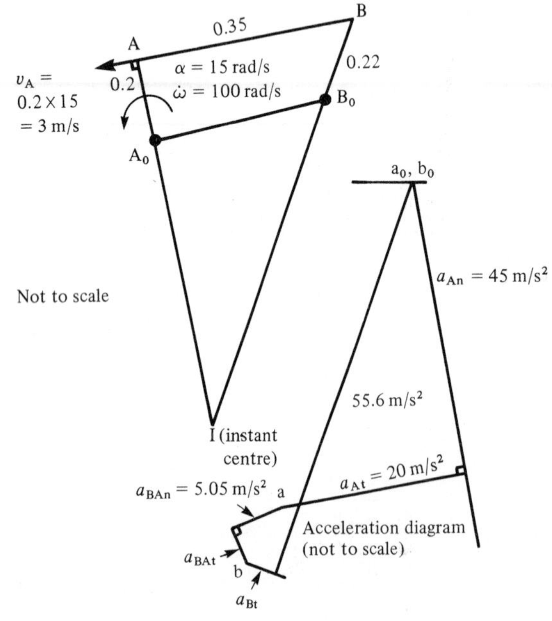

$$\omega_{AB} = \frac{v_A}{AI} = \frac{v_B}{BI} = \frac{3}{0.79} = 3.8 \text{ rad/s} \quad \blacktriangleleft$$

$$v_B = \omega_{AB} \times BI = 3.8 \times 0.92$$

$$= 3.5 \text{ m/s} \quad \blacktriangleleft$$

$$\omega_{BB_0} = 3.5/0.22 = 15.9 \text{ rad/s} \circlearrowright \quad \blacktriangleleft$$

$$\mathbf{a}_{Bn} + \mathbf{a}_{Bt} = \mathbf{a}_{An} + \mathbf{a}_{At} + \mathbf{a}_{BAn} + \mathbf{a}_{BAt}$$

$$a_{An} = \omega_{AA_0}{}^2 \times AA_0 = 15^2 \times 0.2$$

$$= 45 \text{ m/s}^2 \searrow$$

$$a_{At} = \dot{\omega}_{AA_0} \times AA_0 = 100 \times 0.2$$

$$= 20 \text{ m/s}^2 \swarrow$$

$$a_{Bn} = \omega_{BB_0}{}^2 \times BB_0 = 15.9^2 \times 0.22$$

$$= 55.6 \text{ m/s}^2 \downarrow$$

$$a_{BAn} = \omega_{AB}^2 \times AB = 3.8^2 \times 0.35$$

$$= 5.05 \text{ m/s}^2 \swarrow$$

From the acceleration diagram,

$$\alpha_{AB} = \frac{a_{BAt}}{AB} = \frac{3.82}{0.35} = 10.9 \text{ rad/s}^2 \circlearrowright \quad \blacktriangleleft$$

$$\alpha_{BB_0} = \frac{a_{Bt}}{BB_0} = \frac{3.67}{0.22} = 16.7 \text{ rad/s}^2 \circlearrowright \quad \blacktriangleleft$$

3.6

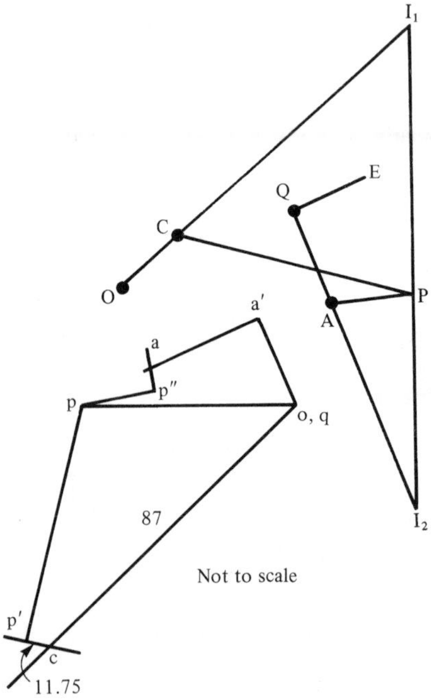

$$v_C = 2\pi \times 250/60 \times 0.127 = 3.32 \text{ m/s}$$

$$v_P = v_C \frac{PI_1}{CI_1} = 3.32 \times \frac{59}{69} = 2.84 \text{ m/s}$$

$$v_A = v_P \times \frac{AI_2}{PI_2} = 2.84 \times 34/33.5$$

$$= 2.88 \text{ m/s}$$

$$\omega_{CP} = v_C/CI_1 = 3.32/0.69 = 4.81 \text{ rad/s}$$

$$\omega_{AP} = v_P/PI_2 = 2.88/0.335 = 8.48 \text{ rad/s}$$

$$\omega_{AQ} = v_A/AQ = 2.88/0.254 = 11.34 \text{ rad/s}$$

$$\mathbf{a}_{Pt} + \mathbf{a}_{Pn} = \mathbf{a}_C + \mathbf{a}_{PCt} + \mathbf{a}_{PCn}$$

$$a_C = a_{Cn} = v_C^2/OC = 3.32^2/0.127$$

$$= 87 \text{ m/s}^2 \downarrow$$

$$a_{PCn} = \omega_{CP}^2 \times CP = 4.81^2 \times 0.508$$

$$= 11.75 \text{ m/s}^2 \leftarrow$$

From the diagram,

$$a_P = op = 62 \text{ m/s}^2$$ ◀

$$a_{An} = \omega_{AQ}^2 \times AQ = 11.34^2 \times 0.254$$

$$= 32.66 \text{ m/s}^2 \uparrow$$

$$a_{APn} = \omega_{AP}^2 \times AP = 8.48^2 \times 0.127$$

$$= 9.13 \text{ m/s}^2 \rightarrow$$

From the diagram,

$$\dot{\omega}_{CP} = \frac{pp'}{CP} = \frac{60}{0.508} = 118 \text{ rad/s}^2$$ ◀

$$\dot{\omega}_{PA} = \frac{ap''}{AP} = \frac{13}{0.127} = 102 \text{ rad/s}^2$$ ◀

$$\dot{\omega}_{AQ} = \frac{aa'}{AQ} = \frac{46}{0.254} = 181 \text{ rad/s}^2$$ ◀

3.7

$$v_A = \frac{2\pi \times 75}{60} \times 0.076 = 0.6 \text{ m/s}$$

From the diagram, by scaling, we find

$$v_x = 0.23 \text{ m/s}$$ ◀

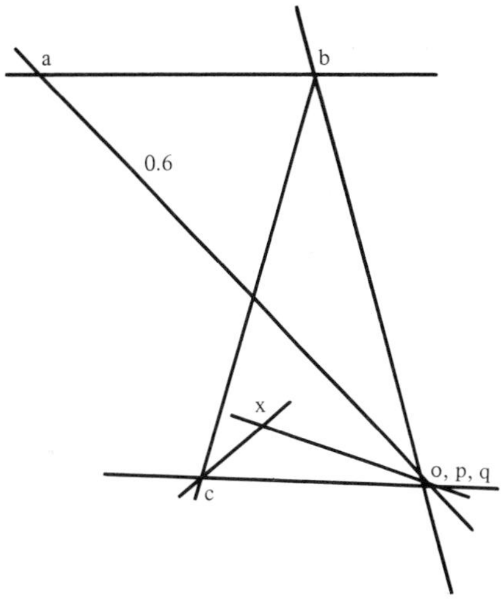

Velocity diagram (not to scale)

3.8

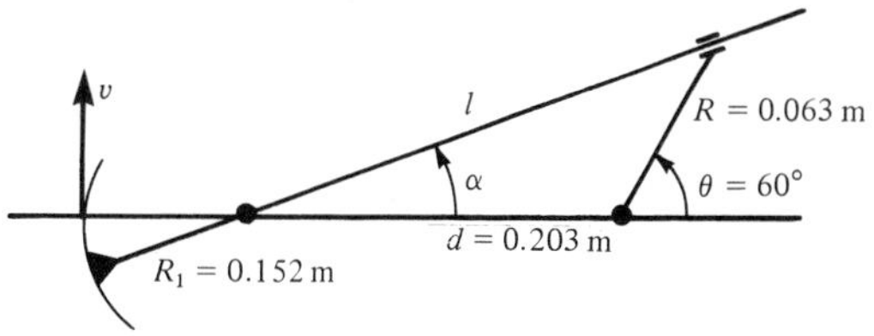

$l \cos\alpha = d + R\cos\theta$; $l \sin\alpha = R\sin\theta$.

Eliminating l, we have

$$\tan\alpha = \frac{R\sin\theta}{d + R\cos\theta}$$

Differentiating with respect to time yields

$$(\sec^2\alpha)\dot{\alpha} = \frac{(d + R\cos\theta)R\cos\theta - R\sin\theta(-R\sin\theta)}{(d + R\cos\theta)^2}\dot{\theta}$$

or $$(\sec^2\alpha)\dot{\alpha} = \frac{d\cos\theta + R}{(d + R\cos\theta)^2}R\dot{\theta}$$

$v = R_1\dot{\alpha}$, and when $\theta = 60°$

$$\alpha = \arctan\left(\frac{0.063 \times \sin 60°}{0.203 + 0.063 \times \cos 60°}\right)$$

$$= 13.1°$$

$$\dot{\alpha} = \frac{0.203 \times \cos 60^\circ + 0.063}{(0.203 + 0.063 \cos 60^\circ)^2} \times 0.063$$

$$\times \frac{2\pi \times 65}{60} \times \cos^2 13.1^\circ$$

$$= 1.21 \text{ rad/s}$$

Hence

$$v = 1.21 \times 0.152 = 0.18 \text{ m/s}$$ ◀

3.9

$$\omega_{OB} = 2\omega_{OA}$$

$$OA = 2OB$$

$$v_A = \omega_{OA} \times OA$$

$$v_B = \omega_{OB} \times OB = 2\omega \times OA/2 = v_A$$

$$\therefore \quad v_A = v_B = \frac{2\pi \times 700}{60} \times 0.073$$

$$= 5.35 \text{ m/s}$$

By scaling

$$v_P = op = 0.53 \text{ m/s}$$ ◀

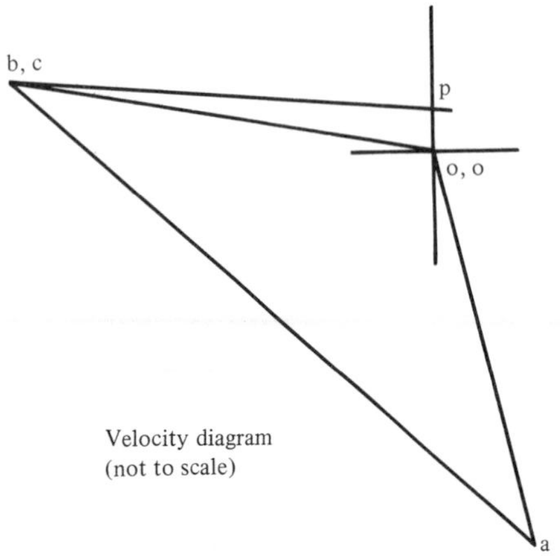

Velocity diagram
(not to scale)

3.10

$$d = \sqrt{0.25^2 + 0.1^2} = 0.2693$$

$$\phi = 100^\circ - \arctan \frac{0.1}{0.25} = 78.2^\circ$$

The angle ψ at the output BB_0 is needed. Referring to the text, from equation (3.16) we have

$$A = \sin\phi = \sin 78.2^\circ = 0.9789$$

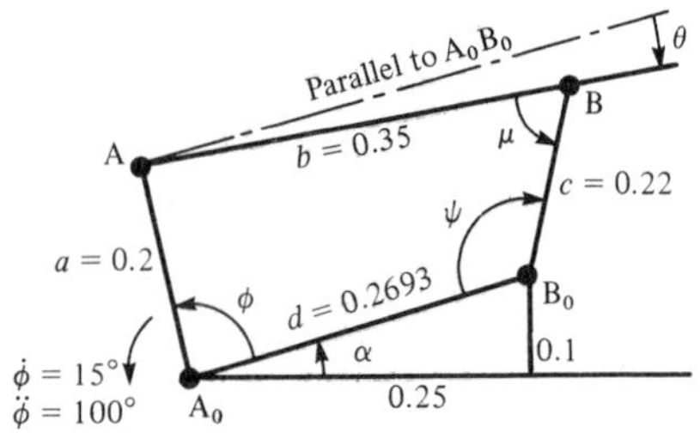

$$B = \cos\phi - \frac{d}{a} = \cos 78.2^\circ - \frac{0.2693}{0.2}$$

$$= -1.1420$$

Also

$$K_3 = (a^2 - b^2 + c^2 + d^2)/2ac$$

$$\therefore \quad K_3 = \frac{0.2^2 - 0.35^2 + 0.22^2 + 0.2693^2}{2 \times 0.2 \times 0.22}$$

$$= 0.4366$$

$$C = \frac{d}{c}\cos\phi - K_3 = \frac{0.2693}{0.22}\cos 78.2^\circ$$

$$- 0.4366 = -0.1863$$

From equation (3.17), by substitution we obtain

$$\psi =$$

$$2 \arctan \left(\frac{0.9789 + \sqrt{0.9789^2 + 1.142^2 - 0.1863^2}}{-1.1420 - 0.1863} \right)$$

$$= -123.49^\circ$$

Substituting in equation (3.15) yields

$$\dot{\psi} =$$

$$\frac{\sin(78.2^\circ + 123.49^\circ) - \dfrac{0.2693}{0.22}\sin 78.2^\circ}{\sin(78.2^\circ + 123.49^\circ) + \dfrac{0.2693}{0.2}\sin(-123.49^\circ)} \times 15$$

$$= 15.8 \text{ rad/s} \circlearrowright$$ ◀

From equation (3.12) we have

$$\sin\theta = -\frac{c \sin\psi + a \sin\phi}{b}$$

$$= -[0.22 \sin(-123.49^\circ)$$

$$+ 0.2 \sin 78.2^\circ]/0.35$$

$$= -0.0351$$

$$\Rightarrow \quad \theta = -2.0135^\circ$$

For the coupler angular velocity, by differentiating equation (3.12) we get

$$\dot{\theta} = -\left(\frac{c\cos\psi\dot{\psi} + a\cos\phi\dot{\phi}}{b\cos\theta}\right)$$

$$= -\left(\frac{0.22\cos 123.49^\circ + 0.2\cos 78.2 \times 15}{0.35\cos 2.0135^\circ}\right)$$

$$= 3.65 \text{ rad/s} \circlearrowleft$$ ◀

In equation (3.15) let

$$\dot{\psi} = (\lambda_1/\lambda_2)\,\dot{\phi}$$

where

$$\lambda_1 = \sin(\phi - \psi) - K_1\sin\phi,$$

$$\lambda_2 = \sin(\phi - \psi) + K_2\sin\psi.$$

On differentiating we have

$$\ddot{\psi} = \frac{\lambda_2\lambda_1' - \lambda_1\lambda_2'}{\lambda_2^2}\dot{\phi}^2 + \frac{\lambda_1}{\lambda_2}\ddot{\phi},$$

where

$$\lambda_1' = \cos(\phi - \psi)\left(1 - \frac{\lambda_1}{\lambda_2}\right) - K_1\cos\phi$$

$$\lambda_2' = \cos(\phi - \psi)\left(1 - \frac{\lambda_1}{\lambda_2}\right) + K_2\frac{\lambda_1}{\lambda_2}\cos\psi$$

Substituting numerical values yields

$$\lambda_1 = -1.5678, \quad \lambda_2 = -1.4925$$

$$\frac{\lambda_1}{\lambda_2} = 1.05$$

$$\lambda_1' = -0.203\,46, \quad \lambda_2' = -0.7336$$

Hence

$$\ddot{\psi} = -3.800\dot{\phi}^2 + 1.05\ddot{\phi}$$

$$= -0.3800 \times 15^2 + 1.05 \times 100$$

$$= 19.5 \text{ rad/s}^2 \circlearrowleft$$ ◀

Differentiating $\dot{\theta}$ yields

$$\ddot{\theta} = \frac{1}{b\cos\theta}(-c\cos\psi\,\ddot{\psi} + c\sin\psi\,\dot{\psi}^2$$

$$- a\cos\phi\,\ddot{\phi} + a\sin\phi\,\dot{\phi}^2 + b\sin\theta\,\dot{\theta}^2)$$

$$= \frac{1}{0.35 \times \cos 2.0135^\circ}(-0.22\cos 123.49^\circ$$

$$- 0.22\sin 123.49^\circ \times 15.8^2$$

$$- 0.2\cos 78.2^\circ \times 100 + 0.2\sin 78.2^\circ$$

$$\times 15^2 - 0.35 \times \sin 2.0135^\circ \times 3.65^2)$$

$$\Rightarrow \quad \ddot{\theta} = -9.91 \text{ rad/s}^2$$ ◀

(*Note*: Using a computer program the following values were obtained: $\psi = -123.4^\circ$, $\theta = -2.0123^\circ$, $\dot{\psi} = 15.75$ rad/s, $\ddot{\psi} = 19.5$ rad/s^2, transmission angle $\mu = 58.5^\circ$, $\dot{\theta} = 3.7$ rad/s, $\ddot{\theta} = -9.7$ rad/s^2.)

3.11

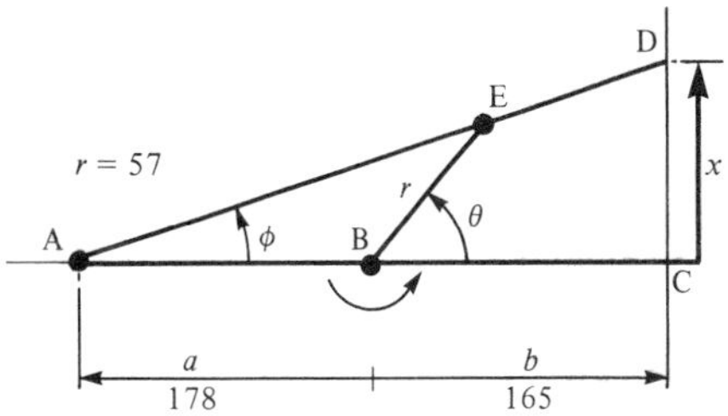

From the triangle ACD we have

$$(a + b)\tan\phi = x$$

From the triangle AEF,

$$r\sin\theta = (a + r\cos\theta)\tan\phi$$

$$\therefore \quad \tan\phi = \frac{r\sin\theta}{a + r\cos\theta}$$

Hence

$$x = \frac{(a + b)r\sin\theta}{a + r\cos\theta} \tag{1}$$

Differentiating yields for the velocity of D

$$v_D = \dot{x} = \omega r(a + b)(a\cos\theta + r)/(a + r\cos\theta)^2 \tag{2}$$

The displacement is a maximum when $v_D = 0$, i.e. when

$$\cos\theta = -\frac{r}{a} = -\frac{57}{178}.$$

(a) Hence $\theta = 108.7^\circ$ and the total stroke of D is given by (1):

$$x_{\text{total}} = 2\frac{(178 + 165) \times 57\sin 108.7^\circ}{178 + 57\cos 108.7^\circ}$$

$$= 232 \text{ mm}$$ ◀

(b) Velocities at mid-stroke, i.e. when $\theta = 0^\circ$ and 180°, are

$$\dot{x}_0 = \omega r(a+b)/(a+r)$$
$$= 57 \times 2\pi \times 343/235$$
$$= 522 \text{ mm/s} \quad \text{or} \quad 0.52 \text{ m/s}$$ ◀

$$\dot{x}_{180} = \omega r(a+b)(r-a)/(a-r)^2$$
$$= 2\pi \times 57 \times 343 \times -121/121^2$$
$$= 1015 \text{ mm/s} \quad \text{or} \quad 1.02 \text{ m/s}$$ ◀

(c) Differentiating (2) yields

$$\ddot{x}_D = \frac{\omega^2 r(a+b)\sin\theta\,(r^2 - a^2 + ar\cos\theta)}{(a + r\cos\theta)^3}$$

Hence

$$\ddot{x}_{60} = (2\pi)^2 \times 343 \sin 60^\circ(57^2 - 178^2 + 57 \times 178 \cos 60^\circ)/(178 + 57\cos 60^\circ)^3$$
$$= 1770 \text{ mm/s}^2$$
$$= 1.77 \text{ m/s}^2$$ ◀

3.12

Recalling Freudenstein's equation,

$$K_1 \cos\phi + K_2 \cos\psi - K_3 = \cos(\phi - \psi)$$

and substituting $\phi = 30^\circ, 45^\circ, 60^\circ$ and $\psi = 200^\circ, 235^\circ, 270^\circ$, we have

$$K_1 \cos 30^\circ + K_2 \cos 200^\circ - K_3 = \cos(30^\circ - 200^\circ) = \cos 170^\circ$$
$$K_1 \cos 45^\circ + K_2 \cos 235^\circ - K_3 = \cos(45^\circ - 235^\circ) = \cos 190^\circ$$
$$K_1 \cos 60^\circ + K_2 \cos 270^\circ - K_3 = \cos(60^\circ - 270^\circ) = \cos 210^\circ$$

i.e.

$$0.8660K_1 - 0.9397K_2 - K_3 = -0.9848 \quad (1)$$
$$0.7071K_1 - 0.5736K_2 - K_3 = -0.9848 \quad (2)$$
$$0.5000K_1 + 0 - K_3 = -0.8660 \quad (3)$$

(*Note*: It is advisable to work to 4 or 5 d.p. when using a calculator.)

(2) − (3) and (1) − (2)

$$\Rightarrow \quad 0.2071K_1 - 0.5736K_2 = -0.1188$$
$$0.1589K_1 - 0.3661K_2 = 0$$
$$\Rightarrow \quad K_1 = 2.3040K_2$$

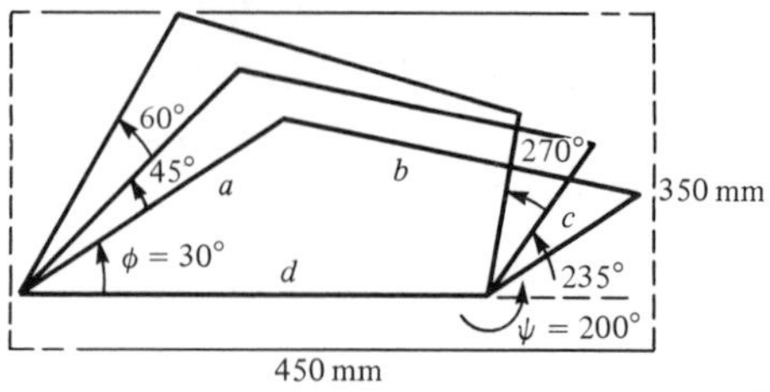

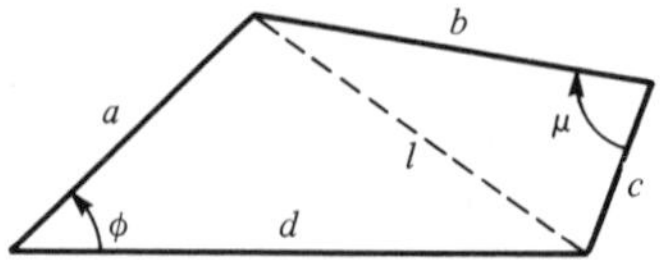

Hence

$$K_2 = \frac{-0.1188}{0.2071 \times 2.3040 - 0.5736} = 1.2318$$

and $K_1 = 2.8381$, $K_3 = 2.2851$

(*Note*: Values obtained by computer were: $K_1 = 2.837\,386$, $K_2 = 1.231\,614$, $K_3 = 2.284\,718$.)

With $d = 1$ unit, $a = 0.8118$, $c = 0.3523$, $b = 0.689$.

For the mechanism to fit in the space given we must ensure that

$$d + c\cos 20^\circ \leqslant 450 \text{ mm}$$

and

$$a \sin 60^\circ \leqslant 350 \text{ mm}$$

By giving d various arbitrary values we find that with $d = 330$ mm, $a = 267.6$ mm, $b = 227.4$ mm, $c = 116.2$ mm. ◀

For the transmission angle μ:

$$l^2 = a^2 + d^2 - 2ad\cos\phi = b^2 + c^2 - 2bc\cos\mu$$

Hence

$$\mu = \arccos \frac{(b^2 + c^2) - (a^2 + d^2) + 2ad\cos\phi}{2bc}$$

When $\phi = 30^\circ$,

$$\mu = \arccos\,[(227.4^2 + 116.2^2 - 267.6^2 - 330^2 + 2 \times 267.6 \times 330 \cos 30^\circ)/(2 \times 227.4 \times 116.2)]$$

$$= 44^\circ \quad ◀$$

Similarly, when $\phi = 45^\circ$,

$$\mu = 79^\circ \quad ◀$$

When $\phi = 60^\circ$,

$$\mu = 121^\circ \quad ◀$$

CHAPTER 4

4.1

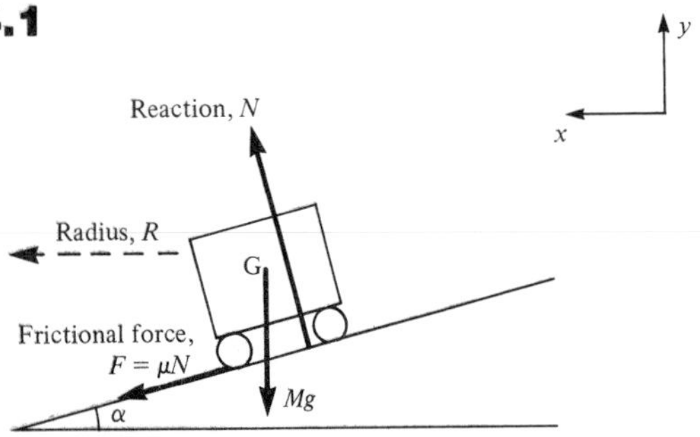

Free body diagram

Centripetal acceleration $= v^2/R$

Resolving horizontally and vertically yields

$$F\cos\alpha + N\sin\alpha = Mv^2/R \qquad (1)$$

$$N\cos\alpha - F\sin\alpha - Mg = 0$$

since $\ddot{y} = 0$ (2)

Solving for N we get

$$N = M\left(g\cos\alpha + \frac{v^2}{R}\sin\alpha\right)$$

$$= 1250\left[9.81\cos 12^\circ + \left(\frac{120}{3.6}\right)^2 \times \frac{\sin 12^\circ}{275}\right]$$

$$= 13\,045\text{ N}$$ ◀

Solving for F,

$$F = \frac{1}{\sin\alpha}(N\cos\alpha - Mg)$$

$$= \frac{1}{\sin 12^\circ}(13\,045\cos 12^\circ - 1250 \times 9.81)$$

$$= 2393\text{ N}$$ ◀

Minimum coefficient of friction

$$\mu = \frac{F}{N} = \frac{2393}{13\,045}$$

$$= 0.18$$ ◀

4.2

Tractive effort $T = \frac{P}{v} = \frac{6 \times 10^6}{270/3.6}$

$$= 80 \times 10^3\text{ N} \quad \text{or} \quad 80\text{ kN}$$

$$M\ddot{x} = T - (A + Bv^2)$$

$$A = 515 \times 10^3 \times 9.81 \times \frac{0.5}{100} = 25.26\text{ kN}$$

When $v = v_{max} = 270$ km/h, $\ddot{x} = 0$.

$$\therefore \quad B = \frac{T - A}{v^2} = \frac{(80 - 25.26) \times 10^3}{(270/3.6)^2}$$

$$= 9.73\text{ N s}^2\text{ m}^2$$ ◀

$$T_{initial} = M\ddot{x}_{initial} + A$$

$$= (515 \times 0.35 + 25.26) \times 10^3$$

$$= 205.5\text{ kN}$$ ◀

4.3

At 75 km/h,

$$T = 125 \times 10^3\text{ N}$$

$$\Rightarrow \quad K = Tv = 125 \times 10^3 \times (75/3.6)$$

$$= 2604 \times 10^3\text{ N m/s}$$

When $v = v_{max}$,

$$\frac{2604 \times 10^3}{v_{max}} = 4750 + kv_{max}^2$$

$$\Rightarrow \quad k = \frac{42\,122}{(200/3.6)^2}$$

$$= 13.65\text{ kg/m}$$

(a) a_{max} occurs when $v = 0$.

$$\therefore \quad a_{max} = \frac{125 \times 10^3 - 4750}{300 \times 10^3} = 0.4\text{ m/s}^2$$ ◀

(b) $m\frac{dv}{dt} = T - R \Rightarrow$ total time t_1 is given by

$$t_1 = m\int_0^{v_1} \frac{dv}{T - R} = m\int_0^{v_0} \frac{dv}{T - A - kv^2}$$

$$+ m\int_{v_0}^{v_1} \frac{dv}{(K/v) - A - kv^2}$$

where $v_0 = \frac{75}{3.6}$ m/s and $v_1 = \frac{175}{3.6}$ m/s.

The first integral can be solved analytically, giving

$$T_0 = \frac{m}{k}\int_0^{v_0} dv/(T'/k) - v^2$$

$$= \frac{m}{k}\left[\sqrt{\frac{k}{T'}}\,\text{artanh}\left(\sqrt{\frac{k}{T'}}\,v\right)\right]_0^{v_0}$$

where $T' = T - A = (125 - 4.75) \times 10^3$
$= 120.25 \times 10^3$ N.

Hence

$$t_0 = \frac{300 \times 10^3}{13.65} \times \sqrt{\frac{13.65}{120.25 \times 10^3}}$$

$$\times \text{artanh} \times \left(\sqrt{\frac{13.65}{120.25 \times 10^3}} \times \frac{75}{3.6}\right)$$

$$= 52.85 \text{ s}$$

The second integral is most easily solved numerically, e.g. using Simpson's rule. We need to calculate $f(v) = \dfrac{1}{K/v - A - kv^2}$ for each value of v. Thus, using 8 strips:

v (km/h)	75	87.5	100	112.5
$f(v)$ (10^{-6}/N)	8.75	10.6	12.75	15.3
$vf(v)$ (10^{-6} m/Ns)	656	928	1275	1724
v (km/h)	125	137.5	150	162.5
$f(v)$ (10^{-6}/N)	18.6	23	29.3	39.7
$vf(v)$ (10^{-6} m/Ns)	2324	3158	4400	6453
v (km/h)	175			
$f(v)$ (10^{-6}/N)	60.1			
$vf(v)$ (10^{-6} m/Ns)	10 518			

$$\text{Total time } t_1 = 52.85 + \frac{12.5}{3 \times 3.6} \times 0.3$$

$$\times [8.75 + 60.1 + 4(10.6 + 15.3 + 23 + 39.7) + 2(12.75 + 18.6 + 29.3)]$$

$$= 240 \text{ s} = 4 \text{ min}$$ ◀

(c) The total distance travelled is obtained in a similar way, and $vf(v)$ is needed as shown. The distance travelled to reach 75 km/h is obtained by integrating:

$$s_0 = m\int_0^{v_0} \frac{v\,dv}{T' - kv^2} = \frac{m}{2k}\ln\left(\frac{T'}{T' - kv_0^2}\right)$$

$$= 555 \text{ m}$$

$$\text{Total distance } s_1 = 555 + \frac{12.5}{3 \times 3.6^2} \times 0.3$$

$$\times [656 + 10\,518 + 4(928 + 1724 + 3158 + 6453) + 2(1275 + 2324 + 4400)]$$

$$= 7900 \text{ m} = 7.9 \text{ km}$$ ◀

(d) For the maximum speed up the incline,

$$0 = \frac{K}{v} - A - kv_{max}^2 - mg\sin\alpha,$$

i.e.

$$2604 - 24.3\,v_{max} - 0.0136 v_{max}^3 = 0$$

Solving by trial and error or a graph between $v = 150$ and 180 km/h gives

$$v_{max} = 170 \text{ km/h}$$ ◀

4.4

Tractive effort T at maximum speed $v_{max} = 160$ km/h when $\ddot{x} = 0$ is

$$T_0 = A + Bv_{max}^2$$

$$A = 55 \times 700 = 38.5 \times 10^3 \text{ N}$$

From Figure 4.13,

$$T_0 = 125 \times 10^3 \text{ N}$$

$$\therefore \quad B = \frac{(125 - 38.5) \times 10^3}{(160/3.6)^2} = 43.79 \text{ N s}^2/\text{m}^2$$

By Newton's second law,

$$m\frac{dv}{dt} = T - A - Bv^2 = T_1 - Bv^2$$

where $T_1 = T - A$.

$$\text{Also } mv\frac{dv}{dx} = T_1 - Bv^2$$

Integrating to obtain the time t_1 and the distance s_1 to reach 120 km/h, we have

$$t_1 = m\int_0^{v_1} f(v)\,dv \quad \text{and} \quad s_1 = m\int_0^{v_1} vf(v)\,dv$$

where $f(v) = \dfrac{1}{T_1 - Bv^2}$.

To evaluate both integrals it is best to use a numerical method. Using Simpson's rule with 6 strips we can compile the following table, T being read off the graph:

v_1 (km/h)	0	20	40	60
T_1 (kN)	340	290	270	260
$A + Bv^2$ (kN)	38.5	39.9	43.9	50.7
$f(v)$ (10^{-6}/N)	3.31	4.0	4.42	4.78
$vf(v)$ (10^{-6} km/Nh)	0	80	176.8	286.8
v_1 (km/h)	80	100	120	
T_1 (kN)	250	190	160	
$A + Bv^2$ (kN)	60.1	72.3	87.2	
$f(v)$ (10^{-6}/N)	5.26	8.49	13.7	
$vf(v)$ (10^{-6} km/Nh)	420.8	849	1644	

Substituting in Simpson's formula yields

$$t_1 = \frac{20}{3 \times 3.6}[3.31 + 13.7 + 4(4 + 4.78 + 8.49) + 2(4.42 + 5.26)] \times 10^{-6} \times 700 \times 10^3$$

$$= 136.6\,\text{s} = 2.28\,\text{min}$$ ◀

and

$$s_1 = \frac{20}{3 \times 3.6^2}[0 + 1644 + 4(80 + 286.8 + 849) + 2(176.8 + 420.8)] \times 10^{-6} \times 700 \times 10^3$$

$$= 2770\,\text{m} = 2.77\,\text{km}$$ ◀

4.5

At v_{max} of 160 km/h, $T = 1700$ N. Since $T = kv_{max}^2$, $k = 1700/(160/3.6)^2 = 0.86\ \text{N s}^2/\text{m}^2$

By Newton's second law,

$$m\frac{dv}{dt} = T - kv^2 - mg\sin\alpha \equiv T' - kv^2,$$

where

$$T' = T - mg\sin\alpha = 1700 - 1300 \times 9.81/20 = 1062\,\text{N}$$

Time taken to speed up from v_1 to v_2 is given by

$$t_1 = m\int_{v_1}^{v_2}\frac{dv}{T' - kv^2}$$

$$= \frac{m}{k}\sqrt{\frac{k}{T'}}\left[\text{artanh}\left(\sqrt{\frac{k}{T'}}v_2\right) - \text{artanh}\left(\sqrt{\frac{k}{T'}}v_1\right)\right]$$

$$= \frac{1300}{0.86}\sqrt{\frac{0.86}{1062}}\left[\text{artanh}\left(\sqrt{\frac{0.86}{1062}} \times \frac{120}{3.6}\right) - \text{artanh}\left(\sqrt{\frac{0.86}{1062}} \times \frac{72}{3.6}\right)\right]$$

$$= 50.4\,\text{s}$$ ◀

$$\text{Power required} = Tv/\eta = 1700 \times \frac{120}{3.6} \times \frac{1}{0.825} = 69\,\text{kW}$$ ◀

4.6

On the level

$$6000 - 64.8\,v_{max} = 300 + 1.8v_{max}^2$$

$$\Rightarrow\quad 1.8v_{max}^2 + 64.8v_{max} - 5700 = 0$$

$$\Rightarrow\quad v_{max} = 147\,\text{km/h}$$ ◀

For motion up the incline

$$mv\frac{dv}{dx} = T - (300 + 54v \text{ or } 1.8v^2) - mg\sin\alpha$$

i.e. $mv\dfrac{dv}{dx} = 5405 - 118.8v$ for $v \leqslant 30$ m/s

and $mv\dfrac{dv}{dx} = 5405 - 64.8v - 1.8v^2$ for $v \geqslant 30$ m/s

For $v \leqslant 30$ m/s,

$$x_1 = 1500\int_0^{30}\frac{v\,dv}{5405 - 118.8v}$$

$$= \frac{1500}{118.8^2}[(5405 - 118.8 \times 30) - 5405\ln(5405 - 118.8 \times 30) - 5405(1 - \ln 5405)]$$

$$= 240\,\text{m}$$

For $v \geqslant 30$ m/s,

$$x_2 = 1500 \int_{30}^{38.9} \frac{v\,dv}{5405 - 64.8v - 1.8v^2}$$

The analytical solution of this integral is awkward; it is therefore better to evaluate it numerically, taking $v = 30$ to 39, as an approximation.

v (m/s)	30	31	32	33
$v/f(v)$ (10^{-2} s/kg)	1.63	1.86	2.15	2.52
v (m/s)	34	35	36	37
$v/f(v)$ (10^{-2} s/kg)	3.03	3.75	4.87	6.81
v (m/s)	38	39		
$v/f(v)$ (10^{-2} s/kg)	11.1	23.9		

Using the trapezium rule yields

$$\begin{aligned} x_2 &= 1500 \times 1[\tfrac{1}{2}(1.63 + 27.9) + 1.86 \\ &\quad + 2.15 + 2.52 + 3.03 + 3.75 \\ &\quad + 4.87 + 6.81 + 11.1] \times 10^{-2} \\ &= 762 \text{ m} \end{aligned}$$

Hence

$$\text{Total distance } x = x_1 + x_2 = 240 + 762 = 1002 \text{ m} \quad ◂$$

4.7

Power = tractive effort × velocity, i.e. $P = Tv$.

When the car is going up an incline,

$$\eta \frac{P}{v} - mg\sin\alpha - kv^2 = m\frac{dv}{dt}$$

where η is the efficiency.

$v = v_{max}$ when $\frac{dv}{dt} = 0$. Hence:

(a) On a level road,

$$\eta P = kv_{max}^3 \Rightarrow v_{max} = \sqrt[3]{\frac{\eta P}{k}}$$

$$= \sqrt[3]{\frac{0.8 \times 55 \times 10^3}{1.025}} = 35 \text{ m/s}$$

$$= 126 \text{ km/h} \quad ◂$$

(b) On an incline of 1 in 10,

$$f(v) = 0.8 \times 55 \times 10^3 - 750 \times \frac{9.81}{10} v_{max} - 1.025 v_{max}^3 = 0$$

$$\therefore \quad 44\,000 - 735.75\, v_{max} - 1.025\, v_{max}^3 = 0$$

If $v_{max} < 35$ m/s, putting $v = 30$ gives $f(30) = -5747.5$; likewise $v = 25 \Rightarrow f(25) = 9590$, $v = 28 \Rightarrow f(28) = 898.2$ and $v = 28.5 \Rightarrow f(28.5) = -697$.

Hence v lies between 28 and 28.5 m/s. Using the Newton–Raphson equation, we have, with $f'(v) = -735.75 - 3.075v_{max}^2$, and $v_1 = 28$ as our first guess,

$$v_2 = v_1 - \frac{f(v)}{f'(v)} = 28 - \frac{898.2}{-3146.6}$$

$$= 28.29 \text{ m/s} \Rightarrow v_{max} = 102 \text{ km/h} \quad ◂$$

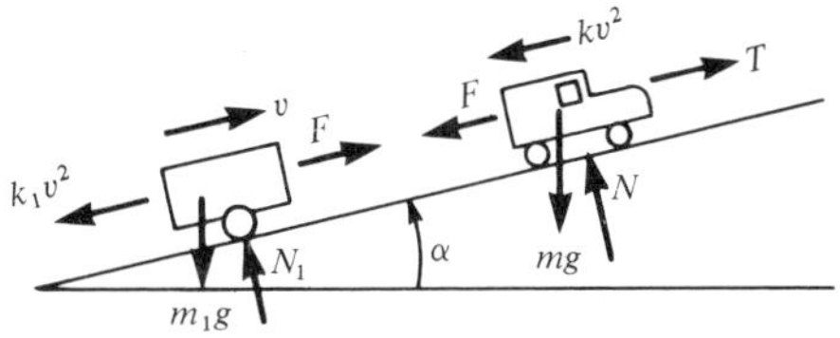

v = 55 km/h = 15.27 m/s
F = tension in the tow-bar

(c) For the trailer, by Newton's second law,

$$F - m_1 g\sin\alpha - k_1v^2 = m_1\frac{dv}{dt}$$

Since the car and trailer are accelerating together,

$$\frac{dv}{dt} = \frac{1}{m_1 + m}\left(\frac{\eta P}{v} - (m_1 + m)g\sin\alpha - (k_1 + k)v^2\right)$$

$$= \frac{1}{1200}\left(\frac{44\,000}{15.27} - \frac{1200 \times 9.81}{10} - 2.275 \times 15.27^2\right) = 0.978 \text{ m/s}^2$$

Hence

$$\begin{aligned} F &= 45 \times 9.81 + 1.25 \times 15.27^2 \\ &\quad + 450 \times 0.978 \\ &= 1173 \text{ N} = 1.17 \text{ kN} \quad ◂ \end{aligned}$$

4.8

(a) Momentum is conserved, and so

$$m_A v_A + m_B v_B = (m_A + m_B)v$$

$$\therefore \quad v = (m_A v_A + m_B v_B)/(m_A + m_B)$$

$$= (60 \times 5 + 80 \times 3)/140 = 3.86\ \text{km/h}$$

(b) Before impact,

$$T_1 = \tfrac{1}{2} m_A v_A^2 + \tfrac{1}{2} m_B v_B^2$$

$$= \frac{10^3}{2 \times 3.6^2}\left\{60 \times 5^2 + 80 \times 3^2\right\}$$

$$= 85.65\ \text{kJ}$$

After impact,

$$T_2 = \tfrac{1}{2}(m_A + m_B)v^2$$

$$= \frac{10^3}{2 \times 3.6^2} \times 140 \times 3.86^2$$

$$= 80.48\ \text{kJ}$$

Energy loss,

$$\Delta T = T_1 - T_2 = (85.65 - 80.48) \times 10^3$$

$$= 5.17\ \text{kJ}$$ ◀

4.9

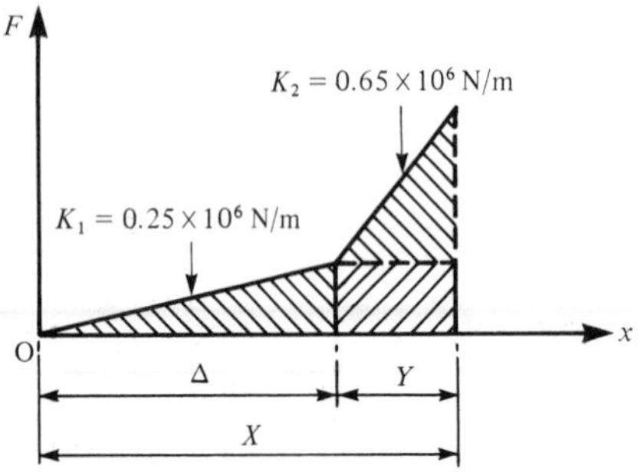

$$\Delta = 0.2\ \text{m}$$

The rolling resistance,

$$R = \frac{3}{100} \times 25 \times 10^3 \times 9.81 = 7357.5\ \text{N}$$

Let X be the distance to come to rest. Then

$$-RX - \int_0^X F\,dx = 0 - \tfrac{1}{2} m v_1^2$$

or $$2RX + 2\int_0^X F\,dx = m v_1^2 \qquad (1)$$

using the work–energy equation.

$$\int_0^X F\,dx = \text{area under the graph}$$

$$= \tfrac{1}{2}K_1\Delta^2 + K_1\Delta(X - \Delta) + \tfrac{1}{2}K_2(X - \Delta)^2$$

$$= X(K_1\Delta - K_2\Delta) + \tfrac{1}{2}K_2X^2 + \tfrac{1}{2}\Delta^2(K_2 - K_1)$$

Hence (1) becomes

$$K_2X^2 + 2[R + \Delta(K_1 - K_2)]X + \Delta^2(K_2 - K_1) - m v_1^2 = 0$$

$$\therefore \quad 0.65 \times 10^6 X^2 + 2[7357.5 + 0.2 \times 10^6(0.25 - 0.65)]X + 0.2^2 \times 0.4 \times 10^6 - 25 \times 10^3 \times \left(\frac{4}{3.6}\right)^2 = 0$$

$$\Rightarrow \quad 0.65 \times 10^6 X^2 - 0.145 \times 10^6 X - 0.015 \times 10^6 = 0$$

giving

$$X = 0.30\ \text{m} = 300\ \text{mm}$$ ◀

Alternatively: Let Y = extra compression; then

$$2\int F\,dy = K_1\Delta^2 + 2K_1\Delta Y + K_2Y^2$$

Hence (1) becomes

$$K_2Y^2 + 2(R + K_1\Delta)Y + 2R\Delta + K_1\Delta^2 - m v_1^2 = 0$$

$$\therefore \quad 0.65 \times 10^6 Y^2 + 2(7357.5 + 0.25 \times 10^6 \times 0.2)Y + 2 \times 7357.5 \times 0.2 + 0.25 \times 10^6 \times 0.2^2 - 25 \times 10^3 \times \left(\frac{4}{3.6}\right)^2 = 0$$

$$\Rightarrow \quad 0.65Y^2 + 0.115Y - 0.018 = 0$$

$$\therefore \quad Y = 0.100$$

$$\text{Total compression} = \Delta + Y = 0.2 + 0.1$$

$$= 0.30\ \text{m as before}$$ ◀

4.10

For the first truck

$$m_1 g \sin\alpha s - \mu m_1 g s = \tfrac{1}{2} m_1 u_1^2$$

$$\Rightarrow \quad u_1 = \sqrt{2sg(\sin\alpha - \mu)}$$

$$= \sqrt{2 \times 305 \times 9.81 \times \left(\frac{1}{70} - \frac{7}{1000}\right)}$$

$$= 6.6\ \text{m/s}$$

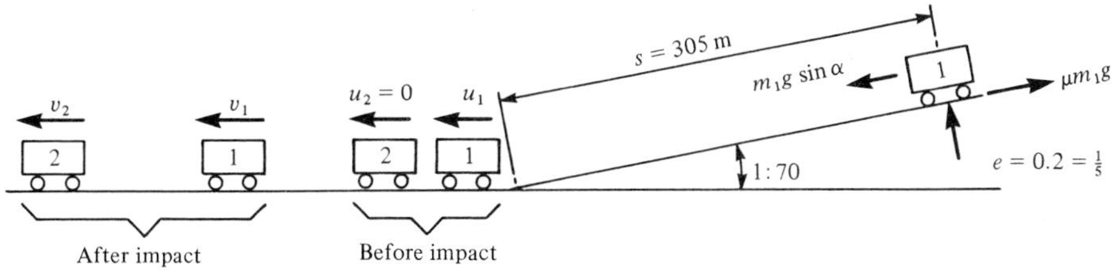

When the trucks collide, $m_2 v_2 + m_1 v_1 = m_2 u_2 + m_1 u_1$ or $v_2 + v_1 = u_2 + u_1$, since $m_2 = m_1$.

But $u_2 = 0$

$\therefore \quad v_2 + v_1 = u_1 \quad$ and $\quad e = -\dfrac{v_2 - v_1}{u_2 - u_1} = \dfrac{v_2 - v_1}{u_1}$

Hence

$$v_2 + v_1 = u_1 = 6.6$$

and $\quad v_2 - v_1 = u_1 e = \dfrac{6.6}{5} = 1.32$

Adding yields

$$v_2 = (6.6 + 1.32)/2 = 3.96 \text{ m/s}$$

and $\quad v_1 = 3.96 - 1.32 = 2.64 \text{ m/s}$

Using the work–energy relationship, we have for the first truck,

$$-m_1 g \mu s_1 = 0 - \tfrac{1}{2} m_1 v_1^2$$

$\Rightarrow \quad s_1 = \tfrac{1}{2} \dfrac{v_1^2}{\mu g} = \tfrac{1}{2} \dfrac{2.64^2}{0.007 \times 9.81} = 50.8 \text{ m} \quad \blacktriangleleft$

and for the second truck,

$$s_2 = \tfrac{1}{2} \dfrac{v_2^2}{\mu g} = \dfrac{3.96^2}{2 \times 0.007 \times 9.81} = 114 \text{ m} \quad \blacktriangleleft$$

4.11

Applying the work–energy relationship,

$$\left(\begin{array}{c}\text{work done}\\\text{by friction}\end{array}\right) + \left(\begin{array}{c}\text{work done}\\\text{in conpressing}\\\text{the gas}\end{array}\right) = \left(\begin{array}{c}\text{change}\\\text{in KE}\end{array}\right)$$

i.e. $\quad -Fx + \displaystyle\int_{V_1}^{V_2} p\, dV = \tfrac{1}{2} m V_2^2 - \tfrac{1}{2} m V_1^2 \quad (1)$

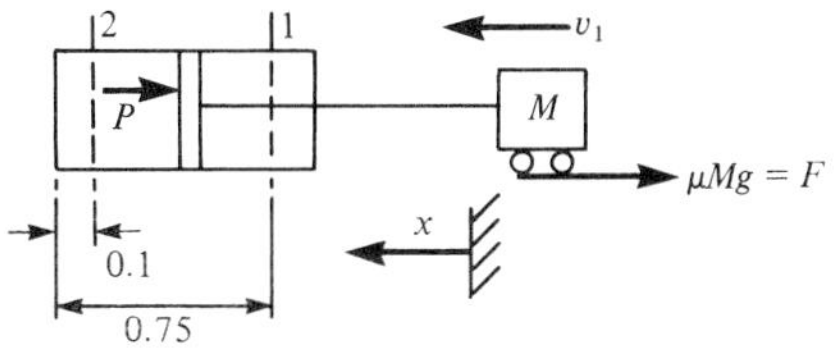

(*Note*: p is in the opposite direction to the displacement x.)

$$\int_{V_1}^{V_2} p\, dV = \int_{V_1}^{V_2} \frac{C\, dV}{V}, \quad \text{since} \quad pV = C.$$

$\therefore \quad C = 10^5 \times \dfrac{\pi}{4} \times 0.2^2 \times 0.75 = 2356 \text{ Pa m}^3$

(*Note*: $1 \text{ bar} = 10^5 \text{ Pa}$, where $1 \text{ Pa} = 1 \text{ N/m}^2$.)

Hence

$$C \int_{V_1}^{V_2} \frac{dV}{V} = C(\ln V_2 - \ln V_1) = C \ln\left(\frac{V_2}{V_1}\right)$$

$$= 2356 \ln\left(\frac{0.1}{0.75}\right) = -4747 \text{ J}$$

Substituting in (1),

$$F \times 0.65 = \tfrac{1}{2} \times 45 \times 10^3 \times \left(\frac{2.5}{3.6}\right)^2 - 4747$$

$\therefore \quad F = 9390 \text{ N}$

$$\left(\begin{array}{c}\text{Coefficient of}\\\text{rolling friction } \mu\end{array}\right) = \frac{F}{mg}$$

$$= \frac{9390}{45 \times 10^3 \times 9.81}$$

$$= 0.02 \quad \blacktriangleleft$$

Also $\quad p_2 = \dfrac{C}{V_2} = \dfrac{2356}{\pi/4 \times 0.2^2 \times 0.1} = 750 \text{ kPa}$

$$= 7.5 \text{ bar} \quad \blacktriangleleft$$

4.12

(a) $(M_0 - mt)\dfrac{dv}{dt} = mu - R$. At $t = 0$,

$$\left(\frac{dv}{dt}\right)_0 = \frac{mu - R}{M_0}$$

$$= \frac{780 \times 2500 - 80 \times 10^3 \times 9.81}{80 \times 10^3}$$

$$= 14.5 \text{ m/s}^2 \quad \blacktriangleleft$$

(b) At burn-out,

$$t_b = \frac{60 \times 10^3}{780} = 76.9\ \text{s}$$

$$\Rightarrow \quad \left(\frac{dv}{dt}\right)_b = \frac{780 \times 2500 - 20 \times 10^3 \times 9.81}{20 \times 10^3}$$

$$= 87.7\ \text{m/s}^2 \quad ◀$$

(c) Thrust,

$$T = mu = 780 \times 2500 = 1.95 \times 10^6\ \text{N} \quad ◀$$

4.13

Velocity at any time t is $v = u \ln\left(\frac{M_0}{M_0 - mt}\right) - gt$

Using the value of t_b from exercise 4.12, at burn-out,

$$v_b = u \ln\left(\frac{M_0}{M_b}\right) - gt_b$$

$$= 2500 \ln\left(\frac{80}{20}\right) - 9.81 \times 76.9$$

$$= 2711\ \text{m/s} \quad ◀$$

$$\frac{ds}{dt} = u \ln\left(\frac{M_0}{M_0 - mt}\right) - gt$$

Integrating yields

$$s = u\left\{\int \ln M_0\, dt - \int \ln (M_0 - mt) dt\right\} - \tfrac{1}{2}gt^2 + C$$

Hence

$$s = ut - \tfrac{1}{2}gt^2 + \frac{u}{m}(M_0 - mt) \ln\left(1 - \frac{mt}{M_0}\right)$$

since $s = 0$ at $t = 0$.

At burn-out,

$$s_b = 2500 \times 76.9 - \tfrac{1}{2} \times 9.81 \times 76.9^2 + \frac{2500}{780} \times 20 \times 10^3 \times \ln(1 - \tfrac{1}{4}) = 145\ \text{km} \quad ◀$$

4.14

(a) The best way is to use the work–energy equation,

$$U_{A\to B} = \Delta T_{A\to B}$$

$$\Delta T_{A\to B} = \tfrac{1}{2}mv^2 - 0 \qquad (1)$$

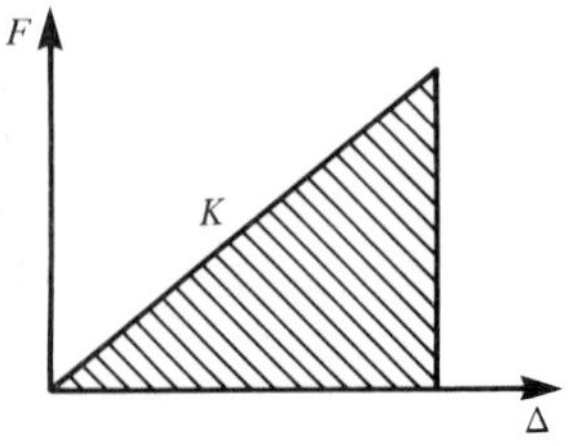

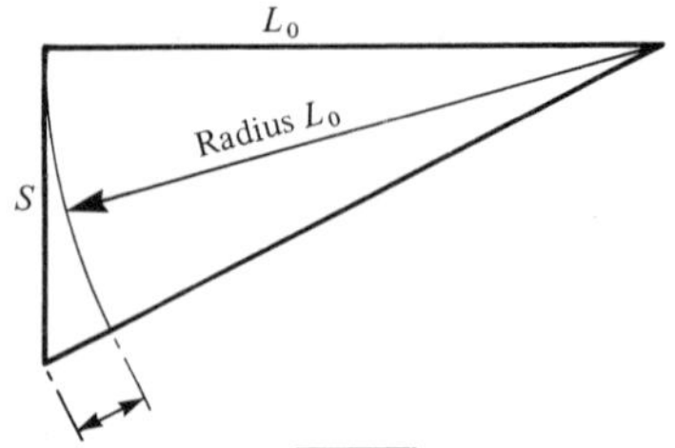

Δ = extension = $\sqrt{S^2 + L_0^2} - L_0$

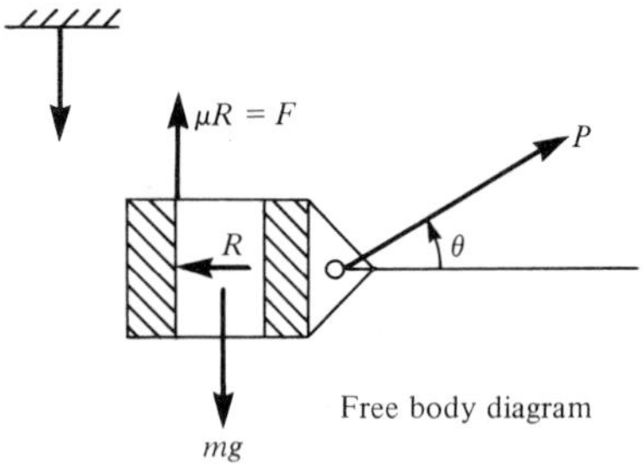

Free body diagram

$$\text{Work done on the spring} = \left(\begin{array}{c}\text{area under}\\ F\text{–}\Delta \text{ graph}\end{array}\right) = \tfrac{1}{2}K\Delta^2$$

Hence

$$U_{A\to B} = mgS - \frac{K}{2}(\sqrt{S^2 + L_0^2} - L_0)^2$$

Substituting in (1) yields

$$v = \sqrt{2gS - \frac{K}{m}(\sqrt{S^2 + L_0^2} - L_0)^2} \quad ◀$$

(b) With friction, $R - P\cos\theta = 0$ and $F = \mu R = \mu P \cos\theta$.

$$\therefore \quad F = \mu K(\sqrt{x^2 + L_0^2} - L_0) \times \frac{L_0}{\sqrt{x^2 + L_0^2}}$$

$$= \mu K\left(L_0 - \frac{L_0^2}{\sqrt{x^2 + L_0^2}}\right)$$

$$\begin{pmatrix}\text{Work done}\\ \text{against friction}\end{pmatrix} = \int_0^S F\,\mathrm{d}x = \mu K\left\{\int_0^S L_0\,\mathrm{d}x - L_0^2\int_0^S \frac{\mathrm{d}x}{\sqrt{x^2+L_0^2}}\right\}$$

$$= \mu K L_0\left\{S - L_0 \ln\left(\frac{S+\sqrt{S^2+L_0^2}}{L_0}\right)\right\}$$

Applying the work–energy equation yields

$$mgS - \tfrac{1}{2}K(\sqrt{S^2+L_0^2}-L_0)^2 - \mu K L_0\left\{S - L_0\ln\left(\frac{S+\sqrt{S^2+L_0^2}}{L_0}\right)\right\}$$

$$= \tfrac{1}{2}mv^2 \text{ and hence } v.$$ ◀

4.15

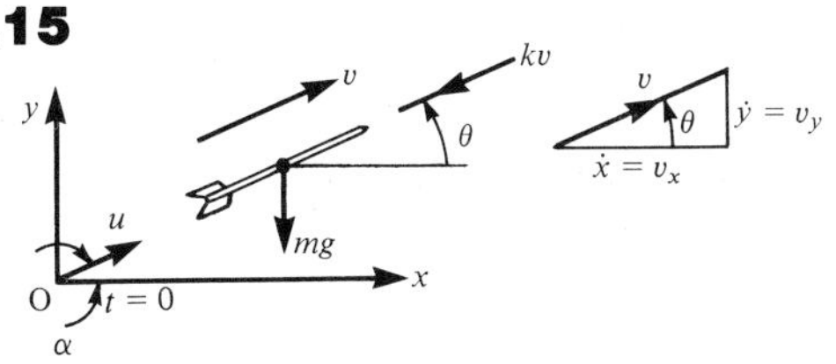

(a) Resolving horizontally, by Newton's second law,

$$-kv\cos\theta = m\ddot{x},$$

i.e. $$-kv_x = m\frac{\mathrm{d}v_x}{\mathrm{d}t}$$

Integrating gives

$$-t = \frac{m}{k}\ln v_x + C$$

When $t = 0$,

$$v_x = u\cos\alpha$$

$$\therefore \quad v_x = u\cos\alpha\, e^{-kt/m}$$

Since $v_x = \dfrac{\mathrm{d}x}{\mathrm{d}t}$, integrating yields

$$x = u\cos\alpha\int_0^t e^{-kt/m}\,\mathrm{d}t + C_1$$

$$\Rightarrow \quad x = \frac{mu\cos\alpha}{k}(1-e^{-kt/m}) \qquad (1)$$

(b) Resolving vertically, by Newton's second law,

$$-mg - kv\sin\theta = m\frac{\mathrm{d}v_y}{\mathrm{d}t}$$

or $$-mg - kv_y = m\frac{\mathrm{d}v_y}{\mathrm{d}t}$$

Separating the variables and integrating, we have

$$m\int\frac{\mathrm{d}v_y}{mg+kv_y} = -t + C_2$$

But when $t = 0$, $v_y = u\sin\alpha$, so that

$$\frac{\mathrm{d}y}{\mathrm{d}t} = v_y = \frac{1}{k}(mg + ku\sin\alpha)e^{-kt/m} - \frac{mg}{k}$$

Integrating once more yields

$$y = \frac{m}{k}\left(u\sin\alpha + \frac{mg}{k}\right)(1-e^{-kt/m}) - \frac{mg}{k}t$$

$$= \frac{m}{k}\left\{\left(u\sin\alpha + \frac{mg}{k}\right)(1-e^{-kt/m}) - gt\right\} \qquad (2)$$

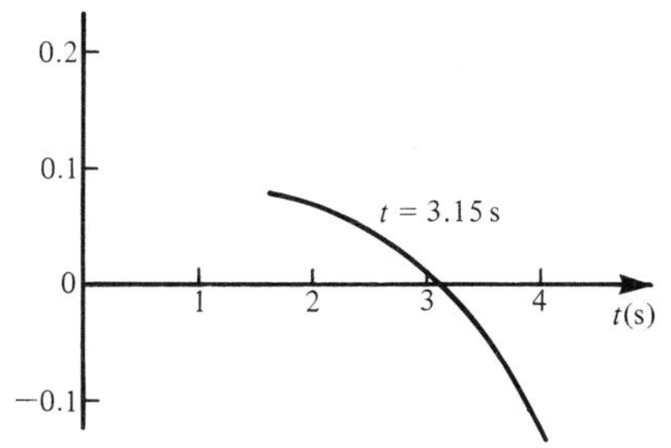

(c) To evaluate the distance covered we need the time taken when $y = 0$ from (2) i.e. when

$$A(1-e^{-kt/m}) - t = 0,$$

where

$$A = \frac{u\sin\alpha}{g} + \frac{m}{k} = \frac{60\sin 15^\circ}{9.81} + \frac{0.15}{0.01}$$

$$= 16.58$$

To calculate the time it is best to plot a graph as shown, giving $t = 3.15$ s. Substituting in (1), the distance travelled

$$x = \frac{0.15 \times 60 \times \cos 15^\circ}{0.01}(1 - e^{-0.01\times 3.15/0.15})$$

$$= 165 \text{ m}$$ ◀

4.16

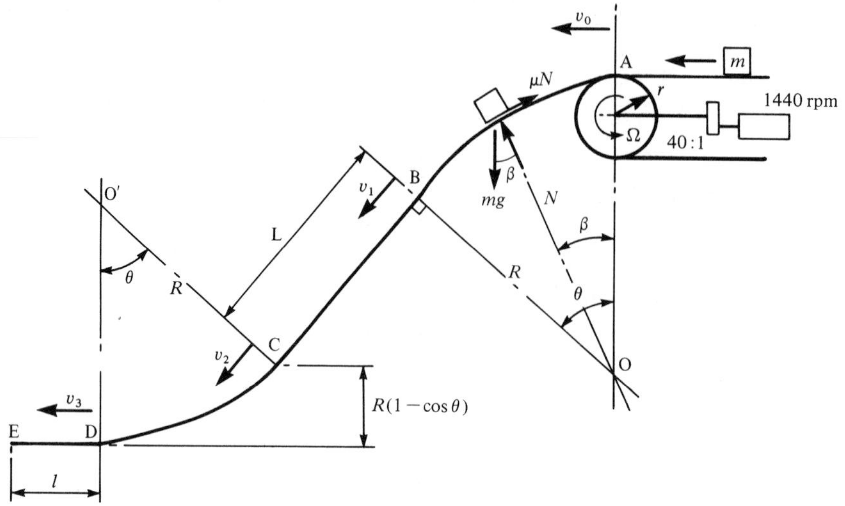

$$u = \frac{2\pi \times 1440}{60} \times \frac{1}{40} \times 0.15 = 0.57 \text{ m/s}$$

At A,

$$T_0 = 0.9T$$

$$\therefore \quad \tfrac{1}{2}mv_0^2 = 0.9 \times \tfrac{1}{2}mu^2$$

$$\Rightarrow \quad v_0 = 0.95u = 0.54 \text{ m/s}$$

For A → B: At any position β we have

$$mg\cos\beta - N = m\dot{\beta}^2 R = m\omega^2 R \qquad (1)$$

$$mg\sin\beta - \mu N = m\ddot{\beta}R = m\dot{\omega}R \qquad (2)$$

From (1) and (2), eliminating N,

$$g(\sin\beta - \mu\cos\beta) + \mu\omega^2 R = \dot{\omega}R$$

or

$$\dot{\omega} - \mu\omega^2 = \frac{g}{R}(\sin\beta - \mu\cos\beta) \qquad (3)$$

But

$$\dot{\omega} = \frac{d\omega}{dt} = \frac{d\omega}{d\beta}\frac{d\beta}{dt} = \omega\frac{d\omega}{d\beta} = \frac{1}{2}\frac{d}{d\beta}(\omega^2)$$

so that (3) becomes

$$\frac{dy}{d\beta} - 2\mu y = \frac{2g}{R}(\sin\beta - \mu\cos\beta) \qquad (4)$$

where

$$y = \omega^2$$

This equation is in the standard form given in the question. If x is the integrating factor, then $x = e^{\int -2\mu d\beta} = e^{-2\mu\beta}$ and the solution of (4) is

$$y = \omega^2 = \frac{-2g}{R(4\mu^2 + 1)}[(1 - 2\mu^2)\cos\beta + 3\mu\sin\beta] + Ce^{2\mu\beta}$$

When $\beta = 0$, $\omega = v_0/R$

$$\therefore \quad C = \left(\frac{v_0}{R}\right)^2 + \frac{2g(1 - 2\mu^2)}{R(4\mu^2 + 1)}$$

When $\beta = \theta$, $v_1 = \omega R$, so that

$$\left(\frac{v_1}{R}\right)^2 = e^{2\mu\theta}\left[\left(\frac{v_0}{R}\right)^2 + \frac{2g(1 - 2\mu^2)}{R(4\mu^2 + 1)}\right] - \frac{2g}{R(4\mu^2 + 1)}[(1 - 2\mu^2)\cos\theta + 3\mu\sin\theta]$$

Substituting values yields

$$\left(\frac{v_1}{R}\right)^2 = 23.34 - 19.64 = 3.69$$

$$\therefore \quad v_1 = 0.89\sqrt{3.69} = 1.61 \text{ m/s}$$

For B → C: The work–energy equation gives

$$mg\sin\theta L - \mu mg\cos\theta L = \tfrac{1}{2}mv_2^2 - \tfrac{1}{2}mv_1^2$$

Hence

$$v_2 = \sqrt{v_1^2 + 2gL(\sin\theta - \mu\cos\theta)}$$
$$= \sqrt{1.61^2 + 2 \times 9.81 \times 1.75(\sin 60° - 0.4\cos 60°)}$$
$$= 5.05 \text{ m/s}$$

For C → D: There is no frictional force, and hence

$$v_3 = \sqrt{v_2^2 + 2gR(1 - \cos\theta)}$$
$$= \sqrt{5.05^2 + 2 \times 9.81 \times 0.84(1 - \cos 60°)}$$
$$= 5.81 \text{ m/s}$$

For D → E: The work–energy equation gives

$$-\mu mgl = 0 - \tfrac{1}{2}mv_3^2$$

Solving for l, we have

$$l = \frac{v_3^2}{2\mu g} = \frac{5.81^2}{2 \times 0.8 \times 9.81} = 2.15 \text{ m}$$ ◀

Note: As a *simple check*, replace the actual chute by a straight one:

$$L' = \sqrt{2.36^2 + 2.33^2} = 3.32 \text{ m}$$

A → D: Potential energy lost $= mgL'\sin\theta$
$= mg \times 2.36$

Friction path $L_f = L + 2R\theta = 1.75 + 2 \times 0.84 \times \frac{60}{57.3} = 3.51$

Work done against friction $= \mu mg\cos\theta L_f$.

Hence

$$v_3 = \sqrt{v_0^2 + 2gH - 2\mu g L_f \cos\theta}$$
$$= \sqrt{0.54^2 + 2 \times 9.81(2.36 - 0.4 \times 3.51 \times \cos 60°)}$$
$$= 5.73 \text{ m/s}$$

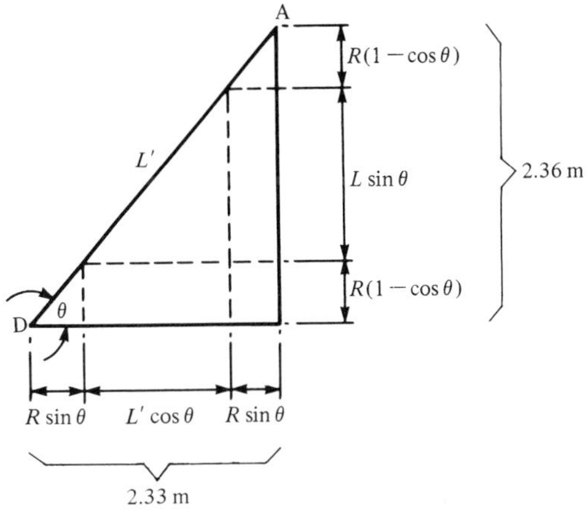

CHAPTER 5

5.1

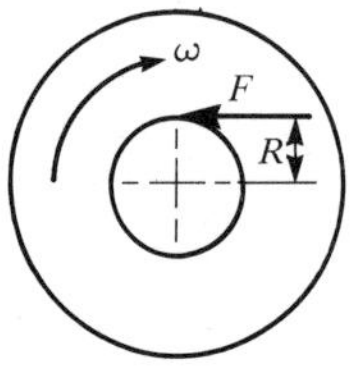

$$\omega_0 = \frac{2\pi \times 120}{60} = 12.57 \text{ rad/s}$$

$$R = 0.04 \text{ m}$$

$$F = 1200 \text{ N}$$

$$I\frac{d\omega}{dt} = -FR \quad \Rightarrow \quad \frac{d\omega}{dt} = -\frac{FR}{I}$$

Integrating, we have

$$\omega = -\frac{FR}{I}t + C_1$$

When $t = 0$, let $\omega = \omega_0$. Then

$$\therefore \quad C_1 = \omega_0$$

Hence

$$\omega = \omega_0 - \frac{FR}{I}t$$

When $\omega = 0$, let $t = T$, so that

$$T = \frac{\omega_0 I}{FR}$$

$$I = Mk^2 = 1000 \times 1.1^2 = 1210 \text{ kg m}^2$$

$$\therefore \quad T = \frac{12.57 \times 1210}{1200 \times 0.04} = 317 \text{ s} = 5.3 \text{ min} \quad ◀$$

Since $\frac{d\theta}{dt} = \omega = \omega_0 - \frac{FR}{I}t$, integrating yields

$$\theta = \omega_0 t - \frac{FR}{2I}t^2 + C_2$$

When $t = 0$, $\theta = 0$.

$$\therefore \quad C_2 = 0$$

Hence

$$\theta_{\text{to rest}} = 12.57 \times 317 - \frac{1200 \times 0.04}{2 \times 1210} \times (317)^2$$

$$= 1992 \text{ rad} = 317 \text{ turns} \quad ◀$$

5.2

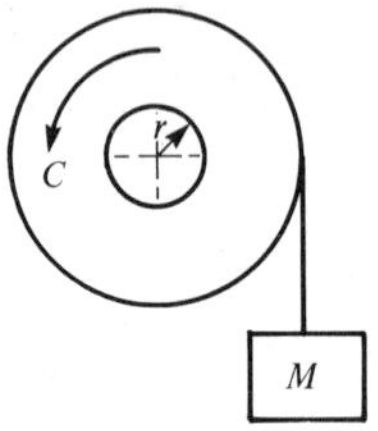

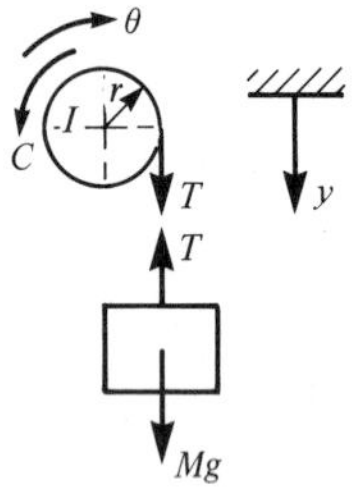

Free body diagram

For the mass:

$$Mg - T = m\ddot{y}$$

For the flywheel:

$$Tr - C = I\ddot{\theta}$$

The kinematic relationship gives

$$r\theta = y \quad \Rightarrow \quad r\ddot{\theta} = \ddot{y}$$

Hence

$$Mg - T = Mr\ddot{\theta} \tag{1}$$

and

$$-\frac{C}{r} + T = \frac{I}{r}\ddot{\theta} \tag{2}$$

Adding (1) and (2) yields

$$\left(Mg - \frac{C}{r}\right) = \left(Mr + \frac{I}{r}\right)\ddot{\theta} = \left(Mr + \frac{I}{r}\right)\omega\frac{d\omega}{d\theta}$$

Integrating and noting that when $\theta = 0$, $\omega = 0$ we find

$$(Mgr - C)\theta = \tfrac{1}{2}(Mr^2 + I)\omega^2$$

When $\theta = A$, let $\omega = \omega_1$, so that

$$(Mgr - C)A = \tfrac{1}{2}(Mr^2 + I)\omega_1^2 \tag{3}$$

After the rope has been released,

$$-C = I\omega\frac{d\omega}{d\theta}$$

Hence

$$-C\theta = \tfrac{1}{2}I\omega^2 + C_2$$

But when $\theta = 0$,

$$\omega = \omega_1 \quad \Rightarrow \quad C_2 = -\tfrac{1}{2}I\omega_1^2$$

and when $\omega = 0$,

$$\theta = B \quad \Rightarrow \quad -CB = -\tfrac{1}{2}I\omega_1^2 \tag{4}$$

Hence from (3) and (4) we get

$$C = \frac{IMgrA}{AI + (Mr^2 + I)B}$$ ◄

5.3

Inertia referred to the road wheels,

$$I = I_e G^2 + I_\omega = 0.08 \times 9^2 + 2.16$$
$$= 8.64 \text{ kg m}^2$$

Torque referred to the road wheels,

$$T = \eta T_m G = 0.88 \times 20 \times 9 = 158.4 \text{ Nm}$$

Tractive effort,

$$P = T/R = 158.4/0.325 = 487.4 \text{ N}$$

where R is the wheel radius.

$$\text{KE of the motorcycle} = \tfrac{1}{2}Mv^2 + \tfrac{1}{2}I\omega^2$$
$$= \tfrac{1}{2}Mv^2 + \tfrac{1}{2}I\left(\frac{v}{R}\right)^2$$
$$= \tfrac{1}{2}v^2[M + I/R^2]$$

where v is the road speed.

Equivalent mass,

$$M_e = M + I/R^2$$
$$= 185 + 8.64/0.325^2 = 266.8 \text{ kg}$$

Road speed,

$$v = \omega R = \frac{2\pi \times 1800}{60} \times \frac{1}{9} \times 0.325$$
$$= 6.81 \text{ m/s} = 24.5 \text{ km/h}$$ ◄

By Newton's second law,

$$M_e \frac{dv}{dt} = P - \text{resistance}$$

Hence the acceleration,

$$\frac{dv}{dt} = \frac{487.4 - 90}{266.8} = 1.49 \text{ m/s}^2$$ ◄

5.4

The equations of motion are:

For the mass:

$$mg - T_1 = ma \quad \text{or} \quad T_1 = m(g-a) \qquad (1)$$

For the winch:

$$R(T_1 - T) - f + C = I\ddot{\theta}$$

$$\text{or} \quad T_1 - T = \frac{I\ddot{\theta} + f}{R} - \frac{C}{R} \qquad (2)$$

For the truck:

$$T - F - Mg \sin\alpha = Ma \qquad (3)$$

From (1) and (2),

$$T = m(g-a) - \frac{I\ddot{\theta} + f}{R} + \frac{C}{R}$$

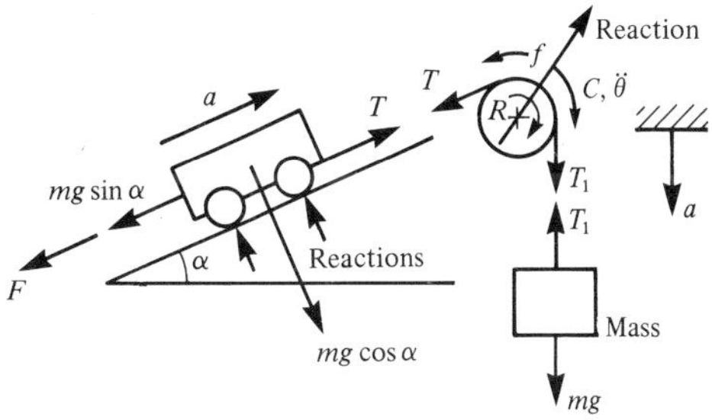

Free body diagram

Substituting in (3) we find

$$m(g-a) - \frac{I\ddot{\theta} + f}{R} + \frac{C}{R} - F - Mg\sin\alpha = Ma$$

Hence

$$Rm(g-a) - I\ddot{\theta} - f + C - FR - Mg\sin\alpha R$$
$$= MaR$$

From kinematics

$$a = R\ddot{\theta} \quad \text{or} \quad \ddot{\theta} = a/R$$

Solving for a we have

$$a = \frac{C - f + R(mg - F - Mg\sin\alpha)}{I + (m+M)R^2} R$$ ◄

5.5

If P is the rated power of the motor, then

$$\text{available power} = \eta P = T_m \omega_{\text{rated}}$$

$$\therefore \quad T_m = \frac{\eta P}{\omega_{\text{rated}}} = \frac{0.65 \times 500}{(2\pi \times 1425/60)} = 2.18 \text{ N m}$$

$$\omega_{\text{rated}} = \frac{2\pi \times 1425}{60} = 149.2 \text{ rad/s}$$

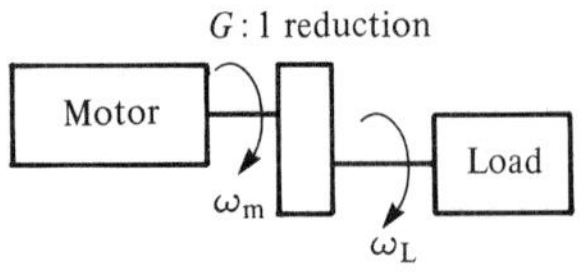

Referred to motor shaft:

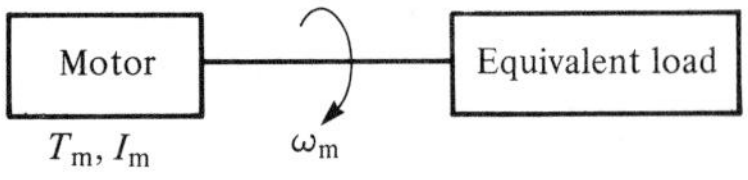

$$T_{Le} = (A + B\omega_L)/G$$
$$= (A + B\omega_m/G)/G$$
$$I_{Le} = I_L/G^2$$

The equation of motion is

$$T_m - \left(A + \frac{B\omega_m}{G}\right)\frac{1}{G} = (I_m + I_L/G^2)\frac{d\omega_m}{dt}$$

or $$a - b\omega_m = I_e\frac{d\omega_m}{dt}$$

where

$$a = T_m - \frac{A}{G} = 2.18 - \frac{40}{50} = 1.38 \text{ N m}$$

$$b = \frac{B}{G^2} = \frac{23}{50^2} = 9.2 \times 10^{-3} \text{ N m s}$$

$$I_e = I_m + \frac{I_L}{G^2} = 0.005 + \frac{56}{50^2}$$
$$= 0.0274 \text{ kg m}^2$$

Integrating yields

$$t = \frac{I_e}{b}\ln\left(\frac{a}{a - b\omega_m}\right),$$

since

$$\omega_m = 0 \quad \text{at} \quad t = 0$$

If t' is the time taken to reach its rated speed, then

$$t' = \frac{I_e}{b}\ln\left(\frac{a}{a - b\omega_{rated}}\right)$$

$$= \frac{0.0274}{9.2 \times 10^{-3}}\ln\left(\frac{1.38}{1.38 - 9.2 \times 10^{-3} \times 149.2}\right)$$

$$= 15.6 \text{ s}$$ ◄

5.6

Referring to exercise 5.5, we have

$$T_m - \frac{A}{G} - \frac{B}{G^2}\omega_m = I_e\frac{d\omega_m}{dt}$$

But $T_m = T_0 - k\omega_m$

so that

$$a' - b'\omega_m = I_e\frac{d\omega_m}{dt}$$

where

$$a' = T_0 - \frac{A}{G} = 2.75 - \frac{40}{50} = 1.95 \text{ N m}$$

$$b' = 0.003\,82 + 0.0092 = 0.013 \text{ N m s}$$

Hence if t'' is now the time taken for the system to reach its rated speed, then

$$t'' = \frac{0.0274}{0.013}\ln\left(\frac{1.95}{1.95 - 0.013 \times 149.2}\right)$$

$$= 11 \text{ s}$$ ◄

5.7

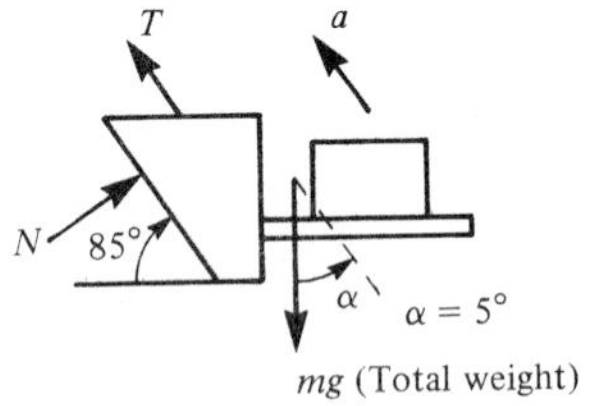

(a) By Newton's second law,

$$T - mg\cos\alpha = ma$$

$$\therefore \quad T = m(g\cos\alpha + a)$$

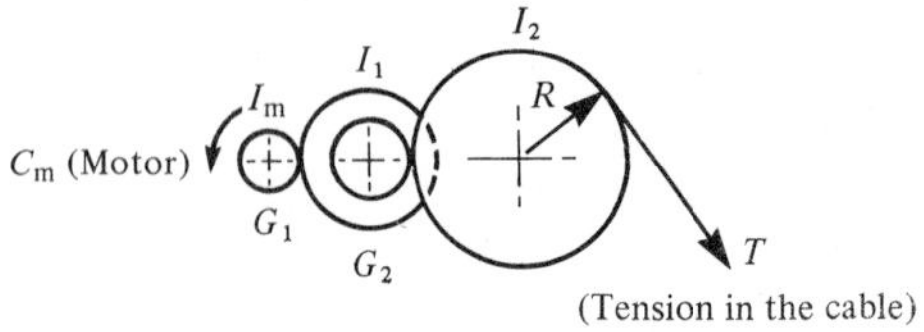

Let I_e = equivalent moment of inertia referred to the motor. Then

$$I_e = I_m + I_1/G_1^2 + I_2/G_2^2G_1^2$$

$$= 0.075 + \frac{2}{5^2} + \frac{12}{5^2 \times 6^2} = 0.17 \text{ kg m}^2$$

Load torque referred to the motor,

$$C_L = TR/G_1G_2 = m(g\cos\alpha + a)R/G_1G_2$$

$$= 147 \times (9.81\cos 5^\circ + a) \times \frac{0.25}{30}$$

$$= 11.97 + 1.225a$$

Hence

$$C_m - C_L = I_e\alpha$$

$$\Rightarrow \quad 25 - 11.97 - 1.225a = 0.17\alpha$$

But

$$\alpha = G_1G_2a/R = 30a/0.25 = 120a$$

Hence

$$13.03 - 1.225a = 0.17 \times 120a$$

$$\text{or} \quad 13.03 = (0.17 \times 120 + 1.225)a$$

$$\therefore \quad a = 0.6\ \text{m/s}^2$$ ◀

(b) Consider a free body diagram of the platform. At the attachment to the trolley there will be a bending moment M, a shear force Q and an axial load F, generally.

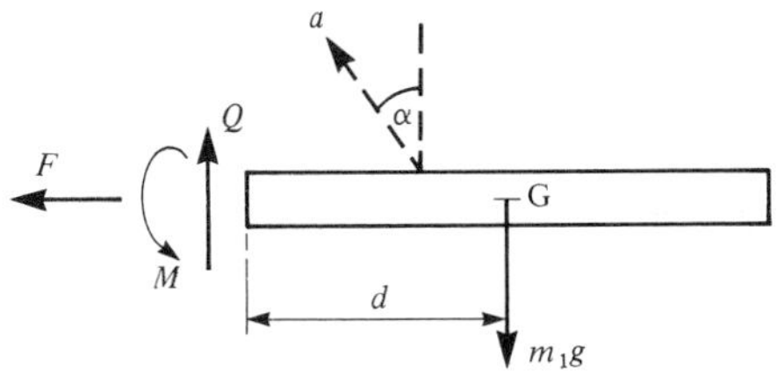

By Newton's second law,

$$Q - m_1g = m_1a\cos\alpha$$

and

$$M - Qd = 0$$

(since the platform is not rotating). Hence

$$M = m_1(g + a\cos\alpha)d$$

$$= 132 \times (9.81 + 0.6\cos 5^\circ) \times 0.5$$

$$= 687\ \text{N m}$$ ◀

5.8

Referring everything to the road wheels,

$$I_e = 0.32 \times 20^2 + 4 \times 1.65 = 134.6\ \text{kg m}^2$$

Equivalent mass,

$$M_e = M + I_e/(\text{radius of wheel})^2$$

$$= 1250 + 134.6/0.375^2 = 2207\ \text{kg}$$

Road speed,

$$v = 25/3.6 = 6.94\ \text{m/s}$$

Resistance to motion

$$R = 200 + 0.45 \times 6.94^2 = 221.4\ \text{N}$$

Let the tractive effort be P. Then

$$M_ea = P - R$$

$$\text{or} \quad P = M_ea + R = 2207 \times 3 + 221$$

$$= 6842\ \text{N}$$

Hence the torque required,

$$T = P \times \text{radius of wheel}$$

$$= 6842 \times 0.375/20 = 128\ \text{N m}$$ ◀

5.9

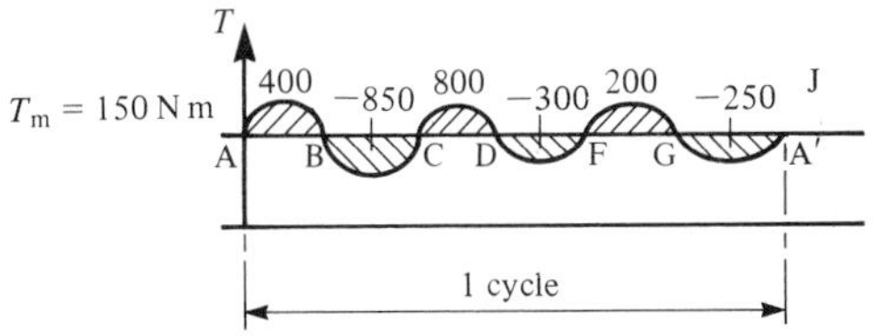

Let E be the energy at the beginning of the cycle, i.e. at A. Then

at B: $E + 400 = E + 400$

at C: $E + 400 - 850 = E - 450$

at D: $E - 450 + 800 = E + 350$

at F: $E + 350 - 300 = E + 50$

at G: $E + 50 + 200 = E + 250$

at A′: $E + 250 - 250 = E$

Hence excess energy during the cycle,

$$\Delta E = E_{max} - E_{min}$$

$$= (E + 400) - (E - 450) = 850\ \text{J}$$

Let I = total moment of inertia

$$= I_{flywheel} + 0.5$$

$$\Delta E = K_sI\omega_0^2 \quad \text{where} \quad K_s = 0.04$$

$$\text{and} \quad \omega_0 = \frac{2\pi \times 1200}{60} = 126\ \text{rad/s}$$

Hence required

$$I = \frac{\Delta E}{K_s \omega_0^2} = \frac{850}{0.04 \times 126^2}$$
$$= 1.34 \text{ kg m}^2$$

so that

$$I_{\text{flywheel}} = 1.34 - 0.5 = 0.84 \text{ kg m}^2$$ ◄

$$\text{Power delivered} = 150 \times 126 = 18.9 \text{ kW}$$ ◄

5.10

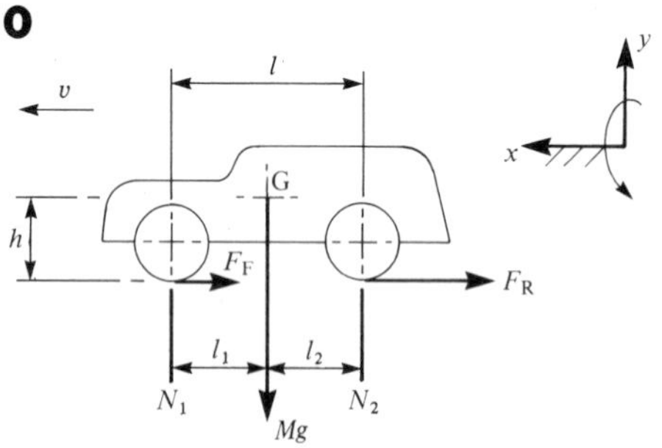

(a) For rear wheel braking the equations of motion are:

$$\Sigma X = M\ddot{x}_G$$

i.e. $-F_R = M\ddot{x}$ (1)

$$\Sigma Y = M\ddot{y}_G$$

i.e. $N_1 + N_2 - Mg = 0$ (2)

since $\ddot{y} = 0$.

$$\Sigma M_G = I\alpha$$

i.e. $F_R h - N_1 l_1 + N_2 l_2 = 0$ (3)

since $\alpha = 0$.

Also

$F_R = \mu N_2$ (4)

From (3), (4) and (2),

$$N_2 = \frac{Mgl_1}{l_1 + l_2 + \mu h} = M\left(\frac{9.81 \times 1.65}{2.85 + 0.6\mu}\right)$$
$$= 5.56M \quad \text{with} \quad \mu = 0.1$$
$$= 5.04M \quad \text{with} \quad \mu = 0.6$$

Hence

$$M\ddot{x} = -\mu N_2$$

and the minimum distance to come to rest is

$$s = -v^2/2\ddot{x}$$

With $\mu = 0.1$,

$$s_{0.1} = 13.9^2/2 \times 0.1 \times 5.56 = 173.5 \text{ m}$$ ◄

With $\mu = 0.6$,

$$s_{0.6} = 13.9^2/2 \times 0.6 \times 5.04 = 32 \text{ m}$$ ◄

(b) For front wheel braking the equations of motion are:

$$-F_F = M\ddot{x}$$
$$N_1 + N_2 - Mg = 0$$
$$N_2 l_2 + F_F h - N_1 l_1 = 0$$
$$F_F = \mu N_1$$

Hence

$$N_1 = \frac{Mgl_2}{l_1 + l_2 - \mu h} = M\left(\frac{9.81 \times 1.2}{2.85 - 0.6\mu}\right)$$
$$= 4.22M \quad \text{with} \quad \mu = 0.1$$
$$= 4.73M \quad \text{with} \quad \mu = 0.6$$

The distance to come to rest is

$$s_{0.1} = 13.9^2/2 \times 0.1 \times 4.22 = 229 \text{ m}$$ ◄

$$s_{0.6} = 13.9^2/2 \times 0.6 \times 4.73 = 34 \text{ m}$$ ◄

(c) For front and rear wheel braking (3) becomes

$$F_R h + N_2 l_2 + F_F h - N_1 l_1 = 0$$

Also $F_R = \mu N_2$ and $F_F = \mu N_1$. Hence

$$N_1 = Mg\left(\frac{l_2 + \mu h}{l_1 + l_2}\right) \quad \text{and} \quad N_2 = Mg\left(\frac{l_1 - \mu h}{l_1 + l_2}\right)$$

Therefore

$$N_1 = 9.81M\left(\frac{1.2 + 0.6\mu}{2.85}\right)$$
$$= 4.34M \quad \text{with} \quad \mu = 0.1$$
$$= 5.37M \quad \text{with} \quad \mu = 0.6$$
$$N_2 = 9.81M\left(\frac{1.65 - 0.6\mu}{2.85}\right)$$
$$= 5.47M \quad \text{with} \quad \mu = 0.1$$
$$= 4.44M \quad \text{with} \quad \mu = 0.6$$

The distance to come to rest is

$$s_{0.1} = 13.9^2/2 \times 0.98 = 98.6 \text{ m}$$ ◄

$$s_{0.6} = 13.9^2/2 \times 5.89 = 16.4 \text{ m}$$ ◄

The ratio $N_1/N_2 = (l_2 + \mu h)/(l_1 - \mu h)$

$$= (1.2 + 0.6\mu)/(1.65 - 0.6\mu)$$

$$= 0.79 \quad \text{with} \quad \mu = 0.1$$ ◄

$$= 1.21 \quad \text{with} \quad \mu = 0.6$$ ◄

5.11

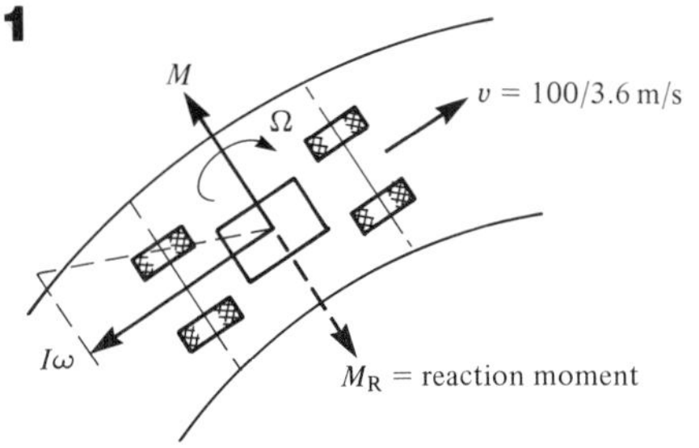

$$\Omega = \frac{v}{R} = \frac{100/3.6}{50} = 0.56 \text{ rad/s}$$

$$\omega = \frac{2\pi \times 3000}{60} = 314 \text{ rad/s}$$

$$M_{gyroscopic} = I\omega\Omega = 3.75 \times 314 \times 0.56 = 659 \text{ Nm}$$ ◄

Hence the pressure is increased at the rear and decreased at the front.

5.12

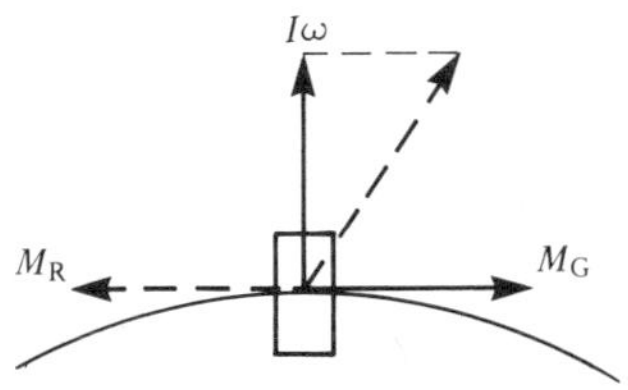

Right-hand bend

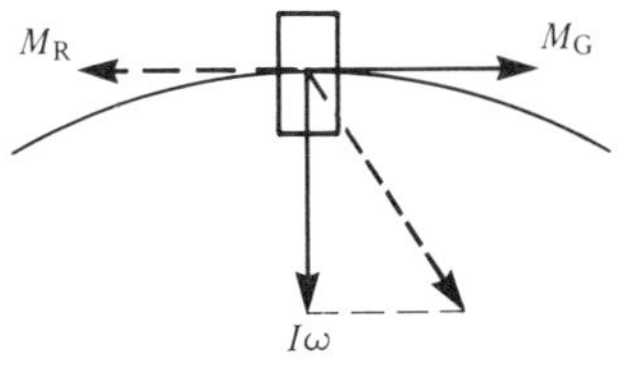

Left-hand bend

$$I = I_{engine} \times G^2 + I_{wheels} = 0.1 \times 5^2 + 2 = 4.5 \text{ kg m}^2$$

$$\Omega = \frac{v}{R} = \frac{16.7}{30} = 0.56 \text{ rad/s}$$

$$\omega = \frac{v}{r} = \frac{16.7}{0.325} = 51.3 \text{ rad/s}$$

$$M_G = I\omega\Omega = 4.5 \times 51.3 \times 0.56 = 129 \text{ N m}$$ ◄

With both LH and RH bends the moment is outwards.

5.13

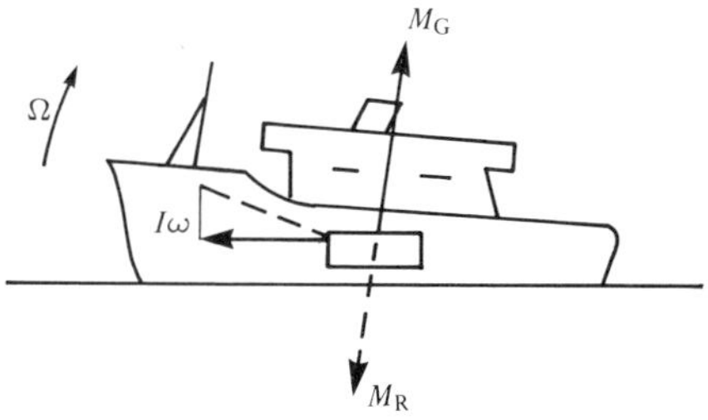

$$I = Mk^2 = 750 \times 0.25^2 = 47 \text{ kg m}^2$$

$$\Omega = 1 \text{ rad/s}; \quad \omega = 2\pi \times 1200/60 = 126 \text{ rad/s}$$

$$M_G = I\omega\Omega = 47 \times 126 \times 1 = 5922 \text{ N m}$$ ◄

When the bow is rising the yacht tends to turn to the right and vice versa when the bow is pitching downwards.

CHAPTER 6

6.1

(a) $\mathbf{P.R} = 4 - 3 \times 2 - 5 \times 7 = -37$

$$\cos\theta = -37/\sqrt{4^2 + 3^2 + 5^2}\sqrt{1^2 + 2^2 + 7^2}$$

$$\Rightarrow \quad \theta = 135.4^\circ \quad ◀$$

(b) $$\mathbf{P}\wedge\mathbf{R} = \begin{vmatrix} \mathbf{i} & \mathbf{j} & \mathbf{k} \\ 4 & -3 & 5 \\ 1 & 2 & -7 \end{vmatrix}$$

$$= (-3 \times -7 - 2 \times 5)\mathbf{i} - (4 \times 7 - 1 \times 5)\mathbf{j} + (4 \times 2 + 1 \times 3)\mathbf{k}$$

$$= 11\mathbf{i} - 23\mathbf{j} + 11\mathbf{k} \quad ◀$$

6.2

(a) $$\mathbf{P} + \mathbf{Q} - \mathbf{R} = \mathbf{i} + \mathbf{j} + \mathbf{k} + 2\mathbf{i} - 3\mathbf{j} + 4\mathbf{k} - \mathbf{j} + 2\mathbf{k}$$

$$= 3\mathbf{i} - \mathbf{j} + 7\mathbf{k} \quad ◀$$

(b) $$\mathbf{P}.(\mathbf{Q} + \mathbf{R}) = (\mathbf{i} + \mathbf{j} + \mathbf{k}).(2\mathbf{i} - 2\mathbf{j} + 2\mathbf{k})$$

$$= 2 - 2 + 2 = 2 \quad ◀$$

$$(\mathbf{P} + \mathbf{Q}).\mathbf{R} = (3\mathbf{i} - 2\mathbf{j} + 5\mathbf{k}).(\mathbf{j} - 2\mathbf{k})$$

$$= 0 - 2 - 10 = -12 \quad ◀$$

(c) $$\mathbf{Q}\wedge\mathbf{R} = \begin{vmatrix} \mathbf{i} & \mathbf{j} & \mathbf{k} \\ 2 & -3 & 4 \\ 0 & 1 & -2 \end{vmatrix} = 2\mathbf{i} + 4\mathbf{j} + 2\mathbf{k}$$

$$\therefore \quad \mathbf{P}\wedge(\mathbf{Q}\wedge\mathbf{R}) = \begin{vmatrix} \mathbf{i} & \mathbf{j} & \mathbf{k} \\ 1 & 1 & 1 \\ 2 & 4 & 2 \end{vmatrix} = -2\mathbf{i} + 2\mathbf{k} \quad ◀$$

$$\mathbf{P}\wedge\mathbf{Q} = \begin{vmatrix} \mathbf{i} & \mathbf{j} & \mathbf{k} \\ 1 & 1 & 1 \\ 2 & -3 & 4 \end{vmatrix} = 7\mathbf{i} - 2\mathbf{j} - 5\mathbf{k}$$

$$\therefore \quad (\mathbf{P}\wedge\mathbf{Q})\wedge\mathbf{R} = \begin{vmatrix} \mathbf{i} & \mathbf{j} & \mathbf{k} \\ 7 & -2 & -5 \\ 0 & 1 & -2 \end{vmatrix} = 9\mathbf{i} + 11\mathbf{j} + 7\mathbf{k} \quad ◀$$

6.3

(a) $\dot{\mathbf{P}} = -15\sin 15t\mathbf{i} + 15\cos 15t\mathbf{j}$

$$P = 1 \quad \Rightarrow \quad \dot{P} = 0 \quad ◀$$

(b) $\dot{\mathbf{R}} = 2\mathbf{i} + 8t\mathbf{j} + 3t^2\mathbf{k} \quad \Rightarrow \quad \ddot{\mathbf{R}} = 8\mathbf{j} + 6t\mathbf{k} \quad ◀$

6.4

$$\mathbf{P.R} = PR\cos\theta$$

When $\theta = 90^\circ$ **P** and **R** are perpendicular to each other.

$\therefore \quad \mathbf{P.R} = 0$

Hence

$$(\mathbf{i} + 2\mathbf{j} + b\mathbf{k}).(b\mathbf{i} - 3\mathbf{j} + 5b\mathbf{k}) = 0$$

$$\therefore \quad b - 6 + 5b^2 = 0 \quad \Rightarrow \quad b = 1 \quad \text{or} \quad -1.2 \quad ◀$$

6.5

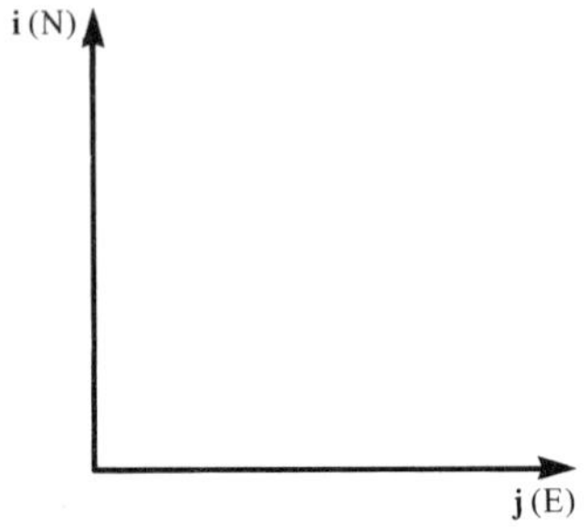

$$\mathbf{v}_{\text{boat}} = \mathbf{v}_{\text{water}} + \mathbf{v}_{\text{boat relative to the water}}$$

$$= \mathbf{i} - 3\mathbf{j} + 3\mathbf{i} + 4\mathbf{j} = 4\mathbf{i} - \mathbf{j} \text{ knots} \quad ◀$$

6.6

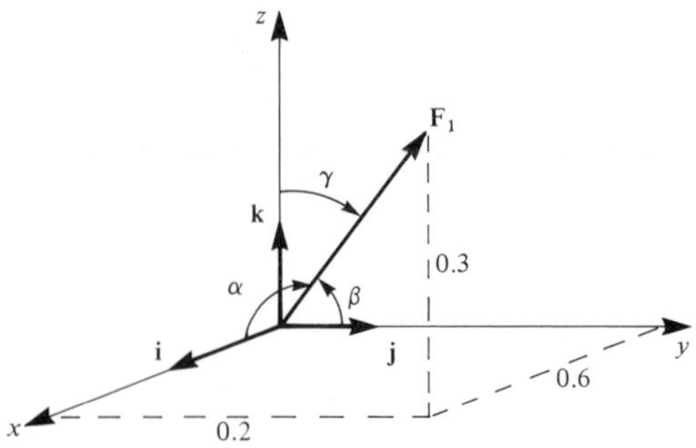

Consider one of the forces, say $\mathbf{F}_1$, where $F_1 = 5$ kN. Then

$$\mathbf{F}_1 = F_1\cos\alpha\mathbf{i} + F_1\cos\beta\mathbf{j} + F_1\cos\gamma\mathbf{k}$$

where

$$\cos\alpha = \frac{0.6}{\sqrt{0.6^2 + 0.2^2 + 0.3^2}} = \frac{0.6}{0.7}$$

$$\cos\beta = \frac{0.2}{0.7}, \quad \cos\gamma = \frac{0.3}{0.7}$$

Hence

$$\mathbf{F}_1 = 4.29\mathbf{i} + 1.43\mathbf{j} + 2.14\mathbf{k} \qquad \text{kN}$$

Similarly

$$\mathbf{F}_2 = 1.29\mathbf{i} - 0.86\mathbf{j} + 2.57\mathbf{k} \qquad \text{kN}$$

$$\mathbf{F}_3 = -0.29\mathbf{i} - 0.43\mathbf{j} - 0.86\mathbf{k} \qquad \text{kN}$$

Resultant

$$\mathbf{F} = \sum_{n=1}^{3} \mathbf{F}_n = 5.29\mathbf{i} + 0.14\mathbf{j} + 3.85\mathbf{k} \qquad \text{kN}$$

The displacement vector,

$$\mathbf{R} = \mathbf{B} - \mathbf{A}$$
$$= 0.3\mathbf{i} + 0.4\mathbf{k}$$

$\therefore$ Work done, $V = \mathbf{F}.\mathbf{R} = (5.29 \times 0.3 + 0 + 3.85 \times 0.4) \times 10^3$

$$= 3.13 \times 10^3 \text{ J}$$
$$= 3.13 \text{ kJ} \quad ◀$$

6.7

$$\omega = 40 \cos\alpha\, \mathbf{i} + 40 \cos\beta\, \mathbf{j} + 40 \cos\gamma\, \mathbf{k}$$
$$= 0\mathbf{i} + 40 \times \frac{0.3}{0.32}\mathbf{j} + 40 \times \frac{-0.1}{0.32}\mathbf{k}$$
$$= 37.95\mathbf{j} - 12.65\mathbf{k} \text{ rad/s}$$

$$\mathbf{R} = \mathbf{P} - \mathbf{A} = (0.4\mathbf{i} - 0.2\mathbf{j} + 0.1\mathbf{k}) - (0.1\mathbf{i} + 0.3\mathbf{j} - 0.1\mathbf{k})$$
$$= 0.3\mathbf{i} - 0.5\mathbf{j} + 0.2\mathbf{k} \text{ m}$$

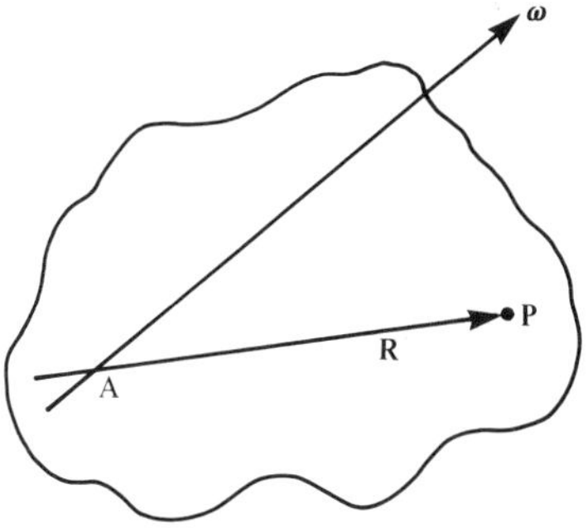

Hence velocity of P,

$$\mathbf{v}_P = \omega \wedge \mathbf{R} = \begin{vmatrix} \mathbf{i} & \mathbf{j} & \mathbf{k} \\ 0 & 37.95 & -12.65 \\ 0.3 & -0.5 & 0.2 \end{vmatrix}$$
$$= 1.27\mathbf{i} - 3.8\mathbf{j} - 11.39\mathbf{k} \text{ m/s}$$

$$v = |\mathbf{v}| = \sqrt{1.27^2 + 3.8^2 + 11.39^2}$$
$$= 12.07 \text{ m/s}$$

$$\alpha = \arccos\left(\frac{1.27}{12.07}\right) = 84° \quad ◀$$

$$\beta = \arccos\left(\frac{-3.8}{12.07}\right) = 108.3° \quad ◀$$

and

$$\gamma = \arccos\left(\frac{-11.39}{12.07}\right) = 160.6° \quad ◀$$

6.8

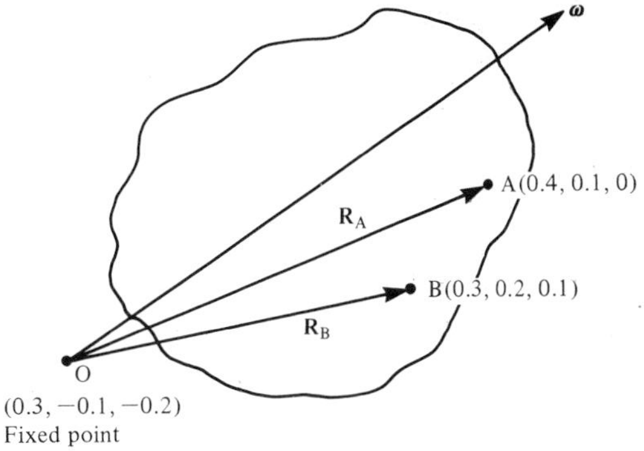

$$\omega = \frac{500}{0.3}(0.2\mathbf{i} + 0.1\mathbf{j} - 0.2\mathbf{k})$$

$$\mathbf{R}_A = (0.4\mathbf{i} + 0.1\mathbf{j}) - (0.3\mathbf{i} - 0.1\mathbf{j} - 0.2\mathbf{k})$$
$$= 0.1\mathbf{i} + 0.2\mathbf{j} + 0.2\mathbf{k} \text{ m}$$

$$\mathbf{v}_A = \omega \wedge \mathbf{R}_A = \frac{500}{0.3} \times \begin{vmatrix} \mathbf{i} & \mathbf{j} & \mathbf{k} \\ 0.2 & 0.1 & -0.2 \\ 0.1 & 0.2 & 0.2 \end{vmatrix}$$
$$= \frac{500}{0.3}\left(0.06\mathbf{i} - 0.06\mathbf{j} + 0.03\mathbf{k}\right)$$
$$= 100\mathbf{i} - 100\mathbf{j} + 50\mathbf{k} \text{ m/s} \quad ◀$$

Also

$$\mathbf{R}_B = (0.3\mathbf{i} + 0.2\mathbf{j} + 0.1\mathbf{k}) - (0.3\mathbf{i} - 0.1\mathbf{j} - 0.2\mathbf{k})$$
$$= 0.3\mathbf{j} + 0.3\mathbf{k} \text{ m}$$

$$\mathbf{v}_B = \omega \wedge \mathbf{R}_B = \frac{500}{0.3} \begin{vmatrix} \mathbf{i} & \mathbf{j} & \mathbf{k} \\ 0.1 & 0.1 & -0.2 \\ 0 & 0.3 & 0.3 \end{vmatrix}$$

$$= \frac{500}{0.3}(0.09\mathbf{i} - 0.06\mathbf{j} + 0.06\mathbf{k})$$

$$= 500(0.3\mathbf{i} - 0.2\mathbf{j} + 0.2\mathbf{k})$$

$$= 150\mathbf{i} - 100\mathbf{j} + 100\mathbf{k} \text{ m/s}$$ ◀

6.9

$$\mathbf{h} = \mathbf{R}\wedge m\mathbf{v} = (0.5\mathbf{i} + 0.4\mathbf{j} + 0.1\mathbf{k}) \wedge 15(27\mathbf{i} + 21\mathbf{j} + 12\mathbf{k})$$

$$= \begin{vmatrix} \mathbf{i} & \mathbf{j} & \mathbf{k} \\ 0.5 & 0.4 & 0.1 \\ 27 & 21 & 12 \end{vmatrix} \times 15$$

$$= 40.5\mathbf{i} - 49.5\mathbf{j} - 4.5\mathbf{k} \text{ kg m}^2\text{/s}$$ ◀

6.10

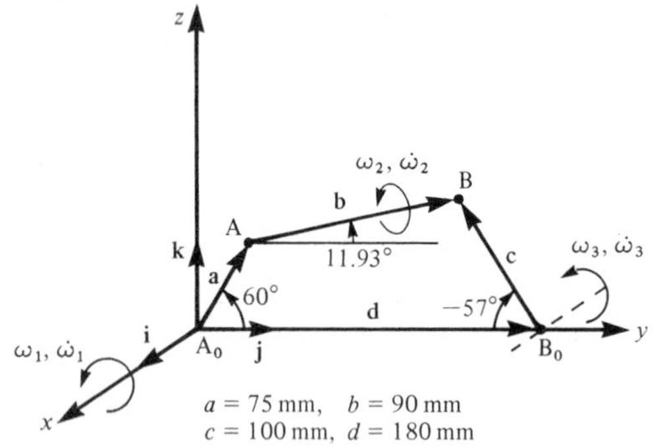

The mechanism is in the *yz* plane. For the velocities:

Vectorially,

$$\omega_1 = 50\mathbf{i}, \quad \omega_2 = \omega_2\mathbf{i}, \quad \omega_3 = \omega_3\mathbf{i}$$

$$\mathbf{a} = 75\cos 60^\circ\mathbf{j} + 75\sin 60^\circ\mathbf{k}$$

$$= 37.5\mathbf{j} + 64.95\mathbf{k} \text{ mm}$$

$$\mathbf{v}_A = 50\mathbf{i}\wedge\mathbf{a} = 50\mathbf{i}\wedge(0.0375\mathbf{j} + 0.064\,95\,\mathbf{k}) \text{ m/s}$$

$$= 1.88\mathbf{k} - 3.25\mathbf{j}$$

$$\Rightarrow v_A = 3.75 \text{ m/s}$$ ◀

$$\mathbf{b} = 90\cos 11.93^\circ\mathbf{j} + 90\sin 11.93^\circ\mathbf{k}$$

$$= 88.06\mathbf{j} + 18.6\mathbf{k} \text{ mm}$$

$$\mathbf{v}_B = \mathbf{v}_A + \omega_2\wedge\mathbf{b}$$

$$= 1.88\mathbf{k} - 3.25\mathbf{j} + \omega_2\mathbf{i}\wedge(0.088\,06\mathbf{j} + 0.0186\mathbf{k})$$

$$= 1.88\mathbf{k} - 3.25\mathbf{j} + 0.088\,06\omega_2\mathbf{k} - 0.0186\omega_2\mathbf{j} \text{ m/s} \qquad (1)$$

$$\mathbf{c} = 100\cos 123^\circ\mathbf{j} + 100\sin 123^\circ\mathbf{k}$$

$$= -54.46\mathbf{j} + 83.86\mathbf{k} \text{ mm}$$

$$\mathbf{v}_B = \omega_3\mathbf{i}\wedge\mathbf{c} = \omega_3\mathbf{i}\wedge(-0.054\,46\mathbf{j} + 0.083\,86\mathbf{k})$$

$$= -0.054\,46\omega_3\mathbf{k} - 0.083\,86\omega_3\mathbf{j} \text{ m/s} \qquad (2)$$

Combining (1) and (2) and equating the **j** and **k** coefficients we obtain

$$1.88 + 0.088\,06\omega_2 = -0.054\,46\omega_3$$

$$-3.25 + 0.0186\omega_2 = -0.083\,86\omega_3$$

$$\therefore \quad \omega_2 = -39.4 \text{ rad/s}$$

and $\omega_3 = 29.77$ rad/s ◀

Also

$$\mathbf{v}_B = -0.054\,46 \times 29.77\mathbf{k} - 0.083\,86 \times 29.77\mathbf{j}$$

$$= -1.59\mathbf{k} - 2.52\mathbf{j}$$

$$\Rightarrow \quad v_B = 2.98 \text{ m/s}$$ ◀

For the accelerations:

$$\mathbf{a}_B = \dot{\omega}_3\mathbf{i}\wedge\mathbf{c} + \omega_3\mathbf{i}\wedge(\omega_3\mathbf{i}\wedge\mathbf{c})$$

$$= \dot{\omega}_3\mathbf{i}\wedge\mathbf{c} - \omega_3^2\mathbf{c} \qquad (3)$$

Also

$$\mathbf{a}_B = \mathbf{a}_A + \mathbf{a}_{BA} = \dot{\omega}_1\mathbf{i}\wedge\mathbf{a} + \omega_1\mathbf{i}\wedge(\omega_1\mathbf{i}\wedge\mathbf{a}) + \dot{\omega}_2\mathbf{i}\wedge\mathbf{b} + \omega_2\mathbf{i}\wedge(\omega_2\mathbf{i}\wedge\mathbf{b})$$

$$= -\omega_1^2\mathbf{a} + \dot{\omega}_2\mathbf{i}\wedge\mathbf{b} - \omega_2^2\mathbf{b}$$

since

$$\dot{\omega}_1 = 0 \qquad (4)$$

Hence, substituting in (3),

$$\mathbf{a}_B = -0.054\,46\dot{\omega}_3\mathbf{k} - 0.083\,86\dot{\omega}_3\mathbf{j} + 47.33\mathbf{j} - 75.02\mathbf{k} \qquad (5)$$

and from (4)

$$\mathbf{a}_B = -93.75\mathbf{j} - 162.28\mathbf{k} + 0.088\,06\dot{\omega}_2\mathbf{k} - 0.0186\dot{\omega}_2\mathbf{j} - 136.7\mathbf{j} - 28.87\mathbf{k} \qquad (6)$$

Equating (5) and (6) we find

$$0.054\,46\dot{\omega}_3 + 0.088\,06\dot{\omega}_2 = 116.32$$

$$0.083\,68\dot{\omega}_3 - 0.0186\dot{\omega}_2 = 277.8$$

$$\therefore \quad \dot{\omega}_2 = -593 \text{ rad/s}^2$$

$$\dot{\omega}_3 = 3155 \text{ rad/s}^2$$ ◀

6.11

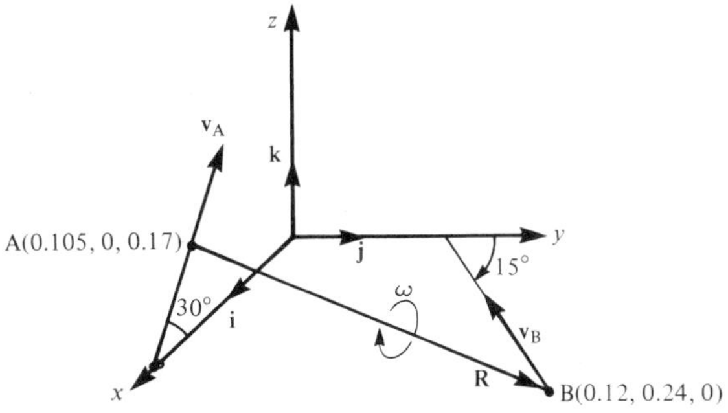

$\boldsymbol{\omega} = \omega_1\mathbf{i} + \omega_2\mathbf{j} + \omega_3\mathbf{k}$

$$\mathbf{v}_B = \mathbf{v}_A + \mathbf{v}_{BA} = \mathbf{v}_A + \boldsymbol{\omega}\wedge\mathbf{R}$$

$$\mathbf{v}_B = -v_B\cos 15^\circ\mathbf{j} - v_B\sin 15^\circ\mathbf{i}$$
$$= (-0.97\mathbf{j} - 0.26\mathbf{k})v_B$$

$$\mathbf{v}_A = -2\cos 30^\circ\mathbf{i} + 2\sin 30^\circ\mathbf{k}$$
$$= -1.73\mathbf{i} + \mathbf{k}\text{ m/s}$$

$$\mathbf{R} = \mathbf{R}_B - \mathbf{R}_A = 0.12\mathbf{i} + 0.24\mathbf{j} - 0.105\mathbf{i} - 0.17\mathbf{k}$$
$$= 0.015\mathbf{i} + 0.24\mathbf{j} - 0.17\mathbf{k}$$

Hence

$$-0.97v_B\mathbf{j} - 0.26v_B\mathbf{k} = -1.73\mathbf{i} + \mathbf{k} + (\omega_1\mathbf{i} + \omega_2\mathbf{j} + \omega_3\mathbf{k})\wedge(0.015\mathbf{i} + 0.24\mathbf{j} - 0.17\mathbf{k}) \quad (1)$$

$$\mathbf{v}_{BA} = \mathbf{v}_B - \mathbf{v}_A = -0.97v_B\mathbf{j} - 0.26v_B\mathbf{k} - (-1.73\mathbf{i} + \mathbf{k})$$

Since $\mathbf{v}_{BA}$ is perpendicular to $\mathbf{R}$, $\mathbf{v}_{BA}.\mathbf{R} = 0$.

Hence

$$(-0.97v_B\mathbf{j} - 0.26v_B\mathbf{k} + 1.73\mathbf{i} - \mathbf{k}).(0.015\mathbf{i} + 0.24\mathbf{j} - 0.17\mathbf{k}) = 0$$

$$\Rightarrow \quad -0.97 \times 0.24v_B + 0.26 \times 0.17v_B + 1.73 \times 0.015 + 0.17 = 0$$

$$\Rightarrow \quad v_B = 1.04\text{ m/s}$$ ◀

Substituting for v_B in (1),

$$1.73\mathbf{i} - 1.01\mathbf{j} - 1.27\mathbf{k} = \mathbf{i}(-0.17\omega_2 - 0.24\omega_3) - \mathbf{j}(-0.17\omega_1 - 0.015\omega_3) + \mathbf{k}(0.24\omega_1 - 0.015\omega_2)$$

Equating the coefficients of **i**, **j** and **k**,

$$-1.73 = 0.17\omega_2 + 0.24\omega_3$$
$$-1.01 = 0.17\omega_1 + 0.015\omega_3$$
$$-1.27 = 0.24\omega_1 - 0.015\omega_2$$

$$\therefore \quad \omega_1 = -5.55$$
$$\omega_2 = -4.13$$
and $$\omega_3 = -4.33\text{ rad/s}$$

$$\therefore \quad \omega = \sqrt{5.55^2 + 4.13^2 + 4.33^2}$$
$$= 8.2\text{ rad/s}$$ ◀

6.12

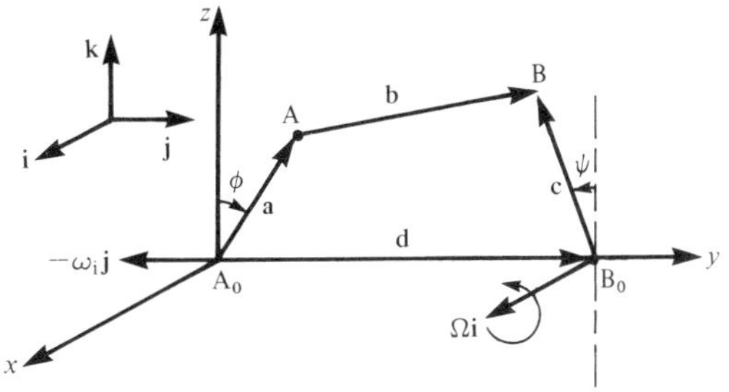

$$\mathbf{a} + \mathbf{b} = \mathbf{c} + \mathbf{d}$$
$$\mathbf{a} = a\cos\phi\mathbf{k} - a\sin\phi\mathbf{i}$$
$$\mathbf{c} = c\cos\psi\mathbf{k} - c\sin\psi\mathbf{j}$$
$$\mathbf{d} = d\mathbf{j}$$
$$\mathbf{b} = \mathbf{c} + \mathbf{d} - \mathbf{a}$$
$$= a\sin\phi\mathbf{i} + (d - c\sin\psi)\mathbf{j} + (c\cos\psi - a\cos\phi)\mathbf{k} \quad (1)$$

To obtain Ω let us consider the link AB of length b given by

$$b^2 = a^2\sin^2\phi + (d - c\sin\psi)^2 + (c\cos\psi - a\cos\phi)^2 = a^2 + c^2 + d^2 - 2cd\sin\psi - 2ac\cos\phi\cos\psi$$

$$\Leftrightarrow \quad A\sin\psi + B\cos\psi = C \qquad (2)$$

where

$$A = 2cd,$$
$$B = 2ac\cos\phi,$$
$$C = a^2 - b^2 + c^2 + d^2 \qquad (3)$$

Differentiating (2) yields

$$\dot{A}\sin\psi + A\cos\psi\,\Omega + \dot{B}\cos\psi - B\sin\psi\,\Omega = \dot{C}$$

From (3),

$$\dot{A} = 0 \quad \dot{B} = -2ac\sin\phi\omega \quad \dot{C} = 0$$

Hence

$$\Omega(A\cos\psi - B\sin\psi) = 2ac\sin\phi\cos\psi\omega$$

$$\therefore \quad \frac{\Omega}{\omega} = \frac{a\sin\phi\cos\psi}{d\cos\psi - a\cos\phi\sin\psi} \qquad (4)$$

for the velocity ratio.

To calculate this ratio ψ is needed. Let

$$t = \tan\frac{\psi}{2}$$

$$\Rightarrow \quad \sin\psi = \frac{2t}{1+t^2}, \quad \cos\psi = \frac{1-t^2}{1+t^2}$$

Substituting in (2) yields

$$(B + C)t^2 - 2At + (C - B) = 0$$

whose roots are

$$\psi = 2\arctan\left(\frac{A \pm \sqrt{A^2 + B^2 - C^2}}{B + C}\right) \qquad (5)$$

(The reader should note the similarity with the two-dimensional four-bar linkage.)

Substituting the given data we obtain

$$A = 2 \times 0.254 \times 0.508 = 0.258 \text{ mm},$$
$$B = 2 \times 0.127 \times 0.254 \times \cos 60^\circ = 0.032 \text{ mm}$$

and $C = 0.127^2 - 0.508^2 + 0.254^2 + 0.508^2 = 0.081$ mm

From (5),

$$\psi = 2\arctan\left(\frac{0.258 \pm \sqrt{0.258^2 + 0.032^2 - 0.081^2}}{0.032 + 0.081}\right) = 154.8^\circ \quad \text{and} \quad 10.9^\circ \qquad ◄$$

$$\therefore \quad \Omega = \frac{0.127\sin 60^\circ\cos 10.9^\circ}{0.508\cos 10.9^\circ - 0.127\cos 60^\circ\sin 10.9^\circ} \times 35 = 7.76 \text{ rad/s} \qquad ◄$$

Alternatively:

$$\mathbf{v}_B = \Omega\mathbf{i}\wedge\mathbf{c} = \Omega\mathbf{i}\wedge(c\cos\psi\,\mathbf{k} - c\sin\psi\,\mathbf{j}) = -\Omega c\cos\psi\,\mathbf{j} - \Omega c\sin\psi\,\mathbf{k}$$

$$\mathbf{v}_A = -\omega\mathbf{j}\wedge\mathbf{a} = -\omega\mathbf{j}\wedge(a\cos\phi\,\mathbf{k} - a\sin\phi\,\mathbf{i}) = -\omega a\cos\phi\,\mathbf{i} - \omega a\sin\phi\,\mathbf{k}$$

$$\mathbf{v}_{BA} = \mathbf{v}_B - \mathbf{v}_A = \omega a\cos\phi\,\mathbf{i} - \Omega c\cos\psi\,\mathbf{j} + (\omega a\sin\phi - \Omega c\sin\psi)\mathbf{k} \qquad (5)$$

Since $\mathbf{v}_{BA}$ is perpendicular to $\mathbf{b}$,

$$\mathbf{v}_{BA}\cdot\mathbf{b} = 0$$

$$\Rightarrow \quad [\omega a\cos\phi\,\mathbf{i} - \Omega c\cos\psi\,\mathbf{j} + (\omega a\sin\phi - \Omega c\sin\psi)\mathbf{k}]\cdot[a\sin\phi\,\mathbf{i} + (d - c\sin\psi)\mathbf{j} + (c\cos\psi - a\cos\phi)\mathbf{k}] = 0$$

i.e. $\omega a^2\sin\phi\cos\phi - \Omega c\cos\psi(d - c\sin\psi) + (\omega a\sin\phi - \Omega c\sin\psi)(c\cos\psi - a\cos\phi) = 0$

or $\omega[a^2\sin\phi\cos\phi + a\sin\phi(c\cos\psi - a\cos\phi)] = \Omega[c\cos\psi(d - c\sin\psi) + c\sin\psi(c\cos\psi - a\cos\phi)]$

$$\therefore \quad \frac{\Omega}{\omega} = \frac{a\sin\phi\cos\psi}{d\cos\psi - a\cos\phi\sin\psi}$$

as in (4) above.

Note: If the angular velocity ω_c of the coupler link AB is needed we proceed thus:

From (5),

$$\mathbf{v}_{BA} = \mathbf{v}_B - \mathbf{v}_A \quad \text{but} \quad \mathbf{v}_{BA} = \omega_c\wedge\mathbf{b}$$

Let $\omega_c = \omega_x\mathbf{i} + \omega_y\mathbf{j} + \omega_z\mathbf{k}$

and $\mathbf{b} = b_x\mathbf{i} + b_y\mathbf{j} + b_z\mathbf{k}$

where b_x, b_y and b_z are obtained from (1).

Also let

$$\mathbf{v}_B - \mathbf{v}_A = A_x\mathbf{i} + A_y\mathbf{j} + A_z\mathbf{k},$$

where A_x, A_y, A_z are obtained from (5).

Then

$$\omega_c \wedge \mathbf{b} = \mathbf{v}_B - \mathbf{v}_A \quad \Rightarrow \quad \begin{vmatrix} \mathbf{i} & \mathbf{j} & \mathbf{k} \\ \omega_x & \omega_y & \omega_z \\ b_x & b_y & b_z \end{vmatrix}$$

$$= A_x\mathbf{i} + A_y\mathbf{j} + A_z\mathbf{k}$$

This will lead to 3 simultaneous equations in ω_x, ω_y and ω_z after equating the coefficients of **i**, **j** and **k**. Then ω_c may be found from

$$\omega_c = \sqrt{\omega_x^2 + \omega_y^2 + \omega_z^2}$$

6.13

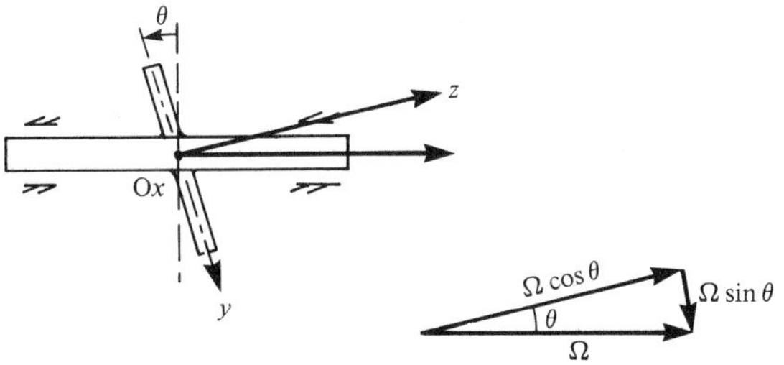

Let I_x, I_y and I_z be the principal moments of inertia of the disc. Then

$$I_x = I_y = \tfrac{1}{4}MR^2, \quad I_z = \tfrac{1}{2}MR^2$$

From the diagram for the angular velocities we have:

$$\omega_x = 0, \quad \omega_y = \Omega\sin\theta, \quad \omega_z = \Omega\cos\theta$$

Since θ is constant,

$$\dot{\omega}_x = 0, \quad \dot{\omega}_y = 0, \quad \dot{\omega}_z = 0$$

Euler's equations give

$$M_x = I_x\dot{\omega}_x - (I_y - I_z)\omega_y\omega_z$$

$$= 0 - (\tfrac{1}{4} - \tfrac{1}{2})MR^2\Omega^2\sin\theta\,\cos\theta$$

$$= \tfrac{1}{8}MR^2\Omega^2\sin 2\theta$$

$$M_y = I_y\dot{\omega}_y - (I_z - I_x)\omega_z\omega_x = 0$$

$$M_z = I_z\dot{\omega}_z - (I_z - I_y)\omega_x\omega_y = 0$$

The moment on the bearings,

$$M_x = \tfrac{1}{8} \times 25 \times 0.225^2 \times \left(\frac{2\pi \times 15\,000}{60}\right)^2 \sin 1^\circ$$

$$= 6812\ \text{N m}$$ ◀

6.14

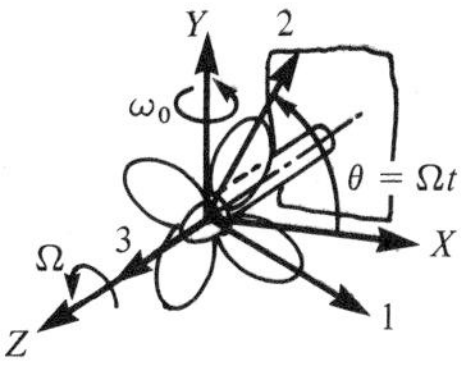

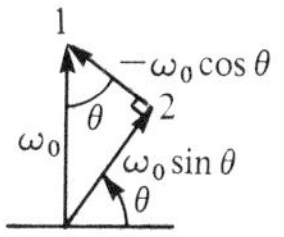

Consider principal axes 1, 2, 3 fixed to the propeller and moving with it, such that O1 and O2 lie in the plane of the fixed axes OXY. Consider an instant t when axis O2 makes an angle $\theta = \Omega t$ with OX.

Then we have

$$\omega_1 = -\omega_0\cos\theta$$

$$\Rightarrow \quad \dot{\omega}_1 = \omega_0\sin\theta\,\dot{\theta} = \omega_0\Omega\sin\theta$$

$$\omega_2 = \omega_0\sin\theta$$

$$\Rightarrow \quad \dot{\omega}_2 = \omega_0\cos\theta\,\dot{\theta} = \omega_0\Omega\cos\theta$$

$$\omega_3 = \dot{\theta} = \Omega \quad \Rightarrow \quad \dot{\omega}_3 = 0$$

since Ω is constant.

Applying Euler's equations, we obtain

$$M_1 = I_1\dot{\omega}_1 - (I_2 - I_3)\omega_2\omega_3$$

$$= I_1\omega_0\Omega\sin\theta - (I_2 - I_3)\omega_0\Omega\sin\theta$$

$$= \omega_0\Omega\sin\theta(I_1 - I_2 + I_3)$$

$$= I_3\omega_0\Omega\sin\theta$$

$$= 2000 \times 0.3 \times \frac{2\pi \times 120}{60}\sin\theta$$

$$= 7540\sin\theta\ \text{N m}$$

$$M_2 = I_2\dot{\omega}_2 - [I_3 - I_1]\omega_3\omega_1$$

$$= I_2\omega_0\Omega\cos\theta + [I_3 - I_1]\,\omega_0\Omega\cos\theta$$

$$= \omega_0\Omega\cos\theta\,[I_2 + I_3 - I_1]$$

$$= I_3\omega_0\Omega\cos\theta$$

$$= 7540\cos\theta\ \text{N m}$$

$$M_3 = I_3\dot{\omega}_3 - [I_1 - I_2]\,\omega_1\omega_2 = 0$$

Hence there is no twisting moment, and the maximum bending moment = 7540 N m ◀

CHAPTER 7

7.1

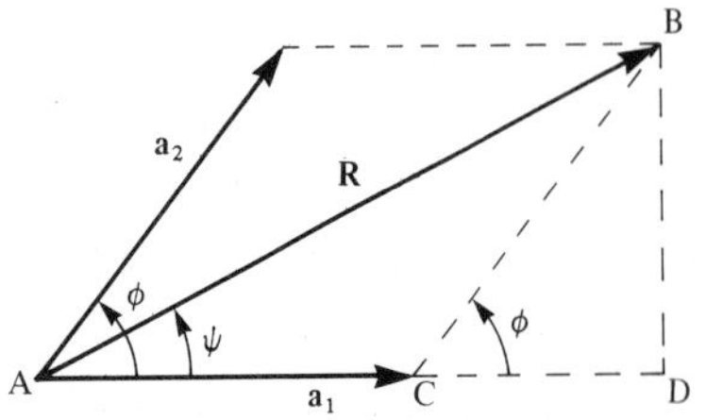

Phasors representing x_1 and x_2 are of lengths a_1 and a_2, with an angle ϕ between them, a_2 leading. The resulting motion is represented by the phasor **R**. Since the whole diagram rotates at ω, **R** is of fixed length, turning at a constant speed and thus generates single harmonic motion. From the triangles ABD and CBD, by Pythagoras' theorem we have:

$$R = [a_1 + a_2 \cos\phi)^2 + (a_2 \sin\phi)^2]^{1/2}$$

and $$\tan\psi = \frac{a_2 \sin\phi}{a_1 + a_2 \cos\phi}$$

Alternatively:

$$x = x_1 + x_2 = a_1 \sin\omega t + a_2 \sin(\omega t + \phi)$$

$$= a_1 \sin\omega t + a_2 \sin\omega t \cos\phi + a_2 \cos\omega t \sin\phi$$

$$= \sin\omega t (a_1 + a_2 \cos\phi) + \cos\omega t \; a_2 \sin\phi$$

$$= A \sin\omega t + B \cos\omega t, \quad \text{say}$$

$$= \sqrt{A^2 + B^2}\left[\frac{A}{\sqrt{A^2 + B^2}} \sin\omega t + \frac{B}{\sqrt{A^2 + B^2}} \cos\omega t\right]$$

$$\therefore \quad X = \sqrt{A^2 + B^2} \sin(\omega t + \psi)$$

where

$$\cos\psi = \frac{A}{\sqrt{A^2 + B^2}}, \quad \sin\psi = \frac{B}{\sqrt{A^2 + B^2}}$$

from which the above results follow. ◀

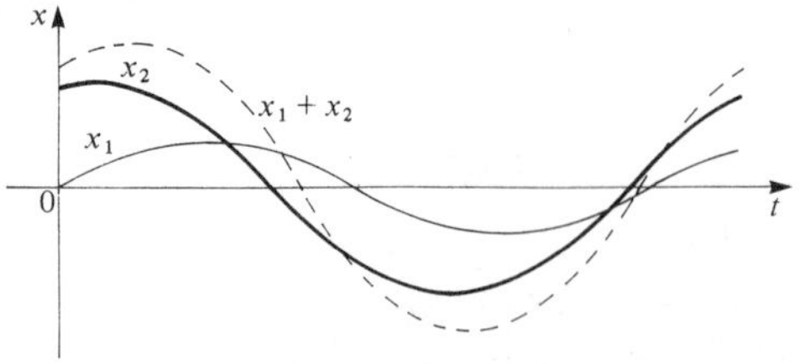

7.2

$$\omega = \frac{2\pi \times 10}{4.3} \text{rad/s} = 14.6 \text{ rad/s}$$

$$f = 10/4.3 \text{ Hz} = 2.33 \text{ Hz}$$

$$= 2.33 \times 60 = 140 \text{ c/min}$$ ◀

$$\tau = 1/f = 1/2.33 = 0.43 \text{ s}$$

7.3

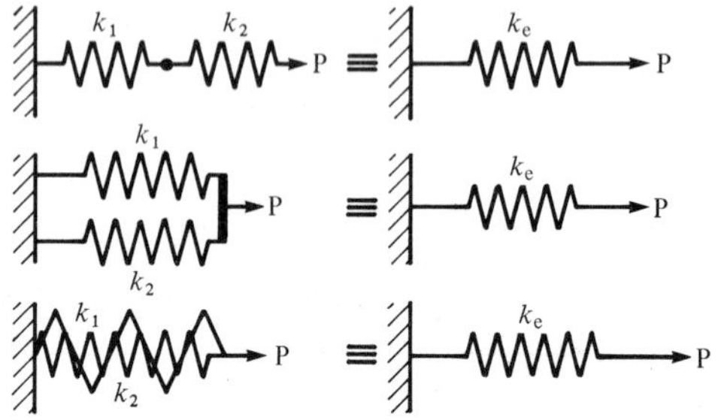

$$k_e = \frac{k_1 k_2}{k_1 + k_2} = \frac{2 \times 4 \times 10^6}{(2 + 4) \times 10^3}$$

$$= 1.33 \times 10^3 \text{ N/m} = 1.33 \text{ kN/m}$$ ◀

$$k_e = k_1 + k_2 = (2 + 4) \times 10^3 = 6 \text{ kN/m}$$ ◀

$$k_e = k_1 + k_2 = 6 \text{ kN/m}$$ ◀

7.4

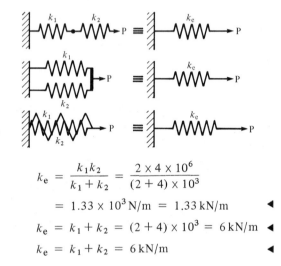

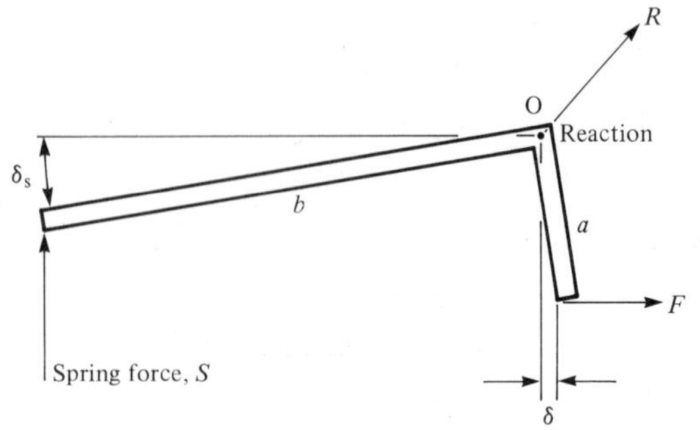

Free body diagram

Taking moments about the hinge O,

$$Fa = Sb \Rightarrow S = Fa/b$$

Since k = spring stiffness, $S = k\delta_s$

Hence

$$\delta_s = \frac{Fa/b}{k}$$

Also

$$\frac{\delta}{a} = \frac{\delta_s}{b}$$

$$\therefore \quad \delta_s = \frac{b}{a}\delta$$

Hence

$$\text{stiffness at P} = \frac{F}{\delta} = k\left(\frac{b}{a}\right)^2$$ ◂

7.5

Cantilever stiffness,

$$k_c = 3EI/l^3$$

since the deflection δ of a cantilever carrying an end load W is given by $\delta = Wl^3/3EI$.

Hence

$$k_c = 3 \times 210 \times 10^9 \times 30 \times 10^{-6}/3^3$$

$$= 0.7 \times 10^6\,\text{N/m} \quad \text{or} \quad 0.7\,\text{MN/m}$$

$$E = \frac{\text{stress}}{\text{strain}} = \frac{\text{load/area}}{\text{extension/length}} = \frac{P/A}{\delta/L}$$

$$\therefore \quad \text{wire stiffness, } k_w = \frac{P}{\delta} = \frac{EA}{L}$$

$$= 210 \times 16^9 \times 10^{-4}/10$$

$$= 2.10\,\text{MN/m}$$

The springs are arranged as in exercise 7.3(a)

$$\Rightarrow \quad k_e = 0.7 \times 2.10/(0.7 + 2.10)$$

$$= 0.525\,\text{MN/m}$$ ◂

7.6

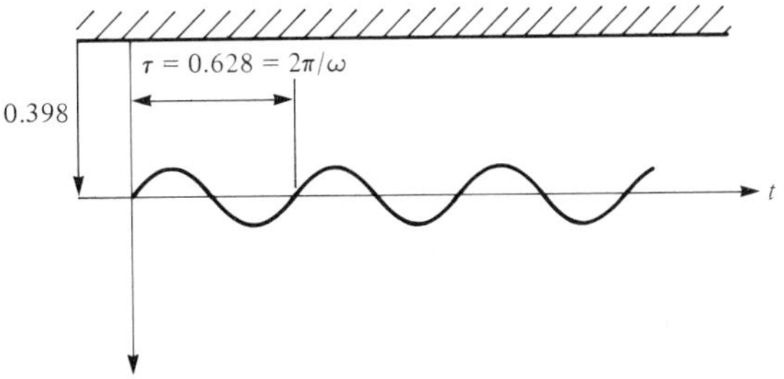

Maximum velocity, $v_{max} = \omega a$

$$\omega = \sqrt{\frac{k}{m}} = \sqrt{\frac{100}{1}} = 10\,\text{rad/s}$$

$$\therefore \quad a = \frac{0.5}{10} = 0.05\,\text{m}$$

Static deflection,

$$\delta_s = mg/k = 1 \times 9.81/100 = 0.0981\,\text{m}$$

Maximum spring extension,

$$\Delta = 0.0981 + 0.05 = 0.1481\,\text{m}$$

$$\therefore \quad \text{Maximum tension} = k\Delta$$

$$= 100 \times 0.1481$$

$$= 14.81\,\text{N}$$ ◂

7.7

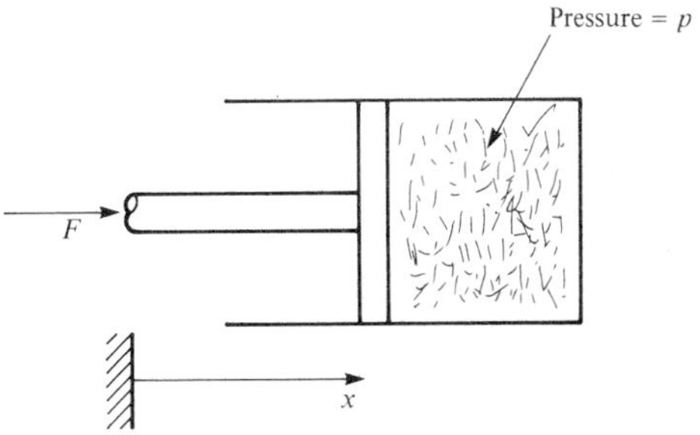

Stiffness,

$$k = \mathrm{d}F/\mathrm{d}x$$

But $F = pA$ and $V = V_0 - Ax$

where V is the volume and V_0 is the volume when the piston is at $x = 0$.

$$\delta F = A\delta p$$

$$\delta x = -\frac{\delta V}{A}$$

$$\therefore \quad \frac{\delta F}{\delta x} = -A^2\frac{\delta p}{\delta V}$$

Hence

$$k = -A^2\frac{\mathrm{d}p}{\mathrm{d}V}$$

Under isothermal conditions,

$$pV = \text{constant}$$

$$\therefore \quad \frac{dp}{dV}V + p = 0 \quad \text{or} \quad \frac{dp}{dV} = -\frac{p}{V}$$

so that

$$k = A^2 p/V$$ ◀

7.8

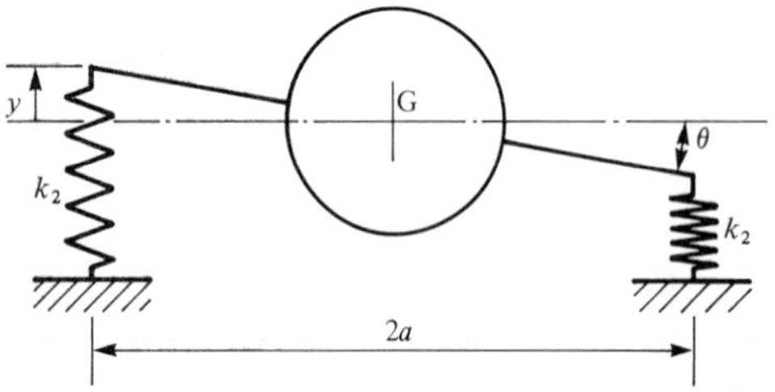

(a) For vertical vibrations,

$$\omega_n = \sqrt{\frac{k}{m}} = \sqrt{\frac{k}{(w/g)}} = \sqrt{\frac{g}{\delta_{st}}}$$

$$= \sqrt{\frac{9.81}{0.014}} = 26.4 \text{ rad/s}$$ ◀

(b) Let

$$k_2 = \text{stiffness of two springs}$$

Then

$$k_2 = \omega_n^2 m/2 = 26.4^2 \times 100/2 = 35 \text{ kN/m}$$

For a deflection θ,

$$y = a\theta$$

Force exerted by the springs $= k_2 a\theta$

Taking moments about G,

$$I_G\ddot{\theta} = -2k_2 a\theta \times a$$

$$\text{or} \quad \ddot{\theta} + \frac{2k_2 a^2}{I_G}\theta = 0$$

Hence the frequency of free angular oscillations,

$$\omega_n' = \sqrt{\frac{2k_2 a^2}{I_G}}$$

$$\therefore \quad \omega_n' = \sqrt{\frac{2 \times 35 \times 10^3 \times 0.125^2}{100 \times 0.08^2}}$$

$$= 41.3 \text{ rad/s}$$ ◀

7.9

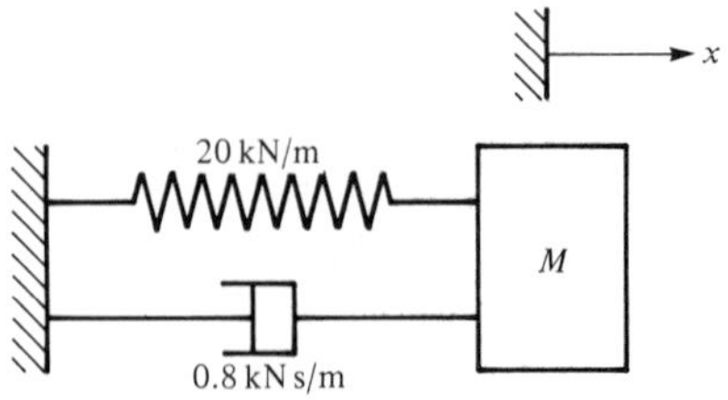

(a)

◀

(b)

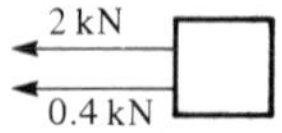

◀

(c)

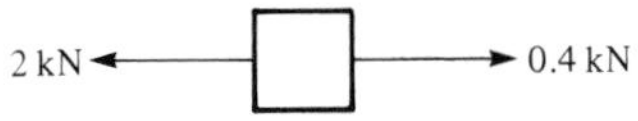

◀

7.10

$$x = Ae^{-\zeta\omega_n t}\cos(\omega_n\sqrt{1-\zeta^2}\,t - \phi)$$

The time constant,

$$\tau = 1/\zeta\omega_n$$

$$\therefore \quad x = Ae^{-t/\tau}\cos(\omega_d t - \phi)$$

The amplitude,

$$X = Ae^{-t/\tau}$$

When $t = 0$,

$$X_0 = A$$

and when $t = 5$ s,

$$X_5 = 0.2X_0 = 0.2A$$

$$\therefore \quad e^{5/\tau} = 5 \quad \Rightarrow \quad 5/\tau = \ln 5$$

Hence

$$\tau = 5/\ln 5 = 3.1 \text{ s}$$ ◀

Since

$$\tau = \frac{1}{\zeta\omega_n},$$

$$\zeta = \frac{1}{\omega_n\tau} = \frac{1}{100/5 \times 2\pi \times 3.1} = 0.002\,56$$ ◀

By equation (7.13) the logarithmic decrement

$$= 2\pi\zeta = 2\pi \times 0.002\,56 = 0.0161$$ ◀

7.11

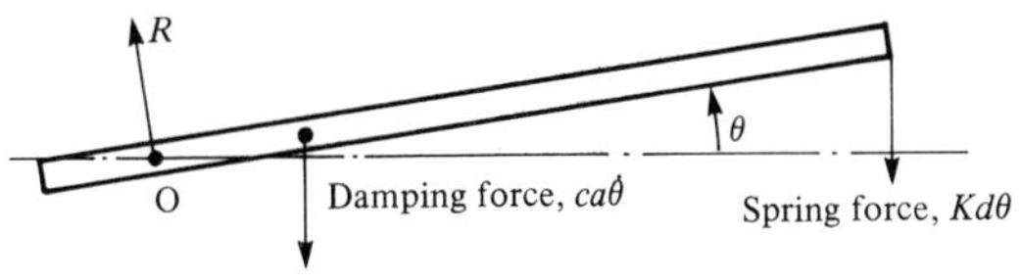

Free body diagram

Assume a small displacement θ.

Taking moments about O,

$$-Kd\theta \times d - ca\dot{\theta}a = I_0\ddot{\theta} = Mb^2\ddot{\theta}$$

$$\therefore \quad \ddot{\theta} + \frac{ca^2}{Mb^2}\dot{\theta} + \frac{Kd^2}{Mb^2}\theta = 0 \qquad ◀$$

Comparing with equation (7.8), i.e.

$$\ddot{x} + \frac{c'}{m}\dot{x} + \frac{kx}{m} = 0,$$

$$\omega_n{}^2 = \frac{Kd^2}{Mb^2} \Rightarrow \omega_n = \frac{d}{b}\sqrt{\frac{K}{M}} \qquad ◀$$

Also $\frac{c'}{m}$ above is equal to $2\zeta\omega_n$, since

$$\zeta = \frac{c'}{2\sqrt{km}}$$

and $\omega_n = \sqrt{\frac{k}{M}}$

Hence

$$2\zeta\omega_n = \frac{ca^2}{Mb^2}$$

$$\therefore \quad \zeta = \frac{ca^2}{2Mb^2} \times \frac{b}{d}\sqrt{\frac{M}{K}} = \frac{a^2c}{2bd\sqrt{KM}} \qquad ◀$$

7.12

Referring to Figure 7.13,

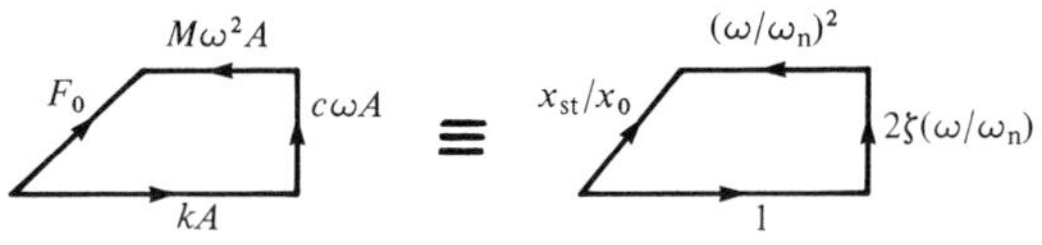

Hence:

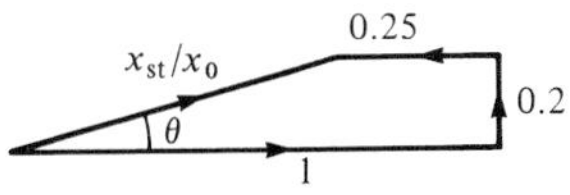

Below resonance

$$\left(\frac{x_{st}}{x_0}\right)^2 = 0.75^2 + 0.2^2 \Rightarrow \frac{x_0}{x_{st}} = 1.288$$

$$\therefore \quad x_0 = 1.29 \text{ mm} \qquad ◀$$

$$\theta = \arctan\frac{0.2}{0.75} = 14.9^\circ \simeq 15^\circ \qquad ◀$$

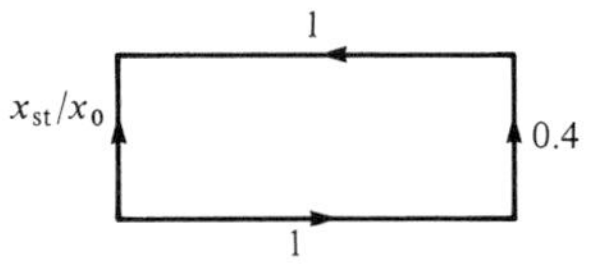

Resonance

$$\frac{x_{st}}{x_0} = 0.4 \Rightarrow x_0 = 2.5 \text{ mm} \quad \theta = 90^\circ \qquad ◀$$

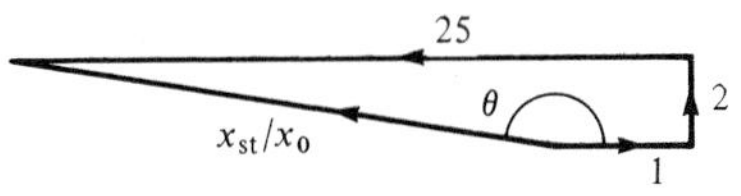

Above resonance

$$\left(\frac{x_{st}}{x_0}\right)^2 = 24^2 + 2^2 \Rightarrow \frac{x_0}{x_{st}} = 0.042$$

$$\Rightarrow x_0 = 0.042 \text{ mm} \qquad ◀$$

$$\theta = 180^\circ - \arctan\frac{2}{2.4} = 175^\circ \qquad ◀$$

7.13

From equation (7.20) we have

$$\left(\frac{x_0}{x_{st}}\right)^2 = \frac{1}{(1-y^2)^2 + 4\zeta^2y^2} \qquad (1)$$

where

$$y = \frac{\omega}{\omega_n}.$$

Thus when $y = 1$,

$$\left(\frac{x_0}{x_{st}}\right) = \frac{1}{2\zeta} \qquad ◀$$

For maximum amplitude,

$$\frac{d}{dy}\left(\frac{x_0}{x_{st}}\right)^2 = 0$$

$$-[2(1-y^2)(-2y) + 8\zeta^2y] = 0$$

$$\Rightarrow \quad 1 - y^2 = 2\zeta^2 \Rightarrow y^2 = 1 - 2\zeta^2$$

Substituting in (1) yields

$$\frac{1}{(x_0/x_{st})_{max}^{\ 2}} = [1-(1-2\zeta^2)]^2 + 4\zeta^2(1-2\zeta^2)$$
$$= 4\zeta^4 + 4\zeta^2 - 8\zeta^4$$
$$= 4\zeta^2(1-\zeta^2)$$

Hence

$$\left(\frac{x_0}{x_{st}}\right)_{max} = \frac{1}{2\zeta\sqrt{1-\zeta^2}}.$$

If ζ is small it follows that

$$\left(\frac{x_0}{x_{st}}\right)_{max} \simeq \frac{1}{2\zeta}$$ ◀

If $$\left(\frac{x}{x_{st}}\right)_{max} = 100 \Rightarrow \zeta = \frac{1}{200} = 0.005$$ ◀

7.14

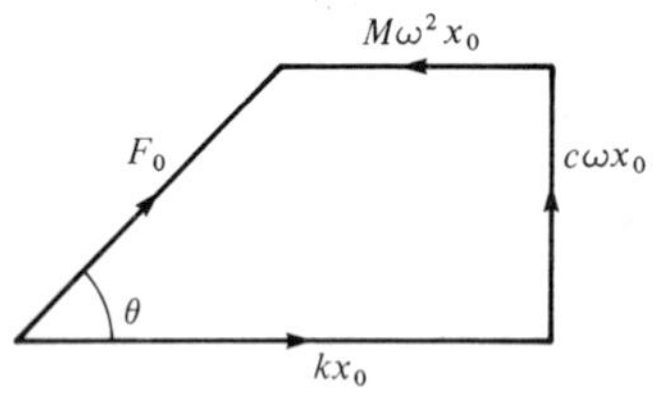

$$k = \frac{Mg}{\delta} = \frac{500 \times 9.81}{2.5 \times 10^{-3}} = 1.962 \times 10^6 \text{ N/m}$$

$$x_{st} = \frac{F_0}{k} = \frac{500}{1.962 \times 10^6} = 0.26 \text{ mm}$$

$$\omega_n = \sqrt{\frac{k}{M}} = \sqrt{\frac{1.962 \times 10^6}{500}}$$
$$= 62.64 \text{ rad/s}$$

$$\omega = \frac{2\pi \times 700}{60} = 73.3$$

$$\therefore \quad y = \frac{\omega}{\omega_n} = \frac{73.3}{62.64} = 1.17$$

Assuming a small value of the damping ratio ζ, from example 7.13,

$$\frac{x_0}{x_{st}} = \frac{1}{2\zeta} \Rightarrow \zeta = \frac{1}{2(x_0/x_{st})}$$

Hence

$$\zeta = \frac{1}{2 \times 6/0.26} = 0.022$$

Therefore ζ is small and the above approximation is valid.

If x_1 is the amplitude of vibration at 700 cycles/min, then by equation (7.20),

$$x_1 = \frac{x_{st}}{\sqrt{(1-y^2)^2 + 4\zeta^2 y^2}}$$
$$= \frac{0.26}{\sqrt{(1-1.17^2)^2 + 4 \times 0.022^2 \times 1.17^2}}$$
$$= 0.7 \text{ mm}$$ ◀

The transmissibility, by equation (7.32), is

$$T = \frac{\sqrt{1+4\zeta^2 y^2}}{\sqrt{(1-y^2)^2 + 4\zeta^2 y^2}}$$
$$= \frac{\sqrt{1+0.022^2 \times 1.17^2}}{\sqrt{(1-1.17^2)^2 + 4 \times 0.022^2 \times 1.17^2}}$$
$$= 2.7$$ ◀

The damping constant,

$$c = 2\zeta\sqrt{kM}$$
$$= 2 \times 0.022 \times \sqrt{1.962 \times 10^6 \times 500}$$
$$= 1378 \text{ N s/m}$$ ◀

7.15

$$\text{Disturbing force} = m\ddot{x}$$
$$= m \times 0.04\omega^2(\cos\omega t + 0.4\cos 2\omega t)$$
$$= 2 \times 0.04 \times 60^2 \times (\cos 60)t + 0.4\cos 120t)$$
$$= 288\cos 60t + 115\cos 120t$$

$$\omega_n = \sqrt{\frac{k}{M}} = \sqrt{\frac{64 \times 10^3}{100}} = 25.3 \text{ rad/s}$$

Then

$$y = \frac{\omega}{\omega_n} = \frac{60}{25.3} = 2.36,$$

$$y_1 = \frac{2\omega}{\omega_n} = 4.72$$

$$\zeta = \frac{c}{2\sqrt{kM}} = \frac{1600}{2 \times \sqrt{64 \times 10^3 \times 100}}$$

$$= 0.32$$

(a) At x_{60} = amplitude due to the force at $\omega = 60$ rad/s. Then

$$x_{60} = \frac{288/64 \times 10^3}{\sqrt{(1 - 2.36^2)^2 + 4 \times 0.32^2 \times 2.36^2}}$$

$$= 0.09 \text{ mm}$$ ◀

(b) Let x_{120} = amplitude due to the force at $\omega = 120$ rad/s. Then

$$x_{120} = \frac{115/64 \times 10^3}{\sqrt{(1 - 4.72^2)^2 + 4 \times 0.32^2 \times 4.72^2}}$$

$$= 0.08 \text{ mm}$$ ◀

(c) Since ω and $2\omega > \omega_n$, $\phi \simeq \pi$.

Hence maximum amplitude,

$$x_{max} \simeq x_{60} + x_{120} = 0.17 \text{ mm}$$ ◀

(d) The transmissibility at ω (since the 2ω component will give a smaller value) is

$$T = \frac{\sqrt{1 + 4\zeta^2 y^2}}{\sqrt{(1 - y^2)^2 + 4\zeta^2 y^2}}$$

$$= \frac{\sqrt{1 + 4 \times 0.32^2 \times 2.36^2}}{\sqrt{(1 - 2.36^2)^2 + 4 \times 0.32^2 \times 2.36^2}}$$

$$= 0.31$$ ◀

Resonance will occur at $\omega = 25.3$ rad/s and 12.6 rad/s.

Index